CONCRETE PIPE HANDBOOK

Published by
AMERICAN CONCRETE PIPE ASSOCIATION
222 West Las Colinas Blvd., Suite 641
Irving, Texas 75039-5423
(972) 506-7216
www.concrete-pipe.org
e-mail: info@concrete-pipe.org

Technical programs of the American Concrete Pipe Association, since its founding in 1907, have been designed to compile engineering data on the hydraulics, loads and supporting strengths and design of concrete pipe. Information obtained is disseminated to producers and consumers of concrete pipe through technical literature and promotional handbooks. Other important activities of the Association include development of product specifications, government relations, participation in related trade and professional societies, advertising and promotion, an industry safety program and educational training. These services are made possible by the financial support of member companies located throughout the United States, Canada, and in more than 40 foreign countries.

Library of Congress catalog number 80-65386
Printed in the United States of America

First printing January, 1980
20,000 copies
Second printing April, 1981
10,000 copies
Third printing January, 1988
10,000 copies
Fourth printing July, 1995
2,000 copies
Fifth printing February, 1998
3,000 copies
Sixth printing June, 2000
2,000 copies
Seventh printing August, 2001
3,000 copies
Eighth printing May, 2005
2,500 copies

ISBN 0-960-38681-6

PREFACE

This *Concrete Pipe Handbook* provides an up-to-date compilation of the concepts and theories which form the basis for the design and installation of precast concrete pipe sewers and culverts. The discussions and analyses have been prepared for use by practicing engineers and engineering students, and the Handbook is a companion volume to the *Concrete Pipe Design Manual* by providing explanations for the charts, tables and design procedures summarized in the Design Manual.

The format and brevity of the Concrete Pipe Design Manual has been advantageous, as is indicated by its widespread use. It is now in its eleventh printing, and 105,000 copies have been published to date. However, the availability of a more comprehensive treatment of the theories and reasons behind pipeline design and installation was believed to be of value and interest to the engineering profession, which resulted in the Board of Directors of the American Concrete Pipe Association authorizing preparation of this Concrete Pipe Handbook.

While some of the data and discussions have never been previously published, most of these practical fundamentals represent an assembly and synthesis of articles and publications from a large number of sources. The history and review of manufacturing in the industry was developed primarily from publications of the American Concrete Pipe Association. *Chapter 3* on Hydraulics and Hydrology was adapted from the Water Pollution Control Federation Manual of Practice No. 9, the Portland Cement Association Handbook of Concrete Pipe Hydraulics, and the Federal Highway Administration Hydraulic Circulars for the Selection of Highway Culverts. Much of *Chapter 4* on Structural Design was derived initially from the early work by A. Marston, M. G. Spangler and W. J. Schlick and their associates at Iowa State University. The latter part of Chapter 4 on the Standard Installation is based on work done by the American Society of Civil Engineer's (ASCE) Standards Committee on Direct Design of Buried Concrete Pipe and Box Sections in conjunction with ACPA. Most of the other chapters are based upon earlier publications of the American Concrete Pipe Association, the American Association of State Highway and Transportation Officials, American Society of Civil Engineers, U.S. Army Corps of Engineers, American Society for Testing and Materials, U.S. Bureau of Reclamation, U.S. Environmental Protection Agency, U.S. Soil Conservation Service, and many others. Credit for much of the data in this Handbook goes to the engineers of these organizations and agencies. Every effort has been made to assure accuracy and technical data presented are considered reliable, but no guarantee is made nor liability assumed.

The Handbook was a time consuming and dedicated effort by the following staff of the American Concrete Pipe Association:

Mike Bealey	(Former) Vice President of Technical Services
John J. Duffy	(Former) Vice President of Marketing Services
Russell B. Preuit	(Former) Director of Engineering Services
Robert E. Stuckey	(Former) Director of Publications
Josh Beakley	Director of Technical Services

We are greatly indebted to the expert advice, encouragement, editing and deadline awareness provided by Robert F. Baker, Consulting Engineer, and to the technical review and assistance of the following representatives of the member companies of the American Concrete Pipe Association who served as the initial review committee:

J. Stuart Boldry	Field Concrete Pipe Company, Inc.
Charles L. Brown	Faulkner Concrete Pipe Company
Robert R. Chisholm	Supercrete Incorporated
Jessie R. Collier	Wilson Concrete Company
Robert A. Parry	Associated Sand & Gravel Company, Inc.
Harry T. Peck	Gifford-Hill Concrete Products
Lee E. Stockton	Price Brothers Company

We are also greatly indebted to the dedicated service and professional advice provided by Richard E. (Rick) Barnes, former president of the American Concrete Pipe Association, in the preparation of this Handbook. Rick served as ACPA president from 1966 until 1990, and was a guiding force in the development and publication of the Handbook . While his death in December, 1997, was a tragic loss to his family as well as our industry, his legacy will continue through his contributions to our profession.

Aside from the immediate use of the Handbook as an educational tool, it is also intended to serve as a basis for continuing growth in the use of precast concrete pipe. The state of the art is presented, not only to assist current practice, but as a point of departure for research and development to produce further economies and continued excellence in performance. Concrete pipe has enjoyed a long and successful history of serving the public interest by transporting sewage and other wastes, and through drainage and flood protection for highways, railroads, airports, and agricultural purposes. To continue to meet the public need, the orderly introduction of new technology is considered vital to the engineering profession and the concrete pipe industry.

John J. Duffy, President
American Concrete Pipe Association
June, 2000

LIST OF CONTENTS

TABLE OF CONTENTS

TABLE OF CONTENTS

FIGURES *Page*

TABLES

CHAPTER 4
LOADS, SUPPORTING STRENGTHS AND STANDARD INSTALLATIONS

FIGURES

TABLES

Page

Figures

Page

FIGURES

Page

CHAPTER 1

DEVELOPMENT OF TECHNOLOGY

The growth of the precast concrete pipe industry has paralleled the rapid advance of technology over the last hundred years. The increased need and concern for waste treatment, water supply, irrigation and drainage for railroads, highways, and airports has resulted in the construction of more and larger pipelines. This chapter traces the development of technology as it relates to modern concrete pipe. From the viewpoint of the concrete pipe industry, history can be organized into the following periods:

- Early days Pre-1800
- Birth of the industry 1800–1880
- Technology and markets 1880–1930
- Advancement of the industry . . . Post-1930

EARLY DAYS . . . PRE-1800

Historical records include many references to engineering feats undertaken by ancient civilizations to collect and convey water. Archaeological explorations indicate an understanding of drainage principles existing very early in human history. For example, a sewer arch constructed about 3750 B.C. was unearthed in an excavation at Nippur, India. Another excavation in Tell Asmar, near Baghdad, exposed a sewer constructed in 2600 B.C. The Minoans, who lived in Crete about 1700 B.C., were master builders and installed elaborate systems of stone drains which carried sewage and drainage.

Most renowned of these early construction efforts were the aqueducts of Rome. The water carried by these aqueducts was used primarily as a supply of drinking water and to carry sewage through Rome's main sewer, the Cloacae Maxima. Built in 800 B.C., and constructed mainly of stone masonry and natural cement, the Cloacae Maxima was the first known man-made waterborne method of sewage disposal. After more than 2000 years, sections of this concrete sewer are still being utilized.

Crude, but functional, sewers also existed in the ancient cities of Babylon, Jerusalem, Byzantium and Paris. Not surprisingly, these cities were noted for their peculiarly bitter and offensive odor.

Early cities tended to develop around waterways. The ancient Britons located Londonium, now the city of London, at the confluence of the Thames River and Fleet Street Creek because they wanted to be on tidewater and adjacent to the sparkling clean drinking water of Fleet Street Creek. As the encampment grew into a town, the water became so polluted with sewage the residents had to go elsewhere for drinking water. As Londonium grew into a city, Fleet Street Creek was covered over with stone and converted into a combined sanitary and storm sewer.

Elsewhere, the sewers of Istanbul were originally creeks supplying drinking water for the Byzantians. The sons of Romulus and Remus camped along the brook which became the Cloacae Maxima, and the Indians of Manhattan Island camped along the banks of what is now the Canal Street Sewer. This universal pattern has been followed by mankind

Illustration 1.1

"After a rain the streets of Paris were a morass of that peculiarly sticky offensive mud compounded of sewage and garbage. The stench was unbelievably bitter and acrid." *Gibbon*

through the ages. A settlement was located near clean drinking water, which eventually became polluted by sewage, and the natural stream became a sewer. It was then often arched over with masonry.

As the great cities grew and people built permanent homes, increasingly greater amounts of sewage, garbage and refuse were deposited in the streets. When the piles became high, and the odor nuisance great enough, the filth was removed using picks, shovels and carts. This condition existed until the early part of the 19th century when water distribution systems made it possible to use water to carry off the sewage. Many cities like Paris, London and Baltimore tried cesspools with disastrous results. The cesspools became breeding areas for disease. It took the waterborne sewage disposal system to clean up the large cities from health and aesthetic standpoints.

Historical records contain many other pre-1800 references relative to drainage. Cato, writing two hundred years before the Christian era, gave explicit directions on drainage and irrigation for agricultural uses.

Very little theoretical pipeline technology existed prior to the 19th century. In 1775, however, the precursor of the modern formula for relating velocity of flow and head loss due to friction in open channel flow was developed by Antoine Chezy, a French engineer and mathematician. It was over 50 years before significant improvements to his concept were recorded.

During the first 5000 years of recorded history, the need for sewers, water supply, and drainage was recognized and practical methods for handling the flow of water were developed. From the remains of ancient structures, it is apparent that the building materials progressed from relatively simple applications of natural materials to cast concrete. In many applications, permanency was a major requirement, and concrete was one of the earliest substitutes for natural stone. While not all stone and concrete structures were able to survive the ravages of time, weather and warfare, concrete has an ancient and notable heritage.

BIRTH OF THE INDUSTRY . . . 1800–1880

The 19th century brought a period of political consolidation and industrial expansion, and the push toward the American West began. Three areas of expansion during this period produced the beginnings of the concrete pipe industry; public health requirements for water and sewage treatment, transportation, and agricultural needs for irrigation and drainage.

PUBLIC HEALTH

Sewage disposal methods did not improve until the early 1840's when the first modern sewer was built in Hamburg, Germany. It was modern in the sense that houses were connected to a sewer system, with the sanitary sewers being separated from the storm sewers.

In 1848, the Metropolitan Commission of Sewers in London reported to Parliament that a need existed for extensive sewer systems and other sanitary improvements. The cholera epidemics that ravaged England around 1854 clearly demonstrated the need for improvements in sewage disposal. However, actual construction of a designed sewer system did not begin until 1859.

As in London, a cholera epidemic in Paris was responsible for more effective sewer systems in that city. The first study of sewerage needs for Paris was made in 1808. At that time there were 14 1/2 miles of drains and approximately 40 outlets into the Seine River. Even though the system was expanded by constructing an additional 10 miles of sewers during the next twenty-five years, cholera again broke out in epidemic proportions in 1832.

Illustration 1.2
Water and sewer system of Paris, cross-section. *Woodcut, circa 1880.*

Many of the early sewers in America were built in small towns and financed with local funds. Because of this, and the lack of accurate records, details of the earlier sewerage projects are unknown. The oldest recorded concrete pipe sanitary sewer installation was in 1842 at Mohawk, New York.

The initial conception of engineered sewer systems in America has been credited to Julius W. Adams who designed the sewers of Brooklyn, New York in 1857. His designs were used as a model for years. The largest sewer at this time was built in Boston, Massachusetts in 1876. This was the first interceptor sewer system in America authorized by a state legislature. It was designed and constructed by Joseph P. Davis who became an internationally famous specialist in the design of sewer systems.

A significant impetus to the growing concern for public health was the yellow fever epidemic which broke out in Memphis, Tennessee in 1873 and caused more than 2000 deaths. In 1878, there were 5150 deaths from this disease. These conditions were largely responsible for the formation of the National Board of Health, the forerunner of the U.S. Public Health Service. The Board assisted Memphis in the design and construction of a sanitary sewer system. By 1880, at least 20 major cities in the United States had concrete pipe sewer lines.

TRANSPORTATION

Waterways, such as Long Island Sound, Albemarle Sound and Chesapeake Bay, provided the principal arteries for travel and commerce. Roads in various stages of development extended from these arteries. A few roads within the large cities had drainage ditches and were sometimes surfaced with gravel, stone or shell. The rest were improved only to the extent of having stumps and boulders removed. Many were impassable for wheeled vehicles in winter or during spring thaws. Travelers crossed small streams by fording and large ones by ferrying.

In the northern regions, earth roads were quagmires during the spring thaw and became distressingly soft during rains at any time of year. Loose sand was also a problem in many areas. After 1820, the ideas of the Scotsman John L. McAdam revolutionized American road building. McAdam was responsible for the good roads around Bristol, England. He asserted that the native soil alone could support the traffic and the only function of the road was to protect the base soil from water and abrasion. **Macadam roads** were 6 to 10 inches thick and made of angular broken stones, packed by traffic into a dense, interlocking mass. The first American road built according to McAdam's principle was the Boonsborough to Hagerstown Turnpike in Maryland, completed in 1822.

Meanwhile, railroads were beginning to expand. The railroad had originated in England with the first line completed between Stockton and Darlington in 1825. In 1827, Maryland chartered the Baltimore and Ohio Railroad Company as the first commercial common carrier. The line ran to the Ohio River and channeled goods from the West across the Allegheny Mountains to the Port of Baltimore. Within ten years, over 200 railroad companies were in some stage of development.

Aided by telegraph and other improvements, the railroads moved westward and played an important role in the development of the West. By 1860, a 30,000 mile network had evolved from a group of disconnected lines. The driving of the *Golden Spike* in 1869 at Promontory Point, Utah, marked the completion by Union Pacific and Central Pacific of the first transcontinental railroad.

One of the earliest railroad culverts was constructed near Salem, Illinois in 1854, an installation that was still in service over a century later. The Memphis Division of the Louisville and Nashville Railroad constructed three nonreinforced concrete pipe culverts in 1855 and 1857. Approximately 40 concrete pipe culverts, ranging in diameter from 10 to 20 inches, were installed in 1877 on the Cambridge Junction line of the Central Vermont Railway.

AGRICULTURE

Early drainage of farm and irrigated lands consisted mainly of small open ditches which served to carry excess water away from low-lying areas. Concrete drain tile was developed in Holland in the 1830's, and introduced in America in the 1840's.

In subsequent years, small size concrete pipe drain tile became increasingly important in the agricultural development of New England and the rolling prairies of the Midwest. Through the use of drain tile, available farm acreage, quality and quantity of farm products, and the value of the farmland were increased. By 1884, in the state of Ohio alone, 11 million acres of land were served by 20,000 miles of drain tile.

The California Gold Rush increased demand for agricultural production because of the heavy influx of miners and settlers. The need for efficient irrigation spurred the development of pipe production and installation technology. In fact, the settlement and development of the western half of the United States depended to a large extent on the irrigation of land.

Scientific knowledge was first applied to the problem of irrigation and drainage in the latter half of the 19th century. Land grant colleges in the midwestern and western states began the investigation of water, crop and soil relationships.

West of the Allegheny Mountains concrete pipe production became increasingly important as the benefits of its use became more widely recog-

Illustration 1.3
1914 method of moving large tile on soft ground.

nized. To effectively utilize irrigation and drainage pipe, farmers needed a continuous supply. As demand outstripped the production capabilities, and the economics of mass production became apparent, machines were developed to maufacture concrete pipe.

THE CONCRETE PIPE INDUSTRY

Concrete sewer pipe was developed during the 19th century after the public became conscious of the needs for sanitation. Many installations of concrete pipe had been made prior to 1880, and its durability characteristics soon became apparent.

The large sewers constructed in Paris during the middle of the 19th century were built of rough stone heavily plastered with cement on the interior. Dr. Rudolph Hering, a well-known sanitary engineer, reported in 1915 that his examination of the interior surfaces of these sewers found them to be "quite good." He attributed this to the density and the smoothness of the plaster. In 1881, he had examined 10 to 20 year old concrete sewers in Vienna and found no deterioration.

Many of the concrete pipelines installed in New England during the latter half of the 19th century are still in use today. In Chelsea, Massachusetts, one of the earliest concrete pipe sewers was installed in 1869 and continues to function satisfactorily.

In 1868, a concrete pipe sanitary sewer was installed in St. Louis, Missouri. An examination in 1962 showed the line to be in excellent condition, and it remained in service. A concrete pipeline installed as a combined sewer in St. Paul, Minnesota in 1875 is serving satisfactorily a century later. Between 1875 and 1888, this city installed over 94,000 linear feet of concrete pipe for combined sewers. These pipelines, varying in size from 9-inch circular to 21-inch by 28-inch oval, have provided 100 years of service.

TECHNOLOGY AND MARKETS . . . 1880–1930

The growth of the concrete pipe industry was greatly influenced by related technical and market developments. Modern design and construction of sewers and culverts, and the design and production of concrete pipe, have evolved from the basic work of the last 100 years. This activity included:

- Development of hydraulic and hydrologic theories
- Concepts for loads on pipe
- Standards for materials and tests

HYDRAULIC AND HYDROLOGIC THEORIES

The basic theory for modern pipeline design was developed over the latter half of the 19th century. Of principal interest were the studies to determine head loss from pipe wall roughness. These studies formed the basis for determining pipe size. Results of these early studies, beginning in the late 19th century, are still being applied, and the following were of major importance:

- Darcy and Weisbach, 1857, extended Chezy's open channel flow formula to pipe flow.
- Ganguillet and Kutter, 1869, published an evaluation of the Chezy friction coefficient.
- Osbourne Reynolds, 1883, discovered the fundamental law of hydraulics distinguishing between laminar and turbulent flow.
- Robert Manning, 1890, published a simplified formula for relating velocity and head loss.
- M. H. Bazin, 1897, published a paper on head loss based upon many different types of pipe materials.
- Hazen and Williams, 1902, developed an equation for flow in pressure and gravity flow pipelines.
- Yarnell, Nagher and Woodward, 1926, published the results of over 3300 experiments conducted at the State University of Iowa on flow of water through culverts.
- F. C. Scobey, 1920, advanced a formula for friction losses in pipe, flumes and canals that became widely used for irrigation pipelines.

Major hydrologic studies were conducted to determine the quantity of precipitation runoff to be carried by storm sewers and culverts, and principal contributors were:

- A. N. Talbot, 1887, developed a formula for runoff.
- Lloyd-Davies, 1906, developed the **Rational Method** that remains the most widely used formula for relating rainfall intensity to runoff.

LOADS ON PIPE

During the first three decades of the 20th century, researchers at Iowa State University developed and tested a theory for estimating loads on buried pipe. The original concept was advanced by Marston-Talbot, and the theory was developed by Marston and Anderson and published in 1913. A. Marston was joined by M. G. Spangler and W. J. Schlick and continued the work on evaluation of design loads. In 1930, Marston published *The Theory of External Loads on Closed Conduits in the Light of the Latest Experiments* which presents the theory in its present form. During this same period, the three-edge bearing test was developed as a method for evaluating the strength of rigid pipe. Other Iowa reports include Schlick's tests of pipe on concrete cradles and Spangler's classic report on the supporting strength of rigid pipe culverts which still serves as the principal design theory.

STANDARDS

The quality of concrete and concrete pipe received extensive attention throughout the early years of the 20th century. The major forum for these studies was the American Society for Testing and Materials, **ASTM.**

The history of concrete pipe standards began virtually with the founding of ASTM in 1898. By 1904, eight technical committees had been organized, and, in 1904, six more were formed. One of these, Committee C-4

Illustration 1.4
Section of 27-inch diameter concrete pipe, 4 feet long during test at Neville Island plant of Concrete Products Company of America, September 1924. First crack 15,250 pounds, ultimate 32,500 pounds.

on Clay and Cement-Concrete Sewer Pipe, was the forerunner of Committee C-13 on Concrete Pipe. Committee C-4 membership included manufacturers of both clay and concrete sewer pipe, and users of these products. By 1918, the following ASTM C-4 subcommittees on concrete pipe were in operation:

I. Absorption and hydrostatic pressure test requirements
II. Chemical requirements
III. Dimensions and their permissible variations
IV. Certain legal definitions
V. Glossary of terms

Subcommittee IV later became Methods of Testing, and Subcommittee V became Nomenclature and Definitions. Subcommittee I was subsequently broadened to Sampling and Physical Test Requirements and a new subcommittee, Required Safe Crushing Strengths of Sewer Pipe to Carry Loads from Ditch Filling, was added.

In 1919, the ASTM Joint Culvert Pipe Committee was formed and consisted of representatives of the American Association of State Highway Officials, American Concrete Institute, American Railway Engineering Association, American Society of Civil Engineers, American Society for Testing and Materials, Bureau of Public Roads, and American Concrete Pipe Association. The purpose of this committee was to develop a standard for reinforced concrete culvert pipe.

The committee's first report, published in 1926, contained a complete tentative standard for reinforced concrete culvert pipe ranging in diameter from 12 to 84 inches. The standard contained two pipe design tables for standard strength and two for extra-strength pipe. Under the direction of W. J. Schlick, strength tests were conducted on these pipe designs and the results used to modify the standard which was ultimately published in 1930 as C76-30T.

Committee C-4 also continued its sewer pipe work and produced tentative standard C 14, Plain Concrete Pipe and tentative standard C 75, Reinforced Concrete Pipe. The committee, however, found that disagreement between the competing material producers resulted in unnecessary debate, and C-4 was reorganized in 1929 into Subcommittee I on Clay Pipe and Subcommittee II on Cement-Concrete Pipe.

In 1930, Committee C-13 was formally organized and acquired jurisdiction over standards C 14, C 75 and C 76. By 1952, C-13 had grown to 54 members and substantially increased its scope of activities. A reorganization of the committee was completed in 1956, establishing an advisory committee and a subcommittee for each of its eight specifications. In 1956, Committee C-13 also acquired jurisdiction of C 412, Concrete Drain Tile, from Committee C-15 on Manufactured Masonry Units.

EXPANDING MARKETS

The demand for sanitary and storm sewers continued into the early decades of the 20th century. By 1915, most major cities had relatively exten-

Illustration 1.5
Layout of rings and forms for making concrete by the hand tamped method. Bent Brothers Company, Henrietta California, 1912.

sive sanitary sewer systems. Many large cities, as well as smaller ones, used concrete pipe for sewer systems.

Major subaqueous sewer outfall installations began in the early 1900's:

- In 1916–18 Cleveland, Ohio extended sewers up to 3200 feet into Lake Erie.
- In 1924 Los Angeles, California completed construction of a 15.4 mile outfall sewer built entirely of reinforced concrete pipe.
- In 1925 Ashtabula, Ohio ran a sewer line 2500 feet into Lake Erie.
- In 1926 Seattle, Washington constructed a seven mile concrete pipe sewer to divert sewage to Puget Sound instead of Lake Washington.

Drainage for agricultural purposes was also experiencing rapid expansion in the United States. The first extensive census of rural land drainage undertaken in 1920 recorded over 157,000 miles of drains serving approximately 66 million acres. It was estimated that an additional 55 million acres were served by private farm drains. The rapid expansion of drainage was directly aided by the introduction of high production methods of drain tile manufacture.

A changing era in transportation began with the shift from the need for local roads and streets to a more general, comprehensive connected system. The Office of Road Inquiry was formed in the U.S. Department of Agriculture in 1893 to deal with local road problems. The increase in the number of automobiles between 1905 and 1918, from 50,000 to 6.2 million, indicated the direction of transportation development. Following ten years of debate the Road Act of 1916 established the concept of a national system of highways. The U.S. Office of Public Roads, formed in 1916, became the U.S. Bureau of Public Roads in 1919, but remained in the Department of Agriculture until 1939.

Local governments were also organizing highway departments. The growth of roads and highways resulted in a rapid increase in the use of concrete pipe. While the needs of the 19th century centered on public health and agriculture, the emphasis of the 20th century was to be on transportation needs. The demand for surfaced roads, reasonable grades and drainage became essential considerations in highway design. By 1930, all states were using concrete pipe in highway construction.

Many railroads were using concrete pipe for culverts. The railroads were the first to jack pipe under railroad embankments, and, in 1926, the first jacked installation using reinforced concrete pipe was completed.

EXPANDING INDUSTRY

The 20th century brought new technology, new standards, and a new rate of growth for the concrete pipe industry. The need to improve quality and

Illustration 1.6
Sixty-nine feet of 96-inch reinforced concrete pipe was jacked under Delaware, Lackawanna & Western Railroad in 1940 in Elmira, New York as a pedestrian underpass.

production capabilities was recognized and on January 23, 1907, the Interstate Cement Tile Manufacturers Association was formed. In 1914, the name of the organization was changed to the American Concrete Pipe Association, *ACPA*.

Organizers of the Association considered the development of a product of standard and uniform quality to be of greatest importance to the new industry. Most of the early discussions at annual meetings were concerned with ways and means of improving quality in concrete drain tile, and, by 1914, a specification for drain tile was under development.

Perhaps the most significant product change during this period came with the introduction of reinforced concrete pipe. Reinforcement was first used in France in 1896 and the concept was brought to America in 1905. The first reinforced concrete culvert pipe was made by C. Frank Wilson of Wilson Concrete Company, Red Oak, Iowa, in 1905 by placing circular rings of reinforcement into the forms as the dry mix was tamped by hand.

During the first three decades of the 20th century, developments in production methods were dramatic. Beginning the century with a handmade product, demand catapulted the industry into automation and mass production techniques. Between 1925 and 1930, the production of concrete pipe doubled, from one to two million tons per year.

Shortly after 1900 in the Northwest, the first tamper machines were developed independently by Thompson, Hammond, Bullen and Ash. These early tampers had a stationary inner form with an outer revolving form. Dry mix concrete was mechanically tamped into the space between the forms by high speed wooden tamper sticks.

In Iowa in 1905, Zeidler and McCracken, working independently made the first packerhead concrete pipe manufacturing machines. At about the same time, Ernest Bent of the Western Concrete Pipe Company, pioneered the packerhead process on the West Coast. The packerhead process uses a stationary outside form. Dry mix is packed against that form by a revolving packerhead extended from a heavy shaft which travels upward within the form.

In 1906 the Quinn Wire and Iron Works of Boone, Iowa started making butt end concrete drain and culvert pipe using steel tamper sticks with both inner and outer forms revolving.

After 1906 almost all concrete pipe over 24 inches in diameter, as well as some as small as 18 inches, were manufactured with reinforcement.

In 1918 in Portland, Oregon, the Tuerck-MacKenzie Company pioneered the use of double tampers, making it possible to tamp on both sides of the reinforcement. Shortly thereafter, several other tamper machines were developed by Martin Iron Works in Los Angeles, California, Sherman in Knoxville, Tennessee and Universal Company of Columbus, Ohio.

Before 1920, Gray in Thomasville, North Carolina and Bullen in Portland, Oregon, working independently, added legs to the lower pallet ring so that when the outside forms were stripped, the forms would drop and break the bond between the fresh concrete and the form.

In 1920 Hume of Melbourne, Australia toured America to establish interest in his centrifugal method of making concrete pipe. His method had been in use since 1912 in plants in Australia, New Zealand, India, Southeast Asia and Peru. Plants were subsequently established in Los Angeles, Detroit, Boston, and Dallas.

In 1922 Mohr-Buchanan centrifugal plants were built in Montreal and Los Angeles by the United Concrete Pipe Company. The Mohr-Buchanan process was a centrifugal method developed in Scotland using a form coated on the inside with a layer of wax. In the curing process, the wax melted, running off to be used again, and the one piece outside form easily stripped.

In 1922 the Lock Joint Pipe Company, using a process differing from the Hume concept, built and operated several centrifugal machines in the eastern United States.

About 1925 Nichols in Detroit, Michigan and Trammel in Forth Worth, Texas and Dayton, Ohio also made concrete pipe by centrifugal processes.

ADVANCEMENT OF THE INDUSTRY . . . Post-1930

The growth of the concrete pipe industry has been spectacular since the 1930's. Following the depression years and World War II, annual produc-

Illustration 1.7
Early 1900's plant for manufacturing small diameter concrete pipe with packerhead equipment.

tion doubled to 4 million tons by 1950. During each of the two succeeding decades, production increased by approximately 3 million tons, reaching a production level of more than 10 million tons annually by 1970. By the middle 1970's, the annual market value of production exceeded one billion dollars.

A series of events significantly influencing public works construction were taking place during this period. With the introduction of industrial production methods the economy was booming in the mid 1920's. The years that followed were a series of cycles that can be grouped into:

- Great depression
- World War II
- Automobile age
- Environmental era
- Energy era

The Depression and World War II were difficult times, an economic crisis followed by a fight for national survival. During the 1930's public works construction was deferred except as undertaken in the Works Progress Administration, WPA, Public Works Administration, PWA, Civilian Conservation Corps, CCC and other programs for providing economic relief through labor intensive activities. Prior to the depression years, concrete pipe had made limited penetration into the 6-inch to 24-inch diameter market. Federal agencies administering the public works pro-

Illustration 1.8
Installation of 72-inch concrete pipe during runway extension at Memphis International Airport during early 1950's.

grams insisted on alternate bidding and production of small diameter pipe increased markedly. The various agencies were designing and constructing projects using more concrete pipe than in any previous period.

The period from 1945 to 1965 was dominated by the needs of the automobile, with main thrust being the construction of the Interstate Highway System. In 1956, the initiation of the $4 billion per year investment produced an irreversible change both in transportation and in daily life.

In the mid-1960's, concerns with air and water pollution had an adverse effect on public works construction and resulted in the passage of the National Environmental Policy Act in 1969. The Act continued and accelerated the trend toward reduction of water and air pollution.

Concern for a cleaner environment had not abated by the early 1970's, when a new crisis arose directing attention to energy. Near the close of the 1970's, the impact of the energy issue on public works was still unclear.

The advancement of the concrete pipe industry from the 1930's to the 1970's can be attributed to the following major factors:

- Analysis of performance surveys
- Increased acceptance of concrete pipe
- Continued advancement in technology
- Improvements in pipe production and quality

PERFORMANCE SURVEYS

The permanence of high quality portland cement concrete under normal field conditions has been demonstrated. Nonetheless, the conservative attitude of engineers and the desire by pipe manufacturers to establish the conditions under which concrete pipe could be best utilized led to a series of performance surveys beginning early in the 1930's. ACPA and many state and federal agencies undertook such studies and have continued to review performance on a periodic basis.

A major series of surveys was started in 1929 and reported periodically in the 1930's by M. W. Loving, Managing Director of ACPA. The 1929 survey included 191 sewers in 43 cities and covered over 24 miles of pipe ranging in size from 30 inches to 108 inches in diameter. All of the pipe had been in place since 1906. Another survey was conducted in 1931 by H. Z. Delzell who examined more than 155 highway and railroad culverts in Pennsylvania, New Jersey, Delaware and Maryland. These, and similar efforts, led to improvements in the bedding of concrete pipe and to the theoretical solutions for earth loads.

During this period of evaluations, many pipelines were examined and the durability of concrete pipe was firmly established. More than any other single factor, these surveys led to the development of standards and to wide acceptance and use of concrete pipe.

ACCEPTANCE OF CONCRETE PIPE

The use of concrete pipe for sanitary and storm sewers and for culverts under highways and railroads had been steadily growing during the years

Illustration 1.9
Part of 12,000 feet of 18-inch sanitary sewer outfall constructed in Norman, Oklahoma in the spring of 1938.

prior to 1930. During the 1930's wide acceptance developed and over 2 million tons of concrete pipe were produced.

Sanitary Sewers

With financial assistance from WPA, many sanitary sewers were installed in the 1930's. Following are some typical installations:

- Chicago, Illinois
  over 50 miles of 6-inch to 102-inch concrete pipe (1935–1940)
- Hammond, Indiana
  over 10 miles of 21-inch to 60-inch concrete pipe (1935–1940)
- Gary, Indiana
  17 miles of 12-inch to 108-inch concrete pipe (1935–1940)
- Henrico Co., Virginia
  over 8 miles of 8-inch to 30-inch concrete pipe (1939)
- Arlington Co., Virginia
  130 miles of 8-inch to 42-inch concrete pipe (1934–1936)
- Fox River Valley, Wisconsin
  46 miles of concrete pipe interceptor (1930–1940)
- Houston, Texas
  over 380 miles of 6-inch to 24-inch concrete pipe (1928–1937)
- Detroit, Michigan
  over 300 miles of concrete pipe sewer lines (1927–1938)

Transportation

New developments in highways during the 1930 decade resulted in increased use of concrete pipe. Extensive use was made of concrete pipe on the 775 miles of the Pan American Highway from Laredo, Texas to Mexico City. Also constructed was the first of the modern freeways, the Pennsylvania Turnpike, which used over 55 miles of concrete pipe ranging in diameter from 12-inch to 72-inch.

Railroads continued to expand and, by 1935, the following major installations of concrete pipe had been made:

- Burlington
  10,000 concrete pipe culverts, 12-inch to 72-inch in diameter
- Chicago, Milwaukee, St. Paul and Pacific
  over 4,000 concrete pipe culverts with a height of earth cover from two to 100 feet
- Northern Pacific
  over 4,000 concrete pipe culverts
- Atcheson, Topeka and Santa Fe
  over 2,000 concrete pipe culverts, 18-inch to 80-inch

The development and construction of major airport facilities began during the 1930's. Between 1930 and 1940, almost 400 miles of 4-inch to 66-inch diameter concrete pipe was used in army, navy and municipal airports.

Table 1.1. Dates When Some Cities Began Using Concrete Pipe Sewers.

City	Year	City	Year
Mohawk, New York	1842	Louisville, Kentucky	1889
Newark, New Jersey	1867	South Bend, Indiana	1889
Hudson, New York	1867	Wausau, Wisconsin	1890
Nashua, New Hampshire	1868	Superior, Wisconsin	1891
Chelsea, Massachusetts	1869	Salt Lake City, Utah	1893
New Haven, Connecticut	1869	Atlanta, Georgia	1895
Savannah, Georgia	1870	Augusta, Georgia	1895
San Francisco, California	1870	Springfield, Massachusetts	1895
Milwaukee, Wisconsin	1871	Bangor, Maine	1896
New London, Connecticut	1873	Eau Claire, Wisconsin	1899
Portland, Maine	1873	Oakland, California	1899
Kokomo, Indiana	1874	Kalamazoo, Michigan	1903
North Adams, Massachusetts	1874	Trenton, New Jersey	1903
Grand Rapids, Michigan	1875	Salem, Oregon	1903
Chicopee, Massachusetts	1875	Janesville, Wisconsin	1904
Indianapolis, Indiana	1878	Jackson, Michigan	1905
Lockport, New York	1879	Cleveland, Ohio	1906
Rutland, Vermont	1879	Springfield, Ohio	1907
Utica, New York	1879	Sacramento, California	1908
Bay City, Michigan	1880	Richmond, Indiana	1908
North Manchester, Indiana	1881	Albuquerque, New Mexico	1908
Racine, Wisconsin	1883	Spokane, Washington	1908
Appleton, Wisconsin	1883	Watertown, New York	1909
Oshkosh, Wisconsin	1884	Tacoma, Washington	1909
Los Angeles, California	1885	Lancaster Pennsylvania	1910
Minneapolis, Minnesota	1886	La Crosse, Wisconsin	1910
St. Paul, Minnesota	1886	Bakersfield, California	1911
Portland, Oregon	1888	Syracuse, New York	1911
Helena, Montana	1889	Lansing, Michigan	1912
Galveston, Texas	1889	Kansas City, Missouri	1912
Greeley, Colorado	1889	Everett, Washington	1913
Waukesha, Wisconsin	1889		

Table 1.2. Dates When States Began Using Concrete Pipe Highway Culverts.

State	Date
Alabama	Prior to 1921
Arizona	1927
Arkansas	Prior to 1927
California	1925
Colorado	Prior to 1920
Connecticut	1923
Delaware	1920
District of Columbia	1935
Florida	1933
Georgia	1920
Hawaii	1925
Idaho	1925
Illinois	1930
Indiana	1919
Iowa	1906
Kansas	1917
Kentucky	1923
Louisiana	1921
Maine	1928
Maryland	1908
Massachusetts	1924
Michigan	1918
Minnesota	1921
Mississippi	1926
Missouri	1930
Montana	1922
Nebraska	1917
Nevada	1924
New Hampshire	1927
New Jersey	1920
New Mexico	1939
New York	1923
North Carolina	1916
North Dakota	1923
Ohio	1929
Oklahoma	Prior to 1924
Oregon	1917
Pennsylvania	Prior to 1916
Rhode Island	1936
South Carolina	1918
South Dakota	1920
Tennessee	1920
Texas	Prior to 1930
Utah	About 1920
Vermont	About 1921
Virginia	1923
Washington	About 1919
West Virginia	1922
Wisconsin	About 1930
Wyoming	1935

Table 1.3. Dates When Concrete Pipe Railway Culverts Were First Installed.

Railway	Date
New York Central (Michigan Division)	1870
Louisville and Nashville	1870
Boston and Maine	1903
Canadian Pacific	1903
Delaware-Lackawanna & Western	1905
Southern Pacific Company	1905
Chicago, Burlington & Quincy	1906
Duluth, Missabe & Iron Range	1908
Northern Pacific	1909
Baltimore & Ohio	1910
Canadian National Railways	1910
Kansas City Southern	1910
Sand Springs Railway Co.	1911
Elgin, Joliet & Eastern	1912
Great Northern	1912
Illinois Central	1912
Mississippi Central	1912
The Pennsylvania Railroad	1912
The Western Pacific	1912
Atlantic Coast Line	1913
Chicago, Milwaukee, St. Paul & Pacific R.R. Co.	1913
Atchison, Topeka & Santa Fe	1914
Chicago & Illinois Midland	1914
Central of Georgia	1914
Southern Railway Co.	1914

Irrigation

The Bureau of Reclamation was instrumental in the expansion of the concrete pipe industry with extensive irrigation installations in Washington, Oregon, California, and Texas from 1925 to 1940. One of the major irrigation programs was the Central Valley Project in California. Another major project was for the irrigation district of the Lower Rio Grande Valley of Texas. More than 650 miles of concrete irrigation pipe were used on this project.

ADVANCEMENT OF TECHNOLOGY

While much of the theory had been developed prior to 1930, subsequent research and standardization contributed greatly to refinement of the earlier standards. In the early 1950's jointing of concrete pipe evolved from the basic mortar joint to flexible joints using rubber gaskets of various designs. In the 1960's, equipment to produce and handle pipe in longer lengths, up to sixteen feet, was introduced.

Research

The major challenge to the concrete pipe industry was to produce a uniform, high quality product while increasing the production rate to meet demand. It was recognized that the future of the industry depended upon products being manufactured as economically as possible, without loss of quality. Research was continued, therefore, as a means of assuring confidence in concrete pipe and its increased use. This research was spon-

Illustration 1.10
Loading large diameter concrete pipe for sand bearing test of 102 and 108-inch sewer pipe for Sacramento, California in 1927.

sored by producers, consumers, trade associations, universities, technical societies, and joint cooperative studies involving two or more of these groups. The following review of research activities will provide some insight into its role in the growth of the concrete pipe industry.

Strength Requirements

A systematic evaluation of the field performance of concrete pipe was conducted, and a series of modifications were made in the theoretical solutions that had been advanced by Talbot in 1908. These empirical approaches were used from 1930 through the 1950's. In the early 1950's, ACPA made a study of the design procedures which led to a report entitled "*D*-Load Design and Tests of Concrete Pipe." The report recommended pipe designs to resist external loadings based upon results of three-edge bearing tests. The recommended designs covered most production conditions in the industry, and are still in ASTM standards for reinforced concrete culvert, storm drain and sewer pipe.

Also in the 1950's, the Bureau of Reclamation published Engineering Monograph No. 6, "Stress Analysis of Concrete Pipe." This contained Olander's analysis of stresses in concrete pipe for a given bedding and backfilling, which considered the weights of the pipe and the water in the pipe.

In the latter part of the 1950's, the American Iron and Steel Institute sponsored a testing program under the direction of Frank J. Heger at Massachusetts Institute of Technology. As a result of the tests, Heger and his associates prepared two reports, *Structural Behavior of Circular Concrete Pipe Reinforced With Welded Wire Fabric* and *The Structural Behavior of Circular Reinforced Concrete Pipe—Development of Theory.*

Pipe Loads

In 1946, Spangler summarized the early work conducted at Iowa State, as well as subsequent refinements. This summary, *Analysis of Loads and Supporting Strength and Principles of Design for Highway Culverts* was published in the 1946 Proceedings of the Highway Research Board and is the most commonly used design reference. In 1956, Ericson, Bridge Engineer of the U.S. Bureau of Public Roads, and his associates simplified the Marston, Schlick, and Spangler equations into tables and charts which were published as *Design and Installation Criteria for Reinforced Concrete Pipe Culverts.*

A major research project was initiated in 1970 at Northwestern University by ACPA. This study, geared to more precise techniques for designing concrete pipe to withstand external loads, is discussed in more detail in *Chapter 10.*

Hydraulics of Concrete Pipe

In 1948 ACPA sponsored research at St. Anthony Falls Hydraulic Laboratory of the University of Minnesota under the direction of Lorenz G. Straub. The results of this work, including authoritative roughness coefficients, entrance losses and energy characteristics, were published in a series of technical papers. The work of Straub was reviewed by the U.S. Bureau of Public Roads, and, in 1961, was accepted and published under the titles *Hydraulic Charts for the Selection of Highway Culverts, Hydraulic Engineering Circular No. 5,* and *Instructions for Use of Culvert Design Charts.*

Hydrogen Sulfide in Sanitary Sewers

Sewage under certain conditions may produce hydrogen sulfide gas, which in turn may be transformed into sulfuric acid. ACPA sponsored research to determine the mechanism for production of hydrogen sulfide and sulfuric acid. One of the early reports on the subject was *Progress Report on Sulfide Control Research* by Pomeroy and Bowlus in 1946. Other authoritative works on the subject include *Influence of Velocity on Sulfide Generation in Sewers* by Davy in 1950; and *Mechanics of Corrosion of Concrete Sewers by Hydrogen Sulfide* by Parker in 1951. Later research and current methods of design and preventive techniques are discussed in detail in *Chapter 7.*

Standards

Throughout the period from 1930 to the 1970's, concrete pipe standards were developed and constant additions, reviews and revisions were made. As discussed in *Chapter 8,* ASTM provides the most representative committees because membership consists of producers, designers and consumers. ASTM standards have been used as the primary source for specifications by government agencies and the private sector.

PRODUCTION

As research, standardization and increases in demand for concrete pipe continued, the industry rapidly changed. In addition to modifications to previously discussed processes, industrialization resulted in the investigation of other processes.

In 1945 Johnson of California, using Johnson-Prosser patents, centrifugated concrete pipe, spinning the form on the bottom, inside a drum spinner. This process was used by plants in California and Texas. About the same time, Peterson and Colosey of the Concrete Products Company of America at Pottstown, Pennsylvania developed and manufactured concrete pipe by a process using a vacuum to remove excess water.

In 1947 and 1948 Fitzpatrick of the Rocla Concrete Pipe Co. Ltd. of Melbourne, Australia made the first of several trips to the United States and established the roller suspension process. Rocla licensed the United States rights to Gifford-Hill-American and under license production began at Valley Concrete Pipe Company at Harlingen, Texas, and Wilson Concrete Pipe Company in Red Oak, Iowa. Later the process was used by the

Gifford-Hill Pipe Company of Dallas, and Lock Joint Pipe Company of New Jersey. In this type of manufacture, a circular form is suspended horizontally on a heavy spindle which, when rotated, revolves the form.

In the early 1950's Jessen of Salt Lake City, Utah developed the Cen-Vi-Ro process which uses a combination of centrifugal, vibration and roller processes. In the Cen-Vi-Ro process the form is spun by rubber truck tires with arrangements so that the form can be also vibrated.

As noted earlier, concrete pipe is produced locally in response to local demand. The production processes are therefore greatly influenced by local conditions. For relatively heavy demand, sophisticated and automated plants have been developed to increase production and reduce costs.

SUMMARY

Modern man cannot live in cities without adequate sanitary sewers, storm sewers and culverts. Concrete pipe is a strong, durable, economical commodity which makes many of our modern sewer systems possible. Most of the Interstate Highway System, many miles of primary and secondary highways, long stretches of railroad lines and airports could not exist without drainage. Concrete pipe provides this drainage and is also widely used for irrigation and farm drainage.

Precast concrete pipe is manufactured in plants under controlled conditions. It is manufactured to meet exacting standards and tested to insure rigorous adherence to these standards.

Concrete pipe is readily available in all parts of the United States and Canada. It is made in modern plants, using local labor, materials and financing. In 1978 production had reached new heights. Sales of concrete sewer and culvert pipe amounted to 12.9 million tons, more than a 300 percent increase over 1947 sales of 4.2 million tons.

REFERENCES

1. "Cement Pipes and Tile," E. S. Hanson, Cement Era Publishing Company, 1911.
2. "Concrete Pipe for Irrigation and Drainage," H. F. Peckworth, American Concrete Pipe Association, 1961.
3. "Concrete Pipe Handbook," H. F. Peckworth, American Concrete Pipe Association, 1967.
4. "Concrete Pipe Lines," M. W. Loving, American Concrete Pipe Association, 1942.
5. "Fiftieth Anniversary History," H. F. Peckworth, American Concrete Pipe Association, 1958.
6. "History of Public Works in the United States 1776–1976," American Public Works Association, 1976.
7. "History of Tile Drainage," M. M. Weaver, 1964.
8. "Modern Sanitation with Concrete Pipe," American Concrete Pipe Association, 1963.
9. "Official Proceedings," American Concrete Pipe Association, 1908 to 1979.
10. "Pictorial History of Road Building," C. W. Wixom, American Road Builders Association, 1975.

CHAPTER 2

MATERIALS AND MANUFACTURE

Many factors have contributed to the success of the concrete pipe industry. Important among these are the ability to use locally available materials, production plants located close to construction projects, and personal services regularly provided by the manufacturer to engineers, contractors and public officials. Included in these services are design and specification assistance, seminars, plant tours and the ability to quickly accommodate the changing needs of contractors by shipping daily to the project site.

Concrete pipe is manufactured throughout North America. The distance concrete pipe is transported from point of manufacture to the installation site varies. In densely populated areas a haul exceeding 75 miles would be unusual, while in less densely populated areas haul distances may exceed 200 miles.

Expansion and improvement of sewer systems and highways are closely tied to the needs and economics of an area. Employees and owners of concrete pipe plants usually live near where the pipe is manufactured and installed. They are dependent on and vitally interested in the services provided by the community. The local nature of the concrete pipe industry allows the pipe manufacturer to contribute to the community and benefit from its expansion.

The quality of precast concrete pipe has also contributed to its success. The quality is obtained from sophisticated facilities, processes and equipment integrated under controlled conditions. While a number of different processes are used, each is capable of producing precast concrete pipe that conform to the requirements of applicable ASTM standards. Discussed briefly in this chapter are the component materials, techniques and equipment used to obtain a consistently high quality product.

MATERIALS

Materials used in the manufacture of precast concrete pipe consist of locally available aggregates and manufactured products, such as portland cement and steel reinforcement. Each of the materials is covered by an ASTM standard relative to its properties and methods of testing.

PORTLAND CEMENT

Portland cement, is a closely controlled chemical combination of calcium, silicon, aluminum, iron, and small amounts of other compounds, to which gypsum is added in the final grinding process to regulate the setting time of the concrete. Some of the raw materials used to manufacture cement are limestone, shells, and chalk or marl, combined with shale, clay, slate or blast furnace slag, silica sand, and iron ore. Lime and silica make up approximately 85 percent of the mass. Each step in the manufacture of portland cement is monitored by frequent chemical and physical tests. The finished product is analyzed and tested to ensure compliance with the applicable standards of specifying agencies.

In the wet manufacturing process, the properly proportioned raw materials are ground with water, thoroughly mixed, and fed into the kiln as a slurry. In the dry process, raw materials are ground, mixed, and fed into the kiln in a dry state. Kilns are mounted with the axis inclined slightly from the horizontal and the finely ground raw material or slurry is fed into the higher end. The raw material is heated to approximately 2700 degrees Fahrenheit in cylindrical steel rotary kilns lined with special firebrick. As the material moves through the kiln, certain elements are driven off in the form of gases. The materials unite to form a substance, called **clinker,** about the size of marbles. Clinker is discharged red hot from the lower end of the kiln and cooled to handling temperature. The clinker is either stockpiled for future use or conveyed immediately to a series of grinding machines where gypsum is added. The final grinding operation reduces the clinker and gypsum to a powder so fine that more than 90 percent will pass through a screen containing 40,000 openings per square inch and more than 80 percent will pass through a screen that has 100,000 openings per square inch.

For practical purposes, portland cements may be considered as being composed of four principal compounds with chemical formulas and abbreviations as shown in *Table 2.1*. Most of the strength developing characteristics are controlled by the tricalcium silicate, C_3S, and dicalcium silicate, C_2S. Together, these two compounds usually total more than 70 percent of the cement for most types.

Portland cements are produced to meet ASTM Standard C 150 and classified into five types described in the following paragraphs. This standard sets limits for chemical composition, fineness of grind, setting time, strength at certain ages, resistance to chemical attack, and rate of development of heat of hydration. All types of cements are not available in every market area, and it is recommended the local pipe manufactures be consulted regarding cement type.

Table 2.1. Four Principal Compounds of Portland Cement.

Compound	Chemical Formula	Abbreviation
Tricalcium silicate	$3CaO \cdot SiO_2$	C_3S
Dicalcium silicate	$2CaO \cdot SiO_2$	C_2S
Tricalcium aluminate	$3CaO \cdot Al_2O_3$	C_3A
Tetracalcium aluminoferrite	$4CaO \cdot Al_2O_2 \cdot Fe_2O_3$	C_4AF

Type I. Normal Portland Cement

Type I cement is a general purpose cement suitable for all uses when the special properties of the other types are not required. It is used in pavement and sidewalk construction, concrete buildings and bridges, railway structures, tanks and reservoirs, sewers, culverts, water pipe, masonry units, soil-cement mixtures, and any use not subject to sulfates or where the heat of hydration is not critical.

Type II. Modified Portland Cement

Type II cement has a lower heat of hydration than Type I, improved resistance to sulfate attack, and is intended for use in structures of considerable size to minimize temperature rise. Applications include large piers, heavy abutments and heavy retaining walls when the concrete is placed in warm weather. In cold weather when heat generation is an advantage, Type I cement may be preferred. Type II cement is also intended for places where protection against sulfate attack is required, as in drainage structures where soil sulfate concentrations are higher than normal but not unusually severe. Type II cement has a maximum allowable tricalcium aluminate content of 8 percent. A detailed discussion of sulfates is included in *Chapter 6*.

Type III. High-Early-Strength Portland Cement

Type III cement is used where high early strengths are desired, such as when forms need to be removed as soon as possible, or when the concrete must be placed in service as quickly as possible. Other uses include cold weather construction so that the required period of protection against low temperatures can be reduced.

Type IV. Low-Heat Portland Cement

Type IV cement is used where the amount and rate of heat generated must be kept to a minimum, but strength development also proceeds at a slower rate. It is intended for use only in mass concrete, such as large gravity dams, where temperature rise is a critical factor.

Type V. Sulfate-Resistant Portland Cement

Type V cement is a special cement intended for use in structures exposed to severe sulfate action. It has a slower rate of strength development than normal portland cement. Type V cement has a maximum allowable C_3A content of 5 percent, which provides better sulfate resistance than Type II cement.

Blended Hydraulic Cements

Blended hydraulic cements are blends of portland cements or lime and one or more natural or manufactured **pozzolans** which, in the presence of moisture, chemically react with calcium hydroxide to form compounds possessing cementitious properties. There are three kinds of blended hydraulic cements manufactured to meet the requirements of ASTM C 595:

- Portland blast-furnace slag cement
- Portland-pozzolan cement
- Slag cement

Portland blast-furnace slag cement consists of a uniform blend of portland cement and fine granulated blast-furnace slag. Blast-furnace slag is a nonmetallic product consisting essentially of silicates and aluminosilicates of calcium and other bases that is developed in a molten condition simultaneously with iron in a blast furnace. **Portland-pozzolan cement** consists of uniform blend of portland cement or portland blast-furnace slag cement and fine pozzolan. Pozzolans are siliceous or siliceous and aluminous materials which possess little or no cementitious value but will chemically react, in finely divided form and in the presence of moisture, with calcium hydroxide to form compounds possessing cementitious properties. **Slag cement** consists of an intimate and uniform blend of granulated blast-furnace slag and hydrated lime.

REINFORCEMENT

The amount of steel reinforcement is specified by ASTM standards or special designs. The type of reinforcement used depends on production processes and local availability. Reinforcement is provided to the pipe producer by steel companies under certified testing procedures.

Welded Wire Fabric

Welded wire fabric is prefabricated from high-strength, cold drawn wires and consists of longitudinal wires welded to transverse wires to form rectangular grids. Each wire intersection is electric resistance-welded by automatic welders. Smooth wires, deformed wires, or a combination of both may be used. Welded wire fabric is manufactured to ASTM Standard A 185 or A 497. The positive mechanical anchorage at each wire intersection of welded smooth wire fabric provides the concrete to steel bond

Illustration 2.1
Mesh roller curves welded wire fabric to proper diameter for cage.

characteristics. Welded deformed wire fabric utilizes wire deformations in addition to the welded intersections to improve bond characteristics.

Cross-sectional area is the basic measure used in specifying wire sizes. Smooth wire sizes are identified by the letter *W* followed by a number indicating the cross-sectional area of the wire in hundredths of a square inch. For example, *W*16 denotes a smooth wire with cross-sectional area of 0.16 square inches. Similarly, deformed wire sizes are identified by the letter *D* followed by a number which also indicates the cross-sectional area in hundredths of a square inch. For example, *D*10 is a deformed wire with a cross-sectional area of 0.10 square inches.

Spacings and sizes of wires in welded wire fabric are identified by style designation. A typical style designation is **2 × 8 – W4 × W2.5.** This denotes a welded wire fabric in which:

Spacing of longitudinal wires = 2 inches
Spacing of transverse wires = 8 inches
Size of longitudinal wires (W4) = 0.04 square inches
Size of transverse wires (W2.5) = 0.025 square inches

Hot Rolled Rod

Hot rolled rod is rolled from steel billets to an approximate round cross section in continuous coils. Rods are not comparable to hot rolled bars in accuracy of cross section or surface finish and as a semifinished product are intended primarily for the manufacture of wire. Hot rolled rod sizes are designated by fractional or decimal parts of an inch. The decimal equivalents are given to three significant figures. The smallest size hot rolled rod commonly made is 7/32 inch, with a nominal diameter of 0.218 inches. It is common practice to produce hot rolled rods to nominal diameters as large as 47/64 inch. Rods that are used in precast concrete pipe are smooth rods produced from Grade 40 steel as described by ASTM Standard A 615.

Illustration 2.2
Vertical cage machine.

Cold Drawn Wire

Cold drawn steel wire is produced from hot rolled rods by one or more cold reduction processes that produce the size desired and improve surface, finish and dimensional accuracy with various mechanical and physical properties. ASTM Standard A 82, and A 496, cover cold-drawn reinforcement used in the manufacture of concrete pipe.

AGGREGATES

Aggregates are granular material of mineral composition, such as sand, gravel or crushed stone, combined with a cementing medium to form concrete. Aggregates should have sufficient strength to develop the full strength of the cementing matrix and be of such character that the binding material will adhere to the surface.

Aggregates are classified by the general terms **fine** and **coarse** aggregate. Fine aggregate consists of material ranging from a size passing a 3/8 inch down to material just passing the number 100-sieve. Coarse aggregate ranges from the maximum size for sand to a varying upper limit determined by the pipe wall thickness and production considerations. The maximum size ordinarily used in pipe manufacture is 3/4 to 1-inch.

Aggregates for concrete pipe meet the requirements of ASTM Standard C 33, except for gradation requirements. This specification limits the amount of deleterious substances and also covers requirements as to grading, strength and soundness.

WATER

Water added to cement produces a chemical reaction termed **hydration.** The physical characteristic of this reaction is the formation of a *gel* when the cement is exposed to water. The gel is formed by the penetration of water into the cement particles causing softening and establishing a colloidal suspension. The taking up of water by the clusters of cement particles is the actual hydration.

A small amount of water is required for hydration but additional water is required to produce a workable mix. There is, however, a relation between the amount of water used and the strength of the resulting concrete. The amount of water must be limited to that which will produce concrete of the quality required. This is seldom a factor in concrete used in precast concrete pipe because the manufacturing processes utilize relatively dry mixes.

Water used for mixing concrete should be free of acids, alkalies and oil, unless tests or experience indicate that water being considered for use and containing any of these materials is satisfactory. Particularly to be avoided is water containing organic matter which may interfere with the hydration of the cement. Most specifications require that the mixing water be suitable for drinking.

MANUFACTURE OF PRECAST CONCRETE PIPE

The basic materials of concrete pipe are fine aggregate, coarse aggregate, portland cement, water and, in some cases, reinforcement. These are combined in a systematic manner, using quantities and proportions specially designed for each product. Fine and coarse aggregates are mixed with cement and water to provide a concrete mix which is formed into pipe by one of several methods. The newly formed pipe is cured and then moved into a storage area until shipment to the construction site. The manufacturing process includes:

- Storage of basic materials
- Materials handling
- Reinforcement fabrication
- Batching and mixing of concrete materials
- Pipe forming
- Offbearing and curing
- Yarding and storage

STORAGE OF MATERIALS

Aggregates of varying gradations are stored in sufficient quantities to enable the continuous operation of the facilities and are most often stored in outside bins. The gradations used at a plant are dependent on the methods

Illustration 2.3
Horizontal cage machine.

of manufacture, the thickness of the pipe wall being produced, and local aggregate sources.

Portland cement is normally stored in a silo located above the manufacturing plant, which enables the cement to flow by gravity into the weighing bins. The cement is pumped into the silo by delivery trucks or by pumping apparatus directly from railroad cars. The capacity of cement storage at any plant is dependent on the size of the plant, the number of types of cement used, and the frequency of delivery.

Steel reinforcement consists of three types: welded wire fabric, wire and rod. It is usually stored near the reinforcement fabricating equipment. The reinforcement inventory is dependent on the various sizes and classes of pipe being produced, and the pipe manufacturer's cage fabrication facilities.

BULK MATERIALS HANDLING

Aggregates are transferred from the storage areas to the weighing bins by loading equipment or a series of conveyor belts. Cement is fed by gravity from the silo into a weighing bin. Weighing bins or hoppers for cement and aggregates are controlled manually or electronically. Water is piped directly to the mixer, and controlled by a manual or electronic system. After the concrete has been mixed, it is delivered directly to the pipe machine or a holding hopper by conveyor belt, skip hoist or front-end loader.

REINFORCEMENT FABRICATION

Cage machines, **mandrels**, and **wire rollers** are the three most common means of fabricating reinforcing cages in a concrete pipe plant. The cage is an assembled unit of steel reinforcement consisting of circumferential and longitudinal bars or wires.

A **cage machine** uses reels of cold drawn steel wire. By means of adjustable guides, it positions the longitudinal wires while wrapping the circumferential wire in a helix around the longitudinals. Intersections of the circumferential and the longitudinal wires are automatically welded. The process produces a continuous cage. When the desired cage length has been reached, the longitudinals and circumferentials are cut with shears.

In using **mandrels** to fabricate cages, the mandrel is adjusted to the required diameter. The longitudinal steel is placed on the mandrel, and the circumferential steel is helically wrapped around the turning mandrel. The intersections of the longitudinals and the circumferentials are automatically welded.

Wire rollers use welded wire fabric in rolls or flat mats with the desired size and spacing of longitudinal and circumferential wires. When the proper length of fabric has been formed by the roller, it is cut and spot welded to form the cage.

Four cage configurations are in common use: **single circular cage, double circular cage, single elliptical cage, and a combination of an elliptical cage and one or more circular cages,** *Figure 2.1*. Additionally, **quadrant**

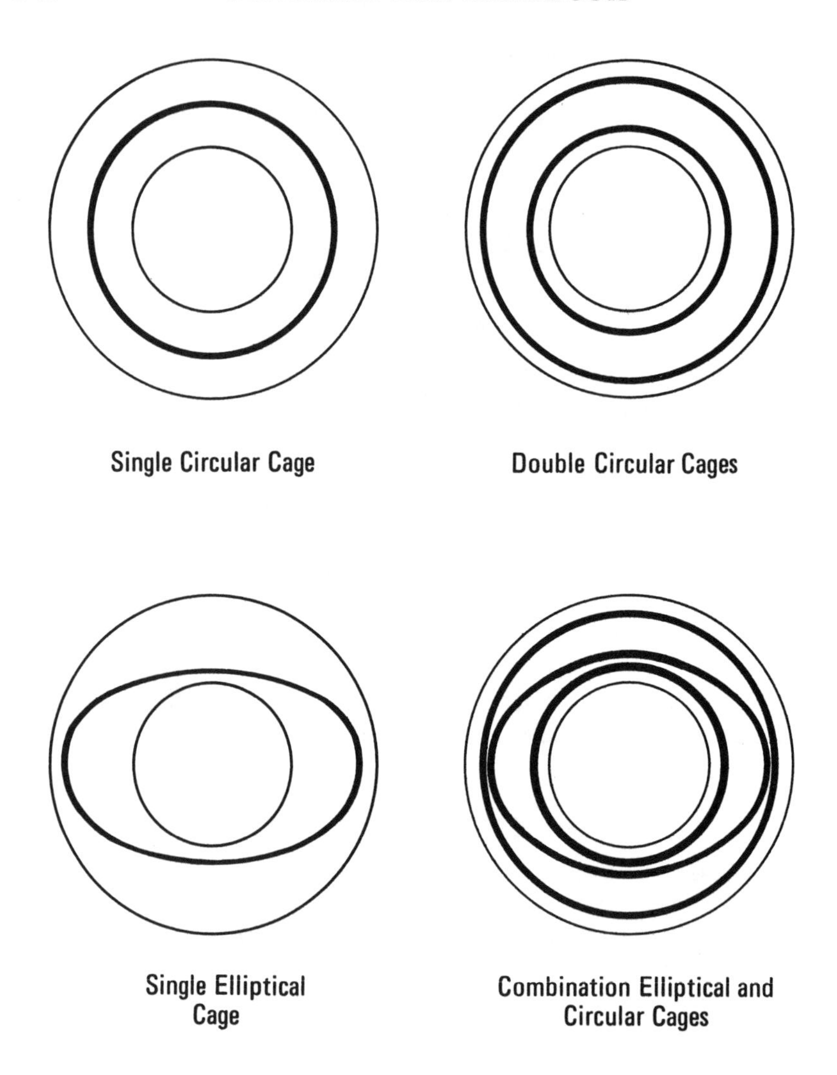

Figure 2.1. Four Cage Configurations Commonly Employed in the Manufacture of Reinforced Concrete Pipe.

reinforcement can be used to provide increased steel areas in the tensile zones of the pipe, *Figure 2.2*. Quadrant reinforcement can be provided by overlapping cages and incorporating mats.

Steel area is a commonly used term for describing the reinforcement in concrete pipe. When the term is used, it refers to the **square inches of circumferential steel per linear foot;** that is, if a section of pipe were to be cut lengthwise, the steel area is the sum of the cross-sectional areas of the exposed circumferential wires in one linear foot of pipe.

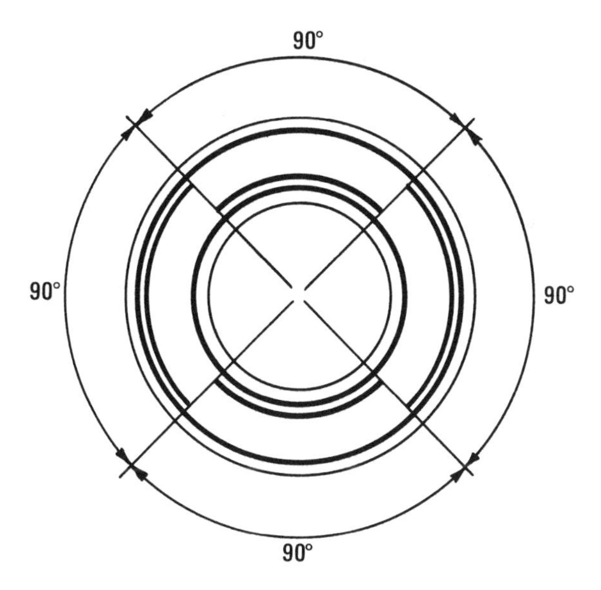

Figure 2.2. Quadrant Reinforcement Provides Additional Reinforcement in Tension Zones of Pipe Wall.

BATCHING

Batching is preceded by design of the mix which provides the proportion of cement, fine aggregate, coarse aggregates, water and admixtures if used.

Cement and both fine and coarse aggregates are fed into weighing bins and then discharged into the mixer. In some processes the materials are mixed and then the proper amount of water and admixture added.

Drum mixers and **pan mixers** are the two most common types used in the concrete pipe industry. A **drum mixer** is an inclined rotating cylinder in which paddles, mounted along the cylinder, mix the concrete. The **pan mixer** consists of a shorter cylinder than the drum mixer and is vertically oriented. Inside the pan, paddles are mounted vertically and rotate to mix the concrete. Components are added from above and the concrete is removed from the bottom. Both drum and pan mixers are efficient in converting the components of the concrete into a homogenous mixture.

The **slump test** is the most common means of measuring the relative water content of cast-in-place concrete mixes. It cannot be effectively applied to the mixes used in concrete pipe machines, because the slump of these mixes is always zero. In fact, concrete mixes for pipe have what is called a **negative slump** in that additional water could be added to the mix before any slump would occur.

PIPE PRODUCTION METHODS

There are five basic methods of producing concrete pipe. Four of the methods, *Figure 2.3*, use mechanical means to place and compact a dry concrete mix into the form. The fifth method uses a more conventional wet mix and casting procedure. The five methods are:

- Centrifugal
- Dry cast
- Packerhead
- Tamp
- Wet cast

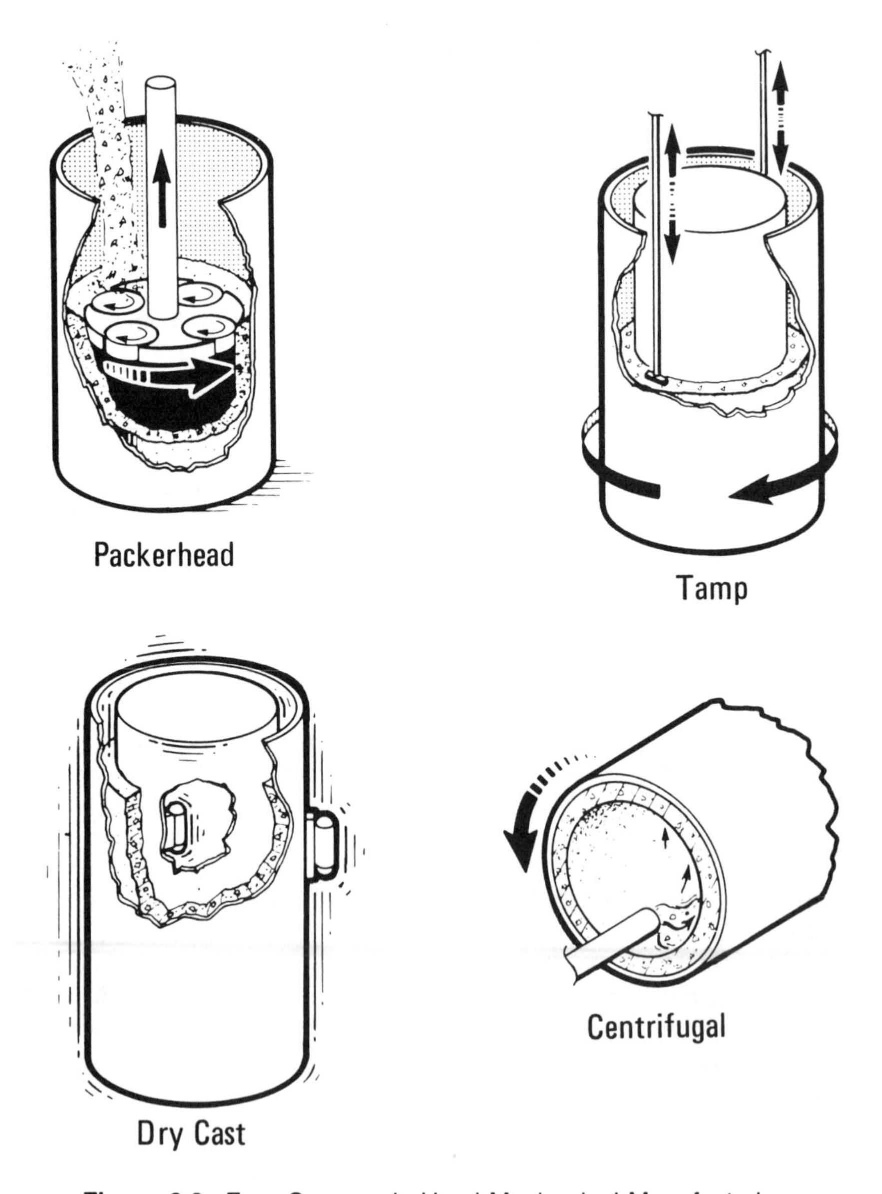

Figure 2.3. Four Commonly Used Mechanical Manufacturing Methods for Production of Precast Concrete Pipe.

Centrifugal or Spinning Process

The **centrifugal or spinning** process uses an outer form that is rotated in a horizontal position during the pipe making process. Vibration and compaction can be used in combination with centrifugation to consolidate the concrete mix. While the mix is wetter than some pipe mixes, water is extracted from the concrete by the centrifugal forces which develop as the pipe is spinning. As the form is rotated, concrete is fed into the form by a conveyor system that is capable of distributing concrete throughout the form length. The finished pipe, still in the form, is moved to the curing area and cured in the form.

Dry Cast Process

The **dry cast** process has several variations but all use low frequency-high amplitude vibration to distribute and densely compact the dry mix in the form. The form is removed immediately as the newly formed pipe can support itself. To get the desired vibration at all points, several different techniques are utilized.

Illustration 2.4
Vibrators on the exterior forms of a two station dry cast machine.

In one method, vibrators are usually attached directly to the exterior form. The mix is fed into the form and the vibrators are operated at various stages during this process. At the completion of the process, the pipe and form is lifted off the machine and moved to the curing area where the form is removed.

Another variation of the dry cast method has a central core that moves up and down and provides vibration and compaction. In this method, when the process is completed, the core retracts and the pipe is stripped and moved to the curing area.

Illustration 2.5
This dry cast machine utilizes an internal vibrating core that rises as the concrete mix is fed into the forms.

Packerhead Process

The **packerhead** process uses a device rotating at a high speed that forms the interior surface of the pipe. It is drawn up through the exterior form as mix is fed in from above. The head has rollers or deflectors mounted on the top which compact the mix. When compaction is complete, the form and pipe are moved to a curing area where the exterior form is removed.

In some packerhead processes a vibrating core follows the packerhead through the pipe making sequence. The core is mounted in a pit below the pipe machine and is retracted before the pipe is moved.

Illustration 2.6
Pipe in outer form is removed from machine and packerhead begins forming another section.

Tamp Process

The **tamp** process uses direct mechanical compaction to consolidate the concrete mix. Inner and outer forms are placed on a rotating table, and the concrete mix is fed into the forms. As the form is rotated and filled the tamper rises automatically. There are usually multiple tampers so that the mix on each side of any reinforcement can be compacted. The pipe is removed from the machine with either the inner or outer form and moved to the curing area where the form is removed.

Illustration 2.7
Packerhead machine forms pipe by compacting dry mix against exterior form.

Wet Cast Process

Wet casting of concrete pipe, as the name implies, uses a concrete mix that is wet relative to the mixes used in the other processes. The mix usually has a slump of less than four inches. The wet cast process is most commonly used for production of large diameter pipe where it is manufactured, cured and stripped at one location. Inner and outer forms are most commonly mounted in a vertical position, but some pipe is cast with forms horizontal. The latter is called **prebed pipe** because the exterior pipe wall has a flat side where the form is open to allow filling.

With vertical forms a cone attached to the inner form is used to direct the concrete mix. The mix is transported to the form by crane, conveyor or similar equipment. As the mix is placed in the form it is vibrated using internal and in many cases external vibrators. After the form has been filled, the cone is removed, and the pipe cured in the form. This is frequently done with canvas tents and steam. Following the curing period, usually overnight, the forms are removed and the pipe moved to the storage area.

OFFBEARING AND CURING

Removal of the pipe from the machine is called **offbearing** and is accomplished in a variety of ways ranging from manual to fully automated. Fork lifts and overhead cranes are used to lift pipe from the machine. The freshly made pipe is transported to the curing **kiln** by fork lifts, hand trucks, overhead cranes or moving floors. Moving floors are commonly found in modern plants providing efficient transport of the pipe into the curing area. A section of moving floor, referred to as a **kiln car,** usually consists of a concrete slab supported on steel trucks. It runs on rails installed in a trench in the floor of the plant. The moving floor passes adjacent to the pipe machine and into the kiln.

Depending on the production method, the pipe is either cured while in the form or immediately removed from the form and cured. Curing is accomplished by a variety of procedures. In some cases, the pipe is placed in a permanent kiln, and in other cases, the pipe is covered by canvas, plastic, or other material which functions as a kiln.

As soon as the concrete pipe is formed, the curing process begins. Curing is optimized by control of kiln conditions and thus, the rate of hydration of the cement. There are three basic methods for curing: steam, water and sealing membranes. In the concrete pipe industry, low pressure steam predominates as a curing method. The principle of low pressure steam curing is that an accelerated rate of hydration produces concrete pipe of required strength in shorter time than is possible when curing at ambient temperatures.

The three essential factors in all known methods of properly curing concrete are time, temperature and moisture. For equivalent strengths, an increase in temperature usually permits a shorter curing period. The time-temperature relationship is not the same for all mixtures, materials, and conditions and is determined by experience.

In low pressure steam curing, it is essential that the relative humidity surrounding the pipe be high, as near as possible to saturation. High humidity, in excess of 80 percent, is provided when the curing temperature is obtained by direct injection of saturated steam into the kiln. With systems combining moisture and hot air, radiant heat, or other forms of dry heat it is necessary to maintain a closer check on the humidity in the kiln. Drying of the concrete can cause damage to the surface. A concrete pipe is sensitive to moisture loss because of the large surface area for the volume of concrete. A moist atmosphere is not necessary when the concrete is entirely encased in a pipe mold. In such cases the water in the concrete mixture is sealed inside the forms.

Concrete pipe can be cured in the open air provided temperatures are high and constant. It is necessary under these conditions to maintain the pipe in a moist condition. A sprinkler system is most commonly used to provide such an environment.

Pipe has been efficiently cured in a chamber by maintaining a constant, warm temperature achieved by the addition of heat or by the heat generated from the hydration of the cement. Moisture is usually provided in the form of a warm spray.

YARDING AND STORAGE

At the completion of the curing cycle the pipe is moved to the storage area. Small diameter pipe is frequently moved in groups of four or six, depending on the size of the pipe and capacity of the equipment. Before moving to the storage area, the pipe receives a final visual inspection to ensure a consistent quality of product. If repairs are needed they are usually done at this time. Marking of the pipe indicating strength class, manufacturing date, manufacturer and other information to conform to ASTM standards is done as the pipe is yarded.

PIPE SHAPES

Concrete pipe is manufactured in five standard shapes: circular, horizontal elliptical, vertical elliptical, arch and rectangular, *Figure 2.4*.

Circular pipe is the most common shape manufactured. The sizes produced have ranged from 4 inches to 204 inches for standard production. The limitation on the size of concrete pipe is usually not a problem of the capability of the producer, but a problem of transportation from the plant to the job site. There are many advantages to a round cross section, from the self centering joint to highly efficient hydraulic characteristics.

Elliptical pipe is manufactured for special applications. **Horizontal elliptical** pipe is sometimes called **low head** because the pipe can be placed where the available head room precludes the use of a standard round section. Where lateral clearance is limited, a **vertical elliptical** pipe can be provided. There is a major difference between horizontal and vertical elliptical pipe in the placement and amount of the reinforcement to resist vertical loading on the pipe.

Arch pipe is another cross section used in some regions, most commonly for highway culverts.

Rectangular sections are also produced by pipe manufacturers and referred to as **box sections.** The precast concrete box section was developed in the early 1970's to provide an alternative to cast-in-place structures. Precast boxes have the advantage of plant control of quality. Precast boxes have the further advantage of being quickly installed, thus reducing time delays during construction.

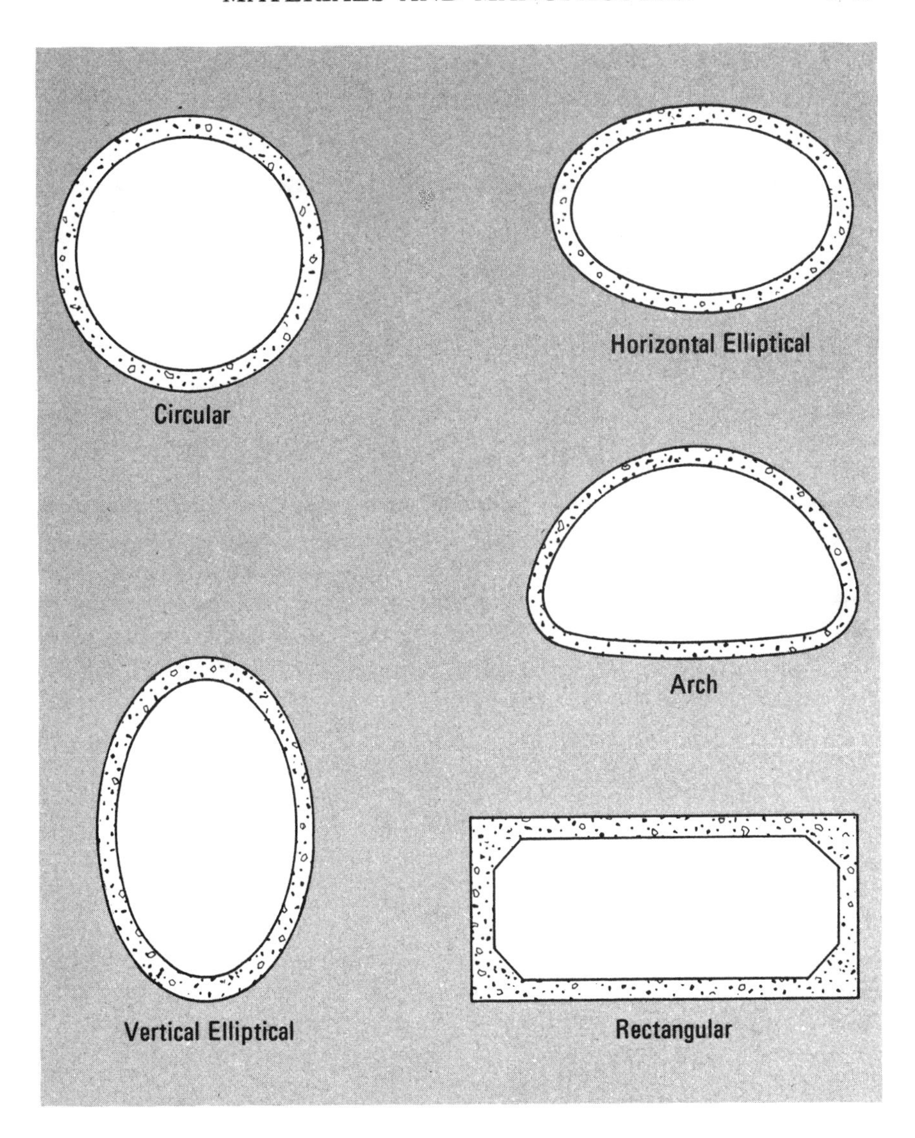

Figure 2.4. Concrete Pipe is Manufactured in Five Common Shapes. Regional Custom and Demand Usually Determine Availability.

SPECIALS

Specials are those precast concrete products other than standard pipe sections, that are used in the construction of a sewer system or culvert. Concrete pipe manufacturers can fabricate almost any size and shape of special product needed. The use of special sections permits a contractor to complete a pipeline more rapidly than if built-in-place structures are used. The high quality of precast concrete products is also advantageous.

Illustration 2.8
Dry cast machine used to manufacture special or standard shapes.

JUNCTIONS

Junctions of almost any shape can be fabricated by a concrete pipe producer. The most common junctions are **tees** and **wyes.** Most pipe manufacturers will fabricate custom junction chambers for a pipe project.

BEVELED PIPE

Beveled, mitered or **radius** pipe incorporate a specific deflection angle into the joint to allow changes in direction of sewer lines without the installation of a manhole. The radius of curvature which may be obtained by beveled pipe is a function of the deflection angle per joint, diameter of the pipe, length of the pipe sections and wall thickness.

Since the maximum permissible bevel for any pipe is dependent on the manufacturing process, the specification must be coordinated with the pipe manufacturer. Many manufacturers have standardized joint configurations and deflections for specific radii, and economies can be realized by utilizing standard sections.

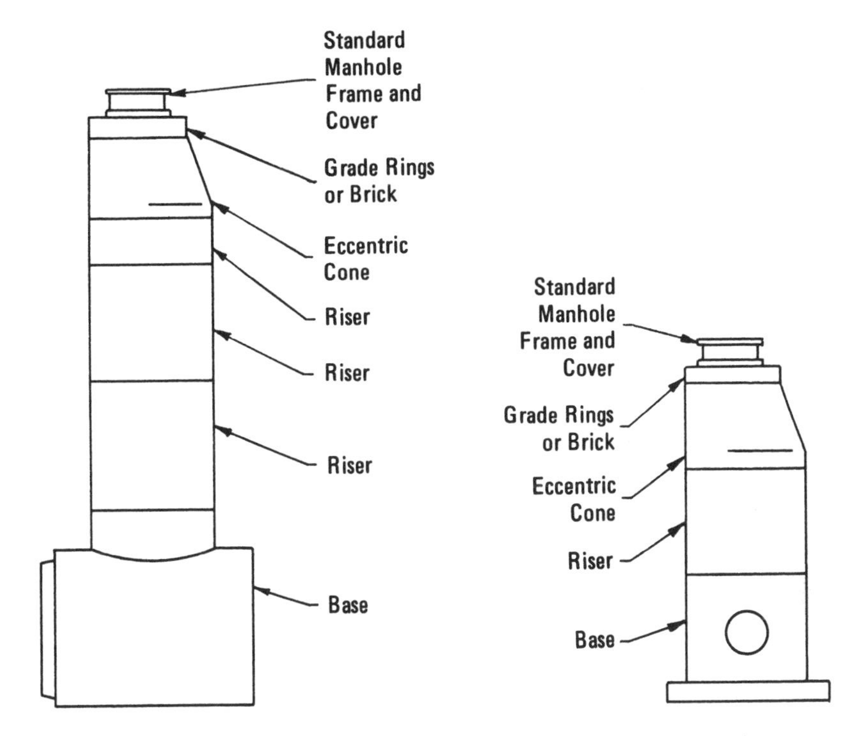

Figure 2.5. Typical Precast Manhole Assembly Combinations.

MANHOLES

Precast concrete manholes are usually installed by the same crew that is installing the pipeline, and a manhole of any depth can be constructed in the field by combining various length sections, *Figure 2.5*. The standard manhole **riser** section is 48 inches in diameter and varies in length. It may be cast with an integral base as part of the manhole section, or the manhole section may be placed on a precast or cast-in-place base. Manholes are used at changes in size, alignment or grade of the pipeline, as well as for convenience in maintenance.

For pipelines of 48 inches in diameter and larger, the lowest manhole section may be cast as a tee, and subsequent riser sections placed on top of the integrally cast tee. This allows installation of the pipeline to proceed with less delay or interruption. It also eliminates the need to use special lengths of pipe to accommodate the manhole.

REFERENCES

1. "ASTM C 76 Reinforcement Design Changes and Related Research," Concrete Pipe Information No. 1, American Concrete Pipe Association, 1971.
2. "Blended Hydraulic Cements," ASTM C 595, American Society for Testing and Materials.
3. "Civil Engineering Handbook," L. C. Urquhart, McGraw-Hill Book Company, 1934.

4. "Cold-Drawn Steel Wire for Concrete Reinforcement," ASTM A 82, American Society for Testing and Materials.
5. "Concrete Aggregates," ASTM C 33, American Society for Testing and Materials.
6. "Concrete Pipe Installation Manual," American Concrete Pipe Association, 1978.
7. "Concrete Pipe Lines," M. W. Loving, American Concrete Pipe Association, Bulletin No. 21, 1940.
8. "Deformed and Plain Billet-Steel Bar for Concrete Reinforcement," ASTM A 615, American Society for Testing and Materials.
9. "Deformed Steel Wire for Concrete Reinforcement," ASTM A 496, American Society for Testing and Materials.
10. "Design and Control of Concrete Mixtures," Portland Cement Association, Tenth Edition, 1952.
11. "Making of Steel," American Iron and Steel Institute, 1950.
12. "Manual of Standard Practice—Welded Wire Fabric," Wire Reinforcement Institute, 1979.
13. "Portland Cement," ASTM C 150, American Society for Testing and Materials.
14. "Welded Deformed Steel Wire Fabric for Concrete Reinforcement," ASTM A 497, American Society for Testing and Materials.
15. "Welded Steel Wire Fabric for Concrete Reinforcement," ASTM A 185, American Society for Testing and Materials.

CHAPTER 3
HYDRAULIC DESIGN

Drainage structures are classified, designed and constructed primarily for three specific applications—sanitary sewers, storm sewers and culverts. **Sanitary sewers** carry domestic, commercial and industrial wastewaters. **Storm sewers** carry precipitation runoff, surface waters and, in some instances, groundwater. **Combined sewers** carry both wastewater and storm water. **Culverts** provide for the free passage of surface drainage water under a highway, railroad, canal, or other embankment.

The purpose of hydraulic design is to establish the size and type of pipe, the pipe gradient or slope, and the inlet and outlet conditions. This chapter presents the principles of hydraulic design and their application to concrete pipe. Also included are the principles and criteria of hydrologic and wastewater disposal design for establishing the quantity of flow for pipelines.

HYDRAULIC PRINCIPLES

The hydraulic design of drainage systems is based upon classical theories for the flow of liquids. These principles, which apply to either open channel flow or closed flow, are covered in the next section, and followed by more specific application to gravity flow pipelines.

BASIC PRINCIPLES

In determining the quantity of flow through pipelines, simplifying assumptions can be made. **Steady flow** occurs when the flow quantity at a given point is constant, and **unsteady** when the flow quantity varies. Usually, steady flow conditions are assumed for design. For special conditions, other assumptions can be made, but such analyses are beyond the scope of this Handbook.

Uniform flow exists in open channels, if the velocity and depth are the same throughout the channel, and in pressure pipelines when there is a uniform cross section as illustrated in *Figure 3.1*. Flow is also classified in terms of whether the flow lines are laminar (straight), or turbulent (irregular). One-dimensional flow analysis is assumed by neglecting variations of flow conditions at any point and considering only changes in mean values.

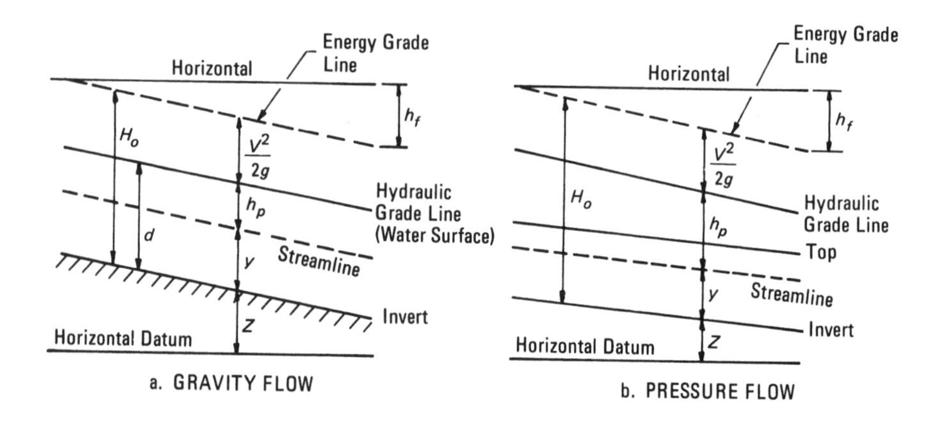

Figure 3.1. Uniform Steady Flow.

One-Dimensional Method of Flow Analysis

Fluid flow is generally nonuniform and thus presents a three-dimensional problem. In most instances, however, uniform flow is assumed at a given cross section, and a one-dimensional method of analysis that neglects any variations of flow characteristics is used. Basic to the one-dimensional method are continuity, momentum, and energy principles.

Continuity Principle

Applying the principle of conservation of mass to fluid flow results in the **continuity principle** which states that in a closed system for, steady incompressible fluid flow, the quantity of flow is constant. As illustrated in *Figure 3.2*, fluid is neither being created nor destroyed between Sections 1 and 2, therefore, in terms of weight:

$$A_1V_1w_1 = A_2V_2w_2 = G \tag{3.1}$$

Where: G = weight flow, pounds per second
A = cross-sectional area of flow, square feet
V = velocity, feet per second
w = specific weight, pounds per cubic foot

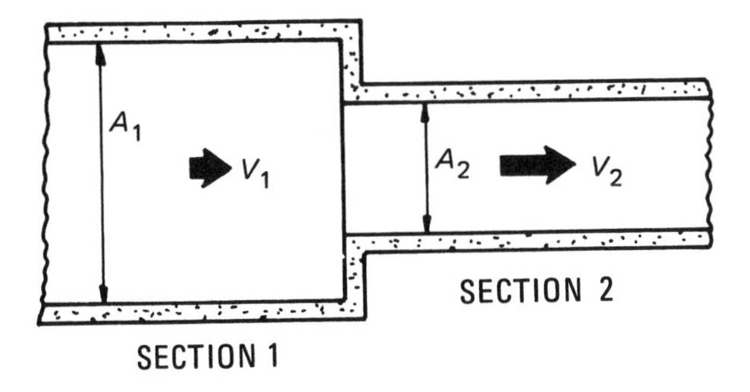

Figure 3.2. Continuity of Flow.

The term G is the weight of flow and is necessary to express gas flows concisely. For liquids, when pressure and temperature changes are negligible, w_1, is equal to w_2, resulting in:

$$A_1V_1 = A_2V_2 = Q \tag{3.2}$$

Where: Q = quantity of flow, cubic feet per second

Momentum Principle

The momentum principle is derived from Newton's second law of motion which states the force on a free body is equal to its mass times acceleration. For steady flow, as illustrated in *Figure 3.3*, the momentum principle states:

$$\overrightarrow{(\Sigma F)}\, dt = d\overrightarrow{(MV)} \tag{3.3}$$

Where: ΣF = resultant of forces applied to fluid
dt = unit time
M = fluid mass
V = velocity of fluid

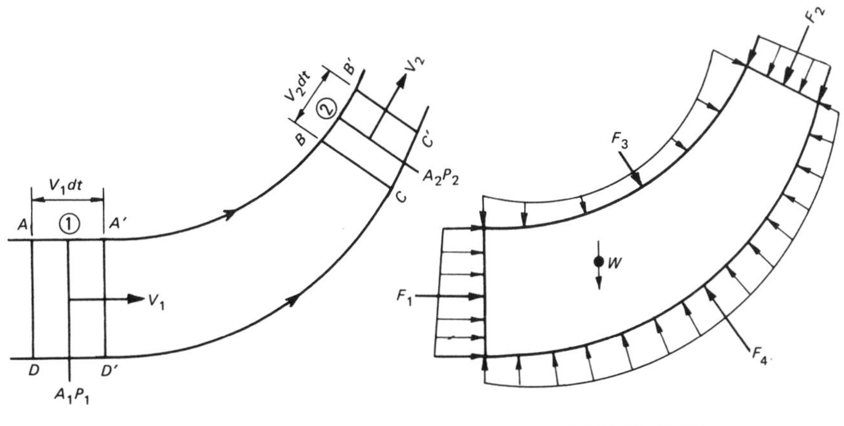

Figure 3.3. Notation for Momentum Relationships.

The term $(\overrightarrow{\Sigma F})dt$ is defined as the **impulse of the resultant force** and $d(\overrightarrow{MV})$, the **change in momentum** of the fluid free body.

The momentum principle provides a basic tool for the solution of fluid flow problems which cannot be solved by the continuity and energy principles alone. Such problems include pressure flows involving pipe bends, transition sections, turbines and hydraulic jumps.

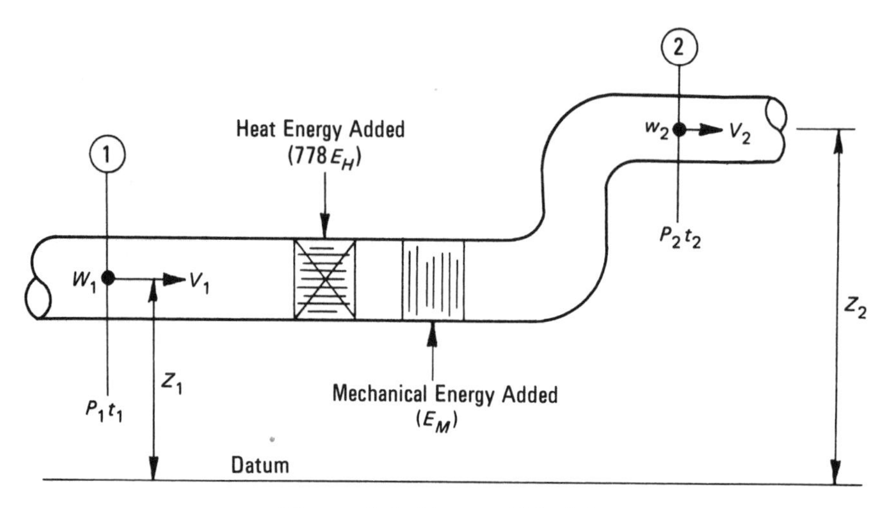

Figure 3.4. Energy Principle.

Energy Principle

The application of the conservation of energy principle is illustrated in *Figure 3.4* in a qualitative manner. The principle states that the fluid energy at Section 1 plus any heat or mechanical energy added is equal to the fluid energy at Section 2. A flowing fluid has four types of energy:

- Internal
- Pressure
- Velocity
- Potential

When heat and mechanical energy are added or lost from the system, the general energy equation is:

$$I_1 + \frac{P_1}{w_1} + \frac{V_1^2}{2g} + Z_1 + 778\ E_H + E_M = I_2 + \frac{P_2}{w_2} + \frac{V_2^2}{2g} + Z_2 \qquad (3.4)$$

Where:

I = internal energy of fluid
P = fluid pressure
P/w = pressure energy
$V^2/2g$ = kinetic or velocity energy
Z = potential energy
$778E_H$ = heat energy
E_M = mechanical energy

For flows in buried pipelines, temperature and density changes are negligible, as are changes in internal energy and heat energy. If the fluid does not pass through a pump or motor, mechanical energy is zero. For these conditions, *Equation 3.4* reduces to the equation proposed by Bernoulli in 1738:

$$\frac{P_1}{w} + \frac{V_1^2}{2g} + Z_1 = \frac{P_2}{w} + \frac{V_2^2}{2g} + Z_2 \quad (3.5)$$

As with the continuity equation, it is evident that the sum of the pressure, velocity and height terms will be equal to a constant. Each term represents unit energies and, as illustrated in *Figure 3.5,* also vertical linear distances.

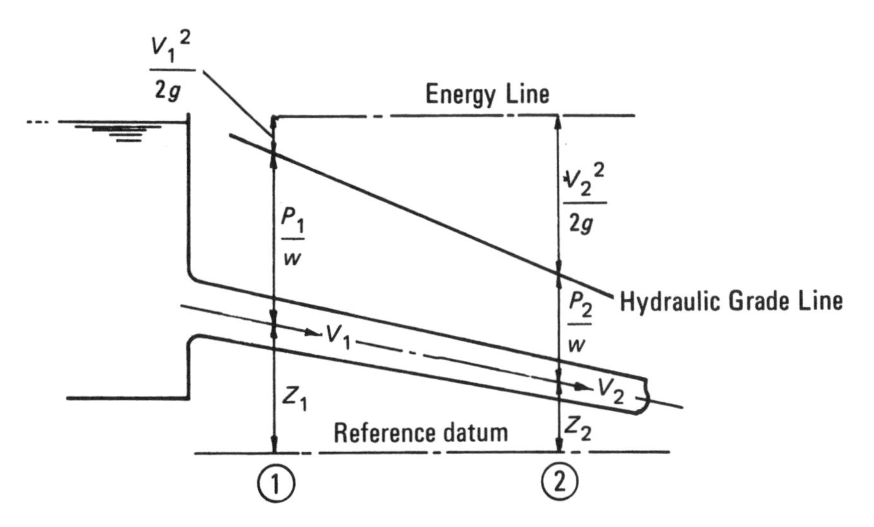

Figure 3.5. Bernoulli Equation.

Gravity Flow Analysis

For uniform flow in an open channel, the slope of the energy and hydraulic grade lines are the same as the slope of the invert, and the depth of flow adjusts itself to a velocity consistent with the friction losses. Flow under this condition is at the **normal depth**, d_n. For non-uniform flow, the energy and the hydraulic grade lines are not parallel. Friction losses, therefore, must be applied to the energy grade line or substantial errors may result in the computations. The factors that influence the difference in elevation of the energy grade line between any two cross sections are the **friction loss** and losses caused by change in alignment or cross-sectional area.

Critical flow, or flow at **critical depth,** is where the total energy above the invert is a minimum for a given discharge or, conversely, the rate of flow is maximum for a given total energy.

Critical flow occurs when the Froude number, F, is equal to unity. If F is less than unity, the flow is **subcritical**, and if it is greater, the flow is **supercritical**. The Froude number is defined as:

$$F = \frac{V}{\sqrt{gd_m}} \tag{3.6}$$

Where: d_m = hydraulic mean depth, feet

The primary significance of the Froude number is that it represents the ratio of the mean flow velocity to the velocity of propagation of a small gravity wave. A gravity wave can be propagated upstream under subcritical flow conditions because the wave velocity is greater than the flow velocity, but can be propagated downstream only in supercritical flow. Consequently, for water surface profile calculations, the analysis begins at the control point and proceeds upstream when the upstream flow is subcritical, and proceeds downstream from the control point when the downstream flow is supercritical.

For a given channel section and discharge, the specific energy head, H_o, *Figure 3.1*, is a function of the depth of flow only. If the depth of flow is plotted against the specific energy head, a specific energy curve, *Figure 3.6* can be obtained. Such curves show that for all flows except critical flow, there are two possible depths at which flow may occur for any value of the specific energy head and discharge. The actual depth of flow depends on the channel slope and friction, and locations of control sections.

For gravity flow, the greater depth results in subcritical flow, and the lesser depth results in supercritical flow. Depths of flow within 10 to 15 percent of the critical depth are likely to be unstable because slight changes in energy may cause great changes in the depth.

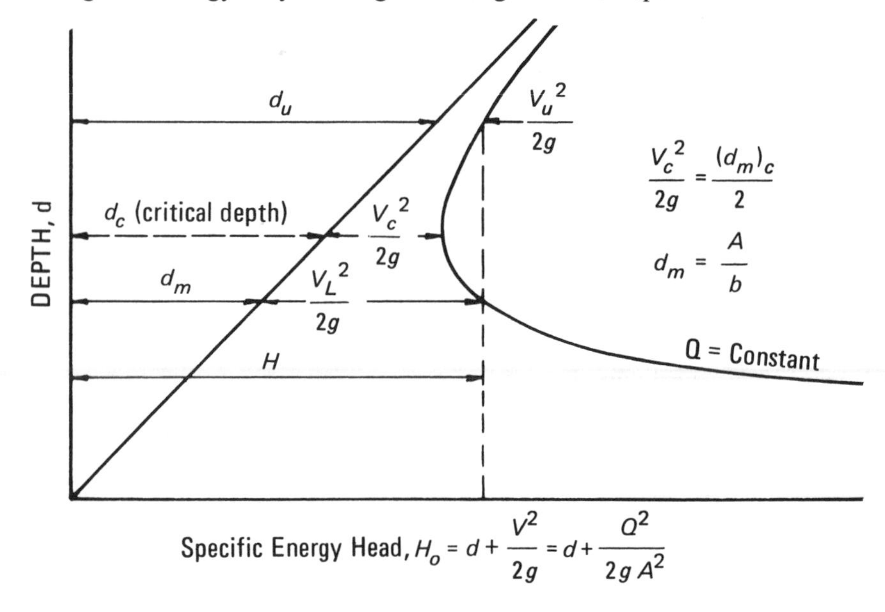

Figure 3.6. Specific Energy Curve.

Since at critical flow the Froude number is equal to unity, the following relationships exist at critical flow, *Figure 3.6:*

Velocity head is equal to one half the hydraulic mean depth:

$$\frac{V_c^2}{2g} = \frac{(d_m)_c}{2} \tag{3.7}$$

Where: $(d_m)_c$ = hydraulic mean depth, feet

Total head is equal to the minimum specific energy head, and equal to the critical depth plus one half the hydraulic mean depth at critical flow:

$$H = H_o = d_c + \frac{(d_m)_c}{2} \tag{3.8}$$

Where: d_c = critical depth, feet

As the flow passes from subcritical on a mildly sloping channel to supercritical on a steeply sloping channel, as shown in *Figure 3.7a,* critical flow occurs in the vicinity of the break in grade. The upstream slope, which is less than critical, is called **subcritical,** or more commonly, a mild slope. The downstream slope, which is greater than the critical, is called **supercritical,** or more commonly, a steep slope.

If the flow passes from a mild to a milder slope channel, or is controlled downstream by discharging into a relatively quiet body of water, or encounters an obstruction such as a weir, a backwater curve is produced in the upstream channel as shown in *Figure 3.7b*.

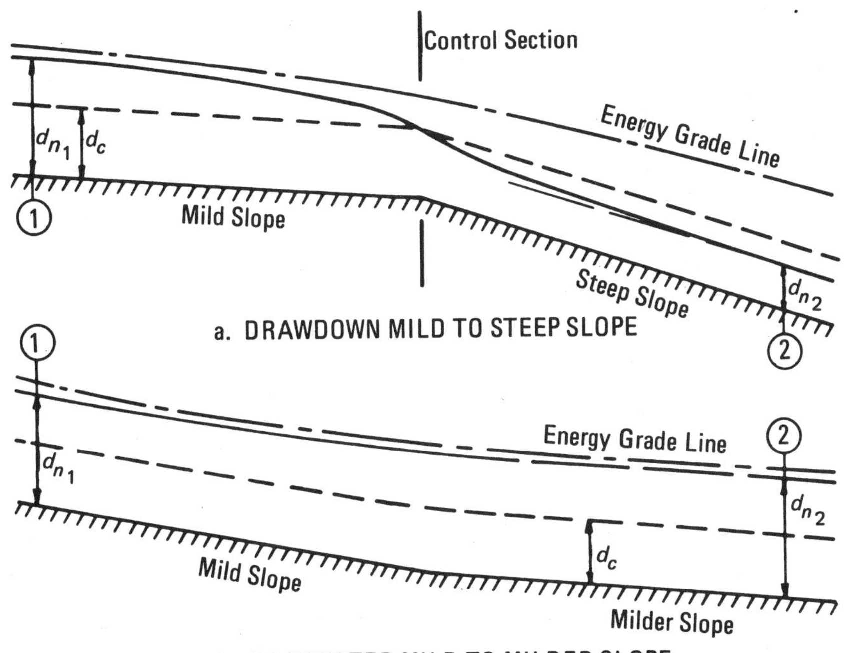

Figure 3.7. Non-Uniform Flow Hydraulic Profiles.

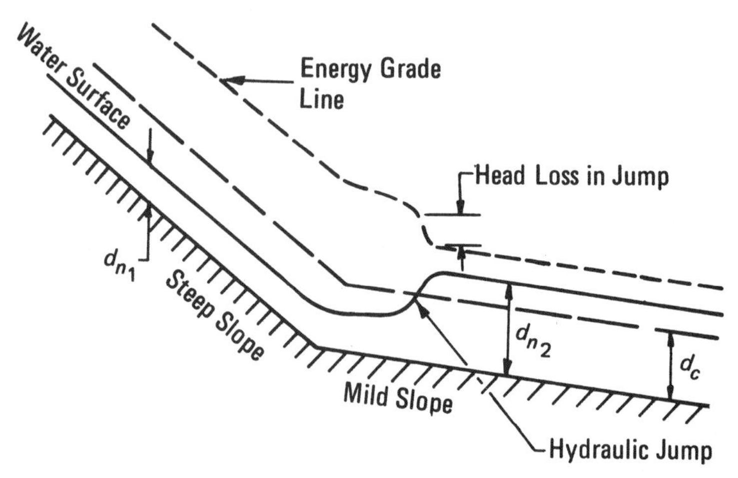

Figure 3.8. Hydraulic Jump Profile.

Figure 3.8 illustrates a possible water surface profile for flow from a steep to a mild slope channel, with supercritical flow on the upper channel and subcritical flow on the lower. In passing from supercritical to subcritical flow, a hydraulic jump occurs with a consequent loss in head. Energy conditions require that the jump occur on the mild slope. If the downstream total energy requirements to transport the flow are greater than those which would result if the jump occurred on the mild slope, the jump takes place on the steep slope. In either case, there is a backwater or drawdown curve from the jump to the break in grade. The loss in head at the jump may be computed by means of the momentum principle. To compute the hydraulic profile, the total energy must be known at some point on the mild slope downstream from the break in grade.

Uniform flow will usually exist at some point both upstream and downstream from the jump.

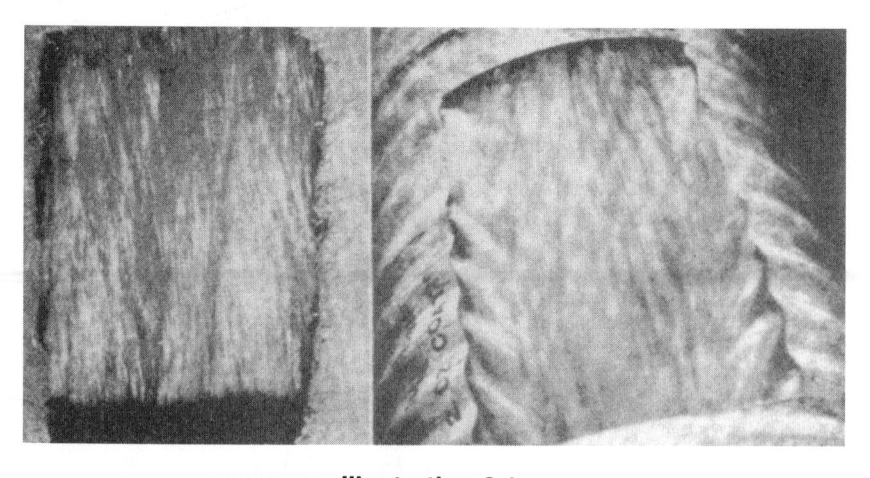

Illustration 3.1
Observation slots provide dramatic visual verification of the differences in flow characteristics between smooth and rough wall pipes.

FRICTION EQUATIONS

A number of formulas have been developed over the years to account for effects of friction and are discussed in the following section. The Manning equation is used extensively for gravity flow and the Hazen-Williams equation for pressure flow.

Chezy Equation

An early empirical equation was published by Chezy in 1775:

$$V = C\sqrt{RS} \tag{3.9}$$

Where: V = mean velocity, feet per second
C = roughness coefficient depending upon channel conditions
S = slope of hydraulic gradient
R = A/W_p = hydraulic radius, feet
A = cross-sectional area of flow, square feet
W_p = wetted perimeter, feet

Chezy hypothesized that for a given channel, the ratio of V^2/RS would be constant, and investigators concentrated on determining the coefficient that would relate various channel conditions.

Darcy-Weisbach Equation

In 1857, the Darcy-Weisbach equation was proposed for pipeline flow, and is still in use. This equation is:

$$h_f = f\frac{l}{D} \cdot \frac{V_f^2}{2g} \tag{3.10}$$

Where: h_f = friction head loss, feet
f = resistance coefficient
l = length, feet
D = pipe diameter, feet
V_f = mean velocity, feet per second
g = acceleration of gravity, 32.16, feet per second

The resistance coefficient, f, has been found to be primarily a function of the **Reynolds number** and the relative roughness of the pipe material. The Reynolds number is normally defined as:

$$\mathbf{R} = \frac{4RV}{v} \tag{3.11}$$

Where: v = kinematic viscosity, pound-second per square foot
R = hydraulic radius, feet

For a circular pressure pipe this reduces to:

$$\mathbf{R} = \frac{DV}{v} \tag{3.12}$$

The Reynolds number is a dimensionless parameter used to compare the significance of viscous effects with relation to roughness effects in determining frictional resistance. The larger the Reynolds number, the greater the influence of the relative roughness in determining the frictional resistance. For design purposes, a graphical representation, *Figure 3.9,* of the various relationships is usually more convenient.

For gravity flow, f requires a trial and error solution because it varies with both the hydraulic radius and the velocity.

A design shortcoming of the Darcy-Weisbach equation is that f is variable with the size of pipe even for the same material. Frictional coefficients in other formulas tend to be more nearly constant with size of pipe, but vary with shape of channel, roughness, etc. Judgment is required in selection of a coefficient regardless which equation is used.

Kutter Equation

Kutter's equation, published about 1869, received wide acceptance and use in estimating gravity flows. The equation is rather unwieldy, but many tables and graphs for its solution were prepared. Through use of the equation, early designers became familiar with the values of the Kutter roughness coefficient, n, applicable to sewers. Kutter's equation is:

$$V = \left[\frac{\frac{1.81}{n} + 41.67 + \frac{0.0028}{S_e}}{1 + \frac{n}{\sqrt{R}}\left(41.67 + \frac{0.0028}{S_e}\right)} \right] \sqrt{RS_e} \tag{3.13}$$

Where: V = the mean velocity of flow, feet per second
R = hydraulic radius, feet
S_e = slope of energy grade line
n = coefficient of roughness

Manning Equation

The Manning equation, developed about 1889, came into general use for sewer design because of greater simplicity and largely has replaced the Kutter equation. The Manning equation is:

$$V = \frac{1.486}{n} R^{\frac{2}{3}} S^{\frac{1}{2}} \tag{3.14}$$

$$Q = \frac{1.486}{n} A R^{\frac{2}{3}} S^{\frac{1}{2}} \tag{3.15}$$

The Manning equation is used for pipe of all shapes flowing either full or partly full. A nomograph, *Figure 3.10,* provides the solution of the Manning equation for circular pipe flowing full.

For a more convenient solution, graphs of slope versus flow have been developed with lines of specific pipe size and velocity. Graphs are usually prepared for each n value as in the Concrete Pipe Design Manual. Hydraulic slide rules are also available for the solution of the Manning equation.

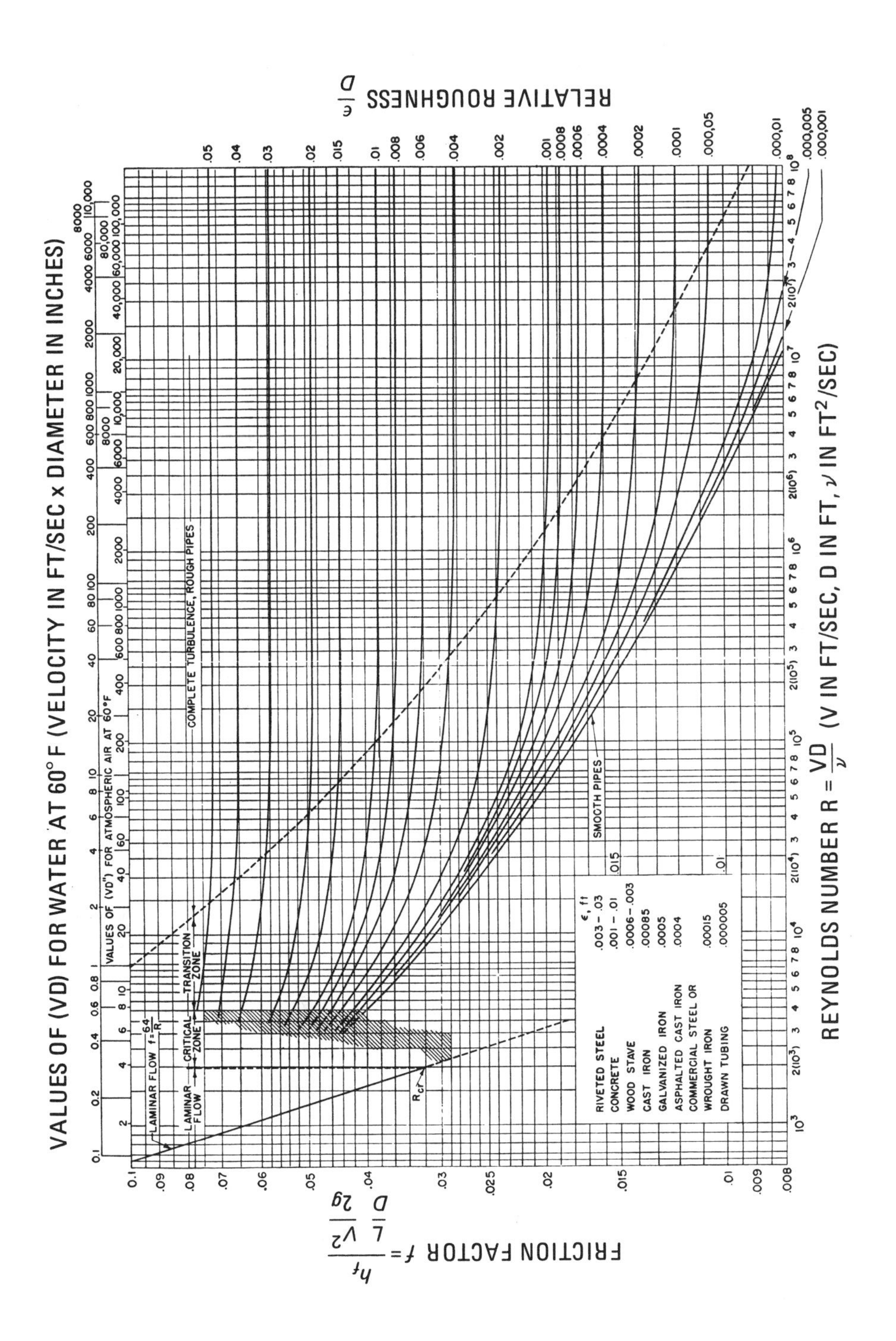

Figure 3.9. Friction Factors as a Function of Reynolds Number and Relative Roughness.

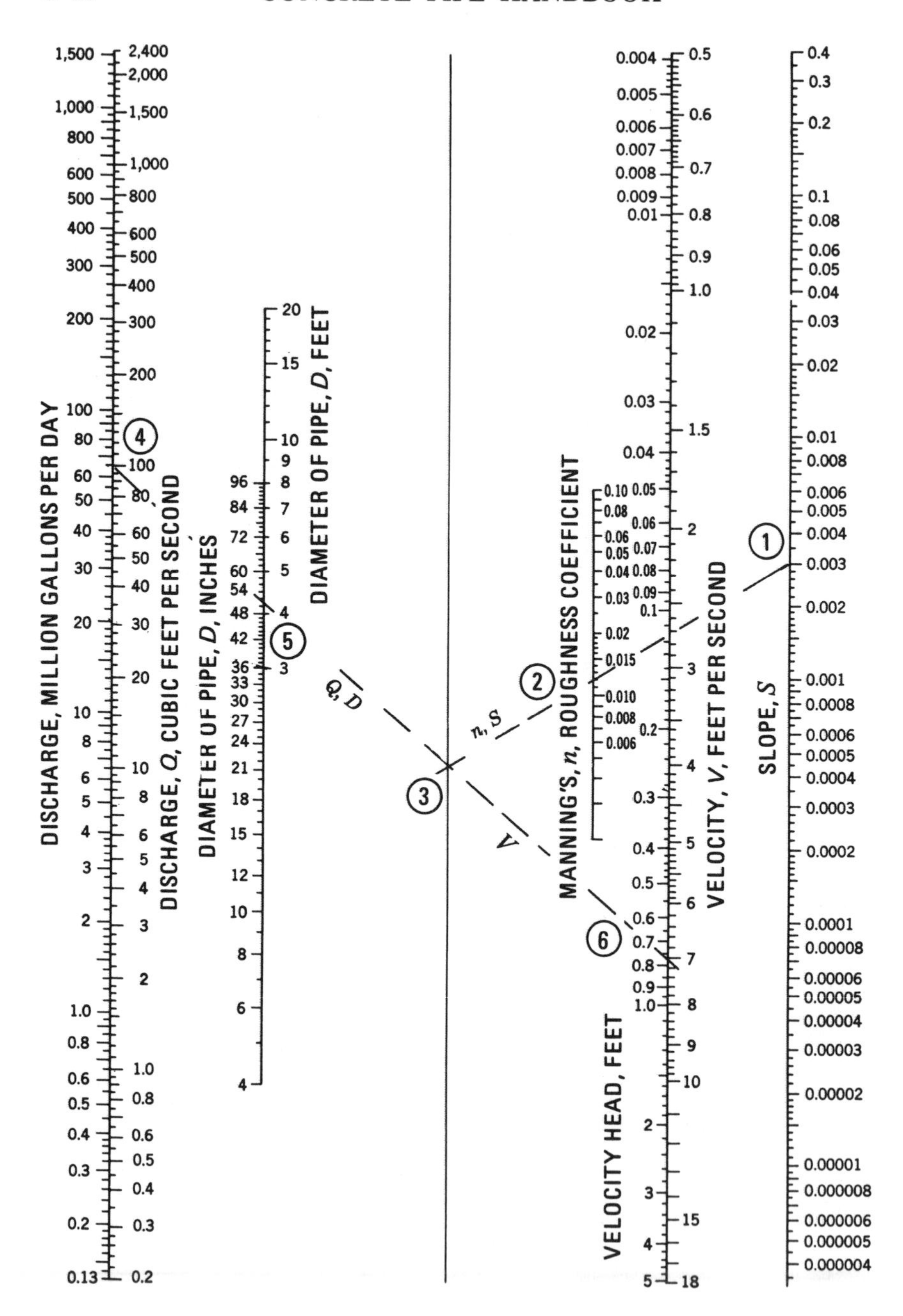

Figure 3.10. Nomograph for Manning's Equation.

Hazen-Williams Equation

The Hazen-Williams equation developed in 1902 is:

$$V = 1.32\ CR^{0.63}S^{0.54} \tag{3.16}$$

Where: C = coefficient related to roughness

The equation is widely used for pressure pipe flow. Values for C have been derived from hydraulic experiments. The following conservative values are suggested for design:

Diameter, inches	*C*
16–48	140
54–108	145
114 and larger	150

These values are applicable to concrete pipelines when fitting losses are a minor part of the total loss and the line is free from organic growths or chemical deposits.

CRITICAL DEPTH

The critical depth for a given flow of water is that depth at which water depth plus velocity head is a minimum. For culvert design, outlet velocity is dependent on the critical depth. For sewer design, drawdown and backwater curve calculations require the determination of critical depth. An expression is determined for critical depth, d_c, from the specific energy equation:

$$d_c = \sqrt[3]{\frac{q^2}{g}} \tag{3.17}$$

Where: q = unit rate of flow, cubic feet per second

This formula pertains specifically to rectangular channels but may be applied to channels of any shape by computing the equivalent average depth d_{avg}. In terms of the critical velocity V_c:

$$\frac{V_c^2}{2g} = \frac{(d_{avg})_c}{2} = \frac{A_c}{2W} \tag{3.18}$$

Where: A_c = cross-sectional area at critical flow, square feet
W = surface width, feet
$(d_{avg})_c$ = average depth at critical velocity, feet

Critical depth in circular pipe can be computed by first determining the average depth at critical velocity, $(d_{avg})_c$, and selecting the depth corresponding to the average depth. Solutions for different sizes and shapes of concrete pipe are presented in graphical form, *Figure 3.11*.

DRAWDOWN AND BACKWATER CURVES

Drawdown and backwater curves are profiles of the water surface, and prediction of the shape of the curves is sometimes required for the design

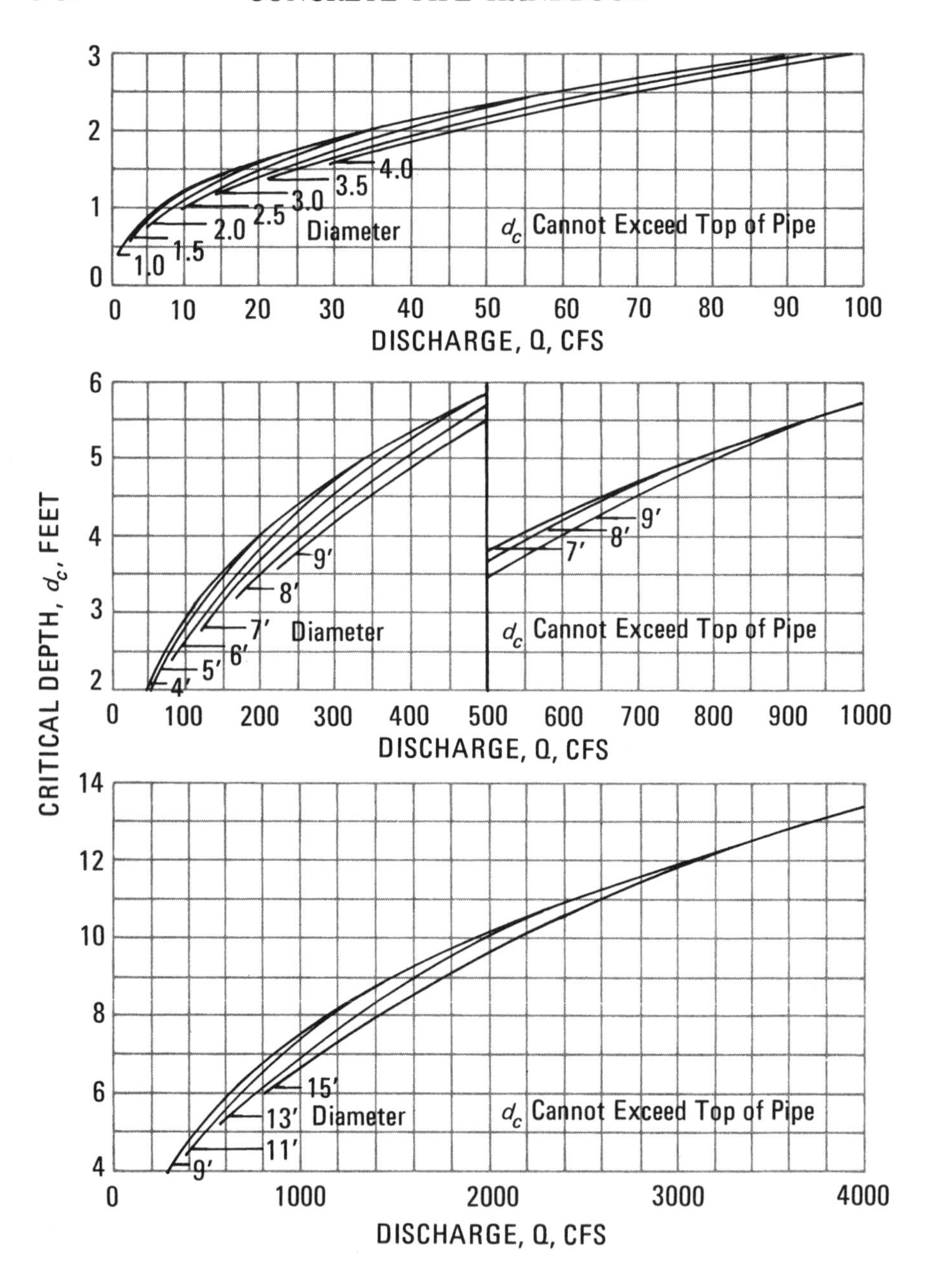

Figure 3.11. Critical Depth Circular Pipe.

of sewers and culverts. Drawdown curves can indicate when a saving in cost may be achieved by reducing the size of the pipe.

The curves depend on flow conditions, control, and channel slope. The curves most frequently encountered for mild and steep slopes are illustrated in *Figure 3.12*.

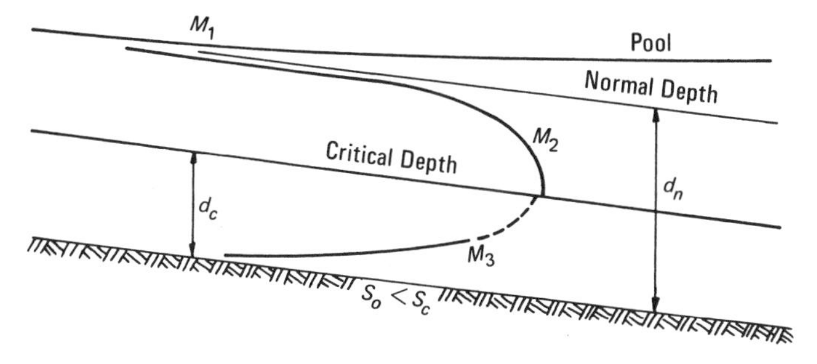

M_1 – Backwater from reservoir or from channel of milder slope ($d > d_n$)
M_2 – Drawdown, as from change of channel of mild slope to steep slope ($d_n > d > d_c$)
M_3 – Flow under gate on mild slope, or upstream profile before hydraulic jump on mild slope ($d < d_c$)

a. MILD SLOPE, $d_n > d_c$

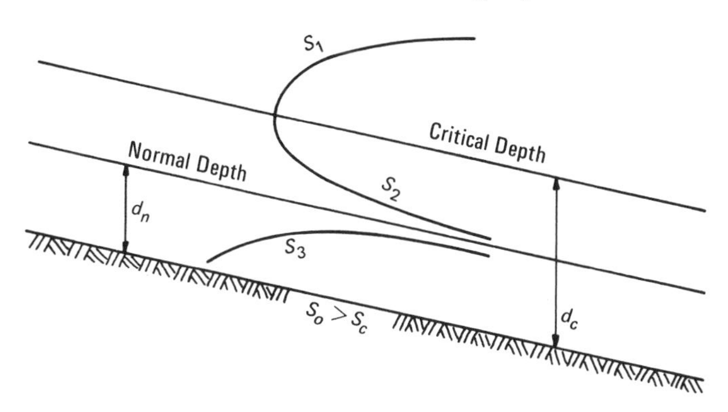

S_1 – Downstream profile after hydraulic jump on steep slope ($d < d_c$)
S_2 – Drawdown, as from mild to steep slope or steep slope to steeper slope ($d_c > d < d_n$)
S_3 – Flow under gate on steep slope, or change from steep slope to less steep slope ($d < d_n$)

b. STEEP SLOPE, $d_n < d_c$

Figure 3.12. Open-Channel Flow Classifications.

Backwater and drawdown profiles may be developed by analytical or graphical integration between cross sections of a given depth:

$$\Delta L = \frac{\Delta(d + h_v)}{S_e - S_o} \tag{3.19}$$

Where: ΔL = unit length of pipe, feet
d = depth of flow, feet
h_v = velocity head, feet
S_e = average slope of the energy grade line
S_o = slope of the invert

The term $\Delta(d + h_v)$ is the change in specific energy between the cross sections. This equation is applicable to uniform channels and requires a trial and error solution.

HYDRAULIC JUMP

A hydraulic jump is created when the flow abruptly changes from supercritical with relatively shallow depth to subcritical with greater depth. Flow in the channel upstream or downstream from the jump may be either uniform or non-uniform depending on the characteristics of the channel.

The hydraulic jump may be employed as a device for dissipation of energy. For example, in stormwater projects, the hydraulic jump may be utilized to avoid scour at the outlet. The location of the jump is critical and methods to approximate the location are presented in technical literature.

The basic equations for an hydraulic jump may be derived from an application of the continuity and momentum principles. For a moderately sloping rectangular channel:

$$\frac{d_2}{d_1} = \frac{1}{2}\left(\sqrt{1 + 8F_1^2} - 1\right) \tag{3.20}$$

$$\Delta H = H_1 - H_2 = \frac{(d_2 - d_1)^3}{4d_1d_2} \tag{3.21}$$

Where: d_1 = depth before the jump, feet
d_2 = depth after the jump, feet
F_1 = Froude number of the upstream flow
ΔH = head loss, feet
H_1 = specific head of the flow before the jump, feet
H_2 = specific head of the flow after the jump, feet

ENERGY LOSSES

Energy losses in bends, junctions and manholes are generally insignificant compared to frictional losses. In situations where these energy losses are critical, evaluations should be made.

DETERMINATION OF DESIGN FLOW

The principal requirement of any pipeline is to carry the maximum flow predicted to occur during the service life for which the structure is designed. The predicted maximum flow is used to establish the pipe size. Sewers and culverts are hydraulically designed assuming that the liquid being transported has the flow characteristics of water.

SANITARY SEWERS

Sanitary sewers are an integral part of an urban area. The extent of a sewer system is largely dictated by the location of the waste treatment facility. The design of the total system is outside the scope of this Handbook, but the elements necessary to establish the design flow are relevant.

Quantity of Wastewater

The elements required to determine the design flow in a sanitary sewer are as follows:

- Design period
- Population estimates
- Per capita sewage flow
- Commercial flow
- Industrial wastes
- Institutional wastes

The relative importance of the preceding elements varies, but each should be considered in development of values for maximum and minimum design flows.

Design Period

The design period is defined as the number of years for which the capacity of the sewer must be adequate and is based on population projections within the area served by the system. Some agencies require a 50-year life while others specify as little as 20 years.

Population Estimates

The design sewage flow is obtained by multiplying the projected estimate of population by the per capita flow. Planning studies are helpful in projecting shifts in the type of activities for the area to be served. Changes from residential to commercial zoning are not unusual, nor are changes from rural and planned residential to industrial zoning.

Population density and migration are important. The average population density is usually less than the saturation density. Representative values for saturation density are:

- For large lots, 2–3 persons per acre
- Small lots, single family, 30 persons per acre
- Small lots, two family, 50 persons per acre
- Multi-story apartments, 1000 persons per acre

Per Capita Sewage Flow

Sewage flow during dry weather periods will be approximately equal to water consumption. In arid regions, evaporation and other losses will lead to less sewage flow per capita than the amount of water consumption.

Changes in water usage must be considered for longer design periods, particularly when there is no problem of water supply. Past trends have been toward a steady increase in the per capita water consumption. Such trends will no doubt be less dramatic in the future, particularly in large urban areas as water supply becomes critical.

Commercial, Industrial and Institutional Wastes

Quantities from commercial areas are frequently considered in small communities as being adequately covered in the peak allowance for per capita sewage flow. Per acre analysis of commercial areas is the standard approach in larger communities. Industrial wastes include human contributions and process wastes which are permitted to enter the system. Industrial wastes are extremely variable insofar as quantity of flow is concerned and range from the normal domestic rate to greater than 200,000 gallons per acre. The type and size of the industry and plant, the supervision and the method of on-site treatment affect the waste quantities. Rates of 8–25 gallons per day per capita per shift is the normal range assumed for the domestic sanitary waste from industry. Institutional wastes are primarily domestic in nature, although process wastes may exist at prisons, municipal owned power plants, garages or any production facility.

Design Flows

The design flow is influenced by predicted and extraneous flows. **Peak, average,** and **minimum** flows are considered in predicting flows. Average flow is determined and a factor is applied to obtain peak flow which is used for selecting pipe size. Minimum flows are analyzed to determine if self-cleaning velocities can be maintained.

Illustration 3.2
Laboratory apparatus for testing hydraulic properties of 8-inch diameter concrete pipe. Manometer connections provide data for flow calculations. The slot enables visual observation and provides access for depth of flow and other measurements.

The average flow is an estimated quantity derived from past data and experience. With adequate local historical records, the average flow from domestic, commercial and industrial sources can be assumed equal to the average rate of water consumption for an area. Without such records, information on probable average flows can be obtained from other sources, including state and national agencies.

Requirements for minimum average flows are usually specified by local, state, and national agencies. *Table 3.1* lists typical design criteria for domestic sewage flows of various municipalities. Bases for estimating commercial and industrial sewage flows for various cities in the United States are listed in *Table 3.2*.

Many studies have been made of hourly, daily and seasonal variations of actual flow. Typical results of one study are shown in *Figure 3.13*. Maximum and minimum daily flows are used in the design of treatment plants, but the sanitary sewer is designed to carry the peak flow. **Peak flow** is defined as the mean rate of the maximum flow occurring during a 15-minute period for any 12-month period, and is determined by multiplying the average flow by an appropriate factor. Values for this factor range from 4.0 to 5.5 for design populations of one thousand, and 1.5 to 2.0 for design populations of one million.

Extraneous flow and its two components, **infiltration** and **inflow** are defined by the United States Environmental Protection Agency, *EPA*, as follows:

Infiltration is the volume of groundwater entering sewers and building sewer connections from the soil, through defective joints, broken or cracked pipe, improper connections, manhole walls, etc.

Inflow is the volume of any kinds of water discharged into sewer lines from such sources as roof leaders, cellar and yard area drains, foundation drains, commercial and industrial so-called clean water discharges, drains from springs and swampy areas, etc. It does not include and is distinguished from infiltration.

Inflow is the major contributor to extraneous flow and should be minimized. Inflow quantities should be based on a survey of the sewer system.

Infiltration, compared to inflow, is a relatively small amount. EPA recommends a construction allowance of about 200 gallons per inch of diameter per mile of sewer per day as a reasonable cost effective construction limit based on a specific average head of groundwater over the pipe. Infiltration and inflow are discussed further in *Chapter 9*.

STORM SEWERS AND CULVERTS

The design flows for storm sewers and culverts are based upon hydrologic principles. These flows include precipitation runoff, surface waters and, in some instances, groundwater. The hydraulic design procedures for storm sewers and culverts are different, but the methods of estimating runoff are the same.

Table 3.1. Sewage Flows Used for Design.

City	Year of Data	Average rate of water consumption, in gpcd[1]	Population served, in thousands	Per capita sewage flow average[2] in gpcd[1]	Sewer design basis in gpcd[1]	Remarks
Baltimore, Md.	–	160	1.300	100	135 x factor	Factor 4 to 2
Berkeley, Calif.	–	76	113	60	92	–
Boston, Mass.	–	145	801	140	150	Flowing half full
Cleveland, Ohio[3]	1946	–	–	100	–	–
Cranston, R.I.[3]	1943	–	–	119	167	–
Des Moines, Iowa[3]	1949	–	–	100	200	–
Grand Rapids, Mich.	–	178	200	189.5	200	–
Great Peoria, Illinois	1960	90	150	75	800 8.500	Based on 12 persons per acre for lateral and trunk sewers respectively
Greenville County, South Carolina	1959	110	200	150	300	Service area includes city of Greenville.[1] Sewers 24" and less designed to flow 1/2 full at 300 gpcd,[1] sewers larger than 24" designed to have 1' freeboard
Hagerstown, Md.	–	100	38	100	250	–
Jefferson County, Ala.	–	102	500	100	300	–
Johnson County, Kans.	1958					
Indian Creek Main Sewer Dist.	–	70	30	60	675	Most houses have basements with interior foundation drains
Mission Township Main Sewer Dist.	–	70	70	60	1.350	Most houses have basements with exterior foundation drains
Kansas City, Mo.	1958	–	500	60	675	For trunks and interceptors
					1.350	For laterals and submains. Many houses have basements and exterior foundation drains
Lancaster County, Neb.	1962	167	148	92	400	Serves City of Lincoln
Las Vegas, Nev.	–	410	45	209	250	–
Lincoln, Neb. (Lateral Dists.)	1964			60	See remarks	For lateral sewers max. flow by formula: peak flow= 5 x avg. flow÷(Pop in 1000's)$^{0.2}$
Little Rock, Ark.	–	50	100	50	100	–
Los Angeles, Calif.	1965	185	2.710	85	•	•85 gpcd[1] residential multiplied by peak factor.
Los Angeles County Sanitation District	1964	200	3.500	70•	–	•Domestic flow only, ranges from 50 to 90 gpcd[1] depending on cost of water, type of residence, etc. Domestic plus industrial averages 90 gpcd[1]
Madison, Wisc.[3]	1937	–	–	–	300	Maximum hourly rate
Memphis, Tenn.	–	125	450	100	100	–
Milwaukee, Wisc.[3]	1945	–	–	125	–	All in 12 hr-250-gpcd[1] rate
Orlando, Fla.	–	150	75	70	190	–
Painesville, Ohio[3]	1947	–	–	125	600	Includes infiltration and roof water
Rapid City, S. Dak.	–	122	40	121	125	–
Rochester, N.Y.[3]	1946	–	–	–	250	New York State Board of Health standard
Santa Monica, Calif.	–	137	75	92	92	–
Shreveport, La.	1961	125	165	–	–	Sewer design is 150 gpcd[1] plus 600 gp acre per day infiltration. Sewers 24" in diameter and less designed to flow 1/2 full, sewers larger than 24" designed to have 1' freeboard
Springfield, Mass.[3]	1949	–	–	–	200	150 gpcd[1] was used on a special project
St. Joseph, Mo.	1960	–	85	125	450	Main Sewers
					350	Interceptors
Toledo, Ohio[3]	1946	–	–	–	160	–
Washington, D. C., Suburban Sanitary District[3]	1946			100	2 to 3.3 x average	–
Wyoming, Mich.	1960	150	50	82•	400	•Calculated actual domestic sewage flow, not including infiltration or industrial flow

[1] *Gallons per capita per day. To convert to liters per capita per day multiply by 3.8.*

[2] *Measure or estimated domestic sewage.*

[3] *"Sewer Capacity Design Practice" by William E. Stanley and Warren J. Kaufman, Journal, Boston Soc. of Civil Engrs., October, 1953, p. 317, Table 2.*

Table 3.2. Sewer Capacity Allowances for Commercial and Industrial Areas.

City	Year data	Commercial	Industrial
Baltimore, Md.[1]	1949	135 gpcd[2] (range 6,750 to 13,500 gpd per acre), resident population	7,500 gpd per acre minimum
Berkeley, Calif	–	–	50,000 gpd per acre
Buffalo, N.Y.[3]	–	60,000 gpd per acre	–
Cincinnati, Ohio[3]	–	40,000 gpd per acre	–
Columbus, Ohio[1]	1946	40,000 gpd per acre; excess added to residential amount	–
Cranston, R.I.[1]	1943	25,000 gpd per acre	–
Dallas, Texas	1960	30,000 gpd per acre added to domestic rate for down town: 60,000 gpd per acre for tunnel relief sewers	–
Detroit, Mich.	–	50,000 gpd per acre	–
Grand Rapids, Mich.	–	40-50 gpcd,[2] office buildings 400-500 gpd per room, hotels 200 gpd per bed, hospitals 200-300 gpd per room, schools	250,000 gpd per acre
Hagerstown, Md.	–	180-250 gpd per room, hotels 150, gpd per bed, hospitals 120-150 gpd per room, schools	–
Houston, Texas	1960	Office Bldgs. – 0.36 gal per sq ft per day (peak) Retail Space – 0.20 gp sq ft pd (peak) Hotels – 0.93 gp sq ft pd (peak)	–
Las Vegas, Nev.	–	310-525 gpd per room, resort hotels 15 gpcd,[2] schools	–
Lincoln, Neb.	1962	7,000 gpd per acre	–
Los Angeles, Calif.	1965	Commercial, 11,700 gpd per acre Industrial, 0.024 cfs per acre Hospital, 0.75 mgd per hospital School, 0.12 mgd per school University, 0.73 mgd per university	
Los Angeles County Sanitation District	1964	10,000 gpd per acre, avg. 25,000 gpd per acre, peak	–
Kansas City, Mo.	1958	5,000 gpd per acre	10,000 gpd per acre
Memphis, Tenn.	–	2.000 gpd per acre	2,000 gpd per acre
Milwaukee, Wis.[1]	1945	60,500 gpd per acre	–
Santa Monica, Calif.	–	9,700 gpd per acre, commercial 7,750 gpd per acre, hotels	13,600 gpd per acre
Shreveport, La.	–	3,000 gpd per acre	–
St. Joseph, Mo.	1962	6,000 gpd per acre	–
St. Louis, Mo.	1960	90,000 gpd per acre avg. 165,000 gpd per acre peak	–
Toledo, Ohio[1]	1946	15,000 to 30,000 gpd per acre, average to peak allowances	–
Toronto	1960	63,500 gpd per acre downtown sewers	–

[1] *"Sewer Capacity Design Practice," by William E. Stanley and Warren J. Kaufman, Journal, Boston Soc. of Civ., Engrs., October, 1953. p. 320. Table 3.*

[2] *Gallons per capita per day.*

[3] *Sludge & Sewage Treatment, Harold Bobbitt, 6-Edition, John Wiley & Sons.*

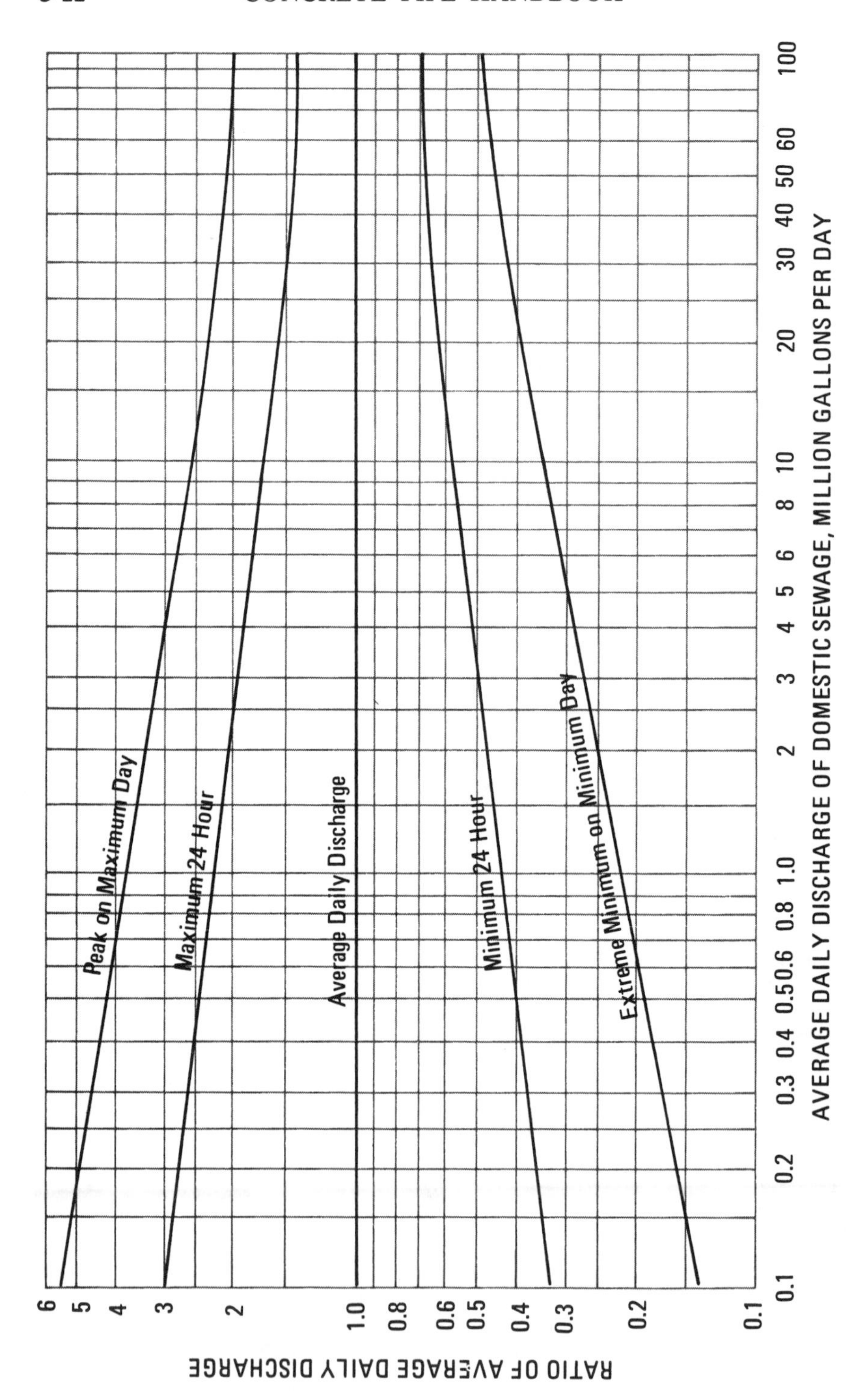

Figure 3.13. Ratio of Extreme Flows to Average Daily Flow in New England.

Hydrologic Principles

Hydrologic analyses are simple in concept but difficult in application. This is because of limited precipitation data for small watersheds, and the hydrologic cycle in which water falls on the land as rain and is retained in temporary storage or disposed of as runoff or evaporation.

Precipitation

Precipitation is the most variable factor affecting runoff. It varies from year to year and from season to season. Certain useful generalizations can be made:

- Intense rainfall occurs infrequently
- Intense rainfall occurs over small areas
- Rainfall distributed over large areas is less intense
- Rainfall of high intensity is of short duration

Based upon statistical analyses, relationships between rainfall frequency, duration, and intensity have been established. As an example, the mean annual rainfall can be used to predict total accumulation without regard to the manner in which it is distributed. The maximum five-year storm has a rainfall intensity that will be equaled or exceeded on the average of one time in five years, without regard to the number of these storms that may occur in any one period.

Rainfall intensity is a function of the **climatology** of the geographical area, the **duration** of the storm, and the storm **area.** Climatology is the study of the movement and interaction of air masses. For example, rain in the midwestern United States is generally produced as a result of the interaction of warm, moisture-laden air from the Gulf of Mexico moving north, and cold, dry air moving southeast from the Pacific Northwest. Local features such as mountains or lakes produce deviations in the general pattern. Since the maximum runoff needs to be determined, the critical storm is one that has maximum intensity, and lasts long enough for all parts of the watershed to contribute to the flow concurrently. A storm of this type is necessarily one with a duration equal to the **time of concentration,** which is discussed elsewhere in this chapter.

The areal distribution of rainfall is important because precipitation is seldom uniform within a given storm area. Rainfall intensity decreases from a maximum near the storm center to zero at the extremities. The rainfall intensity for point locations is illustrated in *Figure 3.14*, and it is necessary to adjust the design data to account for areal distribution.

The most intense rainfall occurs for short periods of time, and intensity is inversely proportional to duration:

$$i = \frac{C}{(d + t)^n} \tag{3.22}$$

Where: i = average intensity of rainfall, inches per hour
C = a constant depending on frequency of occurrence
t = duration of the storm, minutes
d = a constant depending on duration
n = a constant depending on the storm design period

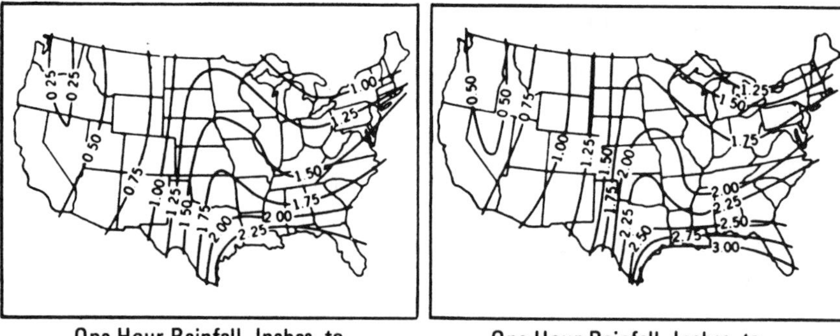

One Hour Rainfall, Inches, to Be Expected Once in 2 Years

One Hour Rainfall, Inches, to Be Expected Once in 5 Years

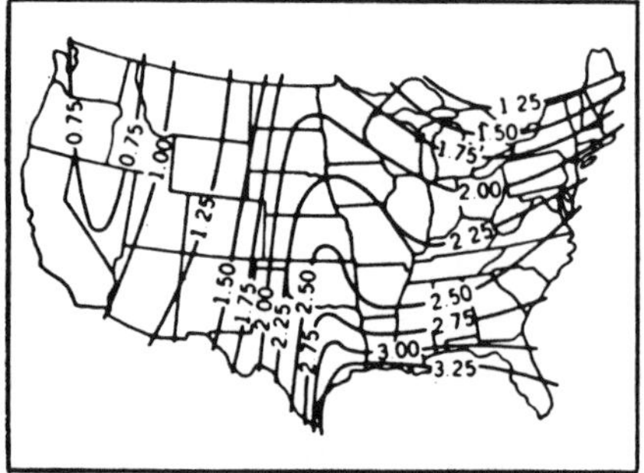

One Hour Rainfall, Inches, to Be Expected Once in 10 Years

One Hour Rainfall, Inches, to Be Expected Once in 25 Years

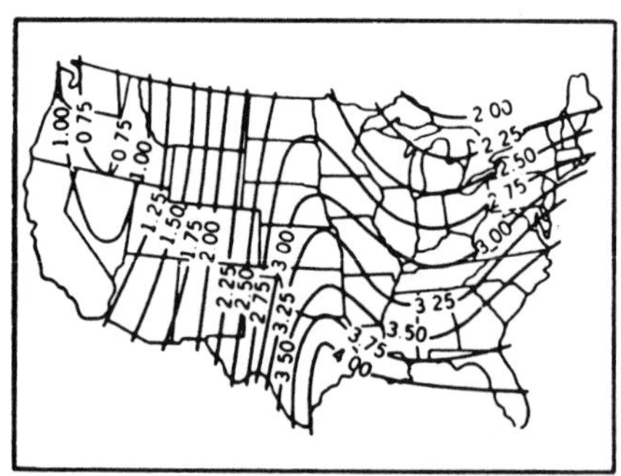

One Hour Rainfall, Inches, to Be Expected Once in 50 Years

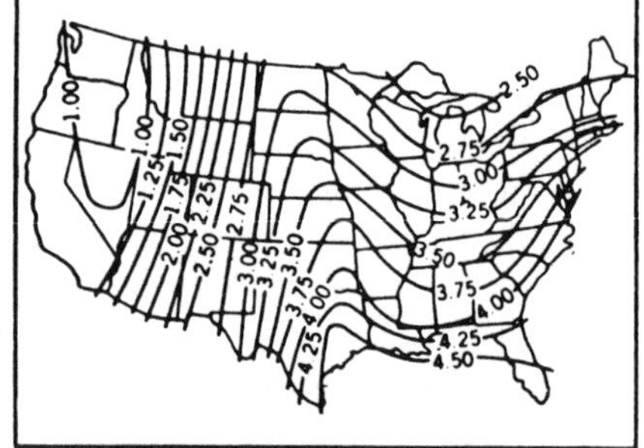

One Hour Rainfall, Inches, to Be Expected Once in 100 Years

Figure 3.14. One Hour Rainfall to be Expected Once in a Given Number of Years.

Figure 3.15 shows relationships for storms varying in duration from five minutes to four hours. These curves may be applied to the one-hour intensities from the charts of *Figure 3.14* to determine the design rainfall applicable to any particular watershed.

Average intensity for a point location can be determined by use of *Figures 3.14* and *3.15*. *Figure 3.16* provides an adjustment to rainfall intensities so as to give an average intensity uniformly distributed over the

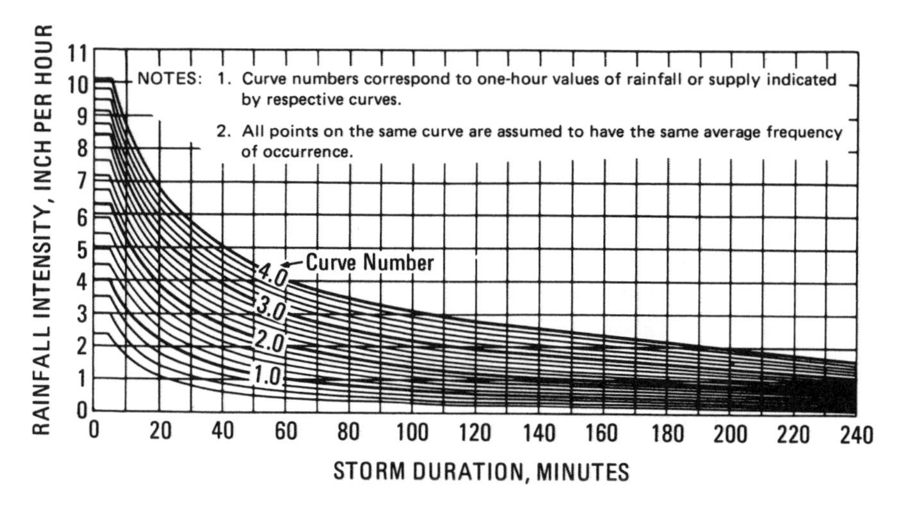

Figure 3.15. Intensity-Duration Curves.

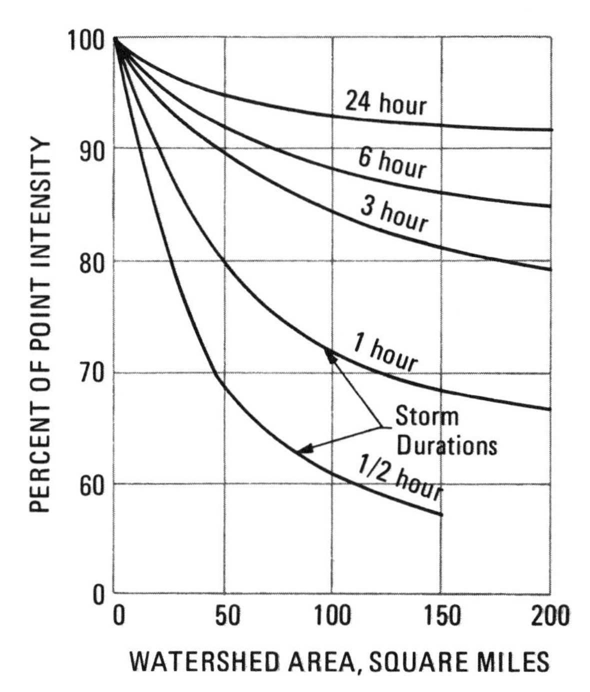

Figure 3.16. Variation of Rainfall Intensity with Area.

watershed. This curve is based on typical storm patterns and is not applicable to areas influenced by mountain conditions.

For small watersheds, areas of less than one square mile, point rainfall intensity data can be used, and for large areas up to 200 square miles, the point rainfall intensity must be adjusted in accordance with *Figure 3.16*. An adjusted intensity is obtained by multiplying the intensity of the design storm by the percent of point intensity, for the area of the watershed.

Runoff

Rain falls on many different types of surfaces. Some surfaces are highly absorbent and very little runoff develops as the rain penetrates into the soil below the vegetation. Others, such as agricultural land, are less absorbent, while impermeable city streets have a high runoff.

Runoff develops when rainfall rate exceeds the infiltration rate into the ground.

As the hydrologic cycle continues, much of the water percolates to the goundwater level, and subsequently through to open stream flow or into deep waterbearing rock strata. Evaporation from the surface and transpiration, release of moisture by trees and plants, are other parts of the hydrologic cycle.

Stream flow consists of surface runoff and groundwater flow from precipitation. *Figure 3.17* is a representative hydrograph that shows stream flow as a time sequence.

The hydrograph illustrates that the rate of runoff varies continuously. Fluctuations are produced by both climatic and topographic variables.

Climatic variables are:

- Type of precipitation
- Rainfall intensity
- Duration of rainfall
- Distribution of rainfall
- Direction of storm movement
- Soil moisture
- Evaporation and transpiration

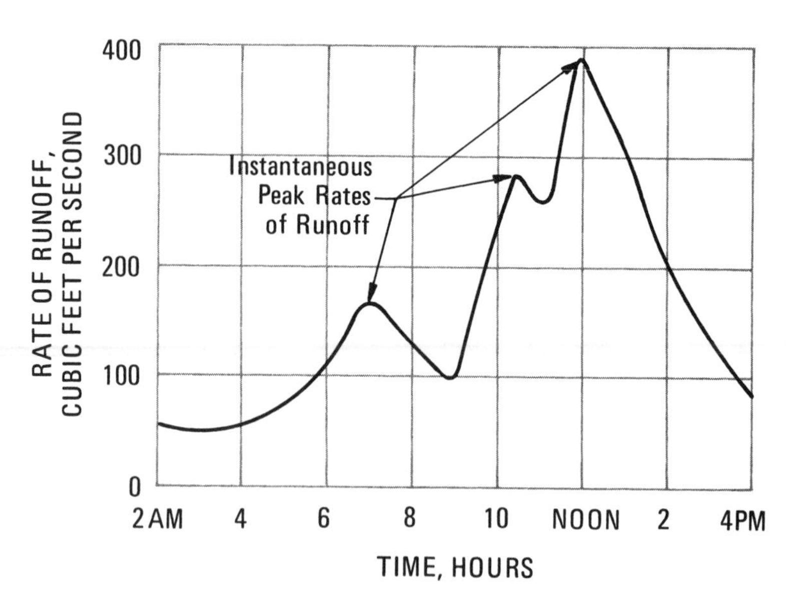

Figure 3.17. Typical Hydrograph of Stream Flow.

Topographic variables include:

- Land use
- Type of soil
- Area
- Land shape or form
- Elevation
- Slope
- Orientation

Research has led to the development of a number of methods for estimating the rate of runoff. These include empirical, statistical and hydrograph methods which are discussed in the following paragraphs. The most generally used technique is the **Rational Method** which is discussed in a later section.

Empirical Equations

Several empirical equations were developed in the late 19th and early part of the 20th centuries. Limited data were available to evaluate the formulas and many variables were not considered. Some of the methods were developed for specific areas so that application to other areas and for other conditions does not provide reasonable results.

Most of these methods were based upon the area of the drainage basin and a topographic feature coefficient.

Talbot Equation, 1887, typical of this type of method is:

$$A = C\ \sqrt[4]{M^3} \qquad (3.23)$$

Where: A = waterway area, square feet
M = drainage area, acres
C = coefficient based upon observations of peak discharges, ranging from 1.0 for mountainous areas to 0.20 for flat areas, feet per second

Myers Equation is:

$$Q = 100p\ \sqrt{M} \qquad (3.24)$$

Where: Q = runoff, cubic feet per second
p = numerical percentage on Myers scale
M = drainage area, square miles

Statistical Method

The statistical approach, often referred to as the frequency analysis, predicts future runoff on the basis of past performance. The reliability of the runoff estimate is primarily a function of the time period, and amount and detail of data.

There are several different approaches to frequency analysis. The usual approach involves three steps:

- The magnitudes of the annual floods are listed in rank order and the largest designated as Number 1.
- The average time interval between flood peaks of equal size, termed the **recurrence interval** or **frequency period,** is computed.

$$T = \frac{N + 1}{M} \tag{3.25}$$

Where: T = recurrence interval
N = length of continuous record
M = order of magnitude of the annual flood peak

- The recurrence interval is plotted against the flood peak on either a logarithmic or probability base. This permits an estimate by extrapolation of larger sized storms with larger recurrence intervals.

Frequency studies have been conducted for a number of areas in an effort to develop a single recurrence curve for different geographic areas. The U.S. Geological Survey and the Federal Highway Administration have made such studies, but limited data have handicapped the efforts.

Hydrograph Method

This method is one of the best techniques for flow determinations. A hydrograph is an accounting system that relates rainfall rates to runoff rates. The relationship is established through data on rainfall, infiltration, sur-

Table 3.3. Runoff Coefficients for Various Areas.

Description of Area	Runoff Coefficients
Business:	
Downtown areas	0.70 to 0.95
Neighborhood areas	0.50 to 0.70
Residential:	
Single-family areas	0.30 to 0.50
Multi units, detached	0.40 to 0.60
Multi units, attached	0.60 to 0.75
Residential (suburban)	0.25 to 0.40
Apartment dwelling areas	0.50 to 0.70
Industrial:	
Light areas	0.50 to 0.80
Heavy areas	0.60 to 0.90
Parks, cemeteries	0.10 to 0.25
Playgrounds	0.20 to 0.35
Railroad yard areas	0.20 to 0.40
Unimproved areas	0.10 to 0.30

face storage, basin size, length of main channels and time for stream flow to reach maximum levels after rainfall begins.

A simple hydrograph describes the runoff characteristics of the watershed, and composite hydrographs include peak discharges and changes in the discharge. The hydrograph is applicable only to the watershed for which it was developed, and its value is limited by the accuracy of rainfall and runoff data.

Rational Method

With the advent of computers, the use of complex equations and models for runoff determination have become commonplace. The relatively simple Rational Method which is described in the following pages, is still widely used for determining design flows in urban and small watersheds. This method assumes that the maximum rate of runoff for a given intensity occurs when the duration of the storm is such that all parts of the watershed are contributing to the runoff at the interception point. The design flow is determined by an empirical equation that relates the quantity of runoff from a given area to a total rainfall that is falling at a uniform rate on the same area and is expressed as:

$$Q = CiA \tag{3.26}$$

Where: Q = peak rate of runoff, cubic feet per second
i = rainfall intensity, inches per hour
A = watershed area, acres
C = runoff coefficient

The runoff coefficient, C, and the drainage area, A, are both constant for a given area at a given time. Rainfall intensity, i, is determined by using an appropriate storm frequency and duration which are selected on the basis of economics and engineering judgment. Storm frequency is selected through consideration of the size of the drainage area, probable flooding, possible flood damage and projected development schedule for the area.

Runoff Coefficient

The runoff coefficient used in the Rational Method is the percent of rainfall that becomes runoff. The value of the coefficient is based on the assumption that conditions of equilibrium will eventually exist.

Table 3.3 lists commonly used runoff coefficients for various areas. In *Figure 3.18* the series of bands present runoff coefficients for varying rates of rainfall with typical soil types and land uses. The bands are an adaptation of several currently used methods of determining C values. The runoff coefficient thus determined may be substituted directly into the equation $Q = CiA$. Adjustment of these curves for local conditions based on measured data may be necessary.

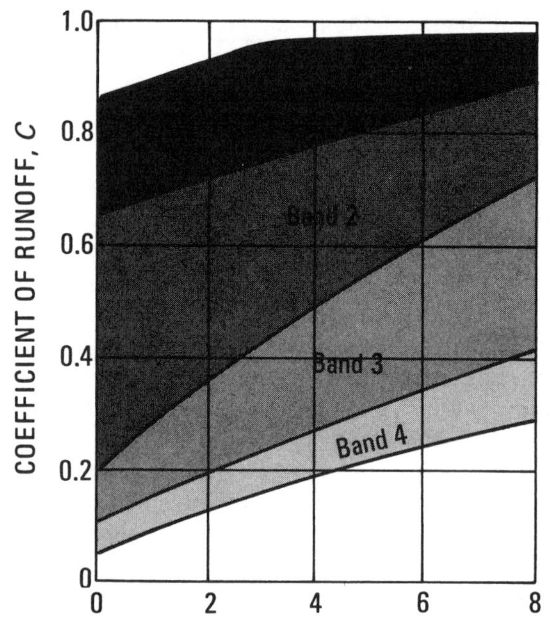

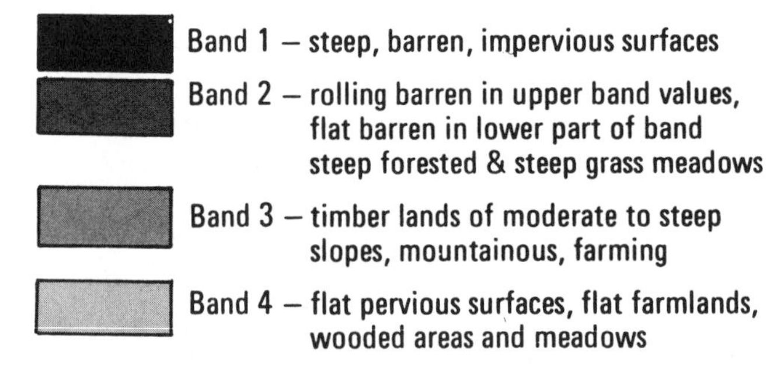

Figure 3.18. Runoff Coefficient, *C*, Related to Rainfall Intensity and Topography.

Intensity

In the Rational Method, intensity is the uniform rate of rainfall in inches per hour for a duration equal to the time of concentration.

The **time of concentration** is defined as the interval of time required for the flow at a given point to become a maximum. This is assumed to occur when all parts of the drainage area are contributing to the flow in the channel.

The usual procedure is to estimate the time of concentration, and then determine the storm intensity consistent with the recurrence frequency and with the duration equal to the time of concentration. This estimate is undoubtedly one of the most serious weaknesses in making a hydrologic analysis by any method because an error has a direct effect on the rainfall intensity value that is used.

Fortunately, errors in selecting time of concentration periods greater than one hour will not be serious because the rainfall intensity does not change rapidly for storms of long duration. Time of concentration for short duration storms is more critical. Development of hydrographs provides better information for estimating the time of concentration.

A relationship between time of concentration, t_c, and the watershed characteristics of length and slope is shown in *Figure 3.19*. Both the maximum length of travel, L, and the average slope over this length, S, are variables. The relationship expresses the time from the beginning of the rainfall until the peak flow at the point in question is attained, and accounts for time lag due to surface travel time and surface storage.

Runoff Area

The watershed area, A, of *Equation 3.26* is the drainage area served by the storm sewer or culvert. This area can be determined from topographic maps or field surveys.

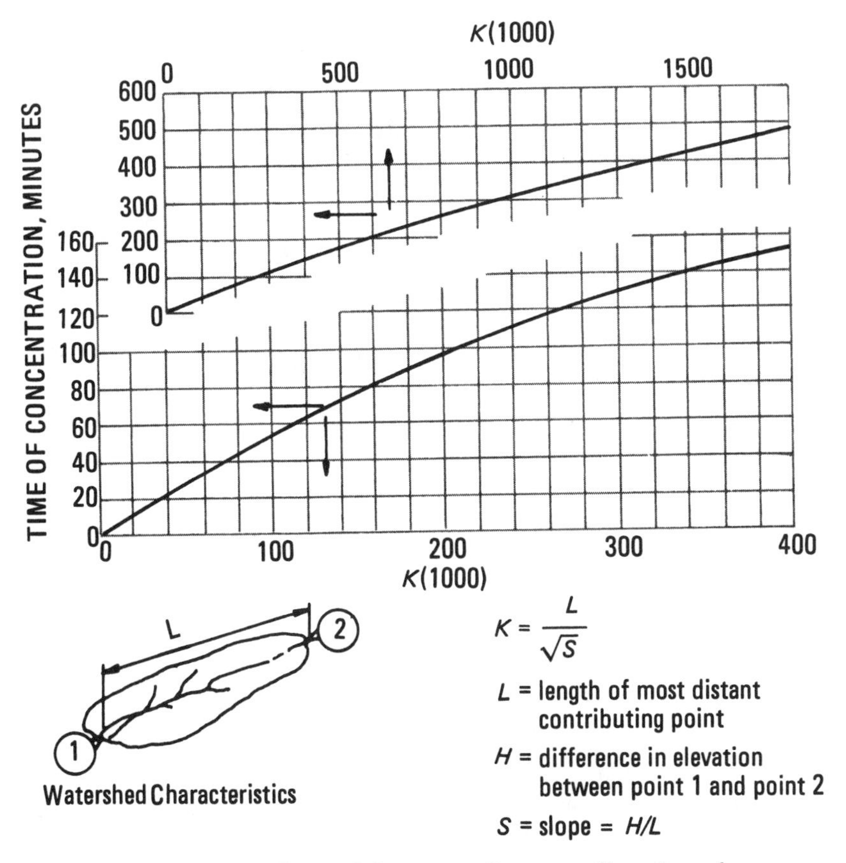

Figure 3.19. Time of Concentration as a Function of Watershed Length and Slope.

FLOOD FREQUENCY DATA

The United States Geological Survey, **USGS,** has developed a nationwide series of water-supply papers. These reports contain tables of maximum known floods and charts for estimating the probable magnitude of floods of frequencies ranging from 1.1 to 50 years. *Figure 3.20* shows the USGS regions, district and principal field offices, and the applicable water-supply paper numbers. Most states have adapted and consolidated those parts of the water-supply papers which pertain to specific hydrologic areas within their boundaries.

It is recommended that the culvert design flow be determined by methods based on USGS data. If such data are not available for a particular culvert location, flow quantities may be determined by the Rational Method or by statistical methods using records of flow and runoff.

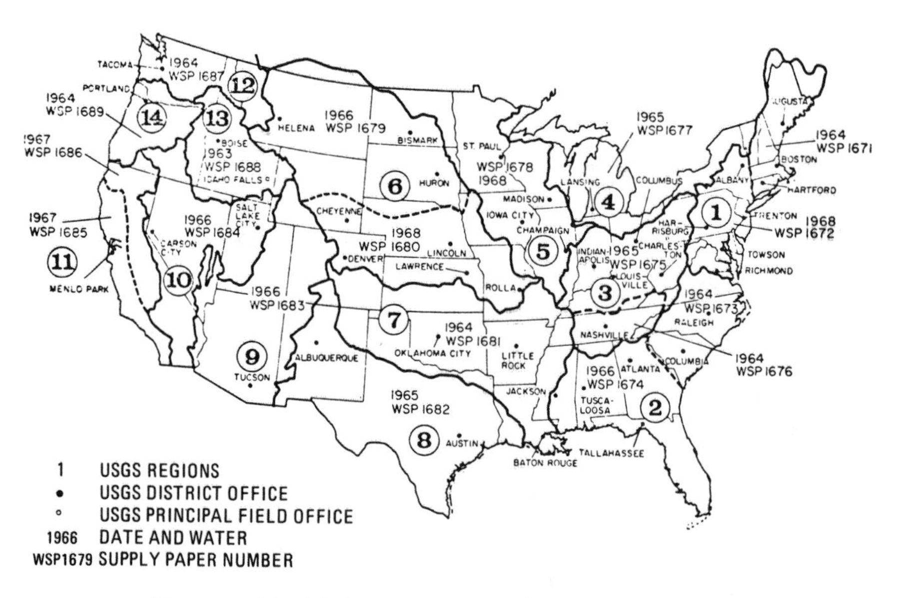

Figure 3.20. Nationwide Flood-Frequency Projects.

DESIGN OF SANITARY AND STORM SEWERS

The hydraulic design of sanitary and storm sewers consists of determining the requirements for transporting water or sewage and utilizing the energy that is available from differences in elevation. The main variables are:

- Pipe size
- Pipe material

Illustration 3.3
A laboratory installation for full scale testing of a 36-inch diameter concrete pipe. The groove and projecting end provides the most hydraulically efficient culvert inlet.

SELECTION OF PIPE SIZE

Sanitary sewers are normally designed to flow partially full and storm sewers almost full, but without pressure. The flow, defined as gravity flow, is maintained by the slope of the sewer. Under such conditions, it is sufficiently accurate to assume that the hydraulic gradient is parallel to the sewer invert, and the flow is uniform as depicted in *Figure 3.1a*.

Sewer velocities are determined by the formulas developed for open channel flow. Major energy losses result from friction between the pipe surface and the flowing fluid. Relating this friction loss to flow is accomplished by Manning's equation:

$$Q = \frac{1.486}{n} AR^{\frac{2}{3}}S^{\frac{1}{2}} \qquad (3.27)$$

For a given flow, this formula can be solved by trial and error by selecting a pipe roughness coefficient and assuming a pipe size and slope. Examples of design aids for solving Manning's equation for full flow conditions are shown in nomograph form in *Figure 3.10* and graphically in *Figure 3.21*.

To use the nomograph, draw a line through the slope, point 1 on the slope scale, and the n value, point 2 on the n scale. From the intersection of this line with the transfer line, point 3, draw another line through the Q value, point 4 on the Q scale. At the intersection of this line with the diameter scale, read the pipe size, point 5, and with the velocity scale, read the velocity, point 6. These values are for full flow conditions.

Figure 3.21 provides solutions to Manning's equation for full flow and an n value of 0.012. Plotted on the horizontal scale is the slope in feet per hundred feet. The vertical scale is the design flow, Q. Diagonal lines are plotted representing pipe diameters from 8 through 144 inches. Velocity lines are also plotted with values along the bottom diagonal line. The required pipe size can be obtained by projection of a horizontal line from the design flow, Q, and of a vertical line from the slope, S. If the intersection falls between two pipe sizes, select the larger size and revise either the slope or the flow. When selecting the pipe size, also interpolate between the velocity lines to obtain the full flow velocity. As an example, using *Figure 3.21* for a given flow of 100 cubic feet per second and a slope of 0.3 feet per 100 feet, the required pipe size is 54-inch diameter and the velocity is greater than seven feet per second.

Since sewers are designed for less than full flow conditions, additional design aids are necessary. The hydraulic properties, velocity, hydraulic radius, quantity and area, vary with the depth of flow and are proportional to the full flow values. A design aid for partial flow conditions is shown in *Figure 3.22* for circular pipe.

Curves are plotted for the hydraulic elements of flow, velocity, area of flow and hydraulic radius. The vertical scale is the ratio of actual depth of flow to the inside diameter. The horizontal scale is the ratio of the value for hydraulic elements at partial flow conditions to full flow conditions. To use the graph, one relationship must be known. For example, if the ratio of design Q to full flow Q is known, from this value on the horizontal scale, project a vertical line to the flow curve. From this intersection, project a horizontal line to any of the other curves, or if depth of flow is desired, to the vertical scale. From the intersection of the horizontal line and one of the other curves, project a vertical line down to the horizontal scale and the value obtained is the ratio of that particular element for partial to full flow conditions. The ACPA Concrete Pipe Design Manual provides design aids for solving Manning's equation and proportional value graphs. These design aids cover circular, elliptical, arch, and box shapes.

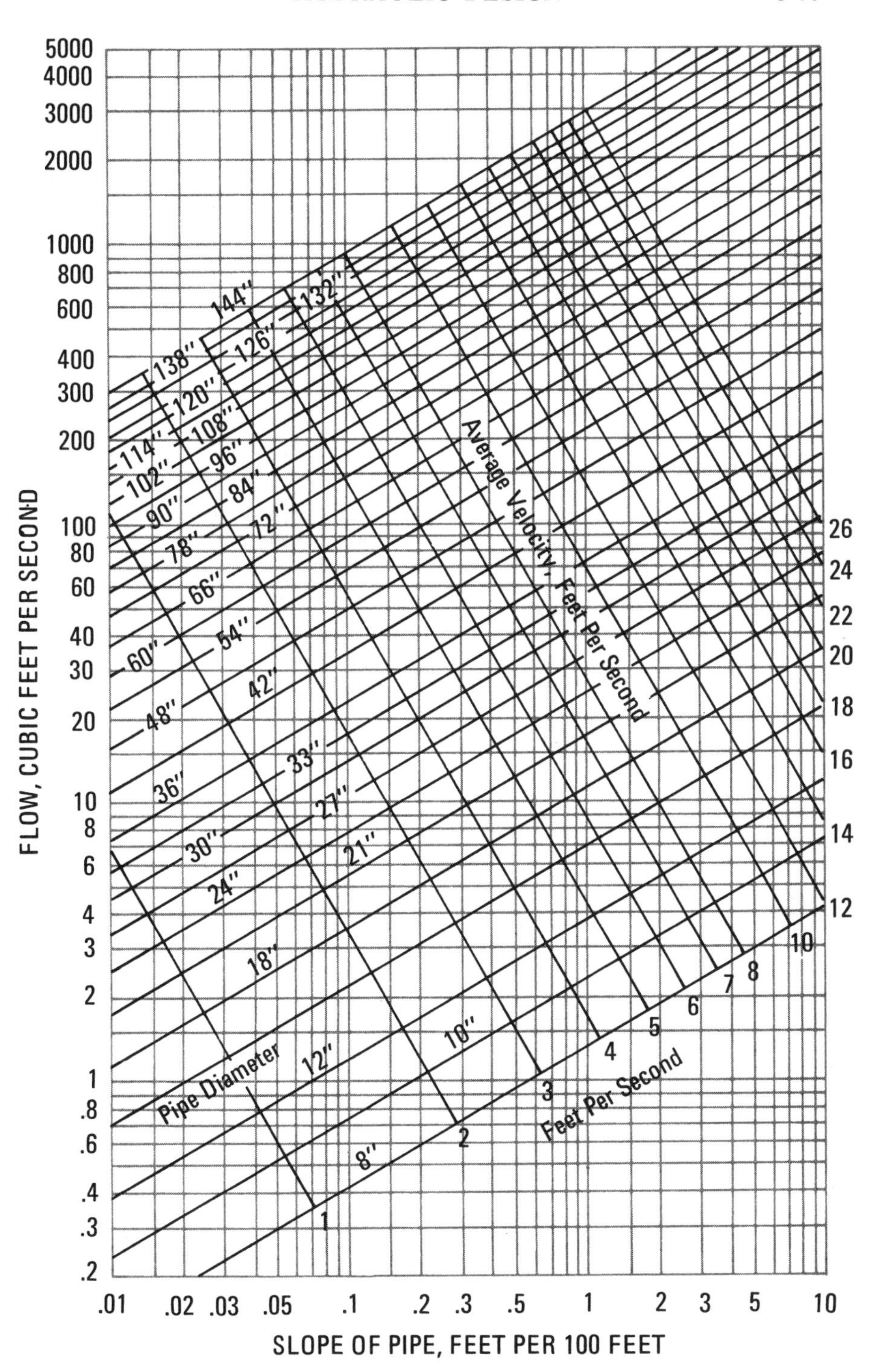

Figure 3.21. Flow for Circular Pipe Flowing Full Based on Manning's Equation, $n = 0.012$.

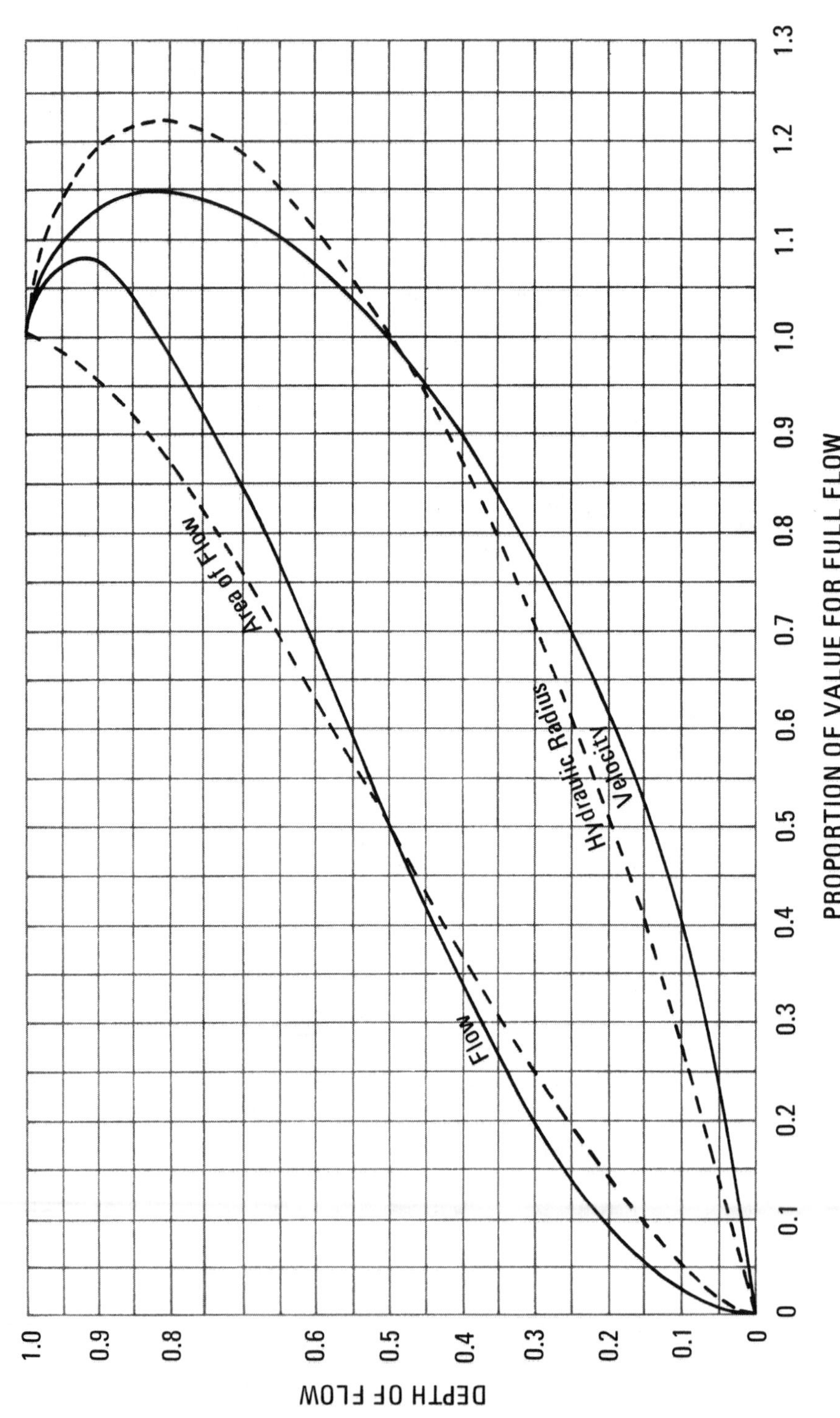

Figure 3.22. Relative Velocity and Flow in Circular Pipe for Any Depth of Flow.

ROUGHNESS COEFFICIENT

Selection of a value for the coefficient of roughness of a pipe is an essential step in determining the pipe size of culverts and sewers. An excessively high value results in oversizing of pipe, while too low a value can result in hydraulically inadequate pipe. Using *Figure 3.10,* if the roughness coefficient for the example shown is increased to a value of 0.029, and the quantity of flow and the slope remain the same (100 cubic feet per second and 0.3 feet per 100 feet), the pipe size required for full flow conditions is increased from 54 to 72 inches.

Values for the coefficient of roughness of pipe have been investigated for many years. Extensive data are available on this subject. Presently accepted values for the coefficient of roughness may appear to be sufficient, but an understanding of how these values were determined is important. The value that is needed is the one which will accurately predict the hydraulic properties of the field installations during service life.

The difference between laboratory test values of Manning's "n" and accepted design values is significant. Numerous tests by public and other agencies have established Manning's "n" laboratory values. However, these laboratory results were obtained utilizing clean water and straight pipe sections without bends, manholes, debris, or other obstructions. The laboratory results indicated the only differences were between smooth wall and rough wall pipes. Rough wall, or corrugated pipe, have relatively high "n" values which are approximately 2.5 to 3 times those of smooth wall pipe.

All smooth wall pipes, such as concrete and plastic, were found to have "n" values ranging between 0.009 and 0.010, but, historically, engineers familiar with sewers have used 0.012 or 0.013. This "design factor" of 20-30 percent takes into account the difference between laboratory testing and actual installed conditions. The use of such design factors is good engineering practice, and, to be consistent for all pipe materials, the applicable Manning's "n" laboratory value should be increased a similar amount in order to arrive at design values. Recommended design values are listed in *Table 3.4*.

The values for corrugated metal pipe in *Table 3.4* exclude any benefits of bituminous linings and pavings because performance records indicate bituminous linings have a relatively short life expectancy.

SELF CLEANING VELOCITY

Sewers should be designed to maintain self cleaning velocities. Flow in a sewer, however, varies with time, which means that the depth of flow and velocity also change. Therefore, the design procedure should include a check for self cleaning velocity at minimum flow. For sanitary sewers, a velocity of 2 feet per second is generally considered adequate. The debris entering a storm sewer will normally have a higher specific gravity than sewage, therefore a minimum velocity of 3 feet per second is usually specified. The slopes required to maintain minimum velocities of 2 feet per second and 3 feet per second for full and half full flow are presented in *Table 3.5*.

Table 3.4. Recommended Values of Manning's *n*.

Type of Pipe	Values of Manning's n	
	Lab Values	Design Values
CONCRETE	0.010	Storm-0.012 Sanitary-0.013
PLASTIC	0.009	Storm-0.012 Sanitary-0.013
ASBESTOS CEMENT	0.010	Storm-0.012 Sanitary-0.013
CLAY	0.010	Storm-0.012 Sanitary-0.013
DUCTILE IRON/CAST IRON	0.010	minimum of 0.013
CORRUGATED METAL*		
2 2/3" x 1/2"	0.024	0.029
3" x 1"	0.027	0.032
6" x 2" structural plate	0.033	0.040
9" x 2 1/2" structural plate	0.037	0.044

* Includes steel and aluminum pipe and helically corrugated pipe.

Table 3.5. Slopes Required To Maintain Minimum Velocities for Full and Half Full Flow.

Pipe Diameter, Inches	V = 2 FPS Slope, Percent				V = 3 FPS Slope, Percent			
	n = 0.010	n = 0.011	n = 0.012	n = 0.013	n = 0.010	n = 0.011	n = 0.012	n = 0.013
8	0.197	0.238	0.284	0.332	0.443	0.536	0.638	0.749
10	0.147	0.178	0.213	0.248	0.329	0.399	0.474	0.557
12	0.115	0.139	0.166	0.194	0.259	0.313	0.372	0.437
15	0.086	0.104	0.123	0.145	0.192	0.232	0.277	0.325
18	0.067	0.081	0.097	0.114	0.151	0.182	0.217	0.255
21	0.055	0.066	0.079	0.092	0.123	0.149	0.177	0.208
24	0.046	0.055	0.066	0.077	0.103	0.124	0.148	0.174
27	0.039	0.047	0.056	0.065	0.088	0.106	0.127	0.149
30	0.034	0.041	0.049	0.057	0.076	0.092	0.110	0.129
33	0.030	0.036	0.043	0.051	0.067	0.081	0.097	0.114
36	0.027	0.032	0.038	0.045	0.060	0.073	0.086	0.101
42	0.022	0.026	0.031	0.036	0.049	0.059	0.070	0.083
48	0.018	0.022	0.026	0.031	0.041	0.049	0.059	0.069
54	0.015	0.019	0.022	0.027	0.035	0.042	0.050	0.059
60	0.013	0.016	0.019	0.023	0.030	0.037	0.044	0.051
66	0.012	0.014	0.017	0.020	0.027	0.032	0.039	0.045
72	0.011	0.013	0.015	0.018	0.024	0.029	0.034	0.040
78	0.010	0.011	0.014	0.016	0.021	0.026	0.031	0.036
84	0.009	0.010	0.012	0.015	0.019	0.024	0.028	0.033
90	0.008	0.010	0.011	0.013	0.018	0.021	0.026	0.030
96	0.007	0.009	0.010	0.012	0.016	0.020	0.023	0.027
102	0.007	0.008	0.010	0.011	0.015	0.018	0.022	0.025
108	0.006	0.007	0.009	0.010	0.014	0.017	0.020	0.024
114	0.006	0.007	0.008	0.010	0.013	0.016	0.019	0.022
120	0.005	0.006	0.008	0.009	0.012	0.015	0.017	0.020
126	0.005	0.006	0.007	0.008	0.011	0.014	0.016	0.019
132	0.004	0.006	0.007	0.008	0.011	0.013	0.015	0.018
138	0.004	0.005	0.006	0.007	0.010	0.012	0.014	0.017
144	0.004	0.005	0.006	0.007	0.009	0.011	0.014	0.016

DESIGN OF CULVERTS

Culverts are constructed to convey water under a highway, railroad, canal, or other embankment.

Hydraulic design of a culvert is primarily influenced by **headwater depth.** As apparent in *Figure 3.23,* if the flow does not pass through the culvert in sufficient quantity, water may go over the embankment or back up and cause flooding with damage and inconvenience upstream. The factors that affect the discharge from the culvert are headwater, pipe size, tailwater, roughness of the pipe, pipe slope, pipe length and inlet geometry.

Culvert flows are classified as being under either **inlet** or **outlet control,** that is, the discharge is controlled by either the outlet or inlet characteristics. The hydraulic capacity of a culvert is determined differently for the two types of control.

Under inlet control, the major factors are:

- Cross-sectional area of the culvert barrel
- Inlet geometry
- Headwater depth

Outlet control involves the additional consideration of:

- Tailwater depth
- Slope, roughness and length of the culvert barrel

Complex hydraulic computations can be used to determine the probable type of flow under which a culvert will operate for a given set of conditions. However, headwater depths for both inlet and outlet control can be easily calculated. The higher value determines the type of control and anticipated headwater depth.

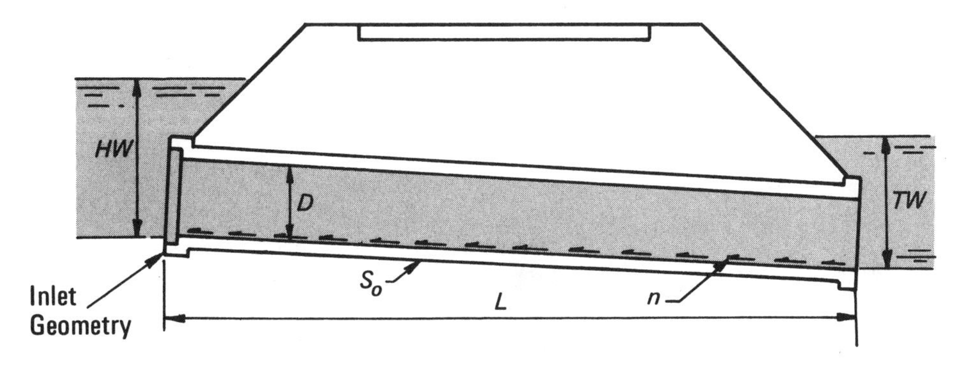

Figure 3.23. Factors Affecting Culvert Discharge.

CULVERTS FLOWING WITH INLET CONTROL

Inlet control means that the discharge capacity is controlled at the culvert entrance, and the condition will exist as long as water can flow through the culvert at a greater rate than water can enter. Inlet conditions depend upon the depth of headwater, *HW*, entrance geometry, area, and shape and type of inlet edge. Types of inlet controlled flow are shown in *Figure 3.24*. As indicated in *Figure 3.24c*, a mitered or beveled entrance moves the control downstream to approximately the top of the miter.

For inlet control conditions, neither roughness, length of the culvert barrel, nor the outlet conditions are factors in determining culvert capacity. The barrel slope has some effect on discharge but a slope adjustment is considered minor and can be neglected for conventional culverts flowing with inlet control. Headwater-discharge relationships for various types of culverts flowing with inlet control have been developed in model studies and verified in some instances by prototype tests. The data were analyzed and nomographs for determining culvert capacity for inlet con-

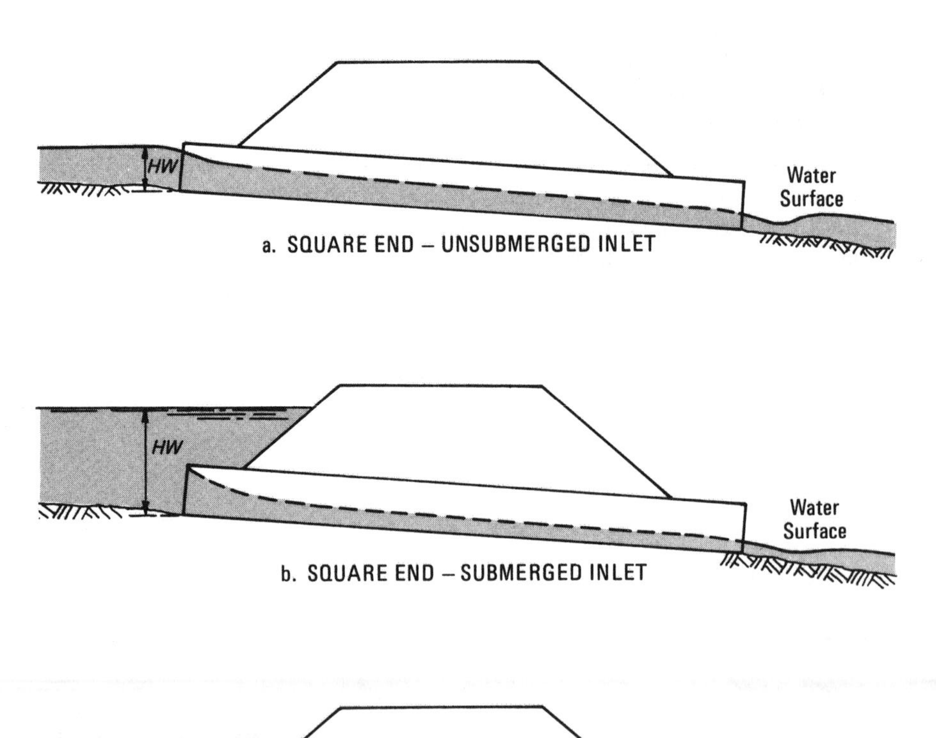

Figure 3.24. Inlet Control.

trol were developed. These nomographs give headwater-discharge relationships for most conventional culverts flowing with inlet control through a range of headwater depths or discharges. An example of these nomographs is shown in *Figure 3.25*.

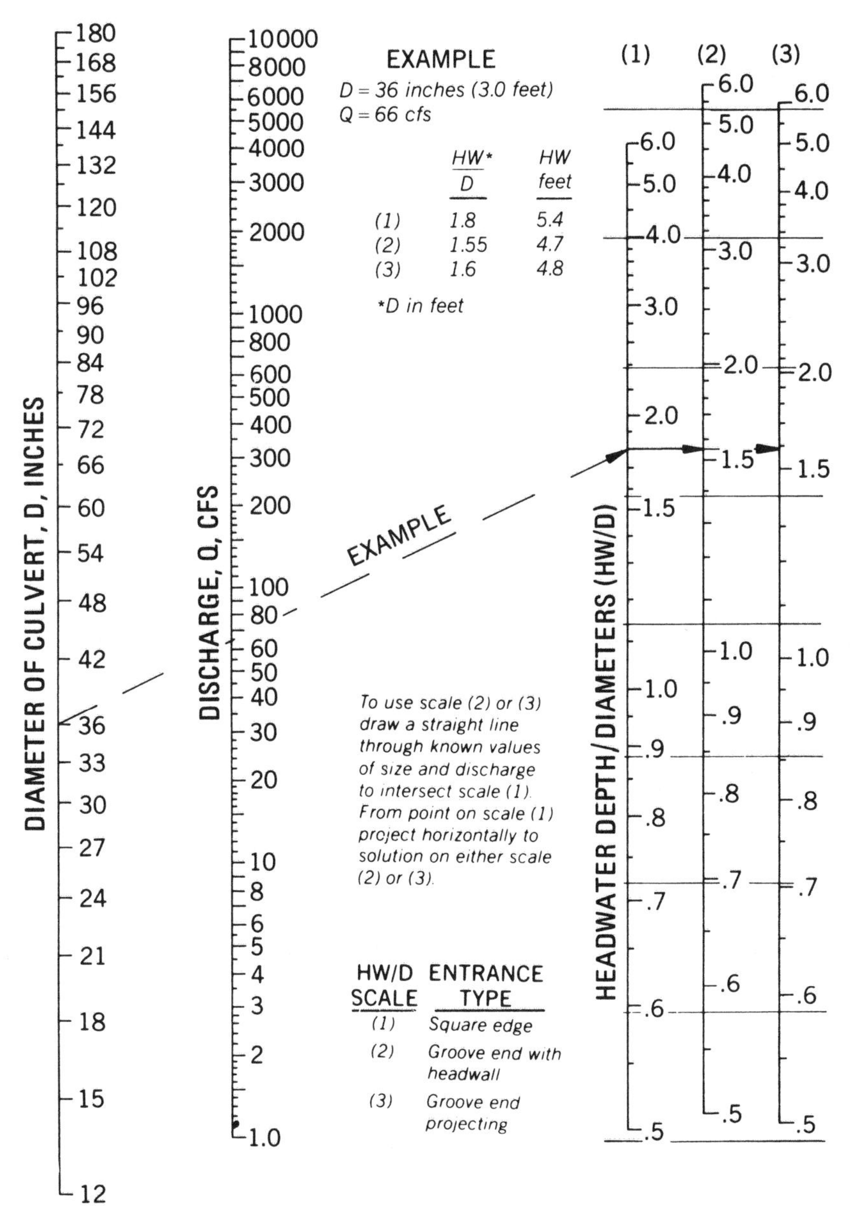

Figure 3.25. Headwater Depth for Circular Concrete Pipe Culverts with Inlet Control.

CULVERTS FLOWING WITH OUTLET CONTROL

Culverts will flow with outlet control as long as water can enter the culvert at a greater rate than water can flow through it. The culvert barrel will flow full or partly full, *Figure 3.26*. When the entire barrel is filled with water for the total length, the culvert is in full flow or flowing full as shown in *Figures 3.26a* and *3.26b*. The other two common types of outlet control flow are shown in *Figures 3.26c* and *3.26d*.

The head, H, required to pass a given quantity of water with the barrel flowing full throughout its length is made up of three major parts:

$$H = H_V + H_e + H_f \tag{3.28}$$

Where: H_V = velocity head loss, feet
H_e = entrance head loss, feet
H_f = friction head loss, feet

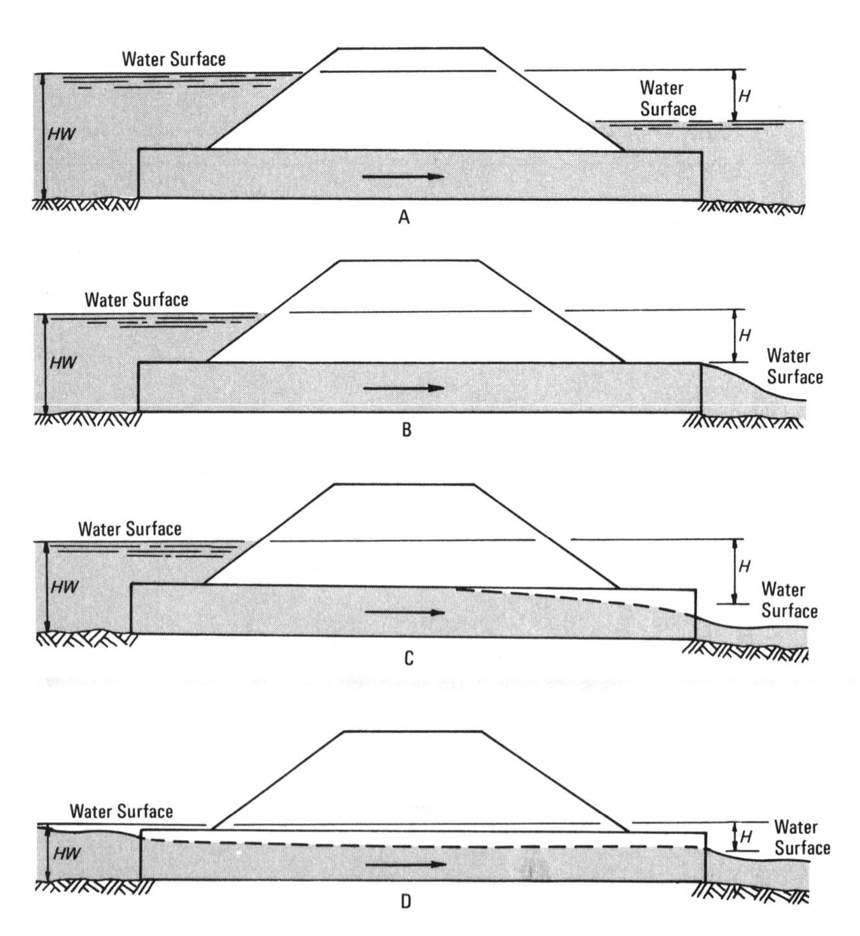

Figure 3.26. Outlet Control.

As noted earlier, the velocity head, H_V, equals $V^2/2g$, where V is the mean or average velocity in the culvert barrel. Energy from the velocity of flow in the approach channel is neglected.

The entrance loss, H_e, varies with the design of the culvert inlet. This loss is expressed as the coefficient, k_e, times the barrel velocity head, or $k_eV^2/2g$. Values of k_e for various types of culvert entrances are presented in *Table 3.6*.

The friction head, H_f, is the energy required to overcome the roughness of the culvert barrel, and can be expressed in terms of Manning's n as follows:

$$H_f = \left[\frac{29n^2L}{R^{1.33}}\right]\frac{V^2}{2g} \tag{3.29}$$

Where: n = coefficient of roughness
L = length of culvert barrel, feet
V = mean velocity of flow in culvert barrel, feet per second
R = hydraulic radius, feet

Table 3.6. Entrance Loss Coefficients.

Type of Structure and Design of Entrance	Coefficient, k_e
Pipe, Concrete	
Projecting from fill, groove end	0.2
Projecting from fill, sq. cut end	0.5
Headwall or headwall and wingwalls	
Groove end of pipe	0.2
Square-edge	0.5
Rounded (radius = 1/12D)	0.1
Mitered to conform to fill slope	0.7
End-Section conforming to fill slope*	0.5
Pipe, or Pipe-Arch, Corrugated Metal	
Projecting from fill (no headwall)	0.9
Headwall or headwall end wingwalls	
Square-edge	0.5
Mitered to conform to fill slope	0.7
End-Section conforming to fill slope*	0.5
Box, Reinforced Concrete	
Headwall parallel to embankment (no wingwalls)	
Square-edged on 3 edges	0.5
Rounded on 3 edges to radius of 1/12 barrel dimension	0.2
Wingwalls at 30° to 75° to barrel	
Square-edged at crown	0.4
Crown edge rounded to radius of 1/12 barrel dimension	0.2
Wingwalls at 10° to 30° to barrel	
Square-edged at crown	0.5
Wingwalls parallel (extension of sides)	
Square-edged at crown	0.7

*Note: "End Section conforming to fill slope", made of either metal or concrete, are the sections commonly available from manufacturers. From limited hydraulic tests they are equivalent in operation to a headwall in both **inlet** and **outlet** control. Some end sections, incorporating a **closed** taper have a superior hydraulic performance.

Substituting these values for H_V, H_e and H_f in *Equation 3.28* and simplifying:

$$H = \left[1 + k_e + \frac{29n^2L}{R^{1.33}}\right]\frac{V^2}{2g} \tag{3.30}$$

Equation 3.30 has been used to develop full flow nomographs, similar to those shown in *Figure 3.27*. There is a separate nomograph for each value of *n*.

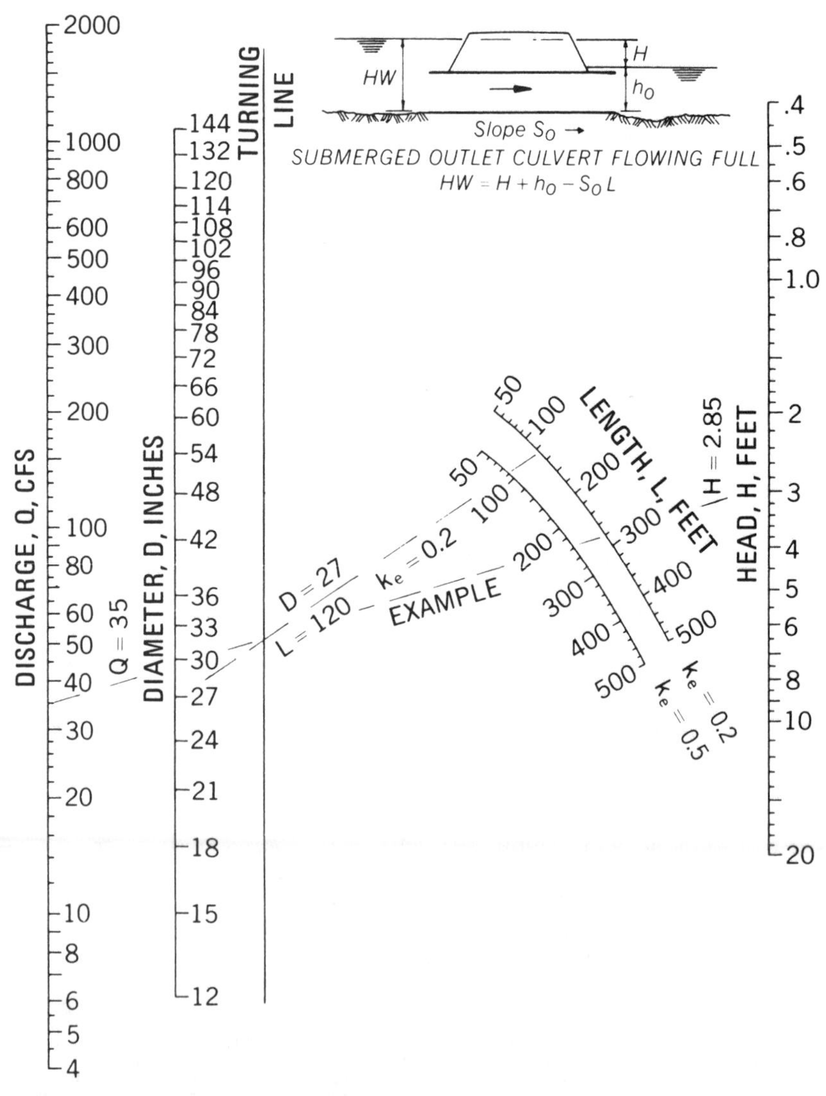

Figure 3.27. Head for Circular Concrete Pipe Culverts Flowing Full.

Headwater depth is determined by:

$$HW = h_o + H - LS_o \tag{3.31}$$

Where: h_o = height of water at outlet, feet
h_o = tailwater depth, TW, feet
$h_o = (d_c + D)/2$
H = head, feet
L = culvert length, feet
S_0 = culvert slope, feet per foot

The determination of h_o is discussed in the following paragraphs.

If the **tailwater surface**, is at or above the crown of the pipe at the outlet, *Figure 3.26a*, h_o is equal to the TW depth, and the relationship of HW to the other terms in *Equation 3.31* is illustrated in *Figure 3.28*.

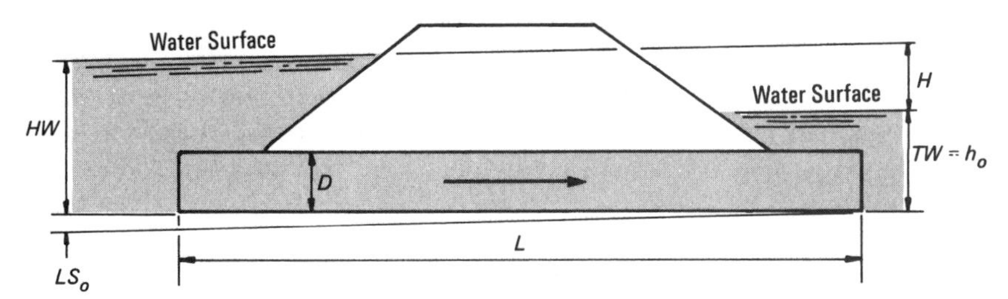

Figure 3.28. Tailwater Above Crown of the Pipe.

If the tailwater surface is below the crown of the pipe at the outlet, the determination of h_o is more complex. *Figures 3.26b, 3.26c* and *3.26d* show the three common types of flow for outlet control with low tailwater condition. In these cases, h_o is assumed to be the larger of two values:

- TW depth in the outlet channel
- $(d_c + D)/2$

The fraction $(d_c + D)/2$ is a simplified means of computing h_o, when the tailwater is low and the discharge does not fill the culvert barrel at the outlet. In this fraction, d_c is critical depth, *Figure 3.11*, and D is the culvert height. The value of d_c can never exceed D, and the upper limit of this fraction is equal to D. *Figure 3.29* shows the terms of *Equation 3.31* for the cases discussed above.

For more rigorous solutions, *Equation 3.31* provides accurate answers if the culvert flows full for a part of the barrel length as illustrated in *Figure 3.29*. This condition of flow will exist when:

$$HW \geq D + (1 + k_e)\frac{V^2}{2g} \tag{3.32}$$

Where: V = mean velocity for the full cross section of the barrel, feet per second
k_e = entrance loss coefficient
D = culvert height, feet

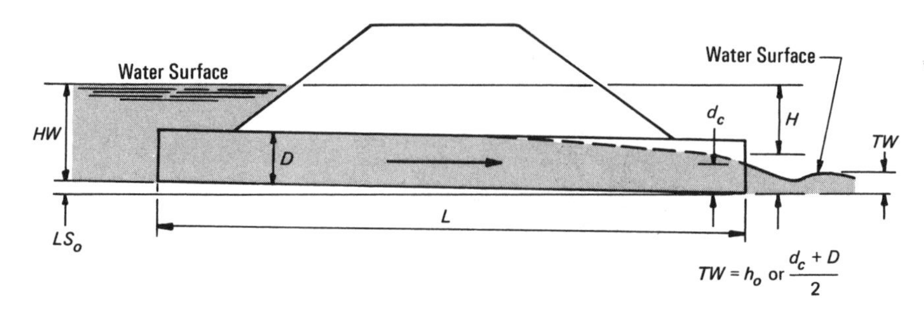

Figure 3.29. Tailwater Below Crown of the Pipe.

If the headwater drops below this point, the water surface will be free throughout the culvert barrel, *Figure 3.26d,* and *Equation 3.31* will not provide precise answers. The correct way to determine HW in this case is by a backwater computation starting at the culvert outlet. However, *Equation 3.31* will give answers of sufficient accuracy for design purposes if the headwater is greater than $0.75D$. In such cases H' is used to show that the head loss is an approximation of H. No solution is given for HW less than $0.75D$.

USE OF DESIGN CHARTS

Although the preceding procedure is primarily for use in selecting a size of culvert to pass a given discharge for a given headwater, a better understanding of culvert operation can be gained by plotting performance curves through some range of discharge and barrel slopes. Such curves can also be used to compare different sizes and types of culverts.

In the ACPA Design Manual simplified culvert capacity charts are provided for conditions of projecting entrance with the outlet submerged and roughness coefficient of 0.012. The capacity charts, one of which is presented in *Figure 3.30,* provide headwater depth for inlet control and headwater depth plus slope times length for outlet control. Therefore, by subtracting slope times length, the headwater depth for outlet control can be obtained and compared to the headwater depth for inlet control. The simplified charts in the Design Manual can be used to solve 90 percent of culvert design problems.

SLOPE

The slope of the barrel can have a significant and controlling influence on the location of the control section. For some cases, a relatively simple analysis will indicate that for a long pipeline the flow will approach or stabilize at normal depth. A comparison of this depth with the critical depth for the specific discharge will tell which type of control will exist. If the normal depth is less than the critical depth, inlet control will exist. If the normal depth is greater than the critical depth, then the pipeline will usually operate under outlet control.

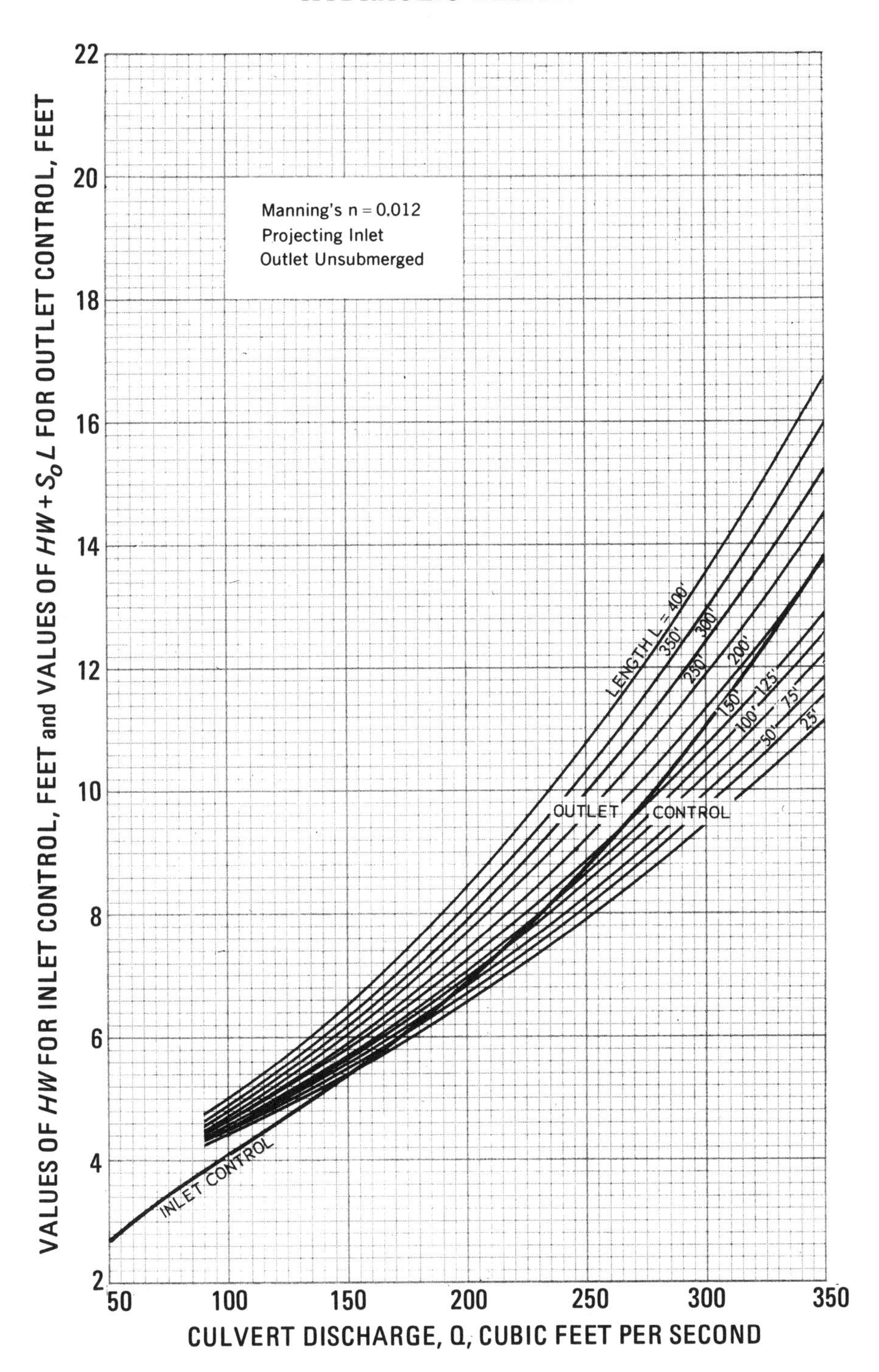

Figure 3.30. Culvert Capacity Chart 60-Inch Diameter Pipe.

INLET DESIGN

The importance of the inlet structure in culvert design has been previously discussed. Two culverts, similar in all other respects, may have different capacities if the inlets are dissimilar.

The inlet should provide a smooth transition from the flow in the inlet channel or reservoir, to the flow in the culvert barrel. This smooth transition is important for two reasons:

- Losses in head due to turbulence at the entrance are kept to a minimum.
- Contraction of the stream of water entering the culvert barrel is prevented or at least decreased.

Experiments have shown that culverts with well rounded inlet edges are very efficient. This inlet is approximated by a concrete pipe with a groove or bell end projecting from the fill. The groove or bell end should not be filled with mortar as the square edge would produce an inlet coefficient two and a half times greater.

A culvert on a steep slope with free fall at the outlet, and a square-edged inlet may flow full when the inlet is submerged by about three or more diameters. The contraction of the entering jet of water, *Figure 3.31*, due to the square corner reduces the effective water area at the inlet to about 70 percent of the pipe area. If the pipe is on a sufficiently steep slope the water will flow too fast for the culvert to flow full.

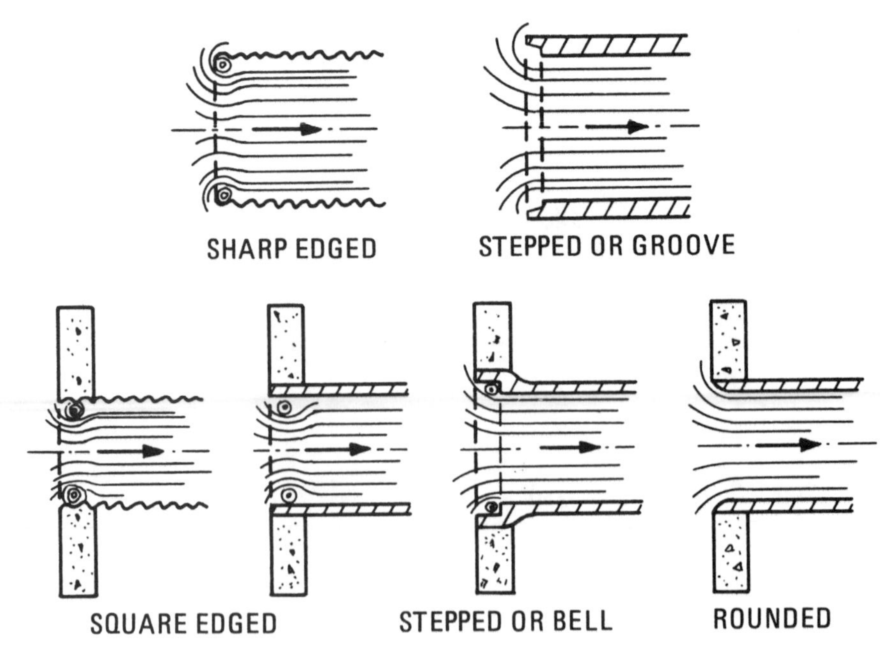

Figure 3.31. Standard Culvert Inlets.

TAILWATER DEPTH

The depth of tailwater is important in determining the hydraulic capacity of culverts flowing with outlet control. In many cases the depth of water in the natural channel is less than the height of water in the outlet end of the culvert and its depth has no effect on culvert discharge capacity or headwater. When the water surface in the outlet channel is established by downstream controls, determination of the tailwater elevation may require special studies. For example these could include:

- Analysis of the stage-discharge relationship of another stream
- Securing of data on reservoir elevations
- Field investigations to locate highwater marks

OUTLET VELOCITY

The hydraulic characteristics of a culvert increase the velocity of flow over that in the natural channel. The higher velocities are most critical just downstream from the culvert outlet, and the erosion potential should be considered.

Energy dissipators have been investigated in the laboratory, and many have been constructed, especially in irrigation channels. Since energy dissipators add to the cost of a culvert, they are only used when required to prevent scour, or as remedial construction.

Illustration 3.4

Prototype testing of 18-inch diameter concrete pipe to determine the hydraulic properties of internal energy dissipator rings. Conclusive results reported in *Chapter 5* enable reduction of culvert outlet velocities without extensive end treatments.

Usually the judgment of engineers working in a particular area is the best guide to the need for energy dissipators at culvert outlets. As an aid in the evaluation, outlet velocities can be computed and compared with actual outlet velocities. A change in size of culvert does not change outlet velocities appreciably in most cases.

For inlet control, outlet velocities may be approximated by computing the velocity for the culvert cross section using Manning's equation for full flow and partial flow hydraulic elements, *Figure 3.22*. The computed outlet velocity for inlet control will be high for culverts having a length-depth ratio less than 20. For these culverts, velocities will be between those computed by Manning's equation and those occurring at critical depth.

For outlet control, the average outlet velocity is equal to the discharge divided by the cross-sectional area of flow at the outlet. When the outlet is unsubmerged, the flow area will be between that corresponding to critical depth and the full area of the pipe.

REFERENCES

1. "Airport Drainage," Federal Aviation Agency, AC 150/5320-5A, U.S. Government Printing Office, 1965.
2. "Applied Hydrology," R. K. Linsley, Jr., M. A. Kohler, and J. L. H. Paulhaus, McGraw-Hill Book Co., Inc., 1949.
3. "California Culvert Practice," Div. Highways, Department of Public Works, State of California, 1960.
4. "Capacity Charts for the Hydraulic Design of Highway Culverts," Bureau of Public Roads, Hydraulic Engineering Circular No. 10, U.S. Government Printing Office, 1965.
5. "Concrete Pipe Handbook," American Concrete Pipe Association, 1978.
6. "Design and Construction of Concrete Sewers," Portland Cement Association, 1968.
7. "Design and Construction of Sanitary and Storm Sewers," WPCF Manual of Practice No. 9, ASCE Manuals and Reports on Engineering Practice No. 37, Water Pollution Control Federation, 1969.
8. "Design Data Series," American Concrete Pipe Association, 1969.
9. "Electronic Computer Program for Hydraulic Analysis of Circular Culverts," Bureau of Public Roads, BPR Program HY-1, U.S. Government Printing Office, 1965.
10. "Elementary Fluid Mechanics," John K. Vennard, John K. Wiley & Sons, Inc., 1947.
11. "Fluid Mechanics," Victor L. Streeter, McGraw-Hill Book Co., Inc., 1958.
12. "Generalized Estimates of Probable Maximum Precipitation for the United States West of the 105th Meridian for Areas to 400 Sq. Miles and Durations to 24 Hr.," Weather Bureau, Technical Paper No. 38, U.S. Government Printing Office, 1960.
13. "Handbook of Applied Hydraulics," McGraw-Hill Book Co., Inc., 1969.
14. "Handbook of Concrete Culvert Pipe Hydraulics," Portland Cement Association, 1964.
15. "Handbook of Hydraulics," H. W. King and E. F. Brater, 5th Edition, McGraw-Hill Book Co., Inc., 1963.
16. "Hydraulic Charts for the Selection of Highway Culverts," Bureau of Public Roads, Hydraulic Engineering Circular No. 5, U.S. Government Printing Office, 1965.
17. "Hydraulic Design of Improved Inlets for Culverts," Hydraulic Engineer Circular No. 13, U.S. Government Printing Office, 1972.
18. "Hydraulic Flow Resistance Factors for Corrugated Metal Conduits," Research and Development Report, U.S. Department of Transportation, U.S. Government Printing Office, 1970.
19. "Hydraulics of Culverts," J. G. Hendrickson, Jr., American Concrete Pipe Association, 1964.

20. "Hydrology," Manual of Practice No. 28, American Society of Civil Engineers, 1949.
21. "Hydrology for Engineers," R. K. Linsley, Jr., M. A. Kohler, and J. L. H. Paulhaus, McGraw-Hill Book Co., Inc., 1958.
22. "Loss of Energy at Sharp-Edged Pipe Junctions in Water Conveyance Systems," Fred W. Blaisdell and Philip W. Manson, Agricultural Research Service, U.S. Department of Agriculture, Technical Bulletin No. 1283, 1963.
23. "Municipal Requirements for Sewer Infiltration," Public Works, 1965.
24. "Nomenclature for Hydraulics," Manual of Engineering Practice No. 43, American Society of Civil Engineers, 1962.
25. "Pressure Changes at Storm Drain Junctions," W. M. Sangster, H. W. Wood, E. T. Smerdon, and H. G. Bossy, University of Missouri Bulletin, Engineering Series Bulletin No. 41, 1958.
26. "Rainfall Frequency Atlas of the United States for Durations from 30-Min. to 24-Hr. and Return Periods from 1 to 100 Yr.," Weather Bureau, Technical Paper No. 40, U.S. Government Printing Office, 1961.
27. "Rainfall Intensity-Frequency Data," D. L. Yarnell, Department of Agriculture, Misc. Publication No. 204, U.S. Government Printing Office, 1935.
28. "Rainfall Intensity-Frequency Regime," Weather Bureau, Technical Paper No. 29, U.S. Government Printing Office: Part 1—Ohio Valley, 1957; Part 2—Southeastern U.S., 1958; Part 3—Middle Atlantic Region, 1958; Part 4—Northeastern U.S., 1959; Part 5—Great Lakes Region, 1960.
29. "Reinforced Concrete Pipe Culverts—Criteria for Structural Design and Installation," Bureau of Public Roads, U.S. Government Printing Office, 1963.
30. "Relation Between Rainfall and Runoff from Small Urban Areas," W. W. Horner and F. L. Flynt, American Society of Civil Engineers Transactions, 1936.
31. "Sewer Capacity Design Practice," William E. Stanley and Warren J. Kaufman, Journal, Boston Society of Civil Engineers, 1953.

CHAPTER 4

LOADS, SUPPORTING STRENGTHS AND STANDARD INSTALLATIONS

The required supporting strength of a buried concrete pipe is determined by the total load that is imposed upon the pipe. The magnitude of the load is influenced by the uniformity and stability of the support soil, as well as the soil conditions around and over the pipe. Presented in this chapter are the generally accepted methods for determining loads on and supporting strengths of concrete pipe based on rational principles of mechanics.

Underground pipelines are classified into several groups and subgroups, shown in *Figure 4.1*, based upon the installation conditions that influence loads. There are two major classes: **trench** pipelines which are placed in natural ground and **embankment** pipelines which are usually bedded in natural ground but are overlayed by a constructed embankment.

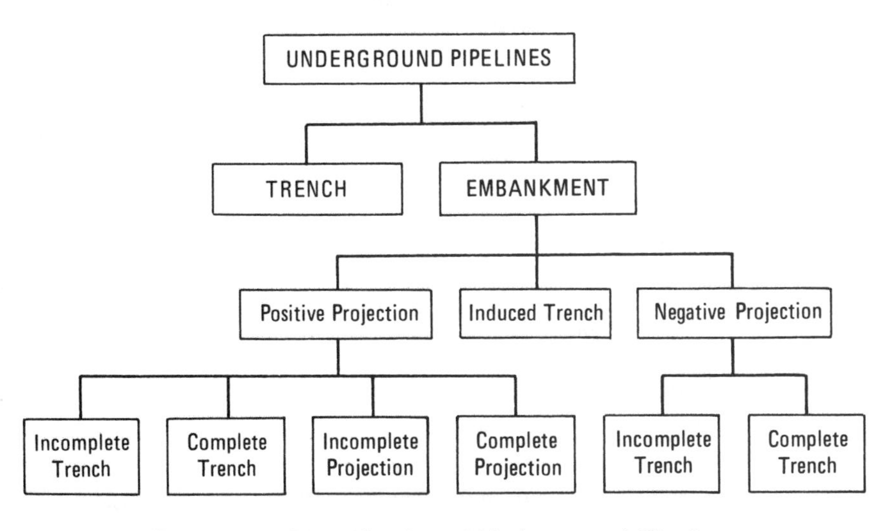

Figure 4.1. Classification of Underground Pipelines.

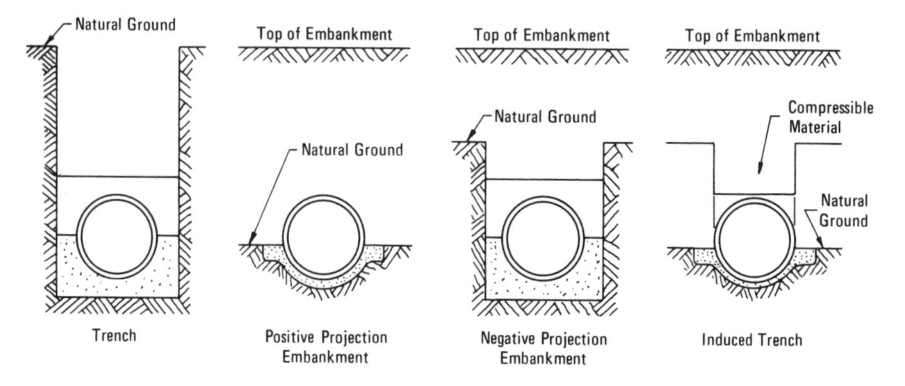

Figure 4.2. Essential Features of Various Types of Installations.

The embankment group is further subdivided into **positive projection, negative projection** and **induced trench** subgroups, based upon the extent the pipe is exposed to direct embankment loading. The essential features of these are illustrated in *Figure 4.2*. There are further subdivisions of the positive projection and negative projection embankment subgroups which are related to whether or not differential settlements may occur throughout the entire depth of backfill. Two additional classifications are **tunneled** and **jacked,** and **multiple pipe** installations.

LOADS ON THE PIPE

Three types of loads must be considered:

1. **Earth loads**
2. **Live loads** from trucks, aircraft, and trains
3. **Surcharge loads** or loads from an additional earth fill or building over an installed pipe

The methods for determining the magnitude of these loads are discussed in the following section.

EARTH LOADS

The **earth load** is the weight of the earth that must ultimately be carried by the pipe. This weight varies with the soil characteristics. More importantly, however, it varies with the installation conditions. The method for determining the earth loading is best approached by considering the two major classes of construction, trench and embankment.

Trench Installations

Trench installations are made in relatively narrow excavations and the pipeline covered with earth backfill which extends to the original ground surface. Sewers, drains and water mains are usually constructed in trenches.

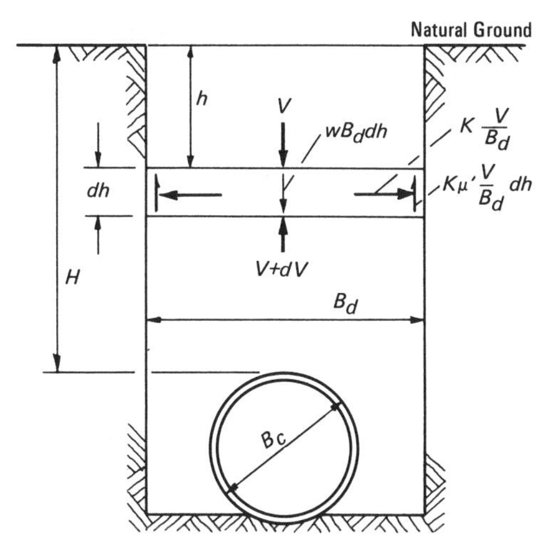

Figure 4.3. Trench Condition.

The trench load theory is based upon certain applied mechanics assumptions concerning the properties of the materials involved. These assumptions are:

- Earth loads on the pipe develop as the backfill settles.
- The resulting earth load on the pipe is equal to the weight of the material above the top of the pipe minus the shearing (frictional) forces on the sides of the trench.
- Cohesion is negligible because with cohesive soils, considerable time must elapse before effective cohesion between the backfill material and the sides of the trench can develop, and with cohesionless soils, would never develop. The assumption of no cohesion yields the maximum probable load on the pipe.
- For a rigid pipe, the sidefills may be relatively compressible and the pipe will carry a large portion of the load developed over the entire width of the trench.
- For rigid pipe, active lateral pressure is neglected which in effect increases the required pipe strength. *Although active lateral pressure against the pipe is usually neglected, it should be taken into account if investigations and experience indicate such pressure is significant.*

Prior to 1913, Marston and Talbot proposed the concept that when a pipe is placed in a narrow trench and backfilled, the backfill material will tend to settle downward; the downward movement of the material within the trench will be resisted by frictional forces along the sides of the trench; and this resistance will reduce the load on the pipe and help support the backfill. Marston subsequently developed the theories and methods for determining earth loads on underground pipelines for all of the common construction conditions. The following derivations of the formulas for earth loads in the trench condition follow the concepts and notations of Spangler.

Referring to *Figure 4.3,* the earth load on the pipe per linear foot of trench, W_d, is obtained by an analysis of the forces existing on a thin horizontal element above the pipe. The vertical pressure, V, is equal to the weight minus the vertical shearing forces along the edges. The shearing forces are equal to the ratio of active lateral unit pressure to vertical unit pressure, K, times the coefficient of internal friction (assuming a cohesionless soil). Thus by summation of the vertical forces acting on the element:

$$V + dV = V + (wB_d)\,dh - 2K\mu'\left(\frac{V}{B_d}\right) dh \qquad (4.1)$$

Solving this differential equation for $h = H$, the total earth load on the pipe is:

$$W_d = wB_d^2\left(\frac{1 - e^{-2K\mu'\frac{H}{B_d}}}{2K\mu'}\right) \qquad (4.2)$$

Where: W_d = load on the pipe for trench installations, pounds per linear foot
w = unit weight of backfill material, pounds per cubic foot
V = vertical pressure on any horizontal plane in backfill, pounds per linear foot
B_d = horizontal width of trench at top of pipe, feet
H = height of fill above top of pipe, feet
h = distance from ground surface down to any horizontal plane in backfill, feet
μ' = tan ϕ', coefficient of friction between fill material and sides of trench
K = ratio of active lateral unit pressure to vertical unit pressure
e = base of natural logarithms

For convenience, the bracketed term is defined as the load coefficient, C_d:

$$C_d = \frac{1 - e^{-2K\mu'\frac{H}{B_d}}}{2K\mu'} \qquad (4.3)$$

and therefore, *Equation 4.2* may be written as:

$$W_d = C_d w B_d^2 \qquad (4.4)$$

In the preceding analysis, the active lateral pressure is obtained from Rankine's ratio, K, the ratio between the lateral and the vertical pressure. The coefficient of friction is tan ϕ', where ϕ' is the friction angle between backfill and soil. The lateral pressure on each side of the element is $K(V/B_d)dh$ and the shearing resistance is $\mu' K(V/B_d)dh$. The value of K is determined by the equation:

$$K = \frac{\sqrt{\mu^2 + 1} - \mu}{\sqrt{\mu^2 + 1} + \mu} = \frac{1 - \sin\phi'}{1 + \sin\phi'} = \tan^2\left(45^\circ - \frac{\phi'}{2}\right) \qquad (4.5)$$

The values of C_d for a number of soils have been plotted against values of H/B_d in *Figure 4.4* and numerical values of C_d are provided in *Table 4.1*. The values of $K\mu'$ and w that are used should be those which result in the maximum calculated load which is probable for the particular type of soil under consideration. In some instances, it will be advisable to determine actual values. When the properties of the soil are unknown, assumed values of w = 120 pounds per cubic foot and $K\mu'$ = 0.13 would provide loads sufficiently accurate for preliminary and comparison calculations.

Figure 4.4 and *Table 4.1* show that as the height of backfill increases for a given trench width, the load coefficient, C_d, and thus the load on the pipe, approaches a constant value. For larger values of the H/B_d ratio, the load coefficent approaches a value of $1/(2K\mu')$. Whenever a project involves deep trenches, K and μ' should be determined for the backfill material.

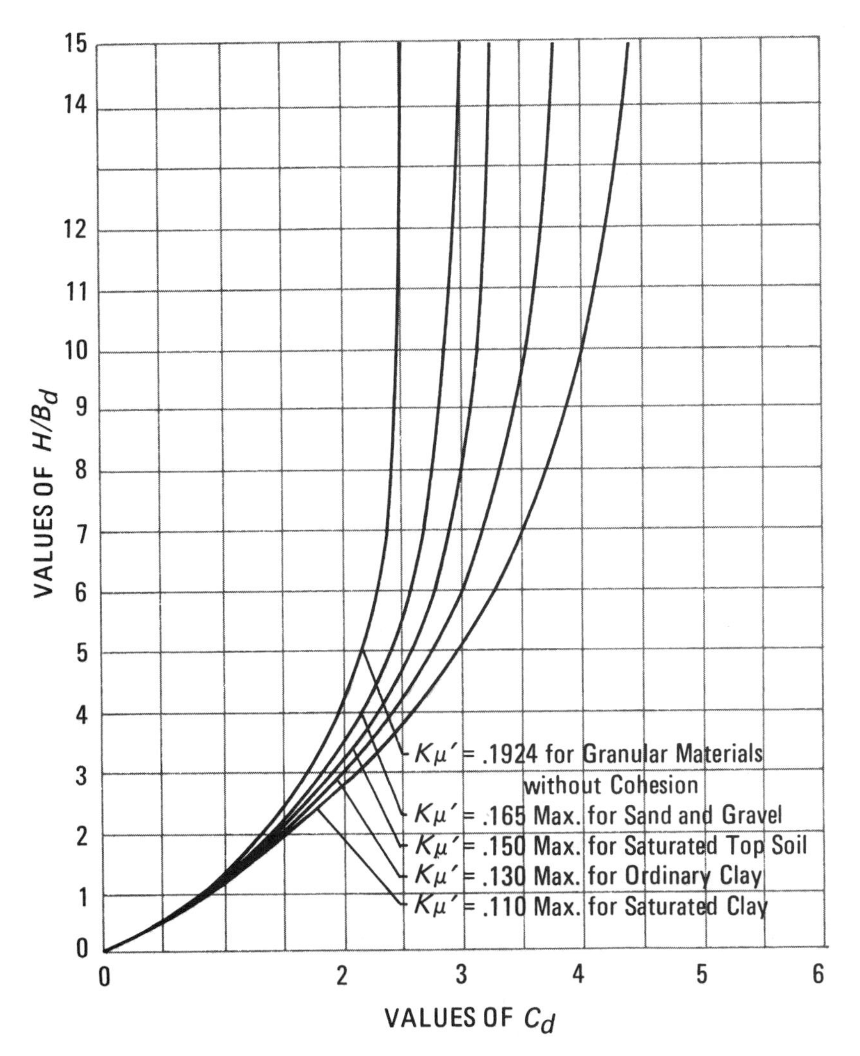

Figure 4.4. Load Coefficient for Trench Installations.

Table 4.1. Values of Trench Load Coefficient, C_d.

Fill Height To Trench Width Ratio H/B_d	Granular Materials Without Cohesion $K\mu=K\mu'=0.1924$	Sand And Gravel $K\mu=K\mu'=0.165$	Saturated Top Soil $K\mu=K\mu'=0.150$	Ordinary Clay $K\mu=K\mu'=0.130$	Saturated Clay $K\mu=K\mu'=0.110$
0.25	0.24	0.24	0.24	0.24	0.24
0.50	0.45	0.46	0.46	0.47	0.47
0.75	0.65	0.66	0.67	0.68	0.69
1.00	0.83	0.85	0.86	0.88	0.90
1.25	0.98	1.02	1.04	1.07	1.09
1.50	1.14	1.18	1.21	1.24	1.28
1.75	1.27	1.33	1.36	1.41	1.45
2.00	1.36	1.46	1.50	1.56	1.62
2.25	1.51	1.59	1.64	1.71	1.77
2.50	1.61	1.70	1.76	1.84	1.92
2.75	1.70	1.81	1.87	1.97	2.06
3.00	1.78	1.90	1.98	2.08	2.20
3.25	1.85	1.99	2.08	2.19	2.32
3.50	1.92	2.08	2.17	2.30	2.44
3.75	1.98	2.15	2.25	2.40	2.55
4.00	2.04	2.22	2.33	2.48	2.66
4.25	2.09	2.28	2.40	2.57	2.76
4.50	2.14	2.34	2.47	2.65	2.86
4.75	2.18	2.40	2.53	2.73	2.95
5.00	2.22	2.45	2.59	2.80	3.03
5.50	2.29	2.54	2.69	2.93	3.19
6.00	2.34	2.61	2.78	3.04	3.33
6.50	2.39	2.68	2.86	3.13	3.46
7.00	2.42	2.73	2.93	3.22	3.57
7.50	2.45	2.78	2.98	3.30	3.67
8.00	2.48	2.81	3.03	3.37	3.76
8.50	2.50	2.85	3.07	3.42	3.84
9.00	2.52	2.87	3.11	3.47	3.92
9.50	2.53	2.90	3.14	3.52	3.98
10.00	2.54	2.92	3.17	3.56	4.04
11.00	2.56	2.95	3.21	3.63	4.14
12.00	2.57	2.97	3.24	3.68	4.22
13.00	2.58	2.99	3.27	3.72	4.29
14.00	2.59	3.00	3.28	3.75	4.34
15.00	2.59	3.01	3.30	3.77	4.38
16.00	2.59	3.01	3.31	3.79	4.41
17.00	2.59	3.02	3.31	3.80	4.44
18.00	2.60	3.02	3.32	3.81	4.46
19.00	2.60	3.02	3.32	3.82	4.48
20.00	2.60	3.03	3.33	3.83	4.49

Through experimental installations, Schlick has shown that the width of the trench, B_d, should be taken as the horizontal trench width at the top of the pipe. For example, if the trench has sloping sides, the load on the pipe would be the same as if calculated for a vertical sided trench with B_d equal to the width of the excavation at the level of the top of the pipe. Since the load on the pipe increases as B_d increases for the same H, the excavation width at the top of the pipe should be held to the minimum required for efficient construction operations.

As the trench width is increased for a given height of cover and pipe diameter, a point is reached at which no additional load is transmitted to the pipe and an embankment condition exists, *Figure 4.2*. This limiting value of trench width is defined as the **transition width.** As an example, for sand and gravel backfill materials, $K\mu' = 0.165$, the width of trench at which this transition occurs can be determined from the curves plotted in *Figure 4.5*. Similar plots can be developed for other type materials. The $r_{sd}p$ term, the **settlement ratio,** is discussed under embankment conditions.

If the trench sides are sloped back, or if the width of trench is large in comparison with the pipe, the earth load on the pipe can be decreased by constructing a narrow subtrench at the bottom of the wider trench, as shown in *Figure 4.6*. In this case, C_d becomes a function of the trench width, B_d, and the height, H.

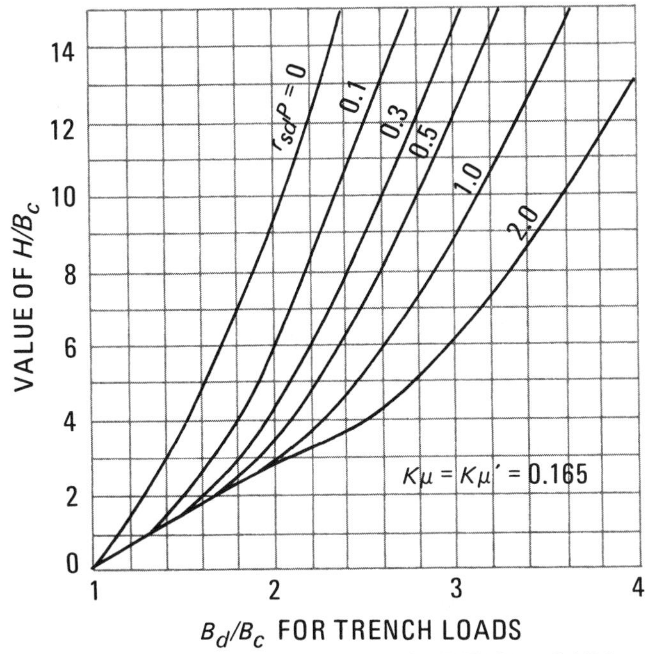

Figure 4.5. Transition Widths.

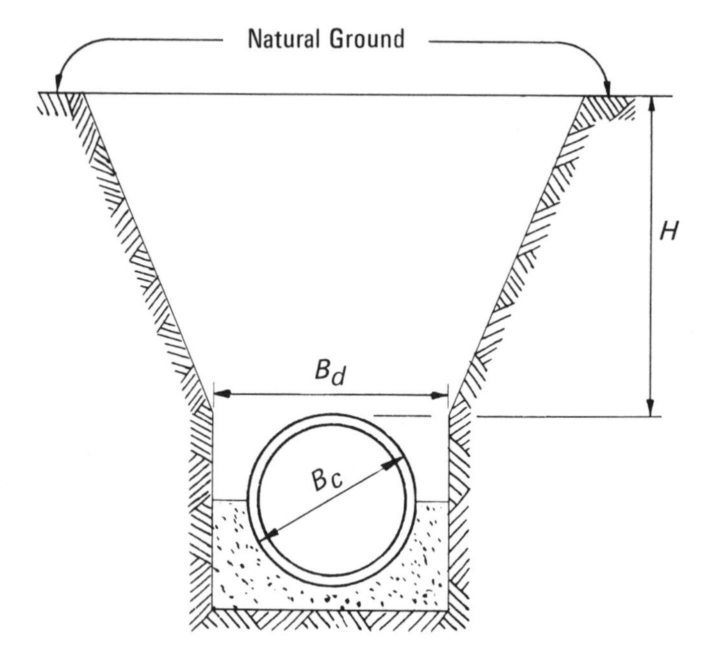

Figure 4.6. Illustration of Sub-Trench and Effective Trench Width.

Embankment Installations

The essential features of embankment installations are illustrated in *Figure 4.2*. Highway and railroad culverts are typically installed under fills or embankments. As shown in *Figure 4.2*, embankment installations are subdivided into three groups:

- **Positive projection** pipe is installed with the top of the pipe projecting above the surface of the natural ground, or compacted fill, and then covered with earth fill. This type also includes pipe installed in extremely wide trenches.
- **Negative projection** pipe is installed in relatively shallow trenches of such depth that the top of the pipe is below the level of the natural ground surface or compacted fill, and then covered with earth fill to a height appreciably greater than the distance from the natural ground surface or original compacted fill surface to the top of the pipe.
- **Induced trench** pipe is initially installed as positive projection. When the embankment fill has been placed to an elevation of at least one pipe diameter over the proposed top of the pipe, a trench is excavated over the pipe and backfilled with a more compressible material, simulating a negative projection installation.

Positive Projection Installations

In considering earth loads in positive projection installations, it is customary to designate the prism of fill directly above the pipe and bounded by vertical planes tangent to the sides of the pipe as the **interior prism,** as illustrated in *Figures 4.7* and *4.8*. The **exterior prisms** are those adjacent to

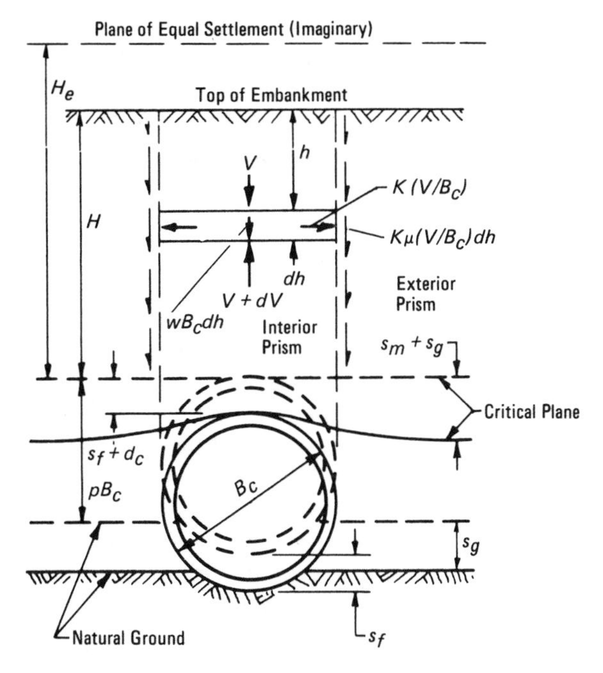

Figure 4.7. Settlements Which Influence Loads on Embankment Pipe, Complete Projection Condition.

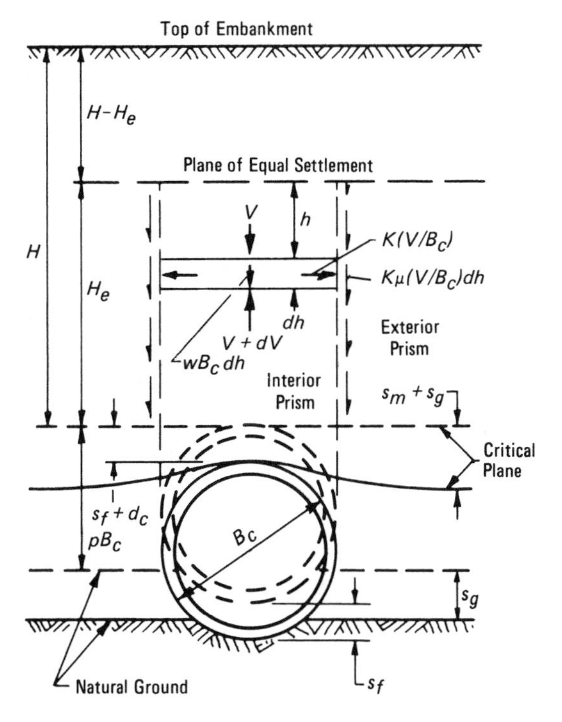

Figure 4.8. Settlements Which Influence Loads on Embankment Pipe, Incomplete Projection Condition.

the vertical planes on both sides of the pipe and of indefinite width. The load transmitted to the top of the pipe is equal to the weight of the interior prism of soil, plus or minus the friction forces which develop along the two vertical planes bounding the interior prism.

The horizontal plane at the top of the pipe is defined as the **critical plane.** Unless the embankment material on each side of the pipe is compacted so as to have the same relative settlement as the pipe, the exterior prism of soil will compress more than the interior prism. In this case, the frictional forces on the vertical planes between the interior and exterior prisms will add to the load on the pipe, and the total load will be the weight of the interior prism of soil plus the frictional forces. Under these conditions, the critical plane will be deformed downward in the exterior prisms with respect to the top of the pipe and the interior prism, and the pipe is defined as being in the **projection** condition as illustrated in *Figures 4.7* and *4.8*.

If the pipe is placed on a slightly yielding foundation, it will settle more than the adjacent soil as the fill is constructed. This would reverse the frictional forces, and reduce the load on the pipe to a value less than the weight of the soil in the interior prism. In this condition, the critical plane will deform downward in the interior prism with respect to the top of the pipe and the exterior prisms, and the pipe is defined as being in the **trench** condition as illustrated in *Figures 4.9* and *4.10*.

The frictional forces are the summation of the active lateral pressure on the two vertical planes multiplied by μ, the coefficient of internal friction of the fill material. If the frictional forces extend up to the surface of the fill, the pipe is defined as being in the **complete projection** condition, *Figure 4.7*, or the **complete trench** condition, *Figure 4.9*. If the frictional forces do not extend to the surface of the fill but cease at a horizontal plane below the top of the fill, the pipe is defined as being in the **incomplete projection** condition, *Figure 4.8*, or the **incomplete trench** condition, *Figure 4.10*. The horizontal plane where the frictional forces cease is defined as the **plane of equal settlement** and its height above the top of the pipe is the **height of equal settlement,** H_e.

The preceding concepts were considered by Marston and the formula for earth loads in the projection and trench condition were mathematically derived as follows, using the same principles and notation as for the analysis of the trench installations.

For the complete projection and trench conditions, considering a horizontal element of fill in the interior prism and summing vertical forces:

$$V + dV = V + (wB_c)dh \pm 2K\mu\left(\frac{V}{B_c}\right)dh \tag{4.6}$$

Solving this differential equation for $h = H$, the total load on the pipe is:

$$W_c = wB_c^2\left(\frac{e^{\pm 2K\mu\frac{H}{B_c}} - 1}{\pm 2K\mu}\right) \tag{4.7}$$

Where: W_c = load on pipe for positive projection conditions, pounds per linear foot

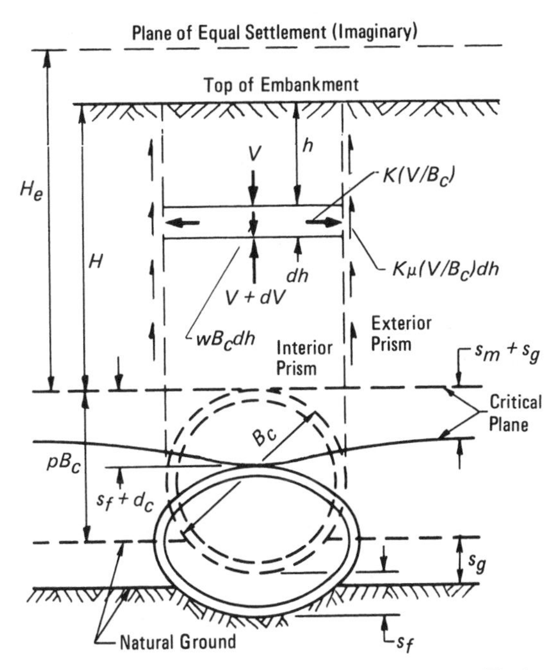

Figure 4.9. Settlements Which Influence Loads on Embankment Pipe, Complete Trench Condition.

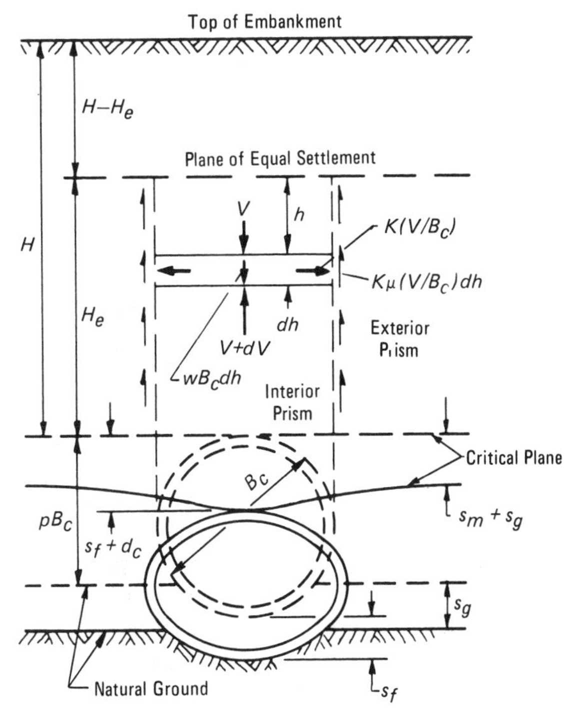

Figure 4.10. Settlements Which Influence Loads on Embankment Pipe, Incomplete Trench Condition.

For convenience the bracketed term is defined as the load coefficient, C_c:

$$C_c = \frac{e^{\pm 2K\mu \frac{H}{B_c}} - 1}{\pm 2K\mu} \tag{4.8}$$

Therefore, *Equation 4.7* may be written as:

$$W_c = C_c w B_c^2 \tag{4.9}$$

In *Equation 4.8*, the upper signs are used for the **complete projection** condition and the lower signs for the **complete trench** condition.

For the incomplete projection and trench condition, the summation of vertical forces on the fill element results in the same equation as *Equation 4.6*:

$$V + dV = V + (wB_c)dh \pm 2K\mu\left(\frac{V}{B_c}\right)dh \tag{4.10}$$

Solving this differential equation for $h = H_e$, with a surcharge of $w(H - H_e)/B_c$, results in an equation similar to *Equation 4.9*:

$$W_c = C_c w B_c^2 \tag{4.11}$$

In this instance, however:

$$C_c = \frac{e^{\pm 2K\mu \frac{H_e}{B_c}} - 1}{\pm 2K\mu} + \left(\frac{H}{B_c} - \frac{H_e}{B_c}\right) e^{\pm 2K\mu \frac{H_e}{B_c}} \tag{4.12}$$

The upper signs are used for the **incomplete projection** condition and the lower signs for the **incomplete trench** condition.

To obtain values for C_c for the incomplete condition, *Equation 4.12*, the height of equal settlement, H_e, must be determined. The analyses are complex, but H_e can be obtained by equating the total settlements of the interior and exterior prisms below the plane of equal settlement. This procedure assumes that the behavior of the soil can be approximated with the elastic theory.

As evaluated by Spangler, the width of the interior and the two exterior prisms at the critical plane, as well as the total height of the fill, H, affect the settlement. The total earthload at the critical plane is $3HwB_c$, assuming that the effective width of the exterior prisms is equal to the interior prism width. From *Equation 4.11*, W_c of the interior prism at the critical plane is $C_c w B_c^2$ and therefore, the combined load of the exterior prisms at the critical plane, with a combined width of $2B_c$ is:

$$3HwB_c - C_c w B_c^2 \tag{4.13}$$

At any depth, h, below the plane of equal settlement, the sum of the vertical loads, $2V'$, on the horizontal element in the exterior prisms is:

$$2V' = 3\,(H - H_e + h)wB_c - V \tag{4.14}$$

In the fill at depth h in the exterior prisms, the stress is V'/B_c and the strain is V'/B_cE, where E is the modulus of elasticity of the soil. Further, if λ' is defined as the **total settlement of the exterior prisms** below the plane of equal settlement, the settlement of an element at depth h is:

$$d\lambda' = \left(\frac{V'}{B_cE}\right)dh \tag{4.15}$$

Substituting for V' from *Equation 4.14*:

$$\lambda' = \int_0^{H_e}\left\{\frac{3(H - H_e + h)wB_c - V}{2B_cE}\right\}dh \tag{4.16}$$

If λ is defined as the total settlement of the **interior prism** below the plane of equal settlement, then the settlement of an element at depth h is:

$$\lambda = \int_0^{H_e}\left(\frac{V}{B_cE}\right)dh \tag{4.17}$$

By definition, the vertical distance from the ground or fill to the top of the pipe is pB_c; p is the **projection ratio**; s_m is the settlement of the soil in the projection height, pB_c, caused by the soil overburden; s_f is the total settlement of the pipe invert; s_g is the settlement of the natural ground surface; and d_c is the vertical deflection of the pipe.

Equating the total settlements of the interior and exterior prisms between the ground level and the plane of equal settlement:

$$\lambda + s_f + d_c = \lambda' + s_m + s_g \tag{4.18}$$

Rearranging terms:

$$\lambda - \lambda' = (s_m + s_g) - (s_f + d_c) \tag{4.19}$$

The right hand side of this equation is the difference in deformation of the critical plane which is simply the settlement of the critical plane at the top of the pipe minus the settlement in the fill. This difference, divided by s_m, is termed the **relative deformation** and is defined as the **settlement ratio**, r_{sd}:

$$r_{sd} = \frac{(s_m + s_g) - (s_f + d_c)}{s_m} \tag{4.20}$$

Therefore, by substitution:

$$\lambda - \lambda' = r_{sd}s_m \tag{4.21}$$

The vertical stress under the exterior prisms at the critical plane is the total load, *Equation 4.13*, divided by width, B_c:

$$\frac{3HwB_c - C_cwB_c^2}{2B_c} \tag{4.22}$$

The settlement in the projection height, pB_c, is equal to the stress divided by E times the projection height:

$$s_m = \left(\frac{3HwB_c - C_cwB_c^2}{2B_c}\right)\frac{pB_c}{E} \tag{4.23}$$

Substituting the values of λ and λ' from the solution to *Equations 4.16* and *4.17* and s_m in *Equation 4.21* and dividing by $3wB_c^2/E$:

$$\left[\frac{1}{2K\mu} \pm \left(\frac{H}{B_c} - \frac{H_e}{B_c}\right) \pm \frac{r_{sd}p}{3}\right]\frac{e^{\pm 2K\mu\frac{H_e}{B_c}} - 1}{\pm 2K\mu} \pm \frac{1}{2}\left(\frac{H_e}{B_c}\right)^2 \tag{4.24}$$

$$\pm \frac{r_{sd}p}{3}\left(\frac{H}{B_c} - \frac{H_e}{B_c}\right)e^{\pm 2K\mu\frac{H_e}{B_c}} - \frac{1}{2K\mu}\cdot\frac{H_e}{B_c} \mp \frac{H}{B_c}\cdot\frac{H_e}{B_c}$$

$$= \pm r_{sd}p\frac{H}{B_c}$$

Again, the upper signs are used for the **incomplete projection** condition where r_{sd} is positive, and the lower signs are for the **incomplete trench** condition where r_{sd} is negative.

Reviewing the three factors in *Equation 4.9* for the load on a positive projection pipe, the horizontal width of the pipe, B_c, is readily determined, and has a constant value throughout the life of the structure. In the case of circular concrete pipe, B_c equals the external diameter of the pipe.

Soil materials differ widely in density, w, a second factor that is relatively simple to evaluate. Since the load on an underground pipe is directly related to the unit weight of the embankment material, the height of fill which will produce a given load on pipe of the same size, B_c, can vary considerably. Unit weights of the majority of embankment soils fall within the range of 100 to 135 pounds per cubic foot.

The third factor in *Equation 4.9* is the most complex; namely, the load coefficient, C_c, which is dependent upon the following physical factors:

H/B_c is the ratio of the height of fill to the horizontal width of the pipe. Since the value of B_c is fixed for a specific installation, the ratio H/B_c will vary with the height of fill H.

μ is the coefficient of internal friction of the soil and may vary from 0.3 to 1.0. The load on a pipe is not directly proportional to μ, and the relationship is such that relatively wide variations in μ cause only minor variations in the load on the structure. In the case of projection pipe, a value of $\mu = 0.6$ is usually used for design purposes. The actual value of the coefficient of internal friction of the soil can be easily measured, but such measurements are rarely necessary.

p is the projection ratio which is the vertical distance between the outside top of the pipe and the natural ground surface, divided by the outside horizontal diameter of the pipe, B_c. The projection ratio is quite easily determined when the natural ground surface, or compacted fill, is fairly level for a considerable distance on each side of the pipe. When the natural ground surface slopes toward or away from the pipe, an average vertical height is used, based upon the elevations for a horizontal distance on each side, approximately equal to the width of the pipe.

r_{sd} is the settlement ratio. This factor determines the direction of action of the frictional forces and is dependent upon the settlement and deflection of the pipe and the compression of the soil adjacent to the pipe. Based on experimental studies, the values listed in *Table 4.2* are recommended for the design of concrete pipe.

Theoretical analyses, *Equation 4.24*, and experimental evidence indicate that the product of the projection ratio, p, and the settlement ratio, r_{sd}, influence the load on a pipe. When concrete pipe is installed in the projection condition, both factors usually have a positive value less than unity and the product of the two is less than either factor individually.

Table 4.2. Design Values of Settlement Ratio.

Installation and Foundation Condition	Settlement Ratio r_{sd}	
	Usual Range	Design Value
Positive Projection	0.0 to +1.0	
Rock or Unyielding Soil	+1.0	+1.0
*Ordinary Soil	+0.5 to +0.8	+0.7
Yielding Soil	0.0 to +0.5	+0.3
Zero Projection		0.0
Negative Projection	−1.0 to 0.0	
$p' = 0.5$		−0.1
$p' = 1.0$		−0.3
$p' = 1.5$		−0.5
$p' = 2.0$		−1.0
Induced Trench	−2.0 to 0.0	
$p' = 0.5$		−0.5
$p' = 1.0$		−0.7
$p' = 1.5$		−1.0
$p' = 2.0$		−2.0

**The value of the settlement ratio depends on the degree of compaction of the fill material adjacent to the sides of the pipe. With construction methods resulting in proper compaction of bedding and sidefill materials, a settlement ratio design value of +0.5 is recommended.*

The solution to *Equations 4.12* and *4.24* are time consuming. *Figure 4.11* is a solution by Spangler, which permits reasonable estimates of C_c for various conditions of H/B_c, r_{sd} and p. Since the effect of μ is nominal, $K\mu$ was assumed to be 0.19 for the projection condition and 0.13 for the trench condition. *Figure 4.11* will provide an estimate for C_c that is well within the accuracy of the theoretical assumptions.

In *Figures 4.11, 4.12* and *4.13*, the family of straight lines represent the incomplete conditions while the curves represent the complete conditions. The straight lines intersect the curves where H_e equals H. These diagrams can therefore be used to determine the minimum height of fill for which the plane of equal settlement will occur within the soil mass.

Where the $r_{sd}p$ product is zero in *Equations 4.9, 4.10, 4.11, 4.12* and *4.24* the load coefficient term C_c is equal to H/B_c. Substituting this value in *Equation 4.9* results in the load, W_c, being equal to the weight of fill above the pipe, wHB_c. For positive values of $r_{sd}p$ the load on the pipe will be greater than the weight of fill above the pipe, and for negative values the load will be less than the weight of fill above the pipe.

Negative Projection Installations

Negative projection installations are those in which the pipe is installed in shallow trenches of such depth that the top of the pipe is below the surface of the natural ground or compacted fill, and then covered with an embankment which extends above the ground level as illustrated in *Figure 4.2*.

The negative projection installation concepts proposed by Spangler in 1950 were similar to those of the positive projection condition. In this theory, load transmitted to the pipe is equal to the weight of the interior prism of soil above the pipe, minus frictional forces along the sides of that prism, *Figure 4.14*. The critical plane was postulated as the horizontal plane through the top of the subtrench, and the width of the interior prism was defined as the width of the subtrench, *Figure 4.15*.

The mathematical derivation and the earth load formula for the complete negative projection condition is the same as for a trench load, except the coefficient of internal friction for the fill, μ, is used instead of μ' for the contact between the fill and the natural ground.

$$W_n = wB_d^2\left(\frac{e^{-2K\mu\frac{H}{B_d}} - 1}{-2K\mu}\right) \text{ when } H \leq H_e \qquad (4.25)$$

Where: W_n = load on the pipe for negative projection conditions, pounds per linear foot

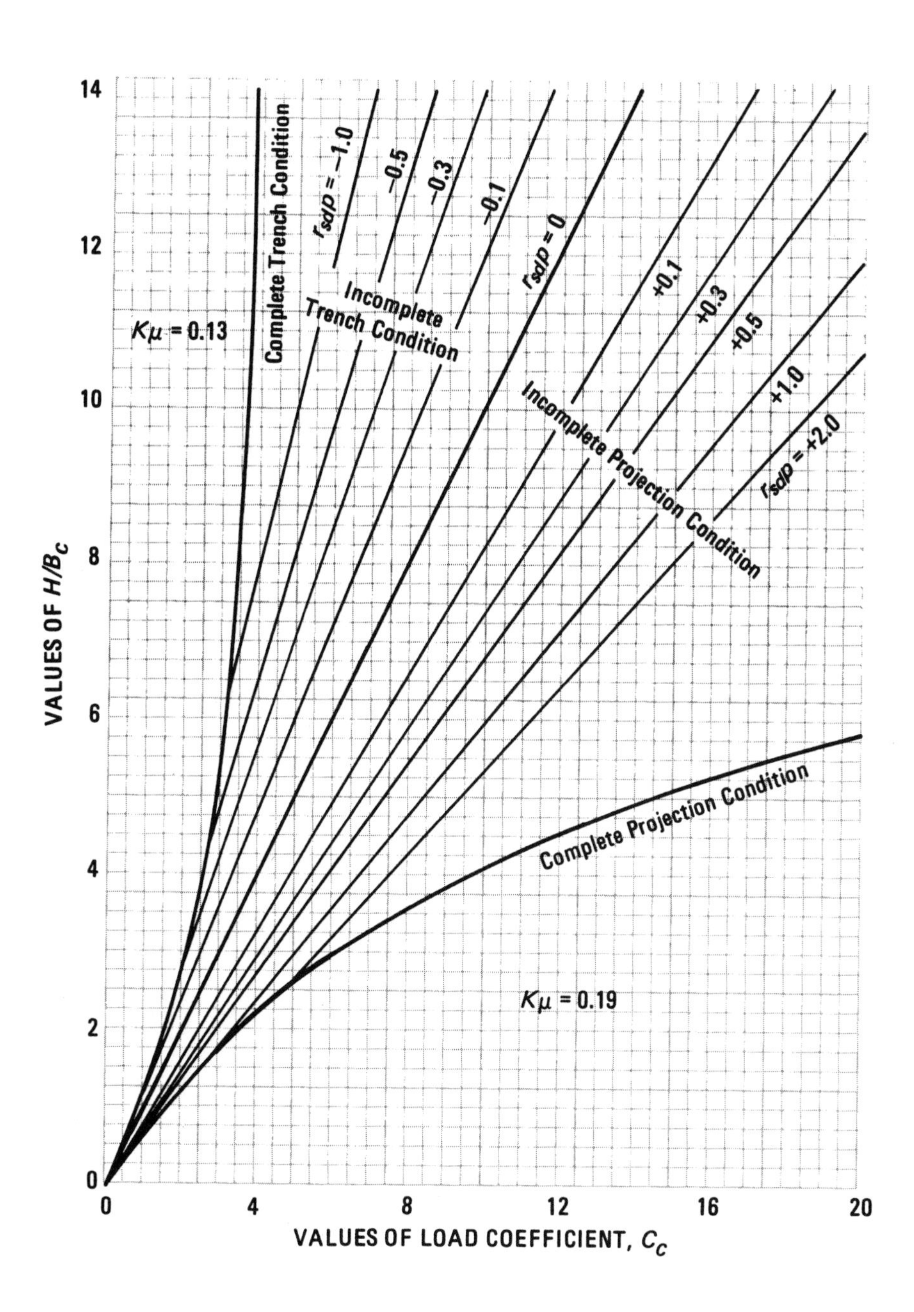

Figure 4.11. Load Coefficient for Positive Projection Embankment Condition.

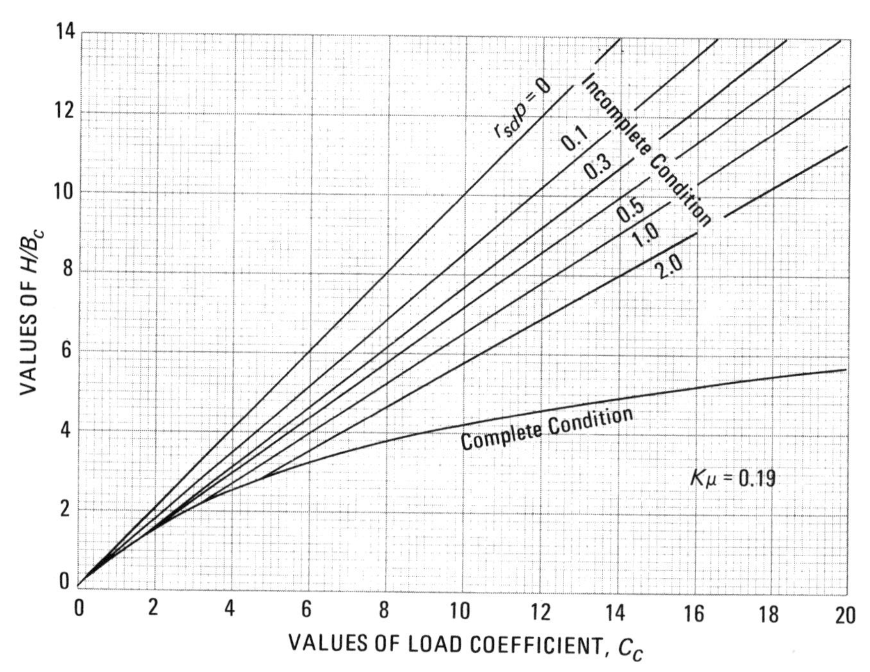

Figure 4.12. Load Coefficient for Horizontal Elliptical and Arch Pipe.

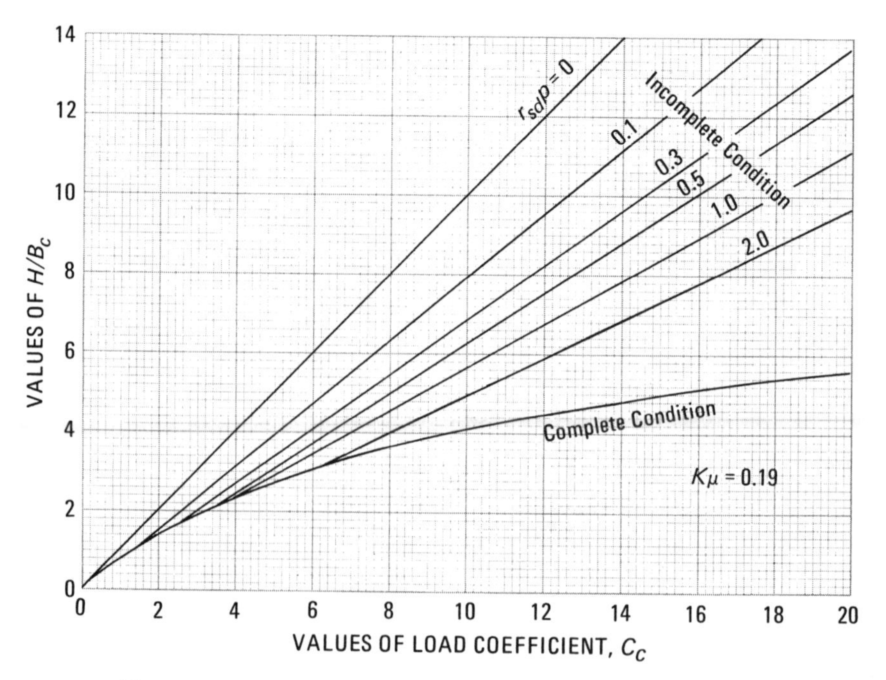

Figure 4.13. Load Coefficient for Vertical Elliptical Pipe.

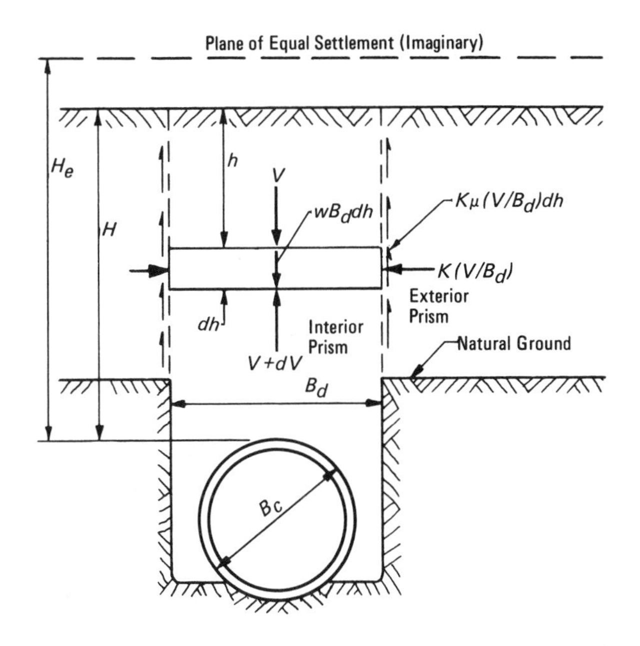

Figure 4.14. Settlement Conditions Which Influence Loads on Embankment Pipe—Complete Negative Projection Condition.

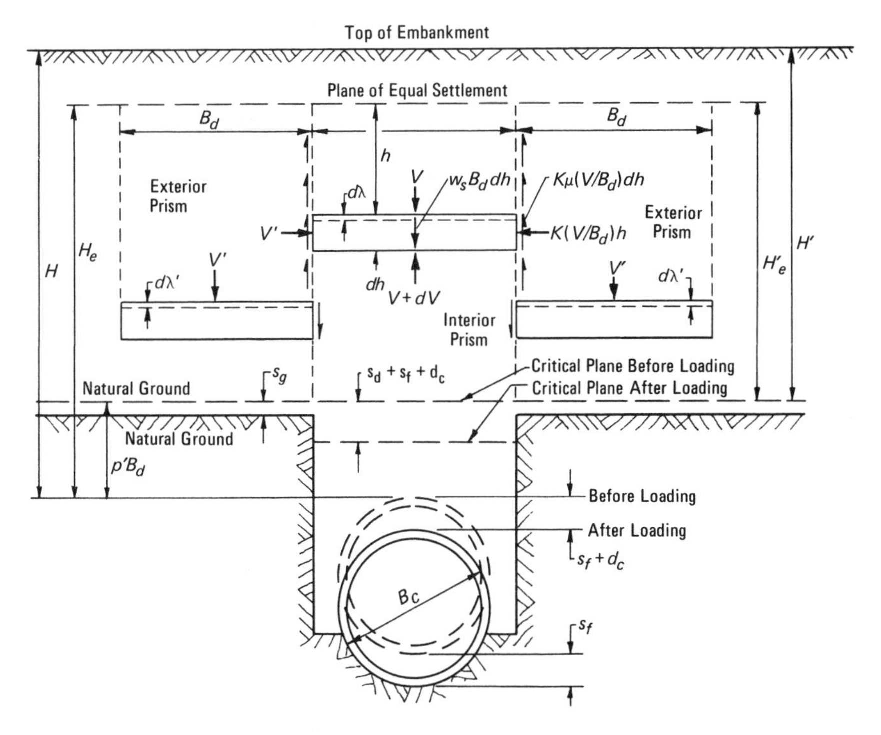

Figure 4.15. Settlement Conditions Which Influence Loads on Embankment Pipe—Incomplete Negative Projection Condition.

The bracketed term is defined as the load coefficient, C_n, for the negative projection condition:

$$C_n = \left(\frac{e^{-2K\mu \frac{H}{B_d}} - 1}{-2K\mu} \right) \text{ when } H \leq H_e \tag{4.26}$$

Therefore, *Equation 4.25* may be written as:

$$W_n = C_n w B_d^2 \tag{4.27}$$

For this condition, Spangler assumes the value of $K\mu$ to be not less than 0.13 so that for greater values of $K\mu$ the values of C_n are somewhat conservative.

For the incomplete negative projection condition, *Figure 4.15*, the mathematical derivation is similar to that of the positive projection condition but somewhat more complex. Summation of vertical forces on the fill element results in:

$$V + dV = V + (wB_d)\, dh - 2K\mu \left(\frac{V}{B_d} \right) dh \tag{4.28}$$

The solution for this differential equation for h equal to H results in *Equation 4.27*, which is the same as for the complete condition but in this instance:

$$C_n = \frac{e^{-2K\mu \frac{H_e}{B_d}} - 1}{-2K\mu} + \left(\frac{H}{B_d} - \frac{H_e}{B_d} \right) e^{-2K\mu \frac{H_e}{B_d}} \text{ when } H > H_e \tag{4.29}$$

As evident in *Equation 4.29*, the exponent of e is always negative and C_n depends on H_e. Again, following Spangler's method of evaluation and considering relative and total settlements, the settlement ratio, r_{sd}, is defined as follows:

$$r_{sd} = \frac{s_g - (s_d + s_f + d_c)}{s_d} \tag{4.30}$$

Where: $(s_d + s_f + d_c)$ = the settlement of the critical plane in feet

In *Equation 4.29*, when H' is equal to $(H - p'B_d)$ and H'_e is equal to $(H_e - p'B_d)$, the equation for H'_e is:

$$\begin{aligned} &\frac{e^{-2K\mu \frac{H'_e}{B_d}} - 1}{-2K\mu} \left[\frac{H'}{B_d} - \frac{H'_e}{B_d} - \frac{1}{2K\mu} \right] \\ &- \frac{H'_e}{B_d} \left[\left(\frac{H'}{B_d} - \frac{H'_e}{B_d} \right) + \frac{1}{2} \frac{H'_e}{B_d} - \frac{1}{2K\mu} \right] \\ &= \frac{2}{3} r_{sd} p' \left[\frac{e^{-2K\mu \frac{H'_e}{B_d}} - 1}{-2K\mu} + \left(\frac{H'}{B_d} - \frac{H'_e}{B_d} \right) e^{-2K\mu \frac{H'_e}{B_d}} \right] \end{aligned} \tag{4.31}$$

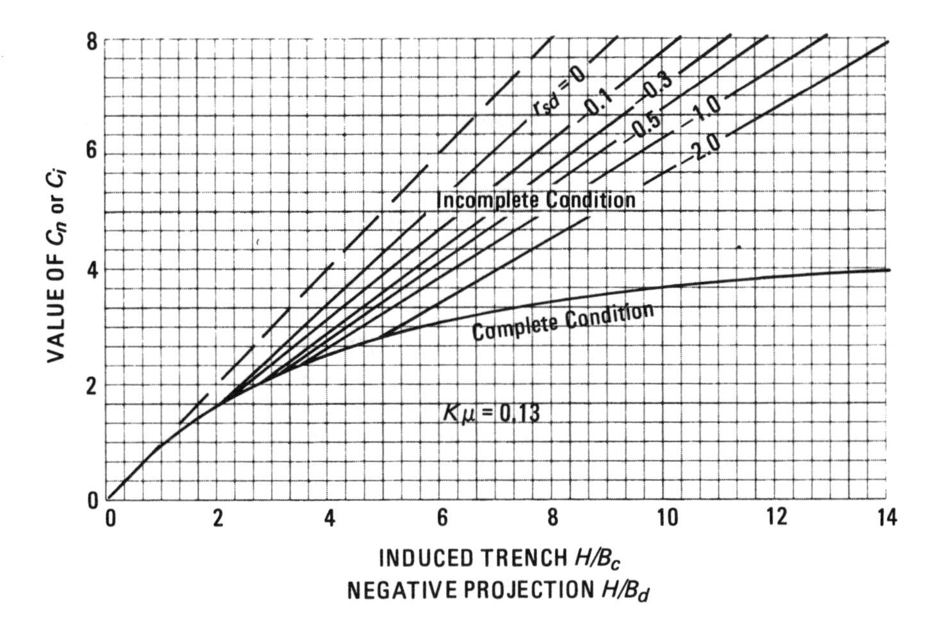

Figure 4.16. Load Coefficient for Negative Projection and Induced Trench Condition (p′ = 0.5).

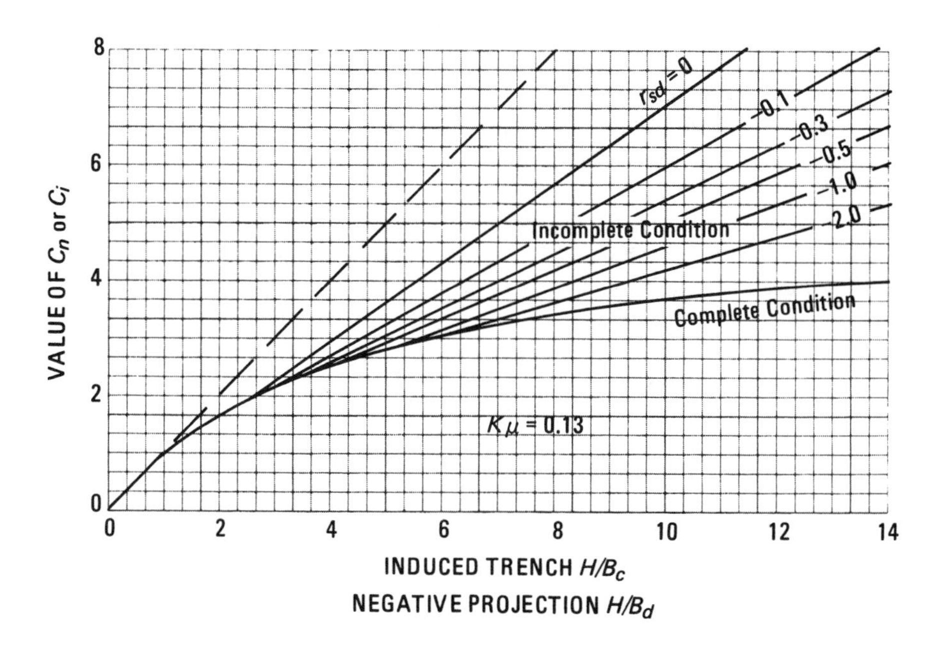

Figure 4.17. Load Coefficient for Negative Projection and Induced Trench Condition (p′ = 1.0).

The notation follows, in general, that given for the positive projection condition, however, the depth of the top of the pipe below the critical plane is defined by $p'B_d$ in which p' is defined as the **negative projection ratio.** If the natural ground surface is on a transverse slope, the vertical distance may be taken as the average distance from the top of the pipe to the top of the trench at both sides of the trench. Furthermore, s_d is defined as the compression within the fill for the height $p'B_d$.

Values of C_n versus H/B_d for various values of r_{sd} are provided in *Figures 4.16* through *4.19* for values of p' equal to 0.5, 1.0, 1.5 and 2.0. For other values of p' between 0.5 and 2.0, values of C_n may be obtained by interpolation. Only one value of $K\mu$ is used, as with the trench condition for positive projection. The family of straight lines representing the incomplete condition intersect the curve for the complete condition. At these intersections, the height of the plane of equal settlement, H_e, equals the height of the top of embankment H. These intersecting points can be used to determine the height of the plane of equal settlement above the top of the pipe.

Induced Trench Installations

The induced trench method of construction is a practical method for relieving the load on pipe placed under high fills. The essential procedures of this method of construction, illustrated in *Figure 4.2*, are as follows:

- Install pipe in a positive projection embankment condition.
- Compact fill material at each side of the pipe for a lateral distance equal to twice the outside diameter of the pipe, or 12 feet, whichever is less. This fill is constructed to an elevation of at least one pipe diameter over the top of the pipe.
- Excavate a trench in the compacted fill directly over the pipe. The depth of the trench should be at least one pipe diameter and the width should coincide as nearly as possible with the outside diameter of the pipe.
- Refill the trench with loose compressible material such as straw, sawdust or organic soil.
- Complete the balance of the fill by normal methods.

An alternate method of induced trench construction is to partially construct the embankment, before the pipe is installed, to an elevation of at least one pipe diameter over the proposed top of the pipe. A trench is then excavated and the pipe installed. Loose compressible material is placed directly above the pipe and the embankment completed by normal methods.

This concept of installation was suggested by Marston and subsequently developed by Spangler as a special case of the negative projection condition. In this case, the width of the subtrench above the top of

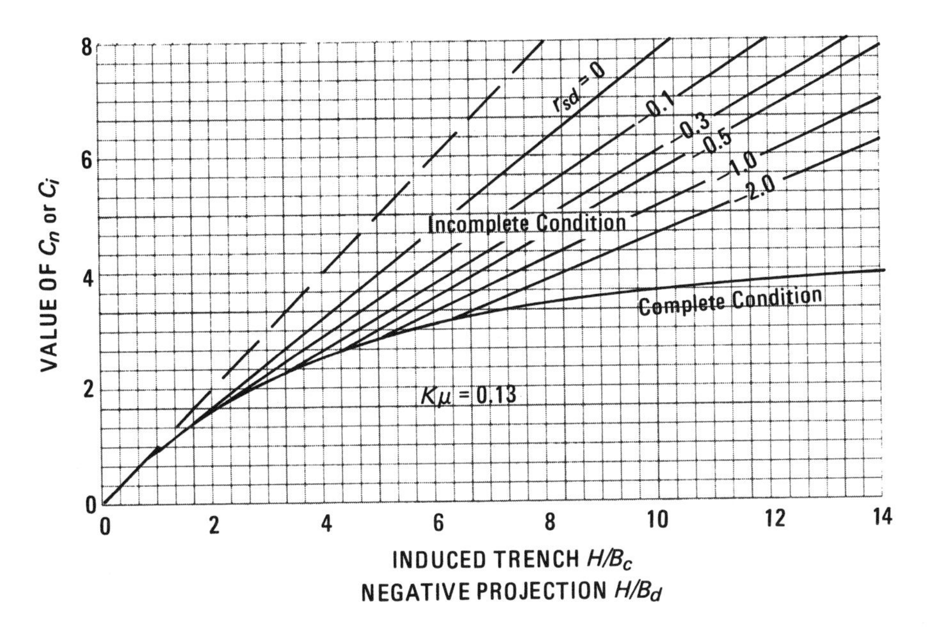

Figure 4.18. Load Coefficient for Negative Projection and Induced Trench Condition (p′ = 1.5).

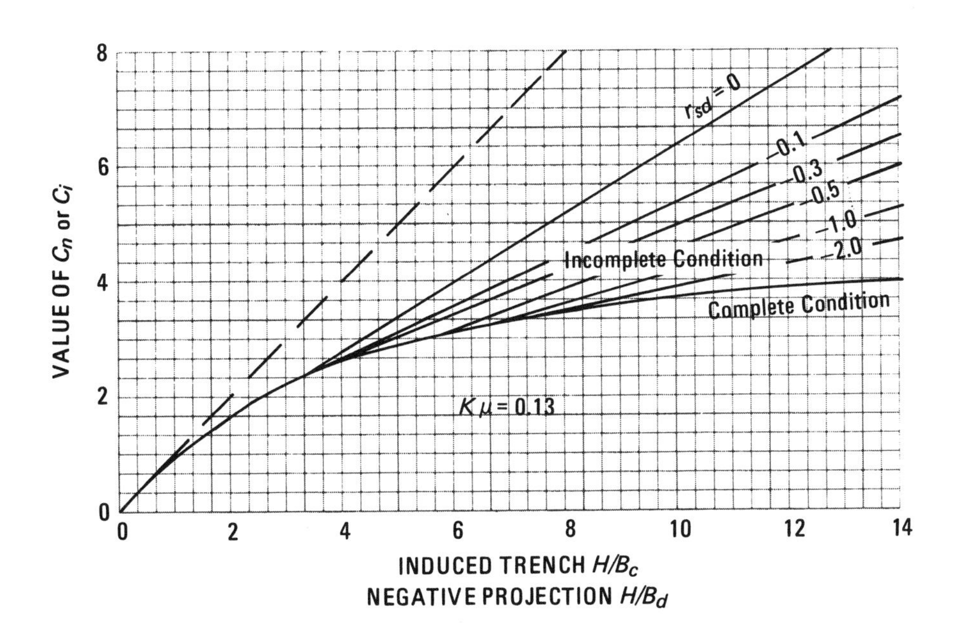

Figure 4.19. Load Coefficient for Negative Projection and Induced Trench Condition (p′ = 2.0).

the pipe determines whether B_c or B_d is used to calculate the load on a pipe installed by the induced trench method in the following equations:

$$W_i = C_i w B_c^2 \tag{4.32}$$

Where: W_i = load on the pipe for induced trench installation, pounds per linear foot
C_i = load coefficient for the induced trench condition:

$$C_i = \frac{e^{-2K\mu\frac{H}{B_c}} - 1}{-2K\mu} \quad \text{when } H \leq H_e \tag{4.33}$$

$$C_i = \frac{e^{-2K\mu\frac{H_e}{B_c}} - 1}{-2K\mu} + \left(\frac{H}{B_c} - \frac{H_e}{B_c}\right) e^{-2K\mu\frac{H_e}{B_c}} \quad \text{when } H > H_e \tag{4.34}$$

The induced trench method results in less load on the pipe than either the positive projection or negative projection embankment conditions. The load reduction is obtained because the fill over the pipe settles downward relative to the adjacent fill, thus generating shearing forces that partially support the backfill. Because of the compressible material placed in the trench, a smaller (larger negative) r_{sd} value is used to account for the larger relative settlement. The net result is a lower value for W_i for any given height of fill and trench width. *Figures 4.16* through *4.19* provide a simple basis for determining C_i for the induced trench method of construction.

Multiple Pipe Installations

A **multiple pipe** installation is the placement of two or more pipelines in a single trench or embankment condition, *Figure 4.20*. This procedure is most commonly used where restrictive cover requirements preclude the use of a single pipe of larger cross sectional area or where a storm sewer and sanitary sewer are being installed in the same trench.

Although multiple pipe installations are rather common, the determination of pipe loads presents some unique problems. The following discussion describes a design method for multiple pipe installations through the application of engineering judgment that produces a reasonable and conservative design solution.

Flat Trench

For multiple pipelines in a single trench, the type of loading, and hence the pipe strength required, can vary from a simple trench condition to a positive projection embankment condition or to a combination of both. A geometric analysis of each installation assists in determining which possible types of loading exist for each pipe.

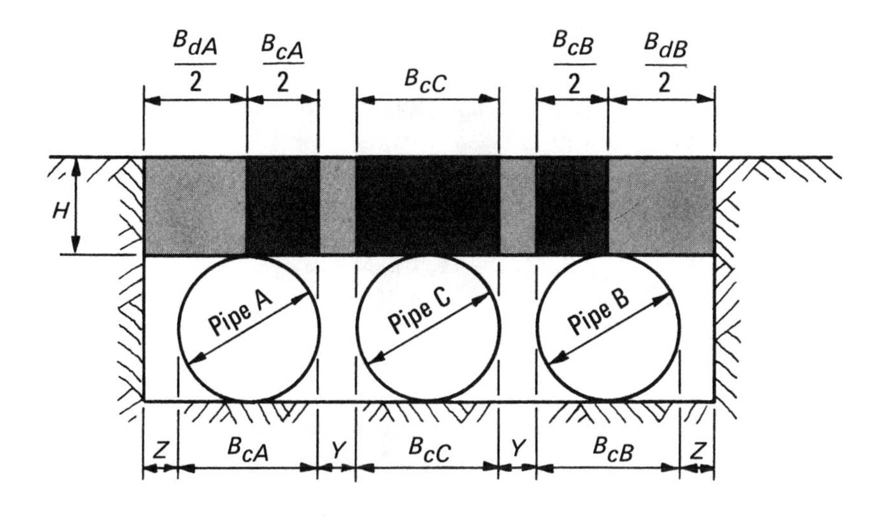

Figure 4.20. Columns of Backfill Associated With Each Pipeline.

Referring to *Figure 4.20*, and considering the center pipe, C, first, if the horizontal span of the outside edges of the pipe, B_{cC}, plus the spacing between the two adjacent pipes, $2Y$, equals or exceeds the transition width for the given size of pipe and depth, H, of backfill above the top of the pipe, then pipe C can be analyzed as a positive projection condition. If B_{cC} plus $2Y$ is less than the transition width, the positive projection condition does not exist and the earth loads on pipe C will be less, since no downward friction forces are exerted by the intermediate soil columns. This would call for an analysis under a negative projection or trench condition. If Y and the spacing between the outside pipe and the trench wall, Z, are small compared to B_C and H, the entire earth load may be shared proportionately by the three pipe, and the entire installation would be analyzed as a trench condition.

Considering pipes A and B, when one-half of the trench width for either pipe, $B_{dA}/2$ or $B_{dB}/2$, is less than one-half the transition width for the given condition, then the respective exterior soil column is functioning as in a trench installation. But, these same exterior columns will function as a positive projection installation when the width of either column equals or exceeds one-half the transition width. Considering the interior soil columns, $B_{cA}/2$ and $B_{cB}/2$, these will function as in a wide trench or a positive projection condition if the width $(B_c/2) + Y$ is equal to or greater than one-half the transition width. If Y is small, there will be little or no differential settlement between the interior soil columns and the positive projection condition will not exist, and the earth loads on the pipe will be correspondingly lower.

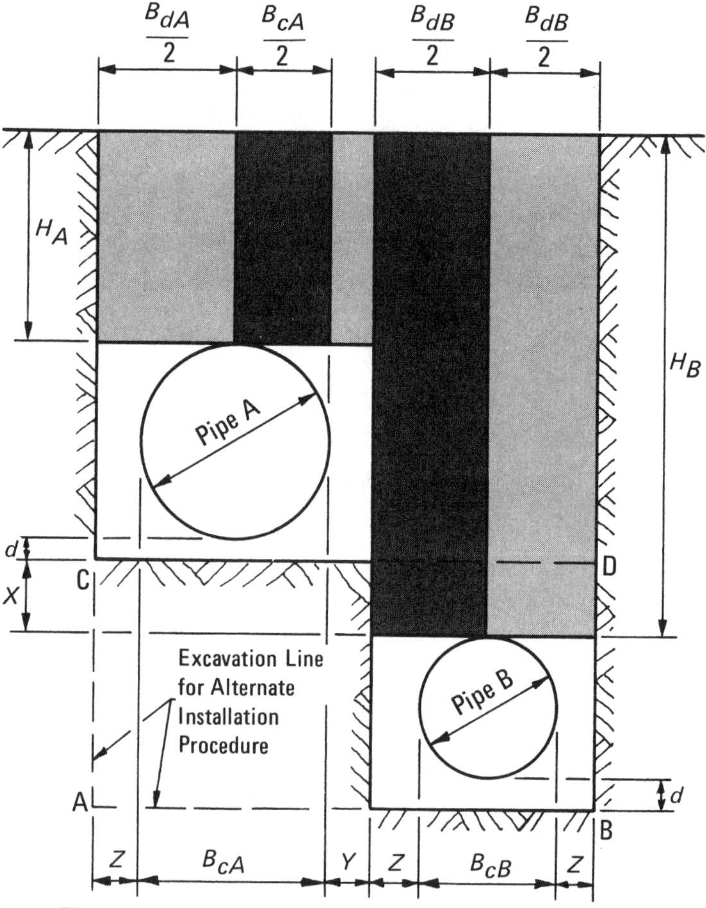

Figure 4.21. Columns of Backfill Associated With Pipelines in a Benched Trench.

Benched Trench

In another common type of multiple pipeline installation, *Figure 4.21*, the pipe are vertically as well as horizontally separated. Usually, the specifications established by the local jurisdiction will include minimum vertical and horizontal separations between pipe and possibly the minimum dimensions of Y with respect to that of X, especially when pipe A is a storm sewer and pipe B is a sanitary sewer, or when there is concern as to the stability of the bench under pipe A. Such specifications affect the geometry of the trench and the ultimate earth loading on each pipe. Any load effects transmitted from pipe A to pipe B through the soil are neglected. These load effects would include a lateral pressure on pipe B which would tend to reduce the required pipe strength. Neglecting this load effect is therefore conservative. Considering the loads on pipe A and B in *Figure 4.21*, the exterior soil columns adjacent to the full-depth trench walls will act as in a trench condition if B_{dA} and B_{dB} are less than the transition width for the given situation, and as in a positive projection condition if both are equal to or greater than the transition width. As for soil column $B_{cA}/2$, it will act as in a positive projection installation since soil column Y tends to settle more than $B_{cA}/2$. However, if Y and X are small, there may be little or no differential settlement between $B_{cA}/2$ and Y, hence the load imposed by column B_{cA} will be reduced from the positive projection installation condition because no downward frictional force would be induced by column Y.

The soil column acting on the left half of pipe B may act in one of three possible ways depending on the relative dimensions of B_{dB}, Y and X. If X is small, approaching zero, there will be very little, if any, differential settlement between the soil column acting on the left half of the pipe and the adjacent soil column Y. Thus, there would be no upward frictional force relieving the loads on this portion of pipe B. This is the neutral condition for a negative projection installation. As X increases, the negative projection ratio, p', also increases and the loads on the pipe decrease, approaching that which would be imposed for the trench condition. A positive projection condition will exist if B_{dB} equals or exceeds the transition width.

A method of construction frequently used for benched trenches is to excavate the full width of the trench for the full depth, *Figure 4.21*, install pipe B, backfill to the level of line CD, install pipe A and complete backfilling. For this type of installation, analysis of the loads for pipe A and the exterior portion of pipe B are the same as previously discussed. However, the interior portion of pipe B is probably loaded in a positive projection condition, since $B_{cB}/2$ plus $2Z$ plus Y plus B_{cA} is almost certain to be greater than one-half of the transition width.

Design Method

A geometric analysis of an installation will indicate the probable types of loading for each pipe and the loads can then be calculated by the appropriate method. If during the analysis of the installation, it appears that the transition point between two loading conditions has been reached, the earth load used should be the greater of the two calculated for each type of loading condition.

Tunneled and Jacked Installations

Two types of loads are imposed upon concrete pipe installed by the tunneling and jacking methods: the axial load due to the jacking pressures applied during installation; and the earth loading due to the overburden, with some possible influence from live loadings, which will usually become effective only after some settlement has occurred. Details of tunneling and jacking installations are discussed and illustrated in *Chapter 5*.

Axial Loads

Because of the axial loading, it is necessary to achieve relatively uniform distribution of the load around the pipe periphery to prevent localized stress concentrations. This is accomplished by using a cushion material between the pipe sections, such as plywood, and insuring that the jacking force is properly distributed through the jacking frame to the pipe and parallel with the axis of the pipe. The cross-sectional area of the concrete pipe wall is more than adequate to resist pressures encountered in any normal jacking operation. For projects where extreme jacking pressures are anticipated due to long jacking distances or excessive frictional forces, higher concrete compressive strengths and additional wall thickness may be required. Little or no increased resistance to axial loads is provided by a higher class of pipe unless a higher concrete compressive strength is used.

Earth Loads

Major factors influencing the vertical earth load on pipe installed by jacking are:

- Weight of the prism of earth directly above the bore
- Upward shearing or frictional forces between the prism of earth directly above the bore and the adjacent earth
- Cohesion of the soil

The vertical earth load on the horizontal plane at the top of the bore, within the width of the excavation, is equal to the weight of the prism of earth above the bore minus the upward frictional forces and minus the cohesion of the soil along the limits of the prism of soil over the bore. This earth load can be computed by the following equations:

$$W_t = C_t w B_t^2 - 2cC_t B_t \quad (4.35)$$

Where: W_t = earth load under tunneled and jacked conditions, pounds per linear foot
C_t = load coefficient for tunneled and jacked pipe
w = unit weight of soil, pounds per cubic feet
B_t = maximum width of bore excavation, feet
c = cohesion of the soil above the excavation, pounds per square foot

$$C_t = \frac{1 - e^{-2K\mu'\frac{H}{B_t}}}{2K\mu'} \quad (4.36)$$

The $C_t w B_t^2$ term is similar to *Equation 4.4* for determining the backfill load on pipe installed in a trench condition where the trench width is the same as the width of the bore. The $2cC_t B_t$ term accounts for the cohesion of undisturbed soil. For cohesive soils, the earth load on a jacked pipe will always be less than on a pipe in a trench installation.

Conservative cohesion design values for various soils are listed in *Table 4.3*. When extensive subsoil exploration and analyses are available for a project area, actual cohesion values should be used.

LIVE LOADS

Pipe is frequently installed under highway and airport pavements and railroad tracks. If the truck, aircraft or train is close to the pipe a live load is added to the other loads which the pipe must carry. However, due to the distributional effect of earth cover, when pipe are installed more than three to five feet below the point of load application the effect of live loads is usually negligible.

Existing theory and design procedures for load distribution through earth masses are based upon the early work of Love, and more specifically, the equations developed by Boussinesq in the mid-nineteenth century. All of the current techniques are based upon the assumption of elastic behavior, modified by an empirical adjustment to account for differences between theoretical and observed behavior. In the following section, the theoretical bases are reviewed and the generally accepted engineering approaches are discussed.

Theoretical Concepts

Theoretical solutions to the distribution of loads through earth masses are based upon the theories of elasticity and specific assumptions relative to material properties and boundary conditions. When applied to live loads on pipelines, the elastic theory solutions are quite conservative, largely because of the short duration of the load, normally a fraction of a second. Therefore, the practical solution to avoid over-design involves an empirical adjustment to the assumed theoretical behavior. The following review of the theory provides a basis for understanding these adjustments.

Table 4.3. Design Values of Cohesion.

Type of Soil	Values of c
Clay	
Soft	40
Medium	250
Hard	1000
Sand	
Loose Dry	0
Silty	100
Dense	300
Top Soil	
Saturated	100

Boussinesq Equations

The Boussinesq equations assume an elastic, homogeneous and isotropic material. The equations were developed for the complete state of stress under a point load applied to the surface of an infinitely wide plane.

The equation for vertical stress is:

$$w = k\left(\frac{kP}{z^2}\right) \tag{4.37}$$

Where:

$$k = \frac{3}{2\pi\left[1 + \left(\frac{r}{z}\right)^2\right]^{5/2}} \tag{4.38}$$

P = point load, pounds
r = radial distance (horizontally), feet
z = depth, feet

This equation produces a bell-shaped curve for load distribution as shown in *Figure 4.22*. On any horizontal plane, a relatively high stress exists under the load, tapering off in all directions. At deeper levels, the values for z are greater and therefore, the pressure intensity is less.

The equations have been extended for loads on circular plates, but solving either application is quite complex. For practical use, simplifications have been developed for the determination of the subsurface pressure

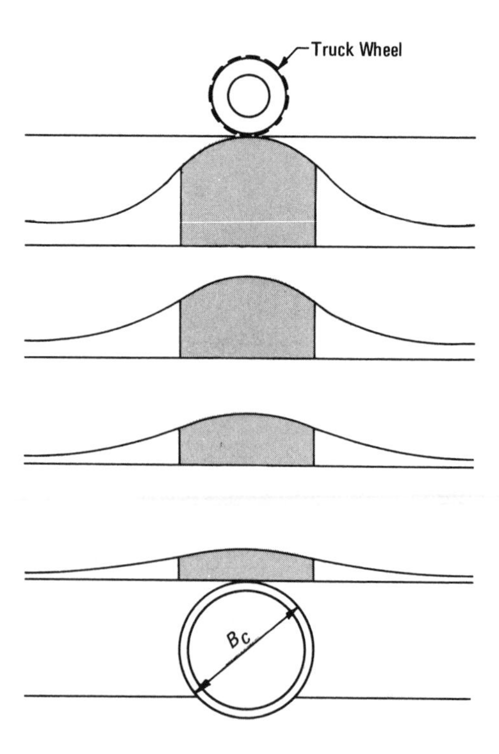

Figure 4.22. Live Load Distribution for Various Heights of Cover.

intensity generated by a load applied on the subgrade or lightly surfaced roadway. A simplification proposed is the following equation developed from the general Boussinesq solution:

$$p_{(H, X)} = Cp_0 \tag{4.39}$$

Where: $p_{(H, X)}$ = vertical pressure intensity at any horizontal distance, X, and any vertical distance, H, within the soil mass, pounds per square foot

C = pressure coefficient dependent on H, X and the radius, r, of the circle of pressure at the surface

p_0 = tire pressure, pounds per square foot

The radius of the circle of pressure at the surface is further defined as:

$$r = \sqrt{\frac{P}{\pi p_0}} \tag{4.40}$$

Where: r = radius of the circle of pressure at the surface, inches

P = single wheel load, pounds

p_0 = tire pressure, pounds per square inch

Equation 4.39 has been solved for a set of conditions in order to simplify the task of estimating the live load. The results are included in *Table 4.4* in the form of pressure coefficients.

Table 4.4. Pressure Coefficients for a Single Load Applied on Subgrade or Flexible Pavement.

Values of C

$p_{(H,X)} = Cp_o$ lb. per sq. ft.

p_o = tire pressure lb. per sq. ft.

r = radius of the circle of pressure at the surface

Single load

H

X

H/r	X/r 0.0	1.0	2.0	3.0	4.0	5.0	6.0	7.0
0.0	1.000	1.000	.000	.000	.000	.000	.000	.000
0.5	.911	.425	.010	.001	.000	.000	.000	.000
1.0	.646	.350	.050	.005	.001	.000	.000	.000
1.5	.424	.250	.075	.012	.004	.001	.000	.000
2.0	.284	.198	.075	.020	.007	.003	.001	.001
2.5	.200	.145	.070	.026	.010	.004	.002	.001
3.0	.146	.110	.066	.029	.013	.006	.003	.002
3.5	.110	.101	.060	.031	.015	.008	.004	.002
4.0	.087	.081	.054	.031	.017	.009	.005	.003
5.0	.057	.054	.041	.028	.017	.011	.006	.004
6.0	.040	.039	.032	.024	.017	.011	.007	.005
7.0	.030	.029	.025	.020	.015	.011	.008	.005
8.0	.023	.023	.020	.017	.013	.010	.008	.006
9.0	.018	.018	.016	.014	.012	.009	.007	.006
10.0	.015	.015	.014	.012	.010	.009	.007	.006

Westergaard Theory

In 1926, Westergaard presented a paper summarizing the results of an extensive study of the effects of loading conditions, subgrade support, and boundary conditions on concrete pavements. These results formed the basis by which he developed a method to calculate the stresses in concrete slabs.

Based upon this early work of Westergaard and others, the Portland Cement Association, PCA, developed a method to determine the vertical pressure on buried pipe due to wheel loads applied to concrete pavements. The PCA approach assumes that both the slab and the earth are elastic materials, the compression of the soil is proportional to the deflection of the slab, and the effect of the load radiates equally in all directions. The following equation for the pressure intensity on concrete pipe under concrete pavements was developed:

$$p_{(H,X)} = \frac{CP}{R_s^2} \qquad (4.41)$$

Where: C = pressure coefficient, dependent on H, X and R_s
P = wheel loads, pounds
R_s = radius of stiffness of the rigid pavement, feet
$p_{(H,X)}$ = vertical pressure intensity at any horizontal distance, X, and any vertical distance, H, within the soil mass, pounds per square foot

R_s is further defined as:

$$R_s = \sqrt[4]{\frac{Eh^3}{12(1 - \mu^2)k}} \qquad (4.42)$$

Where: E = modulus of elasticity of concrete, pounds per square inch
h = thickness of concrete pavement, inches
μ = Poisson's ratio of concrete (assumed a constant 0.15)
k = modulus of subgrade reaction, pounds per cubic inch

Equation 4.41 has been solved for various conditions in order to simplify the task of estimating the live load. The results are included in *Tables 4.5* through *4.9* in the form of pressure coefficients for various values of H, X, and R_s. *Equation 4.42* also has been solved for a range of conditions and R_s is tabulated for various values of h and k in *Table 4.10*. *Figure 4.23* provides a basis for estimating the modulus of subgrade reaction using as a basis the various soil classification systems.

The values given in the tables are used to determine the pressures on horizontal planes at depth H in a semi-infinite elastic body from a single wheel and two wheels at various spacings on the pavement surface. The coefficient values in *Tables 4.6* through *4.8* are larger, for any given fill height, than the coefficient values presented for a single wheel, *Table 4.5*. Thus, the combined pressure on any horizontal plane for wheels at a spacing of 2.4 R_s, or less, is greater than for a single wheel. For the greater wheel spacing of 3.2 R_s, the coefficient values in *Table 4.9* are greater than for a single load, *Table 4.5*, except close to the pavement. Therefore, for a wheel spacing of 3.2 R_s, the combined pressure should be used except

Table 4.5. Pressure Coefficients for a Single Load.

Values of C

$p = \frac{CP}{R_s^2}$ pounds per square foot

P = wheel load, pounds

R_s = radius of stiffness of pavement slab, feet

Single load

H X

H/R_s	X/R_s 0.0	0.4	0.8	1.2	1.6	2.0	2.4	2.8	3.2	3.6	4.0
0.0	.113	.105	.089	.068	.048	.032	.020	.011	.006	.002	.000
0.4	.101	.095	.082	.065	.047	.033	.021	.011	.004	.001	.000
0.8	.089	.084	.074	.061	.045	.033	.022	.012	.005	.002	.001
1.2	.076	.072	.065	.054	.043	.032	.022	.014	.008	.005	.003
1.6	.062	.059	.054	.047	.039	.030	.022	.016	.011	.007	.005
2.0	.051	.049	.046	.042	.035	.028	.022	.016	.011	.008	.006
2.4	.043	.041	.039	.036	.030	.026	.021	.016	.011	.008	.006
2.8	.037	.036	.033	.031	.027	.023	.019	.015	.011	.009	.006
3.2	.032	.030	.029	.026	.024	.021	.018	.014	.011	.009	.007
3.6	.027	.026	.025	.023	.021	.019	.016	.014	.011	.009	.007
4.0	.024	.023	.022	.020	.019	.018	.015	.013	.011	.009	.007
4.4	.020	.020	.019	.018	.017	.015	.014	.012	.010	.009	.007
4.8	.018	.017	.017	.016	.015	.013	.012	.011	.009	.008	.007
5.2	.015	.015	.014	.014	.013	.012	.011	.010	.008	.007	.006
5.6	.014	.013	.013	.012	.011	.010	.010	.009	.008	.007	.006
6.0	.012	.012	.011	.011	.010	.009	.009	.008	.007	.007	.006
6.4	.011	.010	.010	.010	.009	.008	.008	.007	.007	.006	.005
6.8	.010	.009	.009	.009	.008	.008	.007	.007	.006	.006	.005
7.2	.009	.008	.008	.008	.008	.007	.007	.006	.006	.006	.005
7.6	.008	.008	.008	.007	.007	.007	.006	.006	.006	.005	.005
8.0	.007	.007	.007	.007	.006	.006	.006	.006	.005	.005	.005

Table 4.6. Pressure Coefficients for Two Loads Spaced $0.8R_s$ Apart.

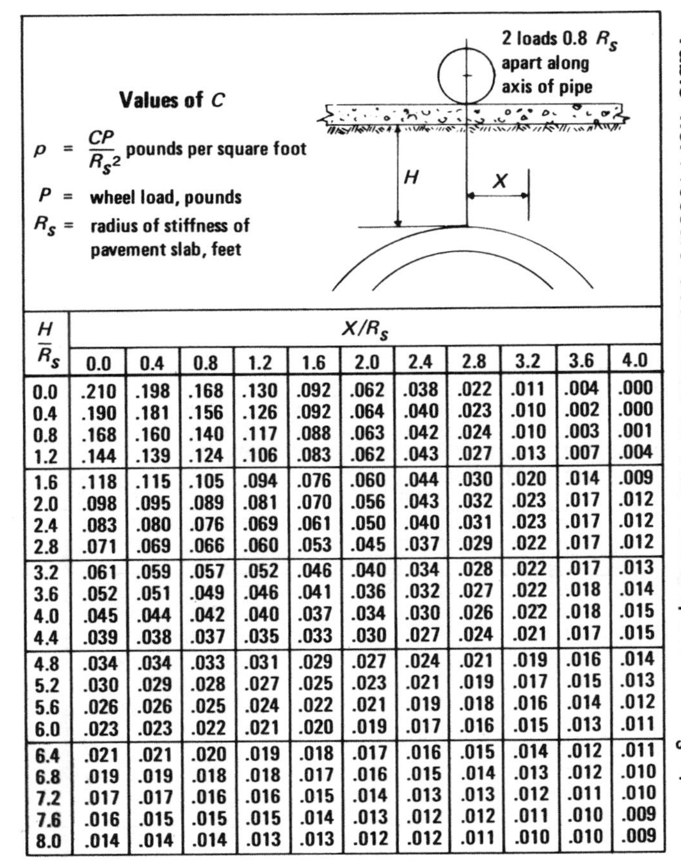

Values of C

$p = \frac{CP}{R_s^2}$ pounds per square foot

P = wheel load, pounds

R_s = radius of stiffness of pavement slab, feet

2 loads 0.8 R_s apart along axis of pipe

H X

H/R_s	X/R_s 0.0	0.4	0.8	1.2	1.6	2.0	2.4	2.8	3.2	3.6	4.0
0.0	.210	.198	.168	.130	.092	.062	.038	.022	.011	.004	.000
0.4	.190	.181	.156	.126	.092	.064	.040	.023	.010	.002	.000
0.8	.168	.160	.140	.117	.088	.063	.042	.024	.010	.003	.001
1.2	.144	.139	.124	.106	.083	.062	.043	.027	.013	.007	.004
1.6	.118	.115	.105	.094	.076	.060	.044	.030	.020	.014	.009
2.0	.098	.095	.089	.081	.070	.056	.043	.032	.023	.017	.012
2.4	.083	.080	.076	.069	.061	.050	.040	.031	.023	.017	.012
2.8	.071	.069	.066	.060	.053	.045	.037	.029	.022	.017	.012
3.2	.061	.059	.057	.052	.046	.040	.034	.028	.022	.017	.013
3.6	.052	.051	.049	.046	.041	.036	.032	.027	.022	.018	.014
4.0	.045	.044	.042	.040	.037	.034	.030	.026	.022	.018	.015
4.4	.039	.038	.037	.035	.033	.030	.027	.024	.021	.017	.015
4.8	.034	.034	.033	.031	.029	.027	.024	.021	.019	.016	.014
5.2	.030	.029	.028	.027	.025	.023	.021	.019	.017	.015	.013
5.6	.026	.026	.025	.024	.022	.021	.019	.018	.016	.014	.012
6.0	.023	.023	.022	.021	.020	.019	.017	.016	.015	.013	.011
6.4	.021	.021	.020	.019	.018	.017	.016	.015	.014	.012	.011
6.8	.019	.019	.018	.018	.017	.016	.015	.014	.013	.012	.010
7.2	.017	.017	.016	.016	.015	.014	.013	.013	.012	.011	.010
7.6	.016	.015	.015	.015	.014	.013	.012	.012	.011	.010	.009
8.0	.014	.014	.014	.013	.013	.012	.012	.011	.010	.010	.009

Table 4.7. Pressure Coefficients for Two Loads Spaced $1.6R_s$ Apart.

Values of C

$p = \frac{CP}{R_s^2}$ pounds per square foot

P = wheel load, pounds

R_s = radius of stiffness of pavement slab, feet

H/R_s	X/R_s 0.0	0.4	0.8	1.2	1.6	2.0	2.4	2.8	3.2	3.6	4.0
0.0	.178	.167	.142	.112	.080	.054	.034	.019	.009	.004	.000
0.4	.164	.156	.136	.109	.080	.056	.036	.019	.008	.002	.000
0.8	.147	.141	.126	.103	.078	.057	.037	.020	.008	.002	.001
1.2	.128	.124	.106	.094	.074	.056	.039	.023	.012	.006	.004
1.6	.108	.105	.097	.082	.070	.054	.040	.028	.019	.014	.009
2.0	.092	.090	.084	.075	.065	.052	.040	.030	.022	.017	.012
2.4	.079	.076	.072	.065	.056	.047	.038	.029	.022	.017	.012
2.8	.068	.066	.062	.058	.050	.043	.035	.028	.022	.017	.012
3.2	.058	.056	.054	.050	.044	.038	.032	.027	.022	.017	.012
3.6	.050	.049	.047	.044	.040	.035	.030	.026	.022	.017	.013
4.0	.043	.042	.041	.039	.036	.033	.030	.026	.022	.018	.015
4.4	.038	.037	.036	.034	.032	.029	.026	.023	.020	.016	.014
4.8	.033	.032	.031	.030	.028	.026	.024	.021	.018	.015	.013
5.2	.029	.028	.027	.026	.025	.023	.021	.019	.016	.014	.012
5.6	.025	.025	.024	.023	.022	.020	.019	.017	.015	.013	.012
6.0	.023	.022	.022	.021	.019	.018	.017	.016	.014	.013	.011
6.4	.020	.020	.019	.019	.018	.016	.015	.015	.013	.012	.011
6.8	.018	.018	.018	.017	.016	.015	.014	.013	.012	.011	.010
7.2	.017	.016	.016	.015	.015	.014	.013	.013	.012	.011	.010
7.6	.015	.015	.014	.014	.014	.013	.012	.012	.011	.010	.010
8.0	.014	.014	.013	.013	.013	.012	.011	.011	.010	.010	.009

Table 4.8. Pressure Coefficients for Two Loads Spaced 2.4 R_s Apart.

Values of C

$p = \frac{CP}{R_s^2}$ pounds per square foot

P = wheel load, pounds

R_s = radius of stiffness of pavement slab, feet

H/R_s	X/R_s 0.0	0.4	0.8	1.2	1.6	2.0	2.4	2.8	3.2	3.6	4.0
0.0	.137	.130	.112	.088	.065	.044	.028	.014	.007	.003	.000
0.4	.130	.125	.109	.087	.066	.047	.028	.013	.005	.001	.000
0.8	.121	.117	.104	.085	.066	.048	.030	.014	.006	.002	.001
1.2	.109	.105	.096	.079	.064	.048	.033	.018	.012	.006	.005
1.6	.095	.092	.084	.072	.060	.047	.035	.025	.018	.012	.009
2.0	.083	.081	.077	.068	.057	.046	.035	.026	.020	.015	.010
2.4	.070	.069	.065	.059	.052	.044	.034	.026	.020	.015	.011
2.8	.062	.060	.058	.053	.046	.039	.033	.027	.020	.015	.011
3.2	.053	.052	.050	.046	.041	.035	.032	.026	.020	.016	.012
3.6	.046	.045	.044	.042	.038	.034	.030	.026	.021	.017	.013
4.0	.040	.040	.039	.037	.035	.032	.029	.025	.021	.017	.014
4.4	.036	.035	.034	.033	.031	.028	.025	.022	.019	.016	.013
4.8	.031	.031	.030	.029	.027	.025	.022	.020	.017	.015	.012
5.2	.027	.027	.026	.025	.024	.022	.020	.018	.016	.014	.012
5.6	.024	.023	.023	.022	.021	.020	.018	.017	.015	.013	.011
6.0	.022	.021	.021	.020	.019	.018	.017	.015	.014	.012	.011
6.4	.019	.019	.019	.018	.017	.016	.015	.014	.013	.012	.010
6.8	.018	.017	.017	.016	.016	.015	.014	.013	.012	.011	.010
7.2	.016	.016	.016	.015	.014	.014	.013	.012	.011	.010	.009
7.6	.015	.014	.014	.014	.013	.013	.012	.011	.011	.010	.009
8.0	.013	.013	.013	.013	.012	.012	.011	.011	.010	.009	.009

Table 4.9. Pressure Coefficients for Two Loads Spaced 3.2 R_s Apart.

Values of C

$$p = \frac{CP}{R_s^2} \text{ pounds per square foot}$$

P = wheel load, pounds

R_s = radius of stiffness of pavement slab, feet

2 loads 3.2 R_s apart along axis of pipe

H/R_s	X/R_s 0.0	0.4	0.8	1.2	1.6	2.0	2.4	2.8	3.2	3.6	4.0
0.0	.097	.093	.080	.065	.048	.032	.020	.011	.004	.000	.000
0.4	.096	.092	.079	.067	.050	.034	.020	.010	.003	.000	.000
0.8	.092	.088	.078	.066	.051	.036	.021	.010	.003	.000	.000
1.2	.086	.082	.074	.066	.050	.038	.025	.014	.007	.003	.001
1.6	.077	.075	.068	.060	.049	.039	.030	.021	.015	.011	.007
2.0	.070	.068	.063	.057	.048	.040	.031	.023	.017	.013	.009
2.4	.061	.060	.056	.051	.045	.038	.030	.023	.017	.013	.010
2.8	.056	.054	.052	.048	.042	.036	.029	.023	.018	.013	.010
3.2	.048	.046	.044	.041	.037	.032	.028	.023	.018	.014	.010
3.6	.043	.041	.040	.038	.034	.030	.027	.022	.019	.015	.012
4.0	.038	.037	.036	.035	.032	.029	.026	.022	.019	.016	.013
4.4	.033	.033	.032	.031	.029	.027	.024	.020	.018	.015	.013
4.8	.029	.029	.028	.027	.025	.023	.021	.018	.016	.014	.012
5.2	.025	.025	.025	.024	.022	.021	.019	.017	.015	.013	.012
5.6	.022	.022	.022	.021	.020	.018	.017	.016	.014	.012	.011
6.0	.020	.020	.020	.020	.020	.017	.016	.015	.013	.011	.011
6.4	.018	.018	.018	.018	.018	.016	.015	.014	.012	.011	.010
6.8	.016	.016	.016	.016	.016	.014	.014	.013	.012	.010	.010
7.2	.015	.015	.015	.015	.015	.013	.013	.012	.011	.010	.009
7.6	.014	.014	.013	.013	.013	.012	.012	.011	.010	.009	.009
8.0	.013	.013	.012	.012	.012	.011	.011	.010	.010	.009	.008

where the pipe is very close to the pavement subgrade elevation when the single wheel load pressure can be used. For wheel spacings greater than 3.2 R_s, the combined pressure of two wheels will never be equal to or greater than the pressure from a single wheel.

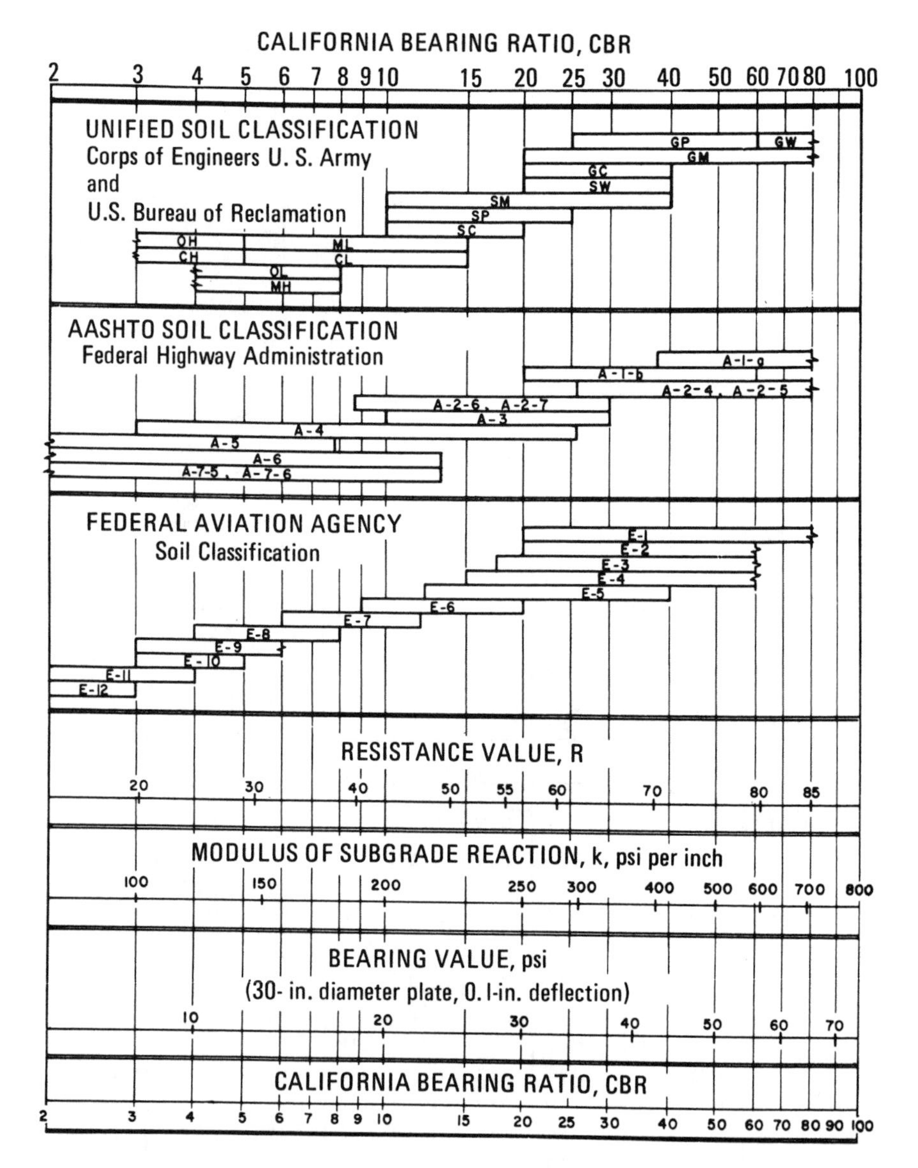

Figure 4.23. Approximate Interrelationships of Soil Classifications and Bearing Values.

The presence of a pipe introduces a boundary condition which, theoretically, creates a case approaching that of an elastic layer of depth H resting on a rigid base. Although pressures based on this concept would be slightly higher than those included in the tabular coefficients, variability of the elastic properties of the backfill over the pipe, the rigidity of the pipe, and the inadequacies of theory are such that precise computations are not justified.

Table 4.10. Values of Radius of Stiffness, R_s.

h (in.)	Values of k								
	50	100	150	200	250	300	350	400	500
6	34.84	29.30	26.47	24.63	23.30	22.26	21.42	20.72	19.59
6.5	36.99	31.11	28.11	26.16	24.74	23.64	22.74	22.00	20.80
7	39.11	32.89	29.72	27.65	26.15	24.99	24.04	23.25	21.99
7.5	41.19	34.63	31.29	29.12	27.54	26.32	25.32	24.49	23.16
8	43.23	36.35	32.85	30.57	28.91	27.62	26.58	25.70	24.31
8.5	45.24	38.04	34.37	31.99	30.25	28.91	27.81	26.90	25.44
9	47.22	39.71	35.88	33.39	31.58	30.17	29.03	28.08	26.55
9.5	49.17	41.35	37.36	34.77	32.89	31.42	30.23	29.24	27.65
10	51.10	42.97	38.83	36.14	34.17	32.65	31.42	30.39	28.74
10.5	53.01	44.57	40.28	37.48	35.45	33.87	32.59	31.52	29.81
11	54.89	46.16	41.71	38.81	36.71	35.07	33.75	32.64	30.87
11.5	56.75	47.72	43.12	40.13	37.95	36.26	34.89	33.74	31.91
12	58.59	49.27	44.52	41.43	39.18	37.44	36.02	34.84	32.95
12.5	60.41	50.80	45.90	42.72	40.40	38.60	37.14	35.92	33.97
13	62.22	52.32	47.27	43.99	41.61	39.75	38.25	36.99	34.99
13.5	64.00	53.82	48.63	45.26	42.80	40.89	39.35	38.06	35.99
14	65.77	55.31	49.98	46.51	43.98	42.02	40.44	39.11	36.99
14.5	67.53	56.78	51.31	47.75	45.16	43.15	41.51	40.15	37.97
15	69.27	58.25	52.63	48.98	46.32	44.26	42.58	41.19	38.95
15.5	70.99	59.70	53.94	50.20	47.47	45.36	43.64	42.21	39.92
16	72.70	61.13	55.24	51.41	48.62	46.45	44.70	43.23	40.88
16.5	74.40	62.56	56.53	52.61	49.75	47.54	45.74	44.24	41.84
17	76.08	63.98	57.81	53.80	50.88	48.61	46.77	45.24	42.78
17.5	77.75	65.38	59.08	54.98	52.00	49.68	47.80	46.23	43.72
18	79.41	66.78	60.35	56.16	53.11	50.74	48.82	47.22	44.66
19	82.70	69.54	62.84	58.48	55.31	52.84	50.84	49.17	46.51
20	85.95	72.27	65.30	60.77	57.47	54.92	52.84	51.10	48.33
21	89.15	74.97	67.74	63.04	59.62	56.96	54.81	53.01	50.13
22	92.31	77.63	70.14	65.28	61.73	58.98	56.75	54.89	51.91
23	95.44	80.26	72.52	67.49	63.83	60.98	58.68	56.75	53.67
24	98.54	82.86	74.87	69.68	65.90	62.96	60.58	58.59	55.41

$$R_s = \sqrt[4]{\frac{Eh^3}{12\,(1-\mu^2)\,k}}$$

where: E = 4,000,000 psi

$\mu = 0.15$

$$R_s = 24.1652\sqrt[4]{\frac{h^3}{k}}$$

Highways

Pavements designed for heavy truck traffic substantially reduce the pressure transmitted through a wheel to the subgrade, and consequently to underlying concrete pipe. The pressure reduction is so great that generally the live load can be neglected. The pressure intensity, however, can be estimated as discussed previously through use of *Equations 4.41* and *4.42* and *Tables 4.5* through *4.10*. For heavy duty asphalt or flexible pavements, the reduction in intensity will be comparable to that for concrete pavements. The economies that can be realized by the reduction of pipe strength requirements can be substantial and should not be overlooked.

For intermediate thicknesses of asphalt or flexibile pavements, there is no generally accepted theory for estimating load distribution effects. The layered system theory, first advanced by Burmister in 1943, has been extended and solved for conditions that could apply to concrete pipe. However, this theory is not in common use. Local engineering practices control the basis for estimating the live load.

Relatively thin pavements do not reduce the pressure transmitted from the wheel to the subgrade to any significant degree. Such pavements are generally considered as unsurfaced roadways for determination of the effect of live loads on buried concrete pipe. As discussed previously, *Equations 4.39* and *4.40* and *Table 4.4* can be used to estimate the pressure intensity. A more practical method as accepted by AASHTO is developed in the following paragraphs.

Load Assumptions

The maximum highway wheel loads generally considered for design purposes are those specified by AASHTO for HS 20 truck and alternate load configurations as illustrated in *Figure 4.24*. The critical axle loads for these configurations are carried on dual wheels. The contact area of the dual wheels is assumed to be oval in shape and is approximately equal to the wheel load divided by the tire pressure. Several assumptions are normally made to simplify the evaluation process. For an HS 20 wheel load, 16,000 pounds, the contact pressure is assumed equal to the tire pressure of 80 pounds per square inch. The contact area, therefore, is 16,000 pounds divided by 80 pounds per square inch, or 200 square inches, and can be approximated by a rectangle, as shown in *Figure 4.25*, with a length of 20 inches and a width of 10 inches. The possible combinations of load applications are a single dual wheel load, two HS 20 trucks passing, and the alternate load configuration in the passing mode. For highway loadings, AASHTO recommends that the live load be increased by an impact factor when the pipe is less than three feet beneath the pavement surface. The recommended impact factors are presented in *Table 4.11*.

Load Distribution Assumptions

At depths, H, below the surface, the length and the width of the rectangle are assumed to increase by the value of 1.75H. The conditions for a single

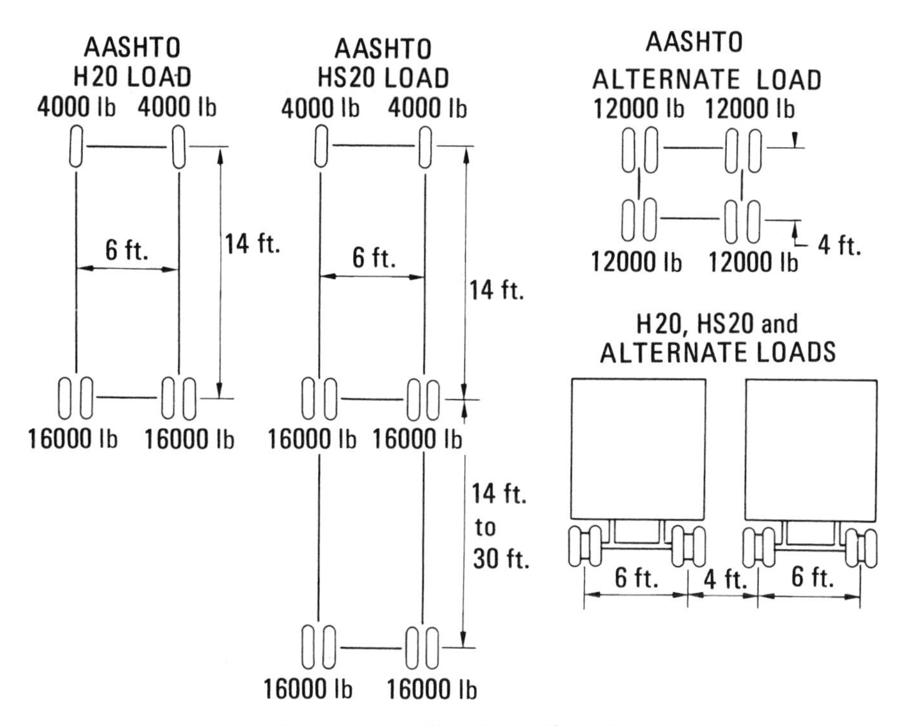

Figure 4.24. Live Load Spacing.

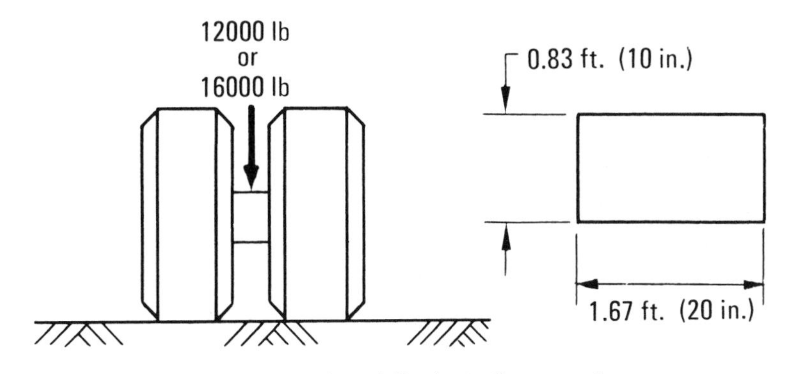

Figure 4.25. Wheel Load Surface Contact Area.

dual wheel, two HS 20 trucks passing, and alternate loads in the passing mode are shown in *Figures 4.26, 4.27* and *4.28*. The maximum value for average pressure intensity is obtained under various conditions of live load and depth of pipe. As shown in *Figures 4.27* and *4.28*, at greater depths the distributed loaded areas overlap, and the maximum pressure will develop under either the truck passing or the alternate loads in passing mode conditions. The depths for these transitions is shown in *Table 4.12*, along with the total loading, and rectangular areas that will produce the critical load effect.

Table 4.11. Impact Factors for Traffic Loads.

Height of Cover	Impact Factor
0′-0″ to 1′-0″	30%
1′-1″ to 2′-0″	20%
2′-1″ to 2′-11″	10%
3′-0″ and Greater	0

Note: Impact factors recommended by the American Association of State Highway and Transportation Officials in "Standard Specifications for Highway Bridges", Twelfth Edition.

Table 4.12. Critical Loading Configurations.

H, feet	P, pounds	A_{LL}, Square Feet
$H < 1.33$	16,000	(0.83 + 1.75H) (1.67 + 1.75H) *(See Fig. 4.26)*
$1.33 \leqslant H < 4.10$	32,000	(0.83 + 1.75H) (5.67 + 1.75H) *(See Fig. 4.27)*
$4.10 \leqslant H$	48,000	(4.83 + 1.75H) (5.67 + 1.75H) *(See Fig. 4.28)*

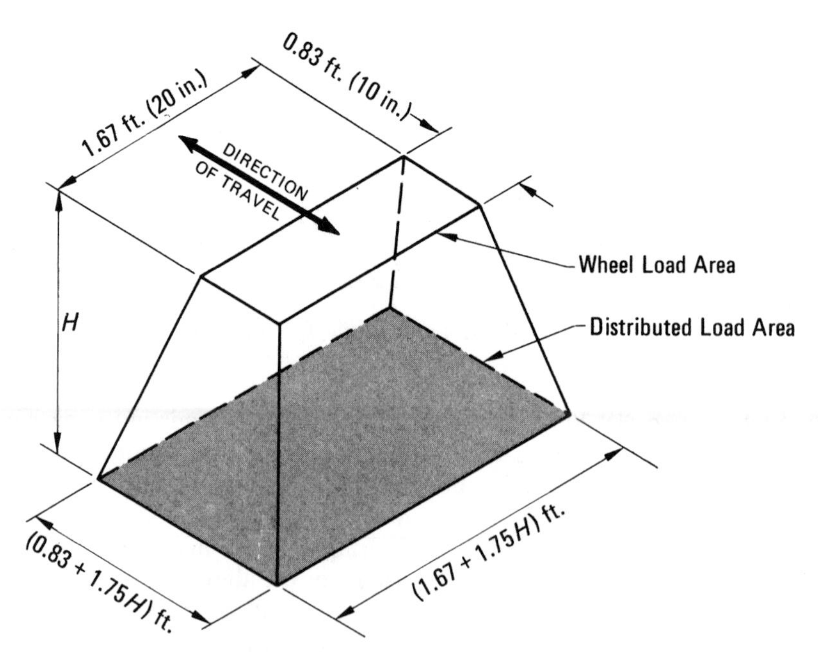

Figure 4.26. Distributed Load Area—Single Dual Wheel.

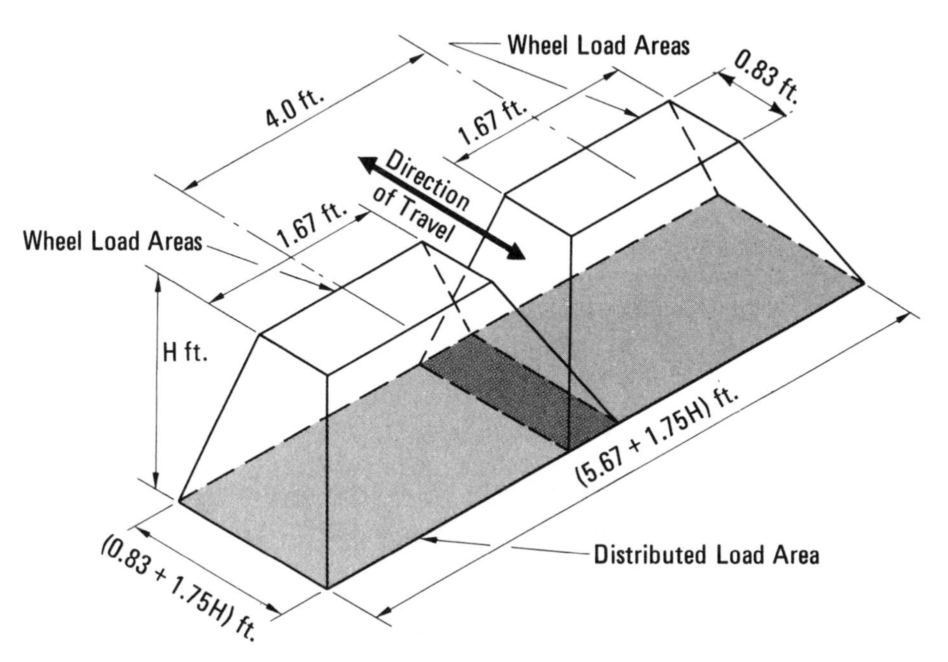

Figure 4.27. Distributed Load Area—Two HS 20 Trucks Passing.

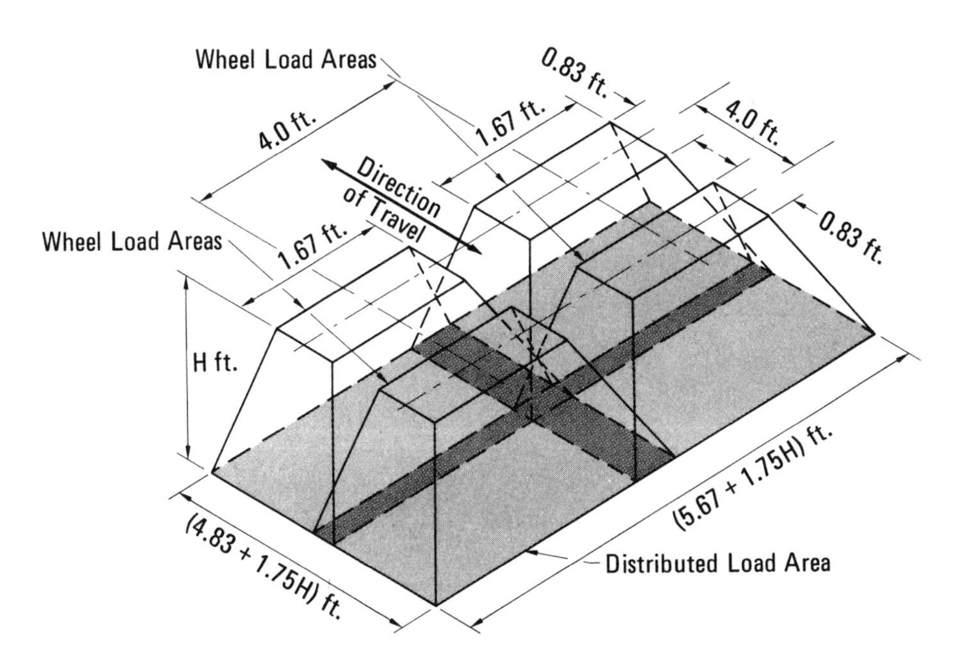

Figure 4.28. Distributed Load Area—Alternate Loads in Passing Mode.

Live Load on Pipe

To determine the live load pressure on a buried concrete pipe, the average pressure intensity at the elevation of the outside top of the pipe is calculated. Then, the total live load acting on the pipe is calculated based upon the average pressure intensity. Finally, the live load pressure per linear foot of pipe is obtained by dividing the total live load on the pipe by the effective supporting length, as shown in *Figure 4.29.*

The average pressure intensity at the level of the outside top of the pipe is obtained by the following equation:

$$w_L = \frac{P(1 + I_f)}{A_{LL}} \tag{4.43}$$

Where: w_L = average pressure intensity, pounds per square foot
P = total applied surface wheel loads, pounds
A_{LL} = distributed live load area on the subsoil plane at the outside top of the pipe, square feet
I_f = impact factor

Given the average pressure intensity that is critical, the total live load, W_T, is obtained by the following equation:

$$W_T = w_L L S_L \tag{4.44}$$

Where: W_T = total live load, pounds
L = length of A_{LL} parallel to longitudinal axis of pipe, feet
S_L = outside horizontal span of pipe or width of A_{LL} transverse to longitudinal axis of pipe, whichever is less, feet

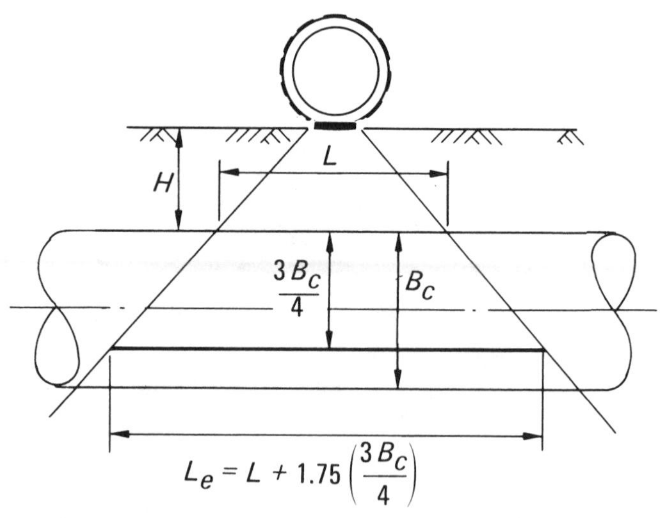

Figure 4.29. Effective Supporting Length of Pipe.

A designer is primarily concerned with maximum loads. The most critical pipe location is one that is centered under the distributed load area. The most critical loading can occur either when the longitudinal pipe axis is parallel or transverse to the direction of truck travel, depending upon the diameter of pipe and depth of cover. Values for L and S_L to be used in *Equation 4.44* are obtained from the orientation of the longitudinal pipe axis with respect to the distributed load area. The maximum value of W_T calculated for the two possible orientations, is used in *Equation 4.45* to determine the live load, W_L:

$$W_L = \frac{W_T}{L_e} \tag{4.45}$$

Where: W_L = live load on pipe, pounds per linear foot
L_e = effective supporting length of pipe, feet

The buried concrete pipe is assumed to be a beam on continuous supports, and that L_e is at a level $B_c/4$ above the bottom of the outside of the pipe, as shown in *Figure 4.29*. Highway live load effects at depths greater than ten feet below the pavement surface are insignificant, and, therefore, for pipes with ten feet or more of cover, live load effects can be neglected. The following equation is used to obtain L_e:

$$L_e = L + 1.75\left(\frac{3B_c}{4}\right) \tag{4.46}$$

Airports

An important factor in airport operations is the proper functioning of its drainage facilities. Because of relatively shallow covers associated with subsurface drainage for airfields, and the magnitude of wheel load concentrations, the effect of aircraft loads on the structural design of underground pipelines is more critical than for most highway facilities.

The pressure distribution of aircraft wheel loads on any horizontal plane in the soil mass is dependent on the magnitude and characteristics of the aircraft loads, including tire pressures, the landing gear configuration, the pavement structure and the subsoil conditions. Larger aircraft have resulted in multiple wheel undercarriages consisting of dual wheel assemblies and dual tandem assemblies to reduce the concentration of load. The net effect is a combination of loadings which impose overlapping pressures, similar to, but heavier than highway loadings.

Major airports are paved with relatively strong surfaces of concrete or asphalt materials, which effectively reduce the load intensity on the subgrade. As discussed previously, *Equations 4.41* and *4.42* and *Tables 4.5* through *4.10* can be used for estimating pressure intensities under concrete pavements. For asphalt surfaces, either local engineering practice or a nominal increase in pressure intensity over that estimated for concrete can be used.

There is a large number of small airports with no surfacing beyond a nominal amount for dust control and to minimize the destructive effect of windblown aggregate particles. For these, *Equations 4.39* and *4.40* and *Table 4.4*, which assume no pavement effect on load distribution, can be used to determine the subsoil pressure intensities from live loads.

Railroads

To evaluate the live load effect for railroad loadings, the American Railway Engineering Association recommends the use of a combination of axle loads and axle spacing represented by the Cooper E 80 loading shown in *Figure 4.30* and an impact factor ranging from 40 percent at zero cover to zero percent with 10 feet of cover. The series of axle loads and spacings is converted into a uniform load at the bottom of the railroad ties. The pressure intensity on a pipe at various depths and various offsets is then computed, based upon the Boussinesq theory. The live load transmitted to a pipe underground is computed by the equation:

$$W_L = C p_0 B_c (1 + I_f) \tag{4.47}$$

Where: W_L = live load transmitted to the pipe, pounds per linear foot
C = pressure coefficient
p_o = intensity of the distributed load at the bottom of the ties, pounds per square foot
B_c = outside horizontal span of the pipe, feet
I_f = impact factor

This equation is similar to the expressions for highway and airport live loadings in that the pressure intensity on the pipe is equal to the pressure on the surface multiplied by an appropriate coefficient.

A locomotive load is assumed uniformly distributed over an area eight feet by 20 feet, and the dead load weight of the track structure to be 200 pounds per linear foot. Live and dead load curves, including impact factors, are plotted in *Figure 4.31* as determined from *Equation 4.47* for a Cooper E 80 loading. For any given height of cover from the top of the pipe to the bottom of the ties, the live load can be read directly from *Figure 4.31*. To obtain the live load per linear foot, it is necessary to multiply the unit load from *Figure 4.31* by the outside horizontal span of the pipe, B_c, in feet.

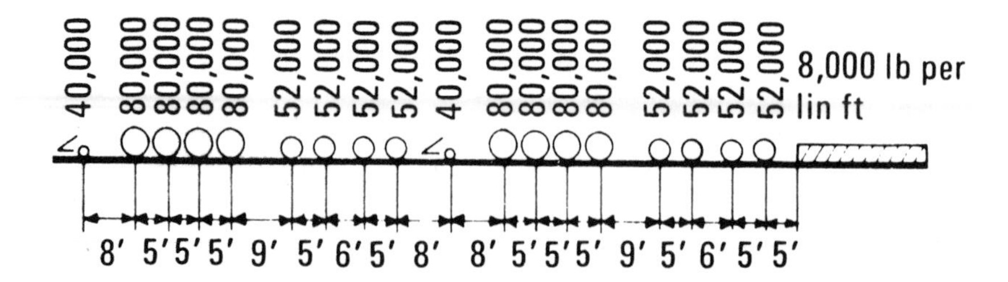

Figure 4.30. Spacing of Wheel Loads Per Axle for a Cooper E 80 Design Loading.

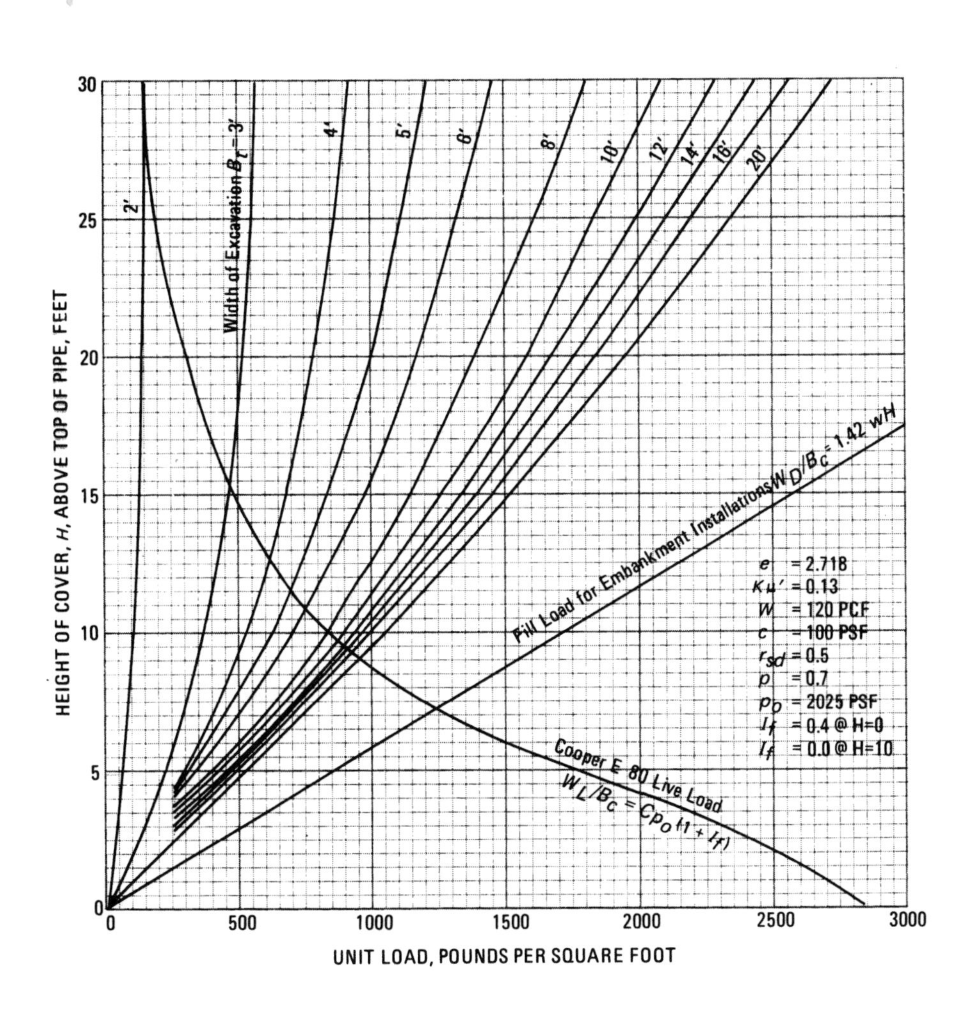

Figure 4.31. Live and Dead Loads on Pipe Installed Under Railroads.

SURCHARGE LOADS

The most common type of **surcharge load** is additional earth fill over an existing pipe installation. If the surcharge load is a building or other surface load, the total weight can be converted to an equivalent frictionless height of fill and evaluated as additional earth fill. After concrete pipe has been in place for a period of time, an improved soil-structure stability is developed. In addition, the load carrying capacity of the pipe increases because of increased concrete strength and favorable load distribution around the periphery of the pipe. If cohesion develops within the soil mass, the amount of the surcharge load transmitted to the pipe may be negligible. All of these time-related factors contribute to the ability of an installed concrete pipe to withstand greater loads than it could at the time of installation. Through site investigations, soils analysis, tests and information on the design and construction of the initial installation, it is possible to evaluate the effect of these factors.

Requirements for an evaluation of surcharge loads are:

- Historical data regarding pipe size and strength class
- Installation data regarding type of installation, type of bedding, type of backfill material and trench width
- Soils analysis to determine whether or not differential settlements will occur between the backfill or fill material over the pipe and soil adjacent to the sides of the pipe, after the surcharge is placed

After the time-related factors have been evaluated, the effect of surcharge loads is estimated by an analysis of the initial installation. The evaluation of two of the most common types, trench and positive projection embankment, will be discussed in detail.

Trench

After placement of the surcharge load, frictional forces may or may not develop in the additional fill depending upon the relative compressibility of the initial backfill material and the original soil in which the trench was excavated. The method of analysis depends upon the height of the additional fill and the relative settlements.

As illustrated in *Figure 4.32,* any one of three possible conditions could develop when a surcharge fill is placed over an existing trench installation:

- Complete condition, *Figure 4.7,* with settlement; i.e., differential settlements occur throughout the entire height of the fill
- Incomplete condition, *Figure 4.8*, with settlement; i.e., differential settlements are dissipated within the surcharge
- Surcharge fill, without settlement; i.e., no differential settlement occurs

The first condition occurs when a surcharge fill is placed over an existing trench installation and differential settlements develop between the initial backfill material and the surrounding soil in which the trench was excavated. In this case, upward frictional forces will be generated in the additional fill.

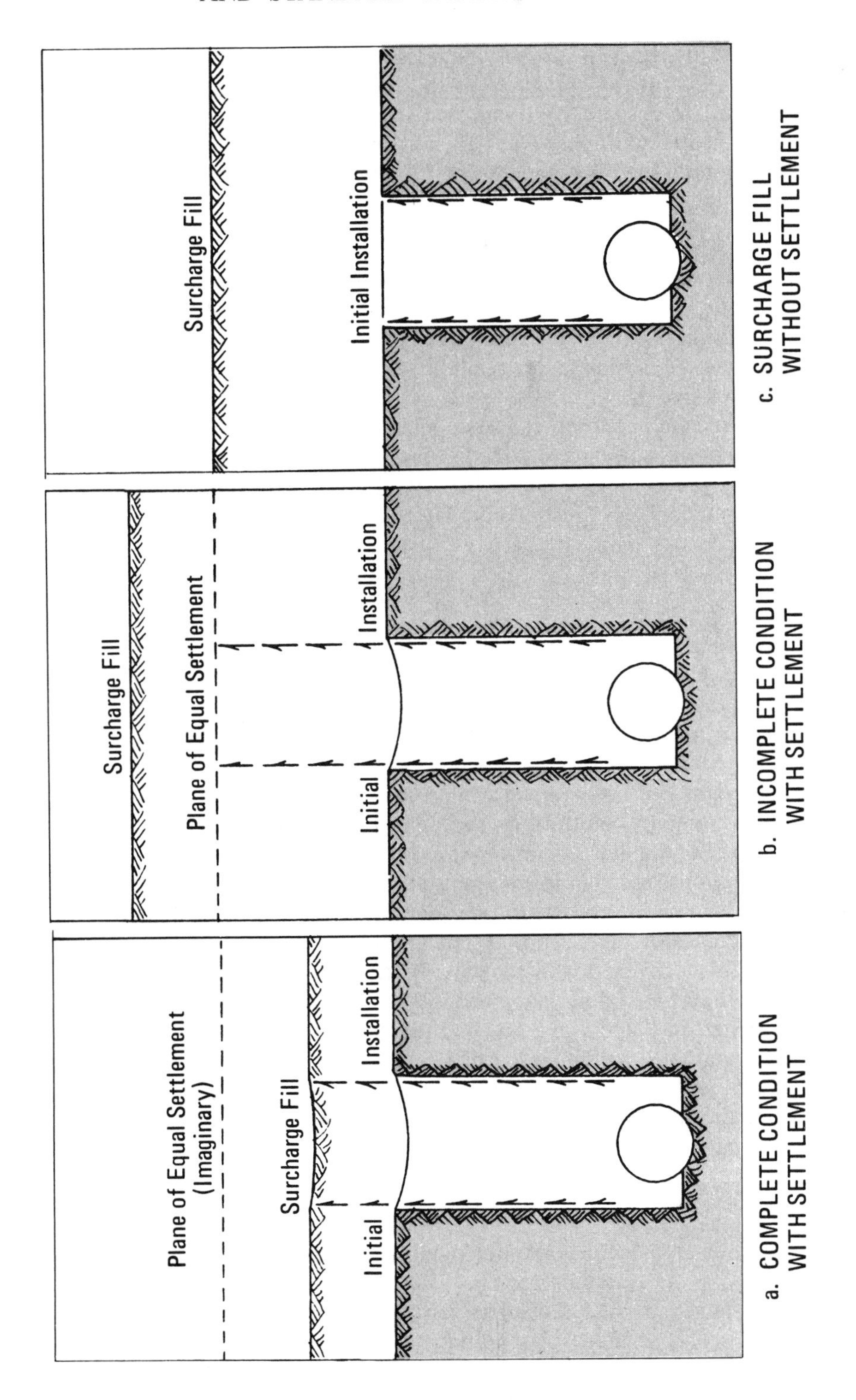

Figure 4.32. Trench Installations with Surcharge Fill Load.

When the height of the surcharge fill is relatively shallow, illustrated in *Figure 4.32 (a),* as compared to the depth of the initial trench, upward frictional forces on the prism will be generated throughout the entire height of the additional fill. This simulates a complete trench condition and the total load is computed by *Equation 4.4:*

$$W_d = C_d w B_d^2 \tag{4.4}$$

Figure 4.4 provides the values of the load coefficient, C_d, for trench installations for various types of soils and H/B_d ratios. The H value to be used in *Figure 4.4* for the surcharge condition is the total height of cover over the pipe, which is the height of the initial backfill plus the height of the surcharge fill.

The second condition exists, as illustrated in *Figure 4.32 (b),* when the surcharge fill is of sufficient height that a plane of equal settlement is developed within the soil mass. This simulates an incomplete negative projection embankment installation and the total load is computed by *Equation 4.27:*

$$W_n = C_n w B_d^2 \tag{4.27}$$

Figure 4.33 presents values of the load coefficient, C_n, for various values of p' and r_{sd}. Recommended design values for the settlement ratio are listed in *Table 4.13*. If differential settlement is expected, the question is whether *Equation 4.4* or *4.27* is applicable, and it is necessary to evaluate the height of surcharge fill required to develop a plane of equal settlement. This height can be obtained from *Figure 4.33* since it is at the point of intersection between the lines for the r_{sd} values and the curved line representing the complete condition; that is, the plane of equal settlement is at the value of H for the intersection. If the incomplete condition is realized, the fill load varies linearly for any given trench width, negative projection ratio and settlement ratio. If the complete trench condition prevails, *Equation 4.4* is used with the value of C_d obtained from *Figure 4.4*.

The third type of surcharge condition, illustrated in *Figure 4.32(c),* exists when the backfill material and the adjacent soil have developed sufficient stability over a period of time so that all material will compress equally, and differential settlements and frictional forces will not develop within the surcharge fill. For this condition, the total load is computed by the equation:

$$W_d = C_d w B_d^2 + C_s w H B_d \tag{4.48}$$

Where: W_d = total load including initial backfill and surcharge load, pounds per linear foot

C_d = load coefficient for trench installations

w = unit weight of backfill material, pounds per cubic foot

B_d = trench width of the initial installation, feet

C_s = load coefficient for surcharge loads

H = height of surcharge fill, feet

Table 4.13. Negative Projection Settlement Ratio Design Values.

Negative Projection Ratio p'	Settlement Ratio r_{sd}
0.5	-0.1
1.0	-0.3
1.5	-0.5
2.0	-1.0
3.0	-2.0

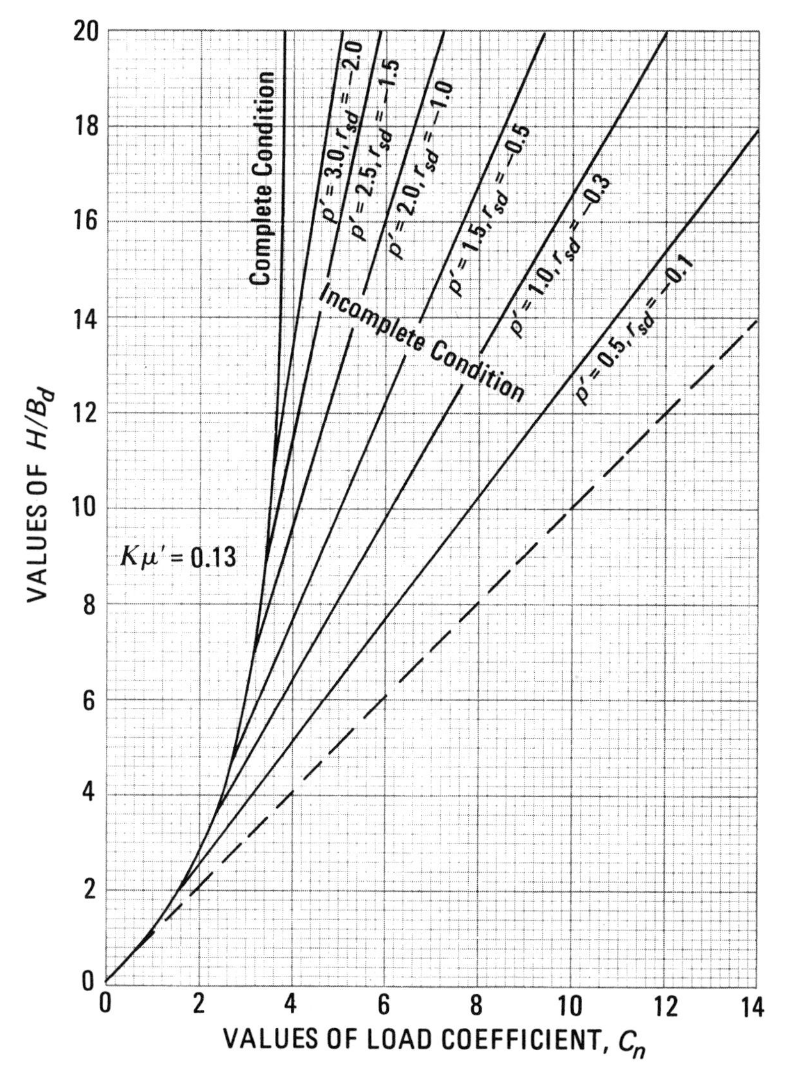

Figure 4.33. Load Coefficient for Trench Installation with Surcharge—Incomplete Condition.

The first term in *Equation 4.48*, $C_d w B_d^2$, accounts for the backfill load of the initial installation, *Equation 4.4*, and the second term, $C_s w H B_d$, accounts for the surcharge load. For uniform surcharge loads that represent buildings or other surface loads, the second term in *Equation 4.48* is expressed as $C_s U_s B_d$.

Where: U_s = uniform pressure at the ground surface, pounds per square foot

Values of the backfill load coefficient, C_d, and the surcharge load coefficient, C_s, are obtained from *Figures 4.4* and *4.34*. The height of backfill, H, is measured from the top of the pipe to the original ground surface for both figures.

Positive Projection Embankment

Any one of the three conditions could develop, as illustrated in *Figure 4.35*, when a surcharge fill is placed over a positive projection embankment installation, as for trench installations:

- Complete condition with settlement
- Incomplete condition with settlement
- Surcharge fill without settlement

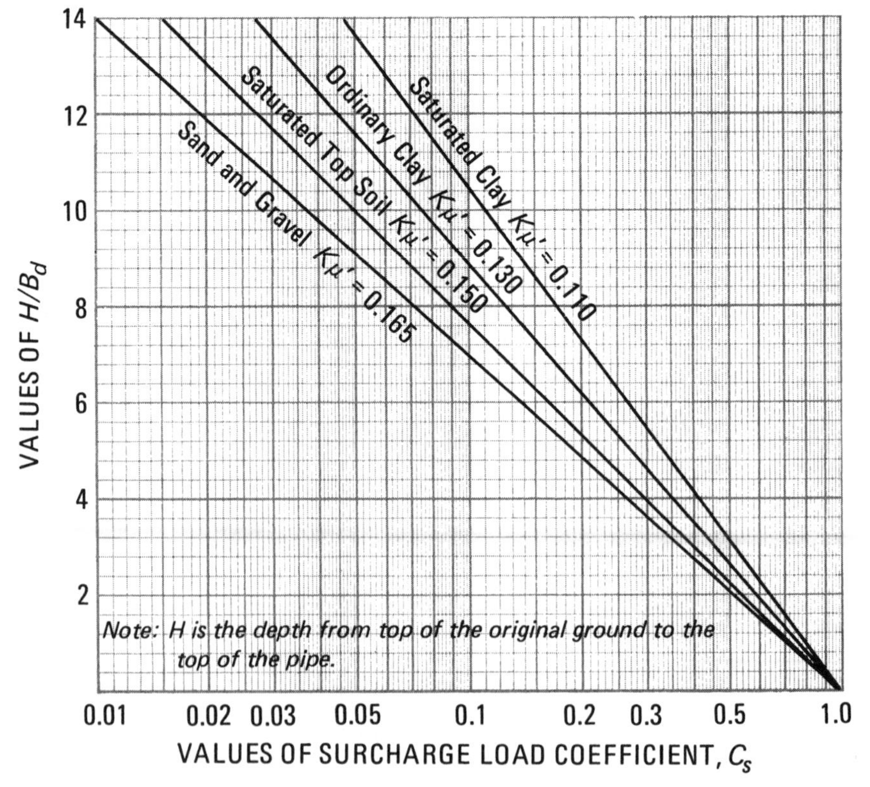

Figure 4.34. Surcharge Load Coefficient—Trench Installations.

When a surcharge fill is placed over an existing embankment installation, differential settlements are expected between the interior and exterior prisms, and downward frictional forces on the interior prism will be generated through the additional fill. Under shallow surcharges, differential settlements and frictional forces will act throughout the completed fill height and a complete condition exists, *Figure 4.35 (a)*. If the fill is of sufficient height, a plane of equal settlement will occur within the soil mass and an incomplete condition will exist, *Figure 4.35 (b)*. If the initial installation is a complete condition, the surcharge may be of sufficient height to enable development of a plane of equal settlement and thus change the complete into the incomplete condition. Once the incomplete condition is realized the fill load varies linearly for any given size of pipe, projection ratio, or settlement ratio, *Equation 4.22*.

Recommended design values for the settlement ratio are listed in *Table 4.2*. The value depends upon the degree of compaction of the fill material adjacent to the sides of the pipe. With construction methods that result in proper compaction of bedding and sidefill materials, lower design values of the settlement ratio may be used.

For both the complete, *Figure 4.35 (a),* and incomplete, *Figure 4.35 (b),* conditions the total load is computed by *Equation 4.9:*

$$W_c = C_c w B_c^2 \tag{4.9}$$

Figures 4.11, 4.12 and *4.13* provide values of the load coefficient for various H/B_c ratios and $r_{sd}p$ products. The value of H to be used in these figures is the total cover over the pipe, which is the height of the initial fill above the pipe plus the height of the surcharge fill. The height of fill required to change from the complete to the incomplete condition can also be determined from *Figures 4.11* through *4.13*. For any given pipe size and $r_{sd}p$ value, this height is at the intersection of the $r_{sd}p$ line and the curved line for the complete condition.

For pipe installed with shallow cover, over a period of time sufficient stability of the surrounding fill may be realized so that placement of a surcharge load will not cause differential settlements. For this stabilized condition, *Figure 4.35 (c),* the total load is computed by the equation:

$$W_{\dot{c}} = C_c w B_c^2 + C_s w H B_c \tag{4.49}$$

Where: W_c = total load including initial fill load and surcharge load, pounds per linear foot

C_c = load coefficient for positive projection embankment installations without surcharge fill

w = unit weight of initial fill material and/or surcharge fill material, pounds per cubic foot

B_c = outside horizontal span of the pipe, feet

C_s = load coefficient for surcharge loads

H = height of surcharge fill, feet

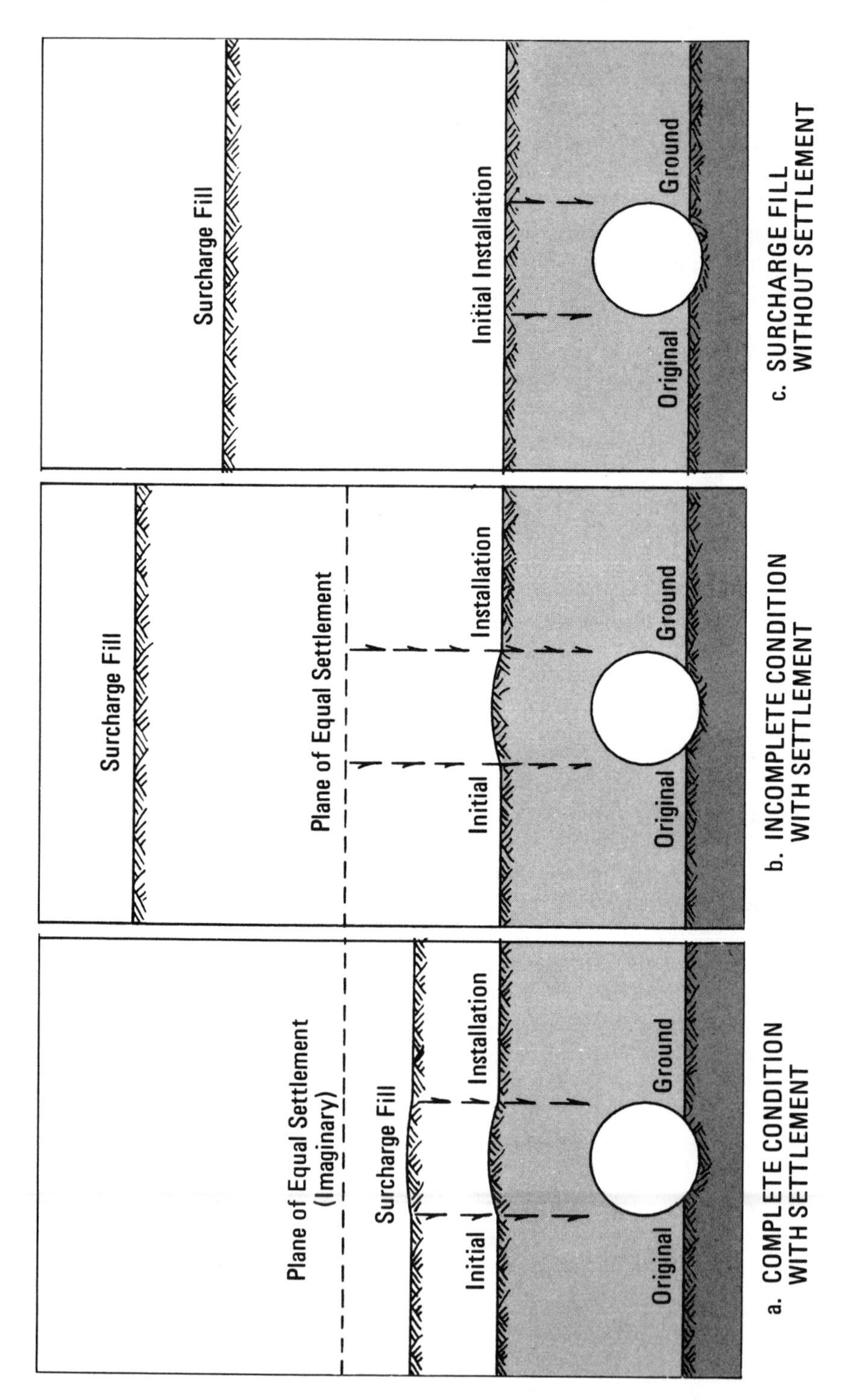

Figure 4.35. Positive Projection Embankment Installations with Surcharge Fill Load.

The first term in *Equation 4.49*, $C_c w B_c^2$, accounts for the initial fill load and the second term, $C_s w H B_c$, accounts for the surcharge fill load. The initial load coefficient is determined from *Figures 4.11* through *4.13* with the H/B_c ratio corresponding to the initial height of fill. *Figure 4.36* presents values of the surcharge load coefficient, C_s, for various H/B_c ratios. The value of H to be used in *Figure 4.36* is the initial height of fill. For uniform loads resulting from buildings or other surcharge loads, the second term of *Equation 4.49* is expressed as $C_s U_s B_c$.

Where: U_s = uniform load on the fill surface, pounds per square foot

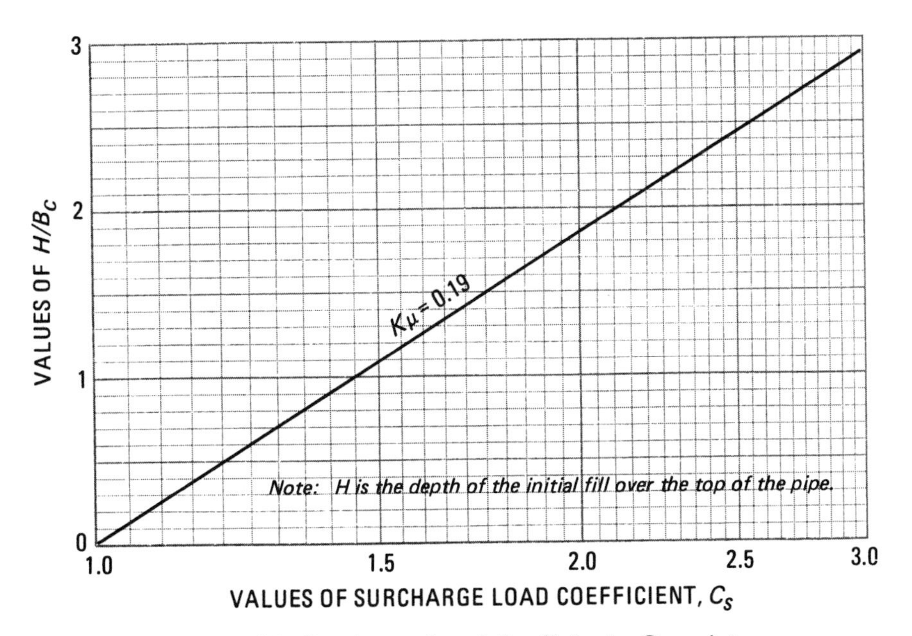

Figure 4.36. Surcharge Load Coefficient—Complete Embankment Installations.

SUPPORTING STRENGTH OF CONCRETE PIPE

The supporting strength of a buried concrete pipeline is dependent on the structural strength of the pipe, the type of foundation, and the compaction of the fill material adjacent to the pipe. Methods for evaluating each of these factors is discussed in the following section.

STRENGTH TESTING

A common method used to determine structural strength is to conduct a three-edge bearing test as illustrated in *Figure 4.37*. The load per linear foot which a pipe will support under this condition is termed the three-edge bearing strength. The three-edge bearing test is the most severe loading to which any pipe will be subjected. There is no lateral support for the pipe, as provided under actual buried conditions, and the applied forces in the test are virtually point loads.

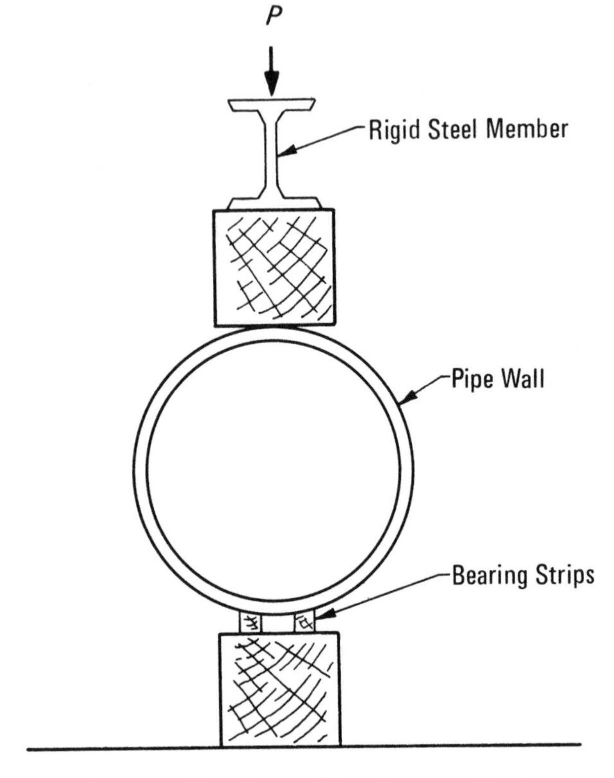

Figure 4.37. Three-Edge Bearing Test.

BEDDINGS

The type of bedding is one of the factors that determines the supporting strength of buried pipe. Four classes of beddings were proposed originally by Spangler and defined by a simplified and idealized distribution of the vertical reactive force acting on the bottom of the pipe. This distribution of the reactive force is described in terms of the central bedding angle, *Figure 4.38:*

- Class D Impermissible, 0 Degree Central Bedding Angle
- Class C Ordinary, 60 Degree Central Bedding Angle
- Class B First Class, 90 Degree Central Bedding Angle

Impermissible, ordinary and first class are the original descriptions used by Spangler. The Class B, C and D descriptions are current designations. The fourth bedding condition is designated as Class A in which the pipe is bedded in concrete.

To transform these mathematically defined loadings into real world conditions, Spangler proposed a series of installation methods. Improvements in construction equipment and methods have resulted in changes to the original installations proposed.

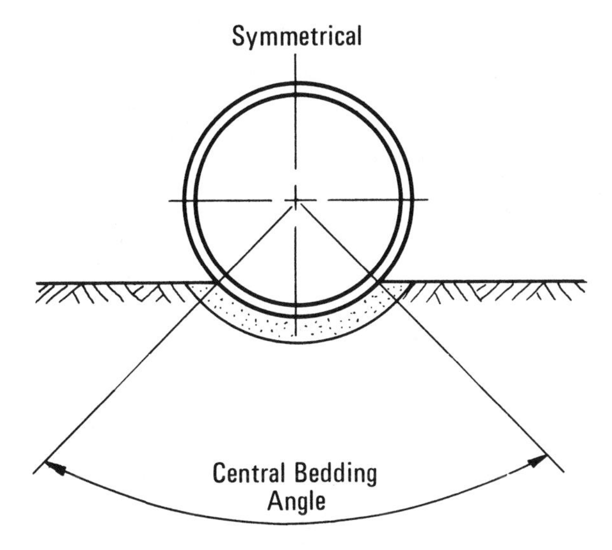

Figure 4.38. Central Bedding Angle.

Classes of bedding for the trench condition are illustrated in *Figures 4.39*, *4.40* and *4.43(a)*:

- **Class A Bedding** can be either a concrete cradle or a concrete arch.
- **Class B Bedding** can be either a shaped subgrade with granular foundation or a granular foundation. A granular foundation without a shaped subgrade is used only with circular pipe.
- **Class C Bedding** can be either a shaped subgrade or a granular foundation. A granular foundation without a shaped subgrade is used only with circular pipe.
- **Class D Bedding** is a flat subgrade, and used only with circular pipe.

Classes of bedding for the embankment condition are illustrated in *Figures 4.41*, *4.42* and *4.43(b)*:

- **Class A Bedding** is a concrete cradle.
- **Class B Bedding** can be either a shaped subgrade with granular foundation, granular foundation or shaped subgrade. A granular foundation without a shaped subgrade is only used with circular pipe and a shaped subgrade by itself is used only with arch and horizontal elliptical pipe.
- **Class C Bedding** can be either a shaped subgrade or a granular foundation. A granular foundation without a shaped subgrade is used only with a circular pipe.
- **Class D Bedding** is a flat subgrade and used only with circular pipe.

Included in *Figures 4.39* and *4.40* is the **bedding factor,** B_f, recommended for trench beddings. Both the trench and embankment bedding factors are discussed in a subsequent section.

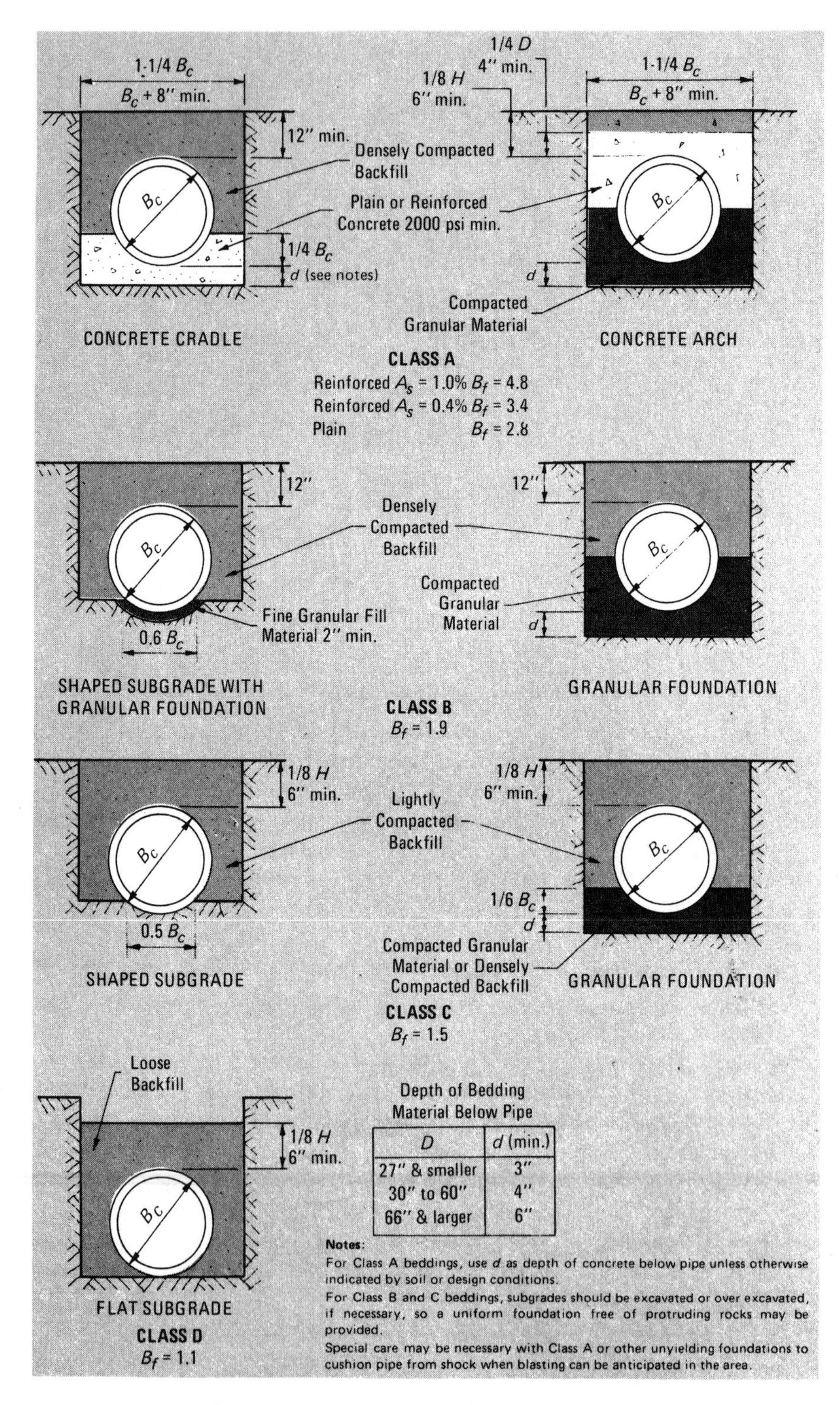

D	d (min.)
27" & smaller	3"
30" to 60"	4"
66" & larger	6"

Notes:

For Class A beddings, use d as depth of concrete below pipe unless otherwise indicated by soil or design conditions.

For Class B and C beddings, subgrades should be excavated or over excavated, if necessary, so a uniform foundation free of protruding rocks may be provided.

Special care may be necessary with Class A or other unyielding foundations to cushion pipe from shock when blasting can be anticipated in the area.

Figure 4.39. Trench Beddings—Circular Pipe.

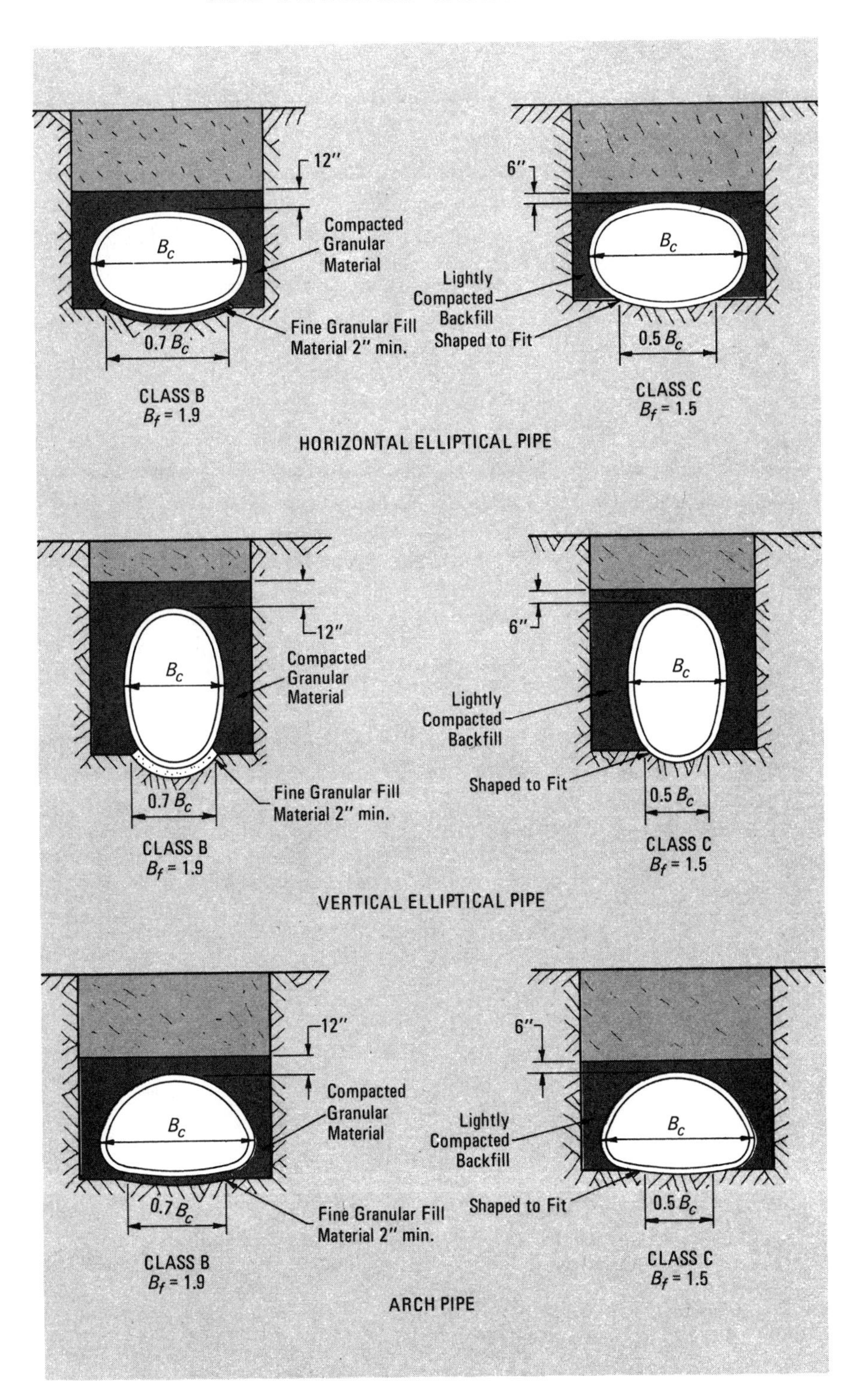

Figure 4.40. Trench Beddings—Elliptical and Arch Pipe.

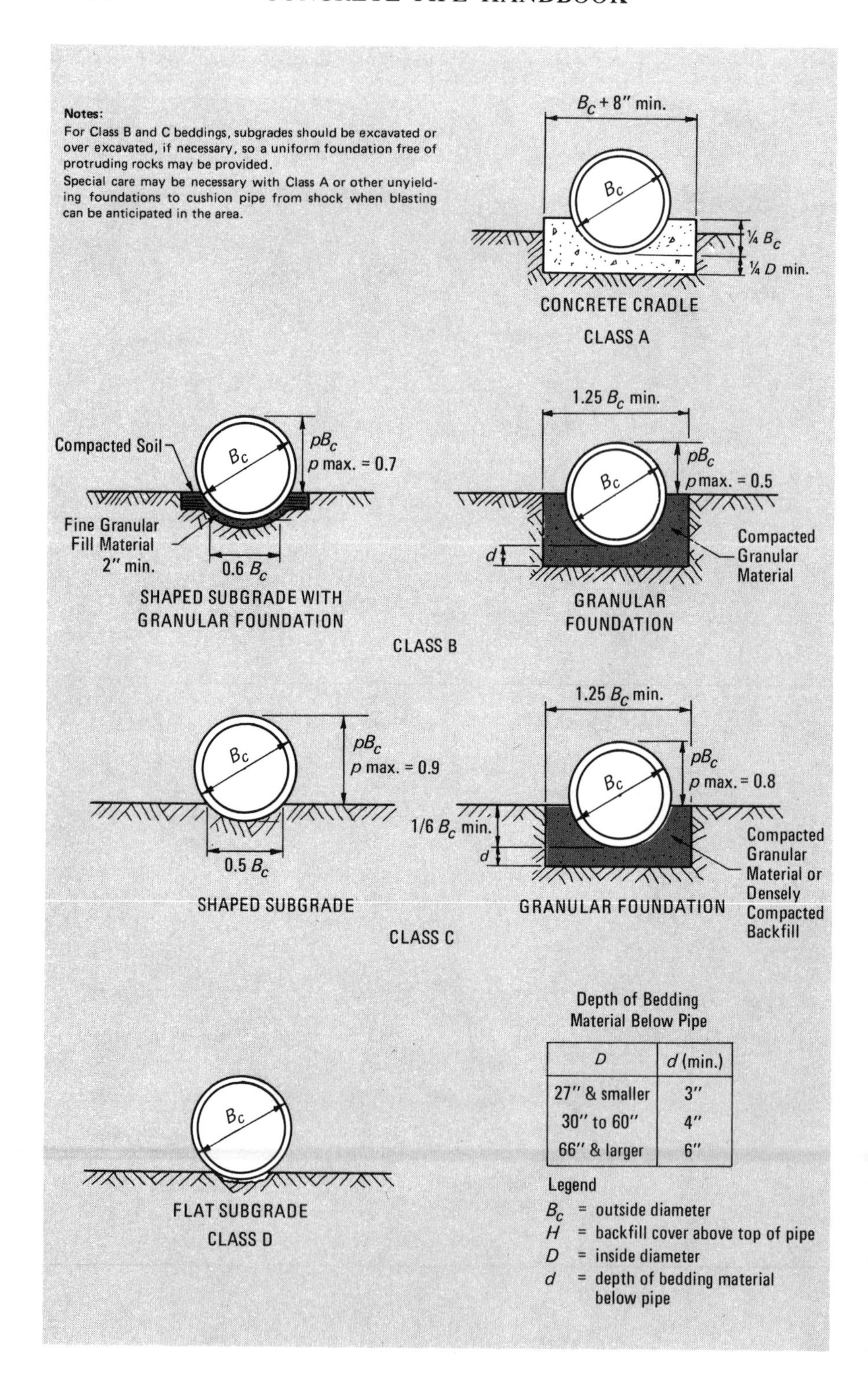

D	d (min.)
27" & smaller	3"
30" to 60"	4"
66" & larger	6"

Figure 4.41. Embankment Beddings—Circular Pipe.

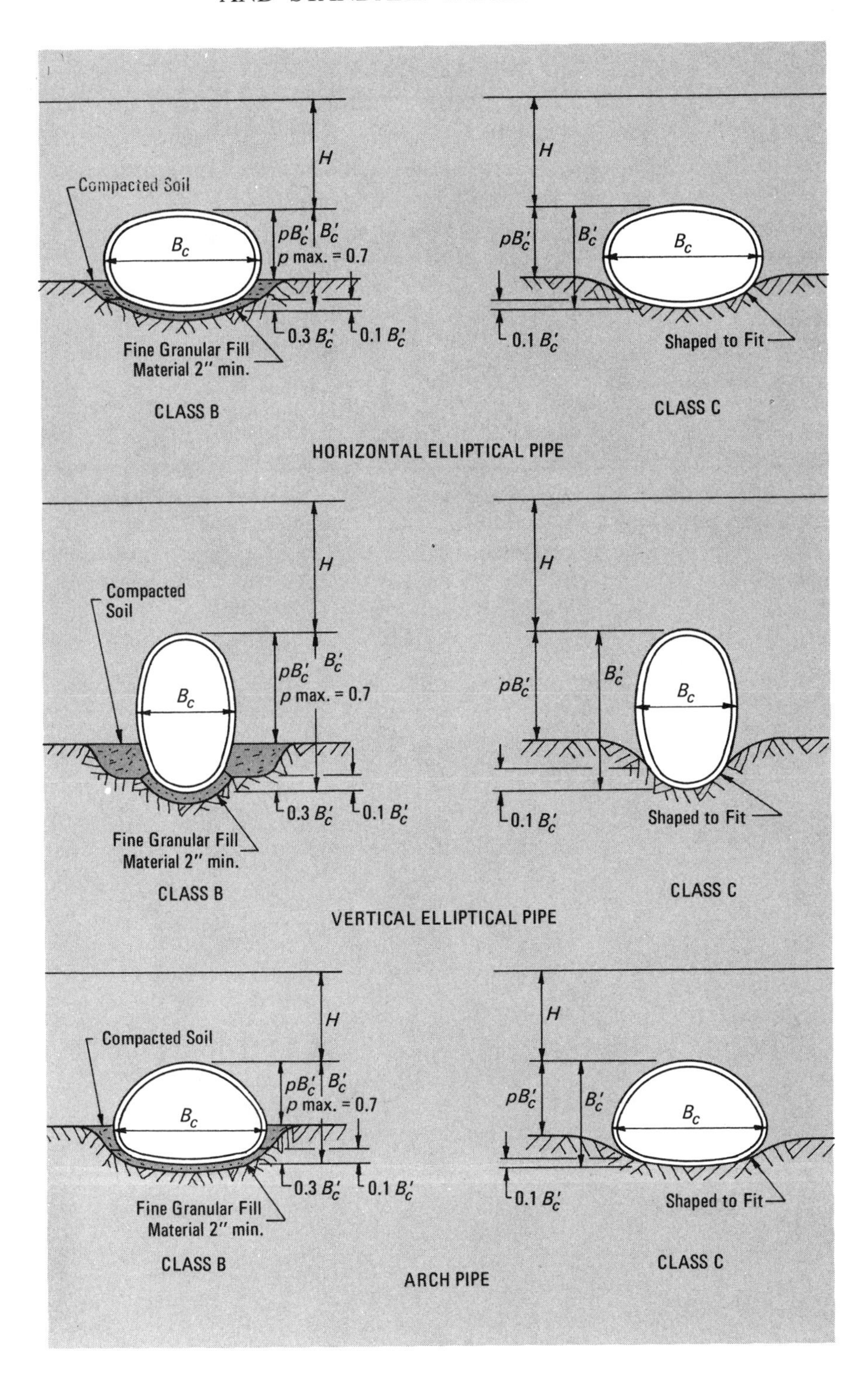

Figure 4.42. Embankment Beddings—Elliptical and Arch Pipe.

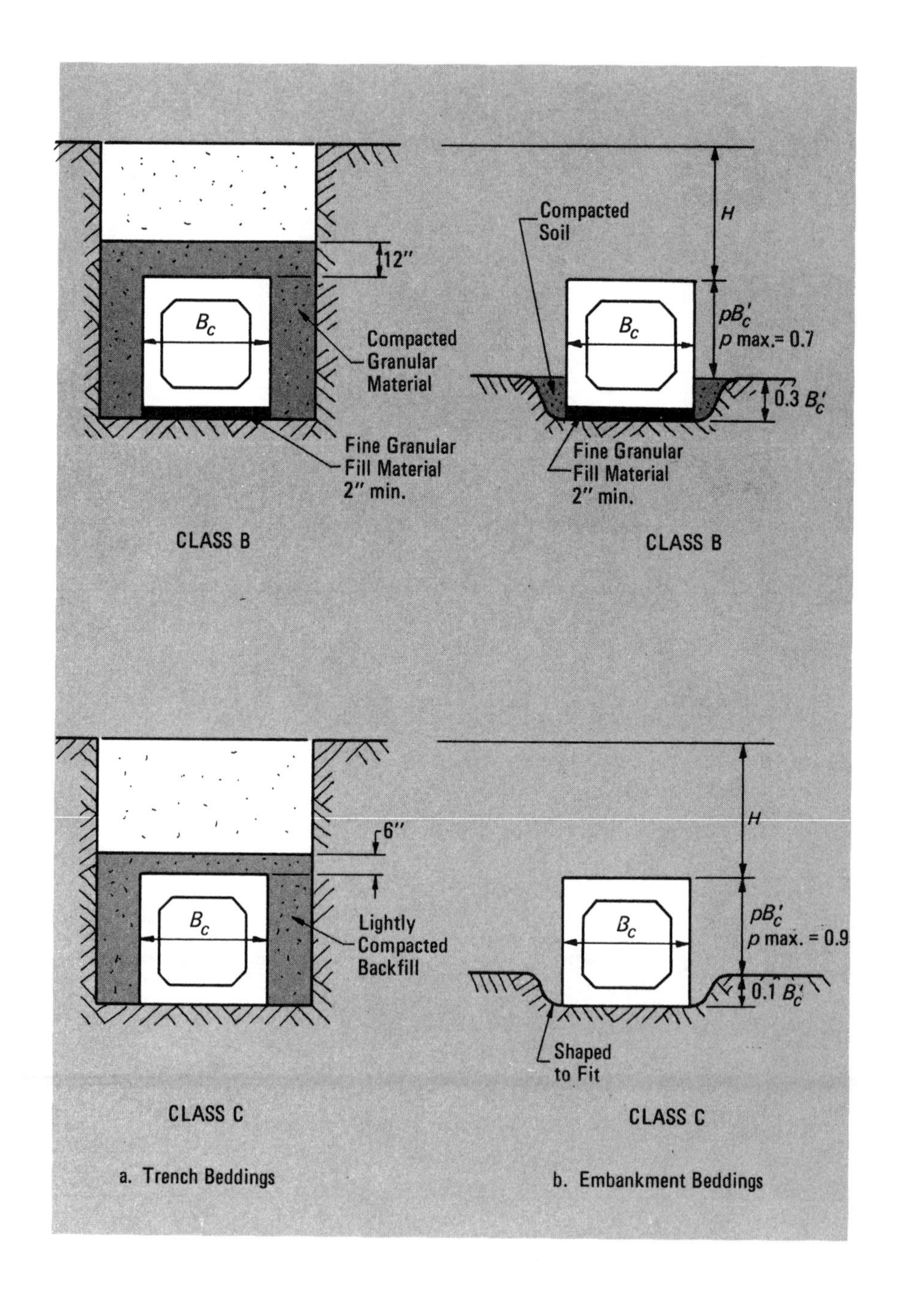

Figure 4.43. Beddings—Precast Concrete Box Sections.

It is assumed that if the pipe is installed in accordance with these drawings, the reactive load of the bedding is uniformly distributed over the central bedding angle. For an actual field installation, the objective is to arrange the bedding under the pipe in such a way as to match the effect of the idealized loading configuration assumed in the design procedure.

Precast reinforced concrete box sections are designed for installed conditions rather than test conditions. Standard designs are presented in ASTM Standards C 789 and C 850. Bedding details are illustrated in *Figure 4.43*. Construction procedures for all beddings are presented in *Chapter 9*.

ROCK OR OTHER UNYIELDING FOUNDATIONS

Where ledge rock, compacted rocky or gravel soil, or other unyielding foundation material is encountered, the pipe should be bedded in accordance with the requirements of one of the previous classes of bedding, but with the following additions:

- For Class B and C beddings, subgrades should be excavated so that a uniform foundation free of protruding rocks may be provided.
- Special care may be necessary with Class A beddings or unyielding foundations to cushion pipe from shock when blasting can be anticipated in the area.

BEDDING FACTORS

Under installed conditions the vertical load on a pipe is distributed over its width and the reaction is distributed in accordance with the type of bedding. When the pipe strength used in design has been determined by plant testing, factors must be developed to relate the in-place supporting strength to the more severe plant test strength.

The **bedding factor** is defined as the ratio between the supporting strength of buried pipe to the strength of the pipe determined in the three-edge bearing test. The same ratio was defined originally by Spangler as the **load factor.** This latter term, however, was subsequently defined in the ultimate strength method of reinforced concrete design with an entirely different meaning. To avoid confusion, therefore, Spangler's term was renamed the bedding factor.

The supporting strength of a buried rigid pipe and the bedding factor for a particular pipeline depend upon two characteristics of the installation:

- Width of the bedding of the pipe and quality of the contact between the pipe and bedding
- Magnitude of the lateral unit pressure acting against the sides of the pipe and area of the pipe over which the lateral pressure acts

The methods for evaluating bedding factors for trench and embankment installations are discussed in the following sections.

Since the sidefill material can be more readily compacted for pipe installed in a positive projection embankment condition, the effect of lateral pressure is considered in evaluating the bedding factor. For trench installations, the effect of lateral pressure was neglected in development of bedding factors. Instead of a general theory as for the embankment condition, Spangler, from analysis of test installations, established conservative fixed bedding factors for each of the standard classes of bedding used for trench installations.

Trench Installations

Conservative fixed bedding factors for pipe installed in a narrow trench condition are listed below the particular standard classes of beddings shown in *Figures 4.39* and *4.40*.

Both Spangler and Schlick, in early Iowa Engineering Experiment Stations publications, postulate that some active lateral pressure is developed in trench installations before the transition width is reached. Experience indicates that the active lateral pressure increases as the trench width increases from a very narrow width to the transition width, provided the sidefill is compacted. Defining the narrow trench width as a trench having a width at the top of the pipe equal to or less than the outside horizontal span plus one foot, and assuming a conservative linear variation, the variable trench bedding factor can be determined by:

$$B_{fv} = (B_{fe} - B_{ft})\left[\frac{B_d - (B_c + 1.0)}{B_{dt} - (B_c + 1.0)}\right] + B_{ft} \qquad (4.50)$$

Where:
- B_c = outside horizontal span of pipe, feet
- B_d = trench width at top of pipe, feet
- B_{dt} = transition width at top of pipe, feet
- B_{fe} = bedding factor, embankment
- B_{ft} = fixed bedding factor, trench
- B_{fv} = variable bedding factor, trench

A six-step design procedure for determining the trench variable bedding factor is:

- Determine the trench fixed bedding factor, B_{ft}
- Determine the trench width, B_d
- Determine the transition width for the installation conditions, B_{dt}
- Determine H/B_c ratio, settlement ratio, r_{sd}, projection ratio, p, and the product of the settlement and projection ratios, $r_{sd}\ p$
- Determine positive projecting embankment bedding factor, B_{fe}
- Calculate the trench variable bedding factor, B_{fv}

Positive Projection Installations

Since the fill material can be compacted more readily in embankment installations, the effect of active lateral pressure in a positive projection condition is considered in evaluating the bedding factor. The supporting strength of the pipe is a function of the distribution of the vertical load, the class of bedding, the magnitude of the active soil pressure against the sides of the pipe, and the area of the pipe over which the active lateral pressure is effective.

The bedding factor for positive projection installations is calculated by the following equation:

$$B_f = \frac{A}{N - xq} \tag{4.51}$$

Where: B_f = bedding factor
A = a constant corresponding to the shape of the pipe
N = a parameter which is a function of the distribution of the vertical load and vertical reaction
x = a parameter which is a function of the area of the vertical projection of the pipe over which active lateral pressure is effective
q = the ratio of the total lateral pressure to the total vertical load

The value of q is determined by the following equation:

$$q = \frac{mK}{C_c}\left(\frac{H}{B_c} + \frac{m}{2}\right) \quad \text{(Circular Pipe)} \tag{4.52}$$

Where: K = the ratio of the unit lateral soil pressure to unit vertical soil pressure (Rankine's coefficient of active earth pressure). A value of 0.33 will usually be sufficiently accurate.
m = fractional part (ratio) of the outside diameter of the pipe over which lateral pressure is effective (usually assumed to equal the projection ratio, p)
C_c = the load coefficient for positive projection pipe

The value of the constant A in the bedding factor equation for circular pipe is 1.431. Design values for the other parameters in *Equation 4.52* for circular pipe are given in *Tables 4.14* and *4.15*. When the concrete cradle method of bedding is used, N' and x' are used for the terms in *Equation 4.51.*

The term m, the fractional part of the outside diameter of the pipe over which the active lateral pressure is effective, is not necessarily the same value as the projection ratio, although assuming so is a rather common practice. When good construction methods are used and proper compaction of both bedding and sidefill materials is attained, effective lateral pressure may develop over the entire height of the pipe. This would result in an m value of 1.0.

Table 4.14. Values of Parameters N and N' in the Bedding Factor Equation.

	Type of Projection Bedding	N	N'
Circular Pipe	Class A		0.505
	Class B	0.707	
	Class C	0.840	
	Class D	1.310	

Table 4.15. Values of Parameters x and x' in the Bedding Factor Equation.

	Effective Height, m	x	x'
Circular Pipe	0.0	0.000	0.150
	0.3	0.217	0.743
	0.5	0.423	0.856
	0.7	0.594	0.811
	0.9	0.655	0.678
	1.0	0.638	0.638

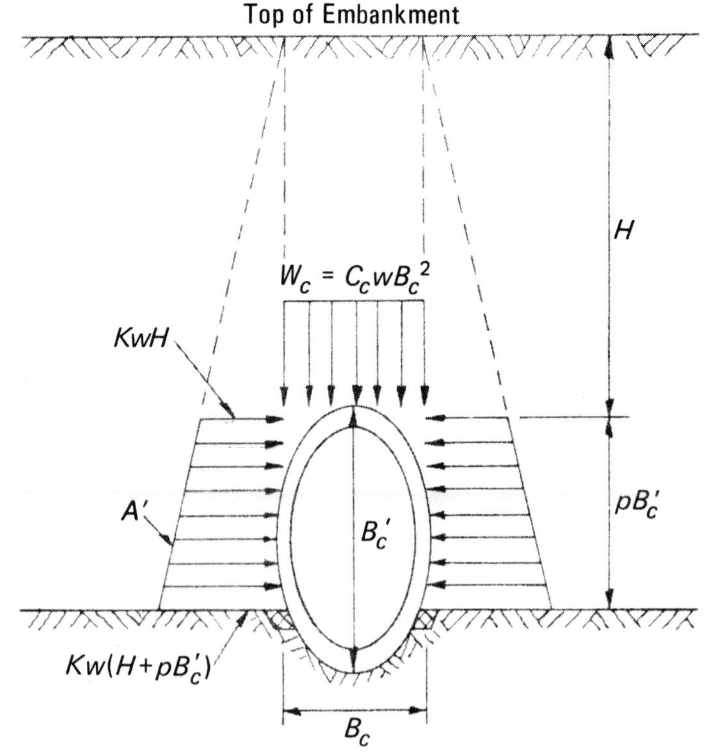

Figure 4.44. Vertical Earth Load and Lateral Pressure.

For elliptical and arch pipe, the expression for pressure ratio, q, is different than for circular pipes. Referring to *Figure 4.44*, for any given height of fill, H, and effective height, pB'_c, over which active lateral pressure acts, the lateral force at the top of the pipe is equal to KwH and the lateral force at the original ground surface is equal to $Kw\,(H + pB'_c)$:

$$q = \frac{pB'_cK}{C_cB_c^2}\left(H + \frac{pB'_c}{2}\right) \quad \text{(Elliptical or Arch Pipe)} \quad (4.53)$$

The total active lateral pressure, A', acting on the pipe is equal to the area of the trapezoid that bounds the pipe:

$$A' = \frac{KwpB'_c(2H + pB'_c)}{2} \quad (4.54)$$

Using *Equation 4.9*, the vertical fill load acting on the pipe is:

$$W_c = C_cwB_c^2 \quad (4.9)$$

By definition, q is equal to the ratio of the total active lateral pressure to the vertical fill load:

$$q = \frac{A'}{W_c} \quad (4.55)$$

Substituting for A' and W_c:

$$q = \frac{pB'_cK}{C_cB_c^2}\left(H + \frac{pB'_c}{2}\right) \quad (4.56)$$

The ratio of B'_c to B_c is 0.69 for horizontal elliptical pipe and approximately 0.69 for arch pipe, and assuming $K = 0.33$:

$$q = \frac{0.23p}{C_c}\left(\frac{H}{B_c} + 0.35p\right) \quad (4.57)$$

For B'_c/B_c equal to 1.45 for vertical elliptical pipe:

$$q = \frac{0.48p}{C_c}\left(\frac{H}{B_c} + 0.73p\right) \quad (4.58)$$

Recommended values of A', N and x to be used in the bedding factor *Equation 4.51* are listed in *Table 4.16*.

Negative Projection and Induced Trench Installations

Selection of the proper bedding factor to be used for determining the supporting strength of a pipe installed in a negative projection embankment condition requires an evaluation of the factors that distinguish this condition from a trench installation. Negative projection or zero projection

Table 4.16. Design Values of Parameters in Bedding Factor Equation.

Pipe Shape	Values of A'	Type of Bedding	Values of N	Projection Ratio	Values of x
HORIZONTAL ELLIPTICAL AND ARCH	1.337	Class B	0.630	0.9	0.421
				0.7	0.369
		Class C	0.763	0.5	0.268
				0.3	0.146
VERTICAL ELLIPTICAL	1.021	Class B	0.516	0.9	0.718
				0.7	0.639
		Class C	0.615	0.5	0.457
				0.3	0.238

conditions are constructed in a trench, and are similar to a typical trench installation. If the backfill between the trench sides and the pipe is well compacted, some lateral pressure against the sides of the pipe will develop. If this condition can be anticipated, a bedding factor can be calculated as for an embankment bedding, *Equation 4.51,* using a K value of 0.15 when determining q.

When a pipe is installed by means of the induced trench method of construction, active lateral pressures will develop. Therefore, the bedding factor for this type of pipe can be calculated in the same way as for a pipe installed in a positive projection embankment condition.

Tunneled and Jacked Installations

Since the jacking method of construction affords positive contact around the lower exterior surface of the pipe and the surrounding earth, an ideal bedding condition is provided. This positive contact can be obtained by close control of the bore excavation to the outside dimensions and shape of the pipe or, if the bore is overexcavated, the space between the pipe and the bore can be filled with sand, grout, concrete or other suitable material. For this type of installation, a bedding factor of three is recommended. If the bore is slightly overexcavated and the space between the pipe and the bore is not filled, a minimum bedding factor of 1.9 is recommended.

The usual procedure in tunnel construction is to complete excavation of the tunnel bore first and then install the pipe. If the pipe is designed to carry the earth load, or a portion of the load, use of trench bedding factors is recommended with the value applied depending on the degree of central bedding angle provided.

FACTOR OF SAFETY AND PIPE STRENGTH

An acceptable balance between economy and safety is an important objective in design of structures. The designer strives for the desired balance by use of a factor of safety. Conservative factors result in projects with higher first costs. Liberal factors produce lower first costs, but will usually result in excessive maintenance or early reconstruction.

In any design procedure, indiscriminate use of safety factors for different items can have a multiplying effect and inadvertently create an excessively conservative design. The multiplication of safety factor by safety factor should be avoided. The current procedure in design of concrete structures is to apply a single factor of safety to the total load or stress. This product is then used for selection of member size and strength. This methodology is also applied to concrete pipe design. The total earth and live load on a buried concrete pipe is first computed and then multiplied by a factor of safety, *F.S.*, to determine the pipe supporting strength required:

$$\text{Pipe Supporting Strength Required} = (W_L + W_E)(F.S.) \qquad (4.59)$$

Pipe strengths are usually presented in terms of ultimate strength in the three-edge bearing test for nonreinforced concrete pipe, and either the 0.01-inch crack strength or ultimate strength in the three-edge bearing test for reinforced concrete pipe. As previously noted, three-edge bearing pipe strengths, *T.E.B.*, are related to buried pipe supporting strengths by the bedding factor, B_f:

$$\text{Pipe Supporting Strength} = T.E.B.(B_f) \qquad (4.60)$$

Combining *Equations 4.58* and *4.59* results in the required three-edge bearing pipe strength:

$$\text{Required T.E.B.} = \frac{(W_L + W_E)(F.S.)}{B_f} \qquad (4.61)$$

Equation 4.61 is used to compute the required ultimate strength in the three-edge bearing test. A factor of safety of 1.25 to 1.5 is commonly used for nonreinforced concrete pipe.

For reinforced concrete pipe, three-edge bearing strength is divided by the inside span of the pipe to obtain a strength classification termed the *D*-load:

$$D\text{-load} = \frac{T.E.B.}{S} \qquad (4.62)$$

Where: S = inside diameter of circular pipe or inside horizontal span of elliptical and arch pipe, feet.

The D-load strength is further classified as the 0.01-inch crack strength, $D_{0.01}$ or the ultimate strength, D_{ult}. The required D-load strength in the three-edge bearing test for reinforced concrete pipe is:

$$D_{ult} = \frac{(W_L + W_E)(F.S.)}{B_f S} \tag{4.63}$$

Equation 4.63 is used to determine the required ultimate strength D-load, and the safety factor, $F.S.$, is defined as the relationship between D_{ult} and $D_{0.01}$:

$$F.S. = \frac{D_{ult}}{D_{0.01}} \tag{4.64}$$

Therefore, *Equation 4.63* can be used to determine the required $D_{0.01}$ strength by substitution of the D_{ult} to $D_{0.01}$ relationship:

$$D_{0.01} = \frac{W_L + W_E}{B_f S} \tag{4.65}$$

The relationship between ultimate D-load and the 0.01-inch crack D-load is specified in the ASTM standards on reinforced concrete pipe:

- For $D_{0.01}$ equal to 2000D or less:
  $$F.S. = 1.5$$
- For $D_{0.01}$ equal to 3000D or more:
  $$F.S. = 1.25$$
- For $D_{0.01}$ more than 2000D but less than 3000D:
  $$F.S. = 1.5 - \left[\frac{D_{0.01} - 2000}{1000}\right](0.25)$$

Thus, the recommended safety factor varies and decreases as the D-load strength increases. The relationships were developed from data obtained on the behavior of concrete pipe in three-edge bearing tests and the buried condition. In the three-edge bearing test, lightly reinforced, low D-load concrete pipe behaves similarly to nonreinforced concrete pipe in that failure generally occurs at the ultimate flexural strength of the pipe. For the more heavily reinforced, high D-load concrete pipe in the three-edge bearing test, structural distress produced by diagonal tension (shear) and radial tension is usually evident before ultimate flexural strength is reached. Radial tension produces a slabbing of the inner cage concrete cover in the pipe tension zone when the concrete tensile force resistance is insufficient to prevent straightening of the inner cage steel. When shear and radial tension criteria govern structural design of the pipe, an ultimate strength in excess of design requirements generally results, and the preceding factors of safety reflect this inherent conservatism.

SPECIFYING PIPE

The design procedure for selection of pipe strength has six logical steps which have been presented in detail in the preceding pages of this chapter.

- Determination of earth load
- Determination of live load
- Selection of bedding
- Determination of bedding factor
- Application of factor of safety
- Selection of pipe strength

The final design step is specifying the pipe in the project bid documents. For most projects, bid items are referenced to one of the ASTM standards on precast concrete pipe. Each standard contains design, manufacturing and testing criteria. The pipe standards normally specified for culvert, storm drain and sewer projects are as follows:

- ASTM Standard C 14 covers three strength classes for nonreinforced concrete pipe which meet minimum ultimate loads.
- ASTM Standard C 76 for reinforced concrete culvert, storm drain and sewer pipe covers five strength classes based on *D*-load at 0.01-inch crack and ultimate load.
- ASTM Standard C 506 for reinforced concrete arch culvert, storm drain and sewer pipe covers strengths based on *D*-load at 0.01-inch crack and ultimate load.
- ASTM Standard C 507 for reinforced concrete elliptical culvert, storm drain and sewer pipe covers strength classes for both horizontal elliptical and vertical elliptical pipe based on *D*-load at 0.01-inch crack and ultimate load.
- ASTM Standard C 655 for reinforced concrete *D*-load culvert, storm drain and sewer pipe covers acceptance of pipe design to meet specific *D*-load requirements.
- ASTM Standard C 789 for precast reinforced concrete culvert, storm drain and sewer box sections covers sections subjected to highway loading with 2 feet or more earth cover, or subjected to dead load only.
- ASTM Standard C 850 for precast reinforced concrete culvert, storm drain and sewer box sections covers sections subjected to highway loading with less than 2 feet of earth cover.
- ASTM Standard C 985 for nonreinforced concrete specified strength culvert, storm drain, and sewer pipe.

For projects involving arch, elliptical or nonreinforced concrete pipe the designer would either match the required pipe strength with the strengths available in the appropriate standard, and specify an appropriate strength class, or contact the pipe manufacturer if nonstandard strengths are required. As an alternative to the standard designs in ASTM Standard C 14 for nonreinforced circular pipe, the engineer could specify a strength under ASTM Standard C 985, which allows the pipe manufacturer to produce the required strength by the most economical method. If the project requires circular concrete pipe, the designer can select from several options. For example, if the required $D_{0.01}$ strength was a little below or a little above 2000*D*, the designer could specify a Class IV, ASTM Standard C 76 pipe. If the required $D_{0.01}$ strength is above 2000*D* but less than 3000*D*, the designer could specify an ASTM Standard C 76 pipe of the required *D*-load and the pipe producer could furnish a pipe designed by interpolation between the tabular reinforcement areas of Class IV and Class V pipe. In addition, if special designs are required for circular concrete pipe, the designer should contact the pipe manufacturer for information on feasibility and availability. An alternative option for the engineer would be to specify the required *D*-load under ASTM Standard C 655. This alternative allows the pipe manufacturer and designer the selection of the most economical methods with which to produce the pipe *D*-load specified and thereby provide the most economical pipe for the project.

Precast reinforced concrete box sections are designed for installed conditions rather than for test conditions. Standard designs are presented in ASTM Standards C 789, Precast Reinforced Concrete Box Sections for Culverts, Storm Drains and Sewers, and C 850, Precast Reinforced Concrete Box Sections for Culverts, Storm Drains and Sewers with Less Than 2 Feet of Cover Subjected to Highway Loadings, for various loading conditions and heights of earth cover. ASTM Standard C 850 covers box sections with less than two feet of earth cover for both the AASHTO HS 20 truck plus dead load conditions and the AASHTO alternate load plus dead load conditions. ASTM Standards C 789 covers box sections with two or more feet of earth cover for both of the preceding loading conditions and also for only the dead load condition. Special designs for sizes and conditions other than as presented in the ASTM standards are also available.

STANDARD INSTALLATIONS AND THE INDIRECT DESIGN METHOD

Foreword

The classic theory of earth loads on buried concrete pipe published in 1930 by A. Marston was developed for trench and embankment conditions (28).

In later work published in 1933, M. G. Spangler presented three bedding configurations and the concept of a bedding factor to relate the supporting strength of buried pipe to the strength obtained in a three-edge bearing test (25).

Spangler's theory proposed that the bedding factor for a particular pipeline and, consequently, the supporting strength of the buried pipe, is dependent on two installation characteristics:

- Width and quality of contact between the pipe and bedding.
- Magnitude of lateral pressure and the portion of the vertical height of the pipe over which it acts.

For the embankment condition, Spangler developed a general equation for the bedding factor, which partially included the effects of lateral pressure. For the trench condition, Spangler established conservative fixed bedding factors, which neglected the effects of lateral pressure, for each of the three beddings. This separate development of bedding factors for trench and embankment conditions resulted in the belief that lateral pressure becomes effective only at transition, or greater, trench widths. Such an assumption is not compatible with current engineering concepts and construction methods. It is reasonable to expect some lateral pressure to be effective at trench widths less than transition widths. Although conservative designs based on the work of Marston and Spangler have been developed and installed successfully for years, the design concepts have their limitations when applied to real world installations.

The limitations include:

- Loads considered acting only at the top of the pipe.
- Axial thrust not considered.
- Bedding width of test installations less than width designated in his bedding configurations.
- Standard beddings developed to fit assumed theories for soil support rather than ease of and methods of construction.
- Bedding materials and compaction levels not adequately defined.

This section discusses the Standard Installations and the appropriate indirect design procedures to be used with them. The Standard Installations are the most recent beddings developed by ACPA to allow the engineer to take into consideration modern installation techniques when designing concrete pipe.

Introduction

In 1970, ACPA began a long-range research program on the interaction of buried concrete pipe and soil. The research resulted in the comprehensive finite element computer program SPIDA, Soil-Pipe Interaction Design and Analysis, for the direct design of buried concrete pipe.

Since the early 1980's, SPIDA has been used for a variety of studies, including development of four new Standard Installations, and a simplified microcomputer design program, SIDD, Standard Installations Direct Design.

The procedure presented here replaces the historical B, C, and D beddings used in the indirect design method with the four new Standard Installations, and presents a state-of-the-art method for determination of bedding factors for the Standard Installations. Pipe and installation terminology as used in the Installations, SIDD, and this procedure is defined in Figure 4.45.

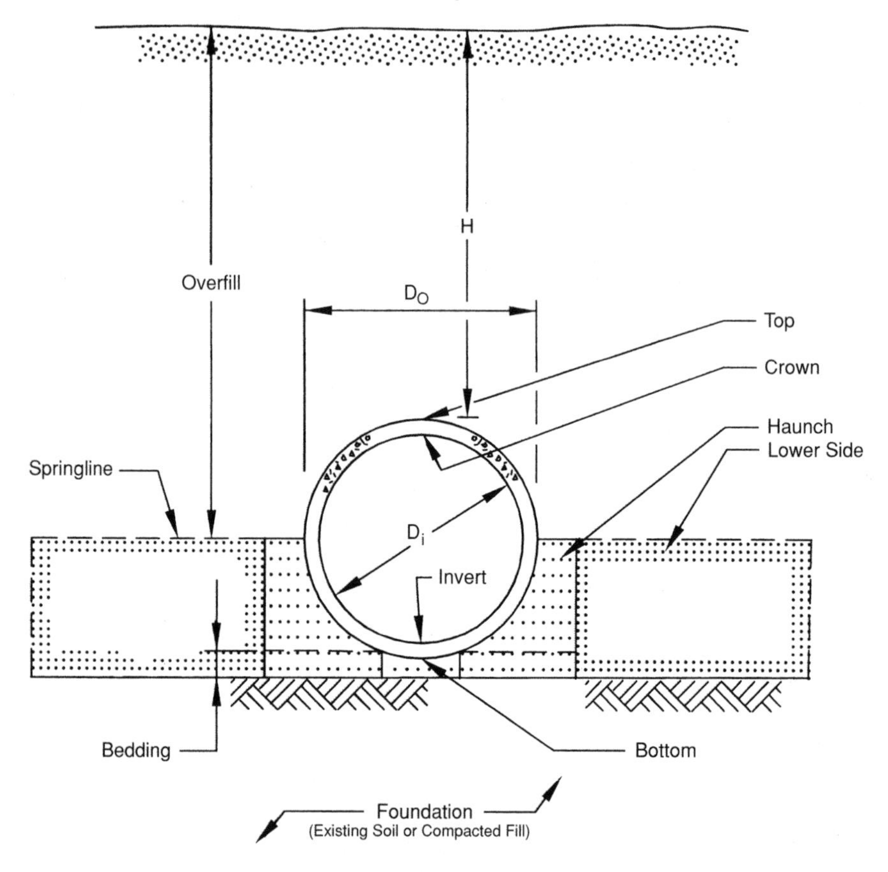

Figure 4.45 Pipe/Installation Terminology

Standard Installations

Through consultations with engineers and contractors, and with the results of numerous SPIDA parameter studies, four new Standard Installations were developed and are presented in Figures 4.46 and 4.47. The SPIDA studies were conducted for positive projection embankment conditions, which are the worst-case vertical load conditions for pipe, and which provide conservative results for other embankment and trench conditions.

The parameter studies confirmed ideas postulated from past experience and proved the following concepts:

- Loosely placed, uncompacted bedding directly under the invert of the pipe significantly reduces stresses in the pipe.
- Soil in those portions of the bedding and haunch areas directly under the

pipe is difficult to compact.

- The soil in the haunch area from the foundation to the pipe springline provides significant support to the pipe and reduces pipe stresses.
- Compaction level of the soil directly above the haunch, from the pipe springline to the top of the pipe grade level, has negligible effect on pipe stresses. Compaction of the soil in this area is not necessary unless required for pavement structures.
- Installation materials and compaction levels below the springline have a significant effect on pipe structural requirements.

Table 4.17 Equivalent USCS and AASHTO Soil Classifications for SIDD Soil Designations

	Representative Soil Types		Percent Compaction	
SIDD Soil	**USCS,**	**AASHTO**	**Standard Proctor**	**Modified Proctor**
Gravelly Sand (Category 1)	SW, SP, GW, GP	A1,A3	100 95 90 85 80 61	95 90 85 80 75 59
Sandy Silt (Category II)	GM, SM, ML, Also GC, SC with less than 20% passing #200 sieve	A2, A4	100 95 90 85 80 49	95 90 85 80 75 46
Silty Clay (Category III)	CL, MH, GC, SC	A5, A6	100 95 90 85 80 45	90 85 80 75 70 40
	CH		100 95 90 45	90 85 80 40

The four Standard Installations provide an optimum range of soil-pipe interaction characteristics. For the relatively high quality materials and high compaction effort of a Type 1 Installation, a lower strength pipe is required. Conversely, a Type 4 Installation requires a higher strength pipe, because it was developed for conditions of little or no control over materials or compaction.

Generic soil types are designated in Figure 4.46 and Figure 4.47. The Unified Soil Classification System (USCS) and American Association of State Highway and Transportation Officials (AASHTO) soil classifications equivalent to the generic soil types in the Standard Installations are presented in Table 4.17.

Load Pressures

SPIDA was programmed with the Standard Installations and many design runs were made. An evaluation of the output of the designs by Dr. Frank J. Heger produced a load pressure diagram significantly different than proposed by previous theories. See Figure 4.48. This difference is particularly significant under the pipe in the lower haunch area and is due in part to the assumption of the existence of partial voids adjacent to the pipe wall in this area. SIDD uses this pressure data to determine moments, thrusts, and shears in the pipe wall, and then uses the ACPA limit states design method to determine the required reinforcement areas to handle the pipe wall stresses (36). Using this method, each criteria that may limit or govern the design is considered separately in the evaluation of overall design requirements. SIDD, which is based on the four Standard Installations, is a stand-alone program developed by the American Concrete Pipe Association.

The Federal Highway Administration, FHWA, developed a microcomputer program, PIPECAR, for the direct design of concrete pipe prior to the development of SIDD. PIPECAR determines moment, thrust, and shear coefficients from either of two systems, a radial pressure system developed by Olander in 1950 and a

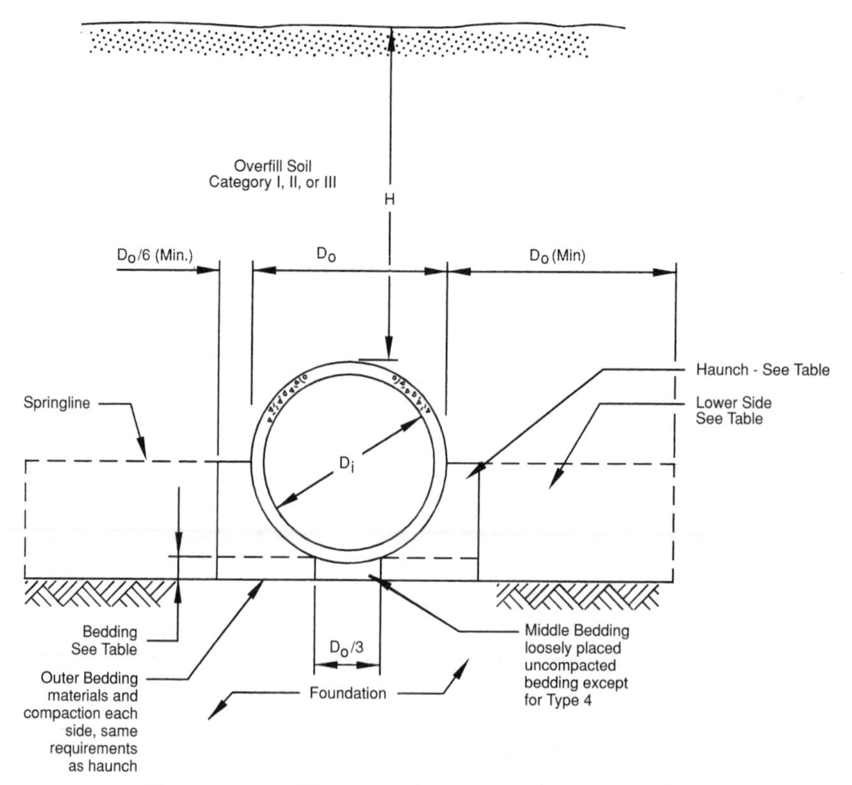

Figure 4.46 Standard Embankment Installations

uniform pressure system developed by Paris in the 1920's, and then also uses the ACPA limit states design method to determine the required reinforcement areas to handle the pipe wall stresses. The SIDD system has been incorporated into PIPECAR as a state-of-the-art enhancement.

Table 4.18 Standard Embankment Installations Soil and Minimum Compaction Requirements

Installation Type	Bedding Thickness	Haunch and Outer Bedding	Lower Side
Type 1	D_o/24 minimum, not less than 75 mm (3"). If rock foundation, use D_o/12 minimum, not less than 150 mm (6").	95% Category I	90% Category I, 95% Category II, or 100% Category III
Type 2	D_o/24 minimum, not less than 75 mm (3"). If rock foundation, use D_o/12 minimum, not less than 150 mm (6").	90% Category I or 95% Category II	85% Category I, 90% Category II, or 95% Category III
Type 3	D_o/24 minimum, not less than 75 mm (3"). If rock foundation, use D_o/12 minimum, not less than 150 mm (6") .	85% Category I, 90% Category II, or 95% Category III	85% Category I, 90% Category II, or 95% Category III
Type 4	D_o/24 minimum, not less than 75 mm (3"). If rock foundation, use D_o/12 minimum, not less than 150 mm (6").	No compaction required, except if Category III, use 85% Category III	No compaction required, except if Category III, use 85% Category III

Notes:

1. *Compaction and soil symbols - i.e. "95% Category I" refers to Category 1 soil material with a minimum standard Proctor compaction of 95%. See Table 4.17 for equivalent modified Proctor values.*
2. *Soil in the outer bedding, haunch, and lower side zones, except within D_o/3 from the pipe springline, shall be compacted to at least the same compaction as the majority of soil in the overfill zone.*

3. ***Subtrenches***
   3.1 *A subtrench is defined as a trench with its top below finished grade by more than 0.1 H or, for roadways, its top is at an elevation lower than 0.3 m (1') below the bottom of the pavement base material.*
   3.2 *The minimum width of a subtrench shall be 1.33 D_o or wider if required for adequate space to attain the specified compaction in the haunch and bedding zones.*
   3.3 *For subtrenches with walls of natural soil, any portion of the lower side zone in the subtrench wall shall be at least as firm as an equivalent soil placed to the compaction requirements specified for the lower side zone and as firm as the majority of soil in the overfill zone, or shall be removed and replaced with soil compacted to the specified level.*

The SPIDA design runs with the Standard Installations were made with medium compaction of the bedding under the middle-third of the pipe, and with some compaction of the overfill above the springline of the pipe. This middle-third area under the pipe in the Standard Installations has been designated as loosely placed, uncompacted material. The intent is to maintain a slightly yielding bedding under the middle-third of the pipe so that the pipe may settle slightly into the bedding and achieve improved load distribution. Compactive efforts in the middle-third of the bedding with mechanical compactors is undesirable, and could produce a hard flat surface, which would result in highly concentrated stresses in the pipe invert similar to those experienced in the three-edge bearing test. The most desirable construction sequence is to place the bedding to grade; install the pipe to grade; compact the bedding outside of the middle-third of the pipe; and then place and compact the haunch area up to the springline of the pipe. The bedding outside the middle-third of the pipe may be compacted prior to placing the pipe.

As indicated in Figures 4.46 and 4.47, when the design includes surface loads, the overfill and lower side areas should be compacted as required to support the surface load. With no surface loads or surface structure requirements, these areas need not be compacted.

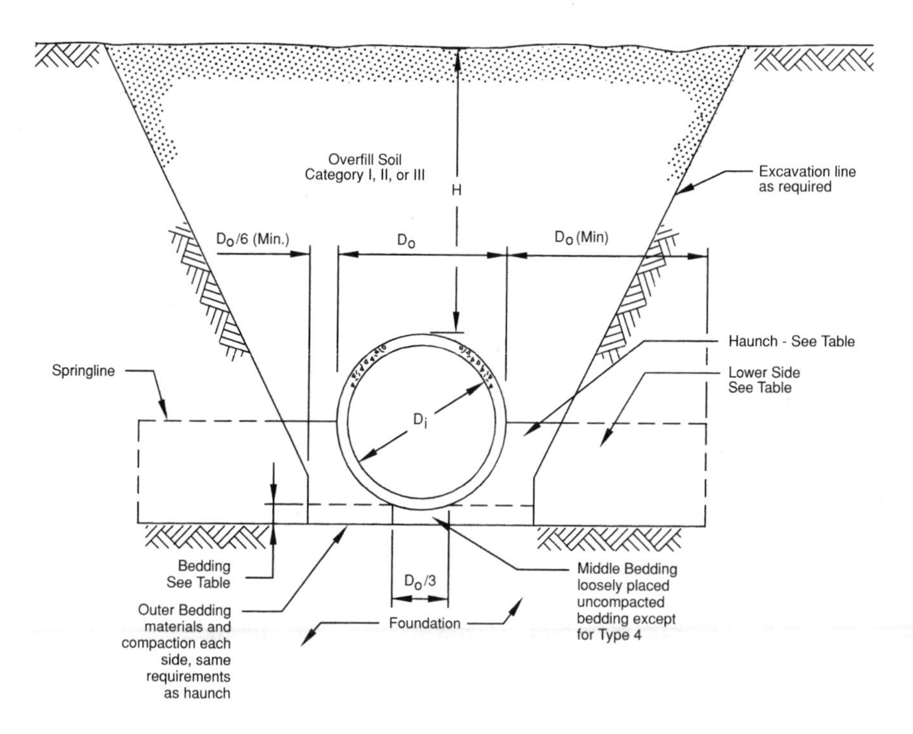

Figure 4.47 Standard Trench Installations

Table 4.19 Standard Trench Installations Soil and Minimum Compaction Requirements

Installation Type	Bedding Thickness	Haunch and Outer Bedding	Lower Side
Type 1	D_0/24 minimum, not less than 75 mm (3"). If rock foundation, use D_0/12 minimum, not less than 150 mm (6").	95% Category I	90% Category I, 95% Category II, or 100% Category III
Type 2	D_0/24 minimum, not less than 75 mm (3"). If rock foundation, use D_0/12 minimum, not less than 150 mm (6").	90% Category I or 95% Category II	85% Category I, 90% Category II, or 95% Category III
Type 3	D_0/24 minimum, not less than 75 mm (3"). If rock foundation, use D_0/12 minimum, not less than 150 mm (6") .	85% Category I, 90% Category II, or 95% Category III	85% Category I, 90% Category II, or 95% Category III
Type 4	D_0/24 minimum, not less than 75 mm (3"). If rock foundation, use D_0/12 minimum, not less than 150 mm (6").	No compaction required, except if Category III, use 85% Category III	No compaction required, except if Category III, use 85% Category III

Notes:

1. *Compaction and soil symbols - i.e. "95% Category I"- refers to Category I soil material with minimum standard Proctor compaction of 95%. See Table 4.17 for equivalent modified Proctor values.*
2. *The trench top elevation shall be no lower than 0.1 H below finished grade or, for roadways, its top shall be no lower than an elevation of 0.3 m (1') below the bottom of the pavement base material.*
3. *Soil in bedding and haunch zones shall be compacted to at least the same compaction as specified for the majority of soil in the backfill zone.*
4. *The trench width shall be wider than shown if required for adequate space to attain the specified compaction in the haunch and bedding zones.*
5. *For trench walls that are within 10 degrees of vertical, the compaction or firmness of the soil in the trench walls and lower side zone need not be considered.*
6. *For trench walls with greater than 10 degree slopes that consist of embankment, the lower side shall be compacted to at least the same compaction as specified for the soil in the backfill zone.*

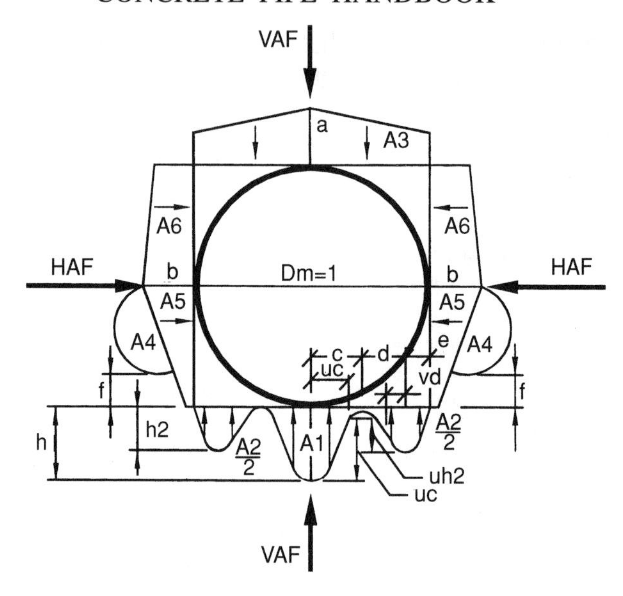

Figure 4.48 Arching Coefficients and Heger Earth Pressure Distributions

Installation Type	VAF	HAF	A1	A2	A3	A4	A5	A6	a	b	c	e	f	u	v
1	135	0.45	0.62	0.73	1.35	0.19	0.08	0.18	1.40	0.40	0.18	0.08	0.05	0.80	0.80
2	1.40	0.40	0.85	0.55	1.40	0.15	0.08	0.17	1.45	0.40	0.19	0.10	0.05	0.82	0.70
3	1.40	0.37	1.05	0.35	1.40	0.10	0.10	0.17	1.45	0.36	0.20	0.12	0.05	0.85	0.60
4	1.45	0.30	1.45	0.00	1.45	0.00	0.11	0.19	1.45	0.30	0.25	0.00	-	0.90	-

Notes:

1. *VAF and HAF are vertical and horizontal arching factors. These coefficients represent non-dimensional total vertical and horizontal loads on the pipe, respectively. The actual total vertical and horizontal loads are (VAF) X (PL) and (HAF) X (PL), respectively, where PL is the prism load.*

2. *PL, the prism load, is the weight of the column of earth cover over the pipe outside diameter and is calculated as:*

$$PL = w\left[\left(H + \frac{D_0\,(4 - \pi)}{96}\right)\right]\frac{D_0}{12}$$

3. *Coefficients A1 through A6 represent the integration of non-dimensional vertical and horizontal components of soil pressure under the indicated portions of the component pressure diagrams (i.e. the area under the component pressure diagrams). The pressures are assumed to vary*

either parabolically or linearly, as shown, with the non-dimensional magnitudes at governing points represented by h_1, h_2, uh_1, vh_2, a and b. Non-dimensional horizontal and vertical dimensions of component pressure regions are defined by c, d, e, vc, vd, and f coefficients.

4. *d is calculated as (0.5-c-e).*
   h_1 is calculated as (1.5A1) / (c) (1+u).
   h_2 is calculated as (1.5A2) / [(d) (1+v) + (2e)]

Bedding Factors

Although developed for the direct design method, the Standard Installations are readily applicable to and simplify the indirect design method, presented previously. The Standard Installations are easier to construct and provide more realistic designs than the historical B, C, and D beddings. Development of bedding factors for the Standard Installations, as presented in the following paragraphs, follows the concepts of reinforced concrete design theories. The basic definition of bedding factor is that it is the ratio of maximum moment in the three-edge bearing test to the maximum moment in the buried condition, when the vertical loads under each condition are equal:

$$Bf = \frac{M_{TEST}}{M_{FIELD}} \qquad [4.66]$$

where:
Bf = bedding factor
M_{TEST} = maximum moment in pipe wall under three-edge bearing test load, Newton-mm (inch-pounds)
M_{FIELD} = maximum moment in pipe wall under field loads, Newton-mm (inch-pounds)

Consequently, to evaluate the proper bedding factor relationship, the vertical load on the pipe for each condition must be equal, which occurs when the springline axial thrusts for both conditions are equal. In accordance with the laws of statics and equilibrium, M_{TEST} and M_{TFIELD} are:

$$M_{TEST} = [0.318N_{FS}] \text{ X } [D + t] \qquad [4.67]$$

$$M_{FIELD} = [M_{FI}] - [0.38tN_{FI}] - [0.125N_{FI}\text{ Xc}] \qquad [4.68]$$

where:

N_{FS} = axial thrust at the springline under a three-edge bearing test load, Newtons per meter (pounds per foot)
D = internal pipe diameter, mm (inches)
t = pipe wall thickness, mm (inches)
M_{FI} = moment at the invert under field loading, (Newton-mm)/m ((inch-pounds)/ft)

N_{FI} = axial thrust at the invert under field loads, Newtons per meter (pounds per foot)
c = thickness of concrete cover over the inner reinforcement, mm (inches)

Substituting equations 4.67 and 4.68 into equation 4.66:

$$Bf = \frac{[0.318 N_{FS}] \text{ X } [D+t]}{[M_{FI}] - [0.38 t N_{FI}] - [0.125 N_{FI} \text{X} c]} \qquad [4.69]$$

Using SIDD, bedding factors were determined for a range of pipe diameters and depths of burial. These calculations were based on one inch cover over the reinforcement, a moment arm of 0.875d between the resultant tensile and compressive forces, and a reinforcement diameter of 0.075t. Evaluations indicated that for A, B. and C pipe wall thicknesses, there was negligible variation in the bedding factor due to pipe wall thickness or the concrete cover, c, over the reinforcement. The resulting bedding factors are presented in Table 4.20.

Design Procedure

The usual six-step indirect design procedure may be followed.

1. Determination of Earth Load
2. Determination of Live Load
3. Selection of Standard Installation
4. Determination of Bedding Factor
5. Application of Factor of Safety
6. Selection of Pipe Strength

Table 4.20 Bedding Factors, Embankment Conditions, B_{fe}

Pipe Diameter	Standard Installation Type 1	Type 2	Type 3	Type 4
300 mm (12 in.)	4.4	3.2	2.5	1.7
600 mm (24 in.)	4.2	3.0	2.4	1.7
900 mm (36 in.)	4.0	2.9	2.3	1.7
1800 mm (72 in.)	3.8	2.8	2.2	1.7
3600 mm (144 in.)	3.6	2.8	2.2	1.7

Notes:

1. *For pipe diameters other than listed in Table 4.20, embankment condition factors, B_{fe} can be obtained by interpolation.*
2. *Bedding factors are based on the soils being placed with the minimum compaction specified in Tables 4.18 and 4.19 for each standard installation.*

The use of the Standard Installations and bedding factors simplifies the indirect design procedure. Changes to and use of each step of the design procedure are described in the following paragraphs.

Determination of Earth Load.

Concrete pipe can be installed in either an embankment or trench condition as discussed previously. The type of installation has a significant effect on the loads carried by the rigid pipe. In many cases, the pipe is installed in a positive projecting embankment condition, or a trench with a width significant enough that it should be considered a positive projecting embankment condition. As explained earlier in this chapter, the soil along side the pipe will settle more than the soil above the rigid pipe structure, thereby imposing additional load to the prism of soil directly above the pipe. With the Standard Installations, this additional load is accounted for by using a Vertical Arching Factor. This factor is multiplied by the prism load (weight of soil directly above the pipe) to give you the total load of soil on the pipe. Unlike the previous design method used for the Marston/Spangler beddings there is no need to assume a projection or settlement ratio. The Vertical Arching Factors for the Standard Installations as well as the equation for soil prism load are as shown in Figure 4.48 and repeated here.

Prism Load

$$PL = w\left[H + \frac{D_o(4 - \pi)}{8}\right] D_o \qquad [4.70]$$

w = soil unit weight, N/m^3 (lbs/ft^3)
H = height of fill, m (ft)
D = Diameter, m(ft)

Vertical Arching Factor (VAF)

Type 1	VAF = 1.35
Type 2	VAF = 1.40
Type 3	VAF = 1.40
Type 4	VAF = 1.45

In narrow or moderate trench width conditions, the resulting earth load is equal to the weight of the material above the pipe minus the shearing (frictional) forces on the sides of the trench. Since the new installed bedding material will settle more than the existing soil on the sides of the trench, the friction along the trench walls will relieve the pipe of some of its soil burden. The Vertical Arching Factors in this case will be less than one. Generic Vertical Arching Factors for the Standard Installations under trench conditions have not been developed, and still need to be computed as explained on pages 4-2 through 4-7 of this handbook.

Determination of Live Load.

A variety of live loads may be applied on the ground or paved surface above the pipe, including truck, railroad, aircraft, etc. The theories used to determine the distribution of these loads through the soil onto the pipe are explained elsewhere in this chapter.

Table 4.21 Relationship of ACPA Design Manual Soil Designations to SIDD Soil Designations

ACPA Design Manual Soils	SIDD Soils
Sand and Gravel	CATEGORY I
Saturated Top Soil	CATEGORY II
Ordinary Clay and Saturated Clay	CATEGORY III

Note:

1. *The USCS and AASHTO soil classifications equivalent to the generic soil types designated in the Standard Installations are presented in Table 4.17.*

Selection of Standard Installation

The selection of a Standard Installation for a project should be based on an evaluation of the quality of construction and inspection anticipated. A Type 1 Standard Installation requires the highest construction quality and degree of inspection. Required construction quality is reduced for a Type 2 Standard Installation, and reduced further for a Type 3 Standard Installation. A Type 4 Standard Installation requires virtually no construction or quality inspection. Consequently, a Type 4 Standard Installation will require a higher strength pipe, and a Type I Standard Installation will require a lower strength pipe for the same depth of installation.

Determination of Bedding Factor

Table 4.20 presents embankment bedding factors, B_{fe}, for each of the Standard Installations.

For trench installations as discussed previously, experience indicates that active lateral pressure increases as trench width increases to the transition width, provided the sidefill is compacted. A SIDD parameter study of the Standard Installations indicates the bedding factors are constant for all pipe diameters under conditions of zero lateral pressure on the pipe. These bedding factors exist at the interface of the pipewall and the soil and are called minimum bedding factors, B_{fo}, to differentiate them from the fixed bedding factors developed by Spangler. Table 4.22 presents the minimum bedding factors.

Table 4.22 Trench Minimum Bedding Factors, B_{fo}

Standard Installation	Minimum Bedding Factor, B_{fo}
Type1	2.3
Type 2	1.9
Type 3	1.7
Type 4	1.5

Note:

1. *Bedding factors are based on the soils being placed with the minimum compaction specified in Figures 4.46 and 4.47 for each Standard Installation.*
2. *For pipe installed in trenches dug in previously constructed embankment, the load and the bedding factor should be determined as an embankment condition unless the backfill placed over the pipe is of lesser compaction than the embankment.*

A conservative linear variation is assumed between the minimum bedding factor and the bedding factor for the embankment condition, which begins at transition width.

The equation for the variable trench bedding factor, modified for use with the Standard Installations, is:

$$B_{fv} = \frac{[B_{fe} - B_{fo}][B_d - B_c]}{[B_{dt} - B_c]} + B_{fo} \qquad [4.71]$$

where:

B_c = outside horizontal span of pipe, mm (feet)
B_d = trench width at top of pipe, mm (feet)
B_{dt} = transition width at top of pipe, mm (feet)
B_{fe} = bedding factor, embankment
B_{fo} = minimum bedding factor, trench
B_{fv} = variable bedding factor, trench

The Design Manual tables (Tables 13 through 42) for trench earth loads present transition width values which are sufficiently accurate for use as values for B_{dt} in the preceding equation.

For pipe installed with 1.95 m (6.5 ft) or less of overfill and subjected to truck loads, the controlling maximum moment may be at the crown rather than the invert. Consequently, the use of an earth load bedding factor may produce unconservative designs. Crown and invert moments of pipe for a range of diameters and burial depths subjected to HS20 truck live loadings were evaluated. Also evaluated, was the effect of bedding angle and live load angle (width of loading on the pipe). When HS20 live loadings are encountered to a significant value, the live load bedding factors, B_{fLL},, presented in Table 4.23A or B are satisfactory for a Type 4 Standard Installation and become increasingly conservative for Types 3, 2, and 1. Limitations on B_{fLL} are discussed in the section on Selection of Pipe Strength.

Application of Factor of Safety

The indirect design method for concrete pipe is similar to the common working stress method of steel design, which employs a factor of safety between yield stress and the desired working stress. In the indirect method, the factor of safety is defined as the relationship between the ultimate strength D-load and the 0.3 mm (0.01-inch) crack D-load. This relationship is specified in the ASTM Standards C 76 and

C 655 on concrete pipe and discussed earlier in this chapter. The relationship between ultimate D-load and 0.3 mm (0.01-inch) crack D-load is 1.5 for 0.3 mm (0.01 inch) crack D-loads of 2,000 or less; 1.25 for 0.3 mm (0.01 inch) crack D-loads of 3,000 or more; and a linear reduction from 1.5 to 1.25 for 0.3 mm (0.01inch) crack D-loads between more than 2,000 and less than 3,000. Therefore, a factor of safety of 1.0 should be applied if the 0.3 mm (0.01 inch) crack strength is used as the design criterion rather than the ultimate strength. The 0.3 mm (0.01 inch) crack width is an arbitrarily chosen test criterion and not a criteria for field performance or service limit.

Section of Pipe Strength

The required three-edge bearing strength of circular reinforced concrete pipe expressed as D-load:

$$D\text{–}load = \left[\frac{W_E}{B_{fe}} + \frac{W_L}{B_{fLL}} \right] \left[\frac{F.S.}{D} \right] \qquad [4.72]$$

where:

W_E = earth load on pipe, kg/m (pounds per linear foot)
W_L = live load on pipe, kg/m (pounds per linear foot)
B_{fe} = earth load bedding factor
B_{fLL} = live load bedding factor
F.S. = factor of safety
D = pipe diameter, mm (feet)

When an HS20 truck live loading is applied to the pipe, use the live load bedding factor, B_{fLL}, as indicated in Equation 4.72, unless the earth load bedding factor, B_{fe}, is of lesser values in which case, use the lower B_{fe} value in place of B_{fLL}. For example, with Type 4 Standard Installation of a 1200 mm (48 inch) diameter pipe under 0.3 m (1.0 feet) of fill, the factors used would be B_{fe}= 1.7 and B_{fLL} = 1.5; but under 0.75 m (2.5 feet) or greater fill, the factors used would be B_{fe}= 1.7 and B_{fLL}, = 1.7 rather than 2.2. For trench installations with trench widths less than transition width, B_{fLL} would be compared to the variable trench bedding factor, B_{fv}.

The use of the six-step indirect design method is illustrated by examples on the following pages.

Table 4.23A Bedding Factors, B_{fLL}, for HS20 Live Loadings

Fill Height, Ft.	Pipe Diamenter, Inches										
	12	24	36	48	60	72	84	96	108	120	144
0.5	2.2	1.7	1.4	1.3	1.3	1.1	1.1	1.1	1.1	1.1	1.1
1.0	2.2	2.2	1.7	1.5	1.4	1.3	1.3	1.3	1.1	1.1	1.1
1.5	2.2	2.2	2.1	1.8	1.5	1.4	1 4	1 3	1.3	1.3	1.1
2.0	2.2	2.2	2.2	2.0	1.8	1.5	1.5	1.4	1 4	1.3	1.3
2.5	2.2	2.2	2.2	2.2	2.0	1.8	1.7	1.5	1.4	1.4	1 .3
3.0	2.2	2.2	2.2	2.2	2.2	2.2	1 8	1 7	1 5	1 5	1 4
3.5	2.2	2 2	2.2	2.2	2 2	2.2	1 9	1.8	1.7	1.5	1.4
4.0	2.2	2.2	2.2	2 2	2.2	2.2	2.1	1.9	1.8	1.7	1.5
4.5	2.2	2.2	2.2	2.2	2.2	2.2	2.2	2.0	1 9	1.8	1.7
5.0	2 2	2.2	2 2	2.2	2 2	2 2	2 2	2.2	2 0	1.9	1.8
5.5	2.2	2.2	2.2	2.2	2.2	2 2	2.2	2.2	2.2	2.0	1.9
6.0	2 2	2.2	2 2	2 2	2.2	2 2	2.2	2.2	2 2	2.1	2.0
6.5	2.2	2.2	2.2	2.2	2.2	2.2	2.2	2.2	2.2	2.2	2.2

Note:

1. *For pipe diameters other than listed in Table 7A, B_{fLL} values can be obtained by interpolation.*

Table 4.23B Bedding Factors, B_{fLL}, for HS20 Live Loadings (Metric)

Fill Height, Meters	Pipe Diamenter, Inches										
	300	600	900	1200	1500	1800	2100	2400	2700	3000	3600
0.15	2.2	1.7	1.4	1.3	1.3	1.1	1.1	1.1	1.1	1.1	1.1
0.30	2.2	2.2	1.7	1.5	1.4	1.3	1.3	1.3	1.1	1.1	1.1
0.45	2.2	2.2	2.1	1.8	1.5	1.4	1 4	1 3	1.3	1.3	1.1
0.60	2.2	2.2	2.2	2.0	1.8	1.5	1.5	1.4	1 4	1.3	1.3
0.75	2.2	2.2	2.2	2.2	2.0	1.8	1.7	1.5	1.4	1.4	1 .3
0.90	2.2	2.2	2.2	2.2	2.2	2.2	1 8	1 7	1 5	1 5	1 4
1.05	2.2	2 2	2.2	2.2	2 2	2.2	1 9	1.8	1.7	1.5	1.4
1.20	2.2	2.2	2.2	2 2	2.2	2.2	2.1	1.9	1.8	1.7	1.5
1.35	2.2	2.2	2.2	2.2	2.2	2.2	2.2	2.0	1 9	1.8	1.7
1.50	2 2	2.2	2 2	2.2	2 2	2 2	2 2	2.2	2 0	1.9	1.8
1.65	2.2	2.2	2.2	2.2	2.2	2 2	2.2	2.2	2.2	2.0	1.9
1.80	2 2	2.2	2 2	2 2	2.2	2 2	2.2	2.2	2 2	2.1	2.0
1.95	2.2	2.2	2.2	2.2	2.2	2.2	2.2	2.2	2.2	2.2	2.2

Note:

1. *For pipe diameters other than listed in Table 7B, B_{fLL} values can be obtained by interpolation.*

Example 1:

Given: A 600 mm (24-inch) diameter circular concrete pipe is to be installed in a positive projecting embankment condition with 10.6 m (35 feet) of 1,922 kg/m^3 (120 pounds per cubic foot) soil overfill.

Find: The required pipe strength in terms of the 0.3 mm (0.01-inch) crack D-load for each of the Standard Installation Types.

Solution:

1. Determination of Earth Load (W_E)

Calculations are shown for the Type 4 Standard Installation, but results for all types are tabulated in the Answer section of this example.

Find the Soil Prism Load

$w = 120$ lbs/ft3
$H = 35$ ft
$D_O = 30$ in
$D_O = 2.5$ ft

$$PL = w\left[\left[H + \frac{D_o \bullet (4-\pi)}{8}\right]\right] \bullet D_o$$

PL = 10,580 lbs/ft

Find the Prism Load in Metric Units

$\rho = 1922$ kg/m^3
$w = \rho \bullet 9.81$
$w = 1.885 \bullet 10^4$ N/m^3
$H = 10.6$ m
$D. = 0.75$ m

$$PL = w\left[\left[H + \frac{D \bullet (4-\pi)}{8}\right]\right] \bullet D.$$

PL = 151,000 N/m

For a Type 4 Installation the Vertical Arching Factor is:

VAF = 1.45

Therefore, the soil load is:

$W_E = VAF \bullet PL$ $\quad$ $W_E = VAF \bullet PL$

$W_E = 15,340$ lbs/ft or $W_E = 219,000$ N/m

2. Determination of Live Load (W_L)

From the Design Manual Table 45, live load is negligible at a depth of 10.6 m (35 feet).

3. Selection of Standard Installation

Calculations for a Type 4 Standard Installation will be shown, but results for all the Standard Installations will be tabulated.

4. Determination of Bedding Factor

From Table 4.20, a bedding factor for the embankment condition, B_{fe}, of 1.7 is obtained for a Type 4 Standard Installation. Since live load is considered negligible under 10.6 m (35 feet) of overfill, a live load bedding factor is not required.

5. **Application of Factor of Safety (F.S.)**
A factor of safety of 1.0 will be used since the D-load for 0.3 mm (0.01-inch) crack strength is desired.

6. **Selection of Pipe Strength**
Equation 4.72 is used to determine the required D-load strength:

$$D_{0.3mm} = \left[\frac{W_E}{B_{fe}} + \frac{W_L}{B_{fLL}}\right] X \left[\frac{F.S.}{D}\right]$$

$$D_{0.3mm} = \left[\frac{219{,}000}{1.7} + 0\right] X \left[\frac{1.0}{600}\right]$$

$$D_{0.3mm} = 215 \text{ N/m/mm}$$

or

$$D_{0.01} = \left[\frac{W_E}{B_{fe}} + \frac{W_L}{B_{fLL}}\right] X \left[\frac{F.S.}{D}\right]$$

$$D_{0.01} = \left[\frac{15{,}340}{1.7} + 0\right] X \left[\frac{1.0}{2}\right]$$

$$D_{0.01} = 4{,}512 \text{ lbs/ft/ft}$$

Answers - Example 1

Installation Type	W_E	B_{fe}	$D_{0.01}$
Type 1	14,280	4.2	1,826
Type 2	14,810	3.0	2,557
Type 3	14,810	2.4	3,196
Type 4	15,340	1.7	4,512
Type 1 (S.I. units)	203,900	4.2	81
Type 2 (S.I. units)	211,400	3.0	117
Type 3 (S.I. units)	211,400	2.4	147
Type 4 (S.I. units)	219,000	1.7	215

Example 2:

Given: A 900 mm (36-inch) diameter, wall B concrete pipe is to be installed in a 1.5 m (5 foot) wide, B_d, trench with 1.5 m (5 feet) of 1,922 kg/m^3 (120 pounds per cubic foot) of sand and gravel overfill.

Find: The required pipe strength in terms of 0.3 mm (0.01-inch) crack D-load for each of the Standard Installation Types.

Solution:

1. Determination of Earth Load (W_E)

Calculations are shown for the Type 1 Standard Installation, and results for all Types of Standard Installations are tabulated in the Answers section of this example. From Design Manual Table 24A, the earth load based on 1,600 kg (100 pounds per cubic foot) overfill of sand and gravel material is 3,175 kg/m (2,129 pounds per linear foot). Increase the earth load by 20 percent for the required 1,922 kg/m^3 (120 pounds per cubic foot) overfill.

$W_E = 1.20x3,175=3,810kg/m$

or

$W_E = 1.20 \text{ x } 2,129 = 2,560$ pounds per linear foot

2. Determination of Live Load (W_L)

From Design Manual Table 45, the live load is 1,000 kg/m (670 pounds per linear foot) at a depth of 1.5 m (5 feet).

3. Selection of Standard Installation

All of the Standard Installations are evaluated and tabulated for this example to illustrate the effects of each.

4. Determination of Bedding Factor

From Table 4.20, an embankment condition bedding factor, B_{fe}, of 4.0 is obtained for a Standard Installation Type 1. From Design Manual Table 24A, a transition width, B_{dt}, is 1.7 m (5.6 feet). For a 900 mm (36 inch) diameter, wall B concrete pipe, the outside diameter, B_c, is 1.1 m (44 inches). From Table 4.22, a trench minimum bedding factor, B_{fo}, of 2.3 is obtained. Equation 4.71 is used to determine the trench variable bedding factor, B_{fv}:

$$B_{fv} = \frac{[B_{fe} - B_{fo}] \text{ X } [B_d - B_c]}{[B_{dt} - B_c]} + B_{fo}$$

$$B_{fv} = \frac{[4.0 - 2.3] \text{ X } [1.5 - 1.1]}{[1.7 - 1.1]} + 2.3$$

$B_{fv} = 3.4$

From Table 4.23, a live load bedding factor, B_{fLL}, of 2.2 is obtained. Since 2.2 is less than B_{fv}, a B_{fLL} of 2.2 will be used.

5. Application of Factor of Safety (F.S.)

A factor of safety of 1.0 will be used since the D-load for 0.3 mm (0.01-inch) crack strength is desired.

6. Selection of Pipe Strength

Equation 4.72 is used to determine the required D-load:

$$D_{0.3mm} = \left[\frac{W_E}{B_{fV}} + \frac{W_L}{B_{fLL}} \right] X \left[\frac{F.S.}{D} \right]$$

$$D_{0.3mm} = \left[\frac{37{,}388}{3.4} + \frac{9{,}810}{2.2} \right] X \left[\frac{1.0}{900} \right]$$

$D_{0.3mm} = 17.1$

or

$$D_{0.01} = \left[\frac{W_E}{B_{fv}} + \frac{W_L}{B_{fLL}} \right] X \left[\frac{F.S.}{D} \right]$$

$$D_{0.01} = \left[\frac{2{,}560}{3.4} + \frac{670}{2.2} \right] X \left[\frac{1.0}{3} \right]$$

$D_{0.01} = 350$

Answers - Example 2

Installation Type	W_E	B_{fe}	B_{fo}	B_{fv}	W_L	B_{fLL}	$D_{0.01}$
Type 1	2,560	4.0	2.3	3.4	670	2.2	350
Type 2	2,560	2.9	1.9	2.6	670	2.2	430
Type 3	2,560	2.3	1.7	2.1	670	2.1	510
Type 4	2,560	1.7	1.5	1.6	670	1.6	670
Type 1 (S.I. units)	3,810	4.0	2.3	3.4	1000	2.2	17.1
Type 2 (S.I. units)	3,810	2.9	1.9	2.6	1000	2.2	21.1
Type 3 (S.I. units)	3,810	2.3	1.7	2.1	1000	2.1	25.0
Type 4 (S.I. units)	3,810	1.7	1.5	1.6	1000	1.6	32.2

REFERENCES

1. "Analysis of Loads and Supporting Strengths and Principles of Design for Highway Culverts," M. G. Spangler, Proceedings, Volume 26, Highway Research Board, 1946.
2. "Buried Pipelines, A Manual of Structural Design and Installation," N. W. H. Clarke, MacLaren and Sons, London, United Kingdom, 1968.
3. "Computenzed Design of Precast Reinforced Concrete Box Culverts," R. W. Latona, F. J. Heger and M. Bealey, Research Record Number 443, Transportation Research Board, 1973.
4. "Concrete Cradles for Large Pipe Conduits," W. J. Schtick and J. W. Johnson, Bulletin Number 80, Iowa State College, 1926.
5. "Concrete Pipe and the Soil-Structure System," Special Technical Publication Number 630, American Society for Testing and Materials, 1976.
6. "Concrete Pipe Design Manual," American Concrete Pipe Association, 1978.
7. "Concrete Pipe Handbook," American Concrete Pipe Association, 1959.
8. "Design and Construction of Sanitary and Storm Sewers," Manual of Practice Number 37, American Society of Civil Engineers, and Manual of Practice Number 9, Water Pollution Control Federation, 1974.
9. "Effects of Cracks in Reinforced Concrete Culvert Pipe," Concrete Pipe Information No. 7, American Concrete Pipe Association, 1977.
10. "Effects of Cracks in Reinforced Concrete Sanitary Sewer Pipe," Concrete Pipe Information No. 6, American Concrete Pipe Association, 1977.
11. "Factors of Safety in the Design of Buried Pipelines," M. G. Spangler, Research Record Number 269, Highway Research Board, 1969.
12. "Highway Live Loads on Circular Concrete Pipe," Design Data Number 1, American Concrete Pipe Association, 1977.
13. "Loads on Negative-Projecting Conduits," W. J. Schtick, Proceedings, Volume 31, Highway Research Board, 1952.
14. "Loads on Pipe in Wide Ditches," W. J. Schtick, Bulletin 108, Iowa State College, 1932.
15. "Negative Projecting Conduits," M. G. Spangler and W. J. Schlick, Report Number 14, Iowa State College, 1953.
16. "A Practical Application of the Imperfect Ditch Method of Construction," M. G. Spangler, Proceedings, Volume 37, Highway Research Board, 1958.
17. "Precast Concrete Box Sections," Concrete Pipe Information No. 5, American Concrete Pipe Association, 1973.
18. "Soil Engineering," M. G. Spangler and R. L. Hardy, Intext Educational Publishers, 1973.
19. "Soils Engineering," M. G. Spangler, International Textbook Company, 1966.
20. "Standard Tests for Drain Tile and Sewer Pipe," A. Marston, Proceedings, American Society for Testing and Materials, 1911.
21. "Stresses in Concrete Pavements Computed by Theoretical Analysis," H. M. Westergaard, Public Roads, April, 1926.
22. "Structural Analysis and Design of Pipe Culverts," R. J. Krizek, R. A. Parmelee, J. N. Kay and H. A. Elnaggar, National Cooperative Highway Research Program Report Number 116, Highway Research Board, 1971.
23. "Structural Characteristics of Reinforced Concrete Elliptical Sewer and Culvert Pipe," Harold V. Swanson and Mason D. Reed, Highway Research Record Number 56, Highway Research Board, 1964.
24. "Supporting Strength of Drain Tile and Sewer Pipe Under Different Pipe-Laying Conditions," W. J. Schtick, Bulletin Number 57, Iowa State College, 1920.
25. "The Supporting Strength of Rigid Pipe Culverts," M. G. Spangler, Bulletin 112, Iowa State College, 1933.
26. "The Supporting Strength of Sewer Pipe in Ditches and Methods of Testing Sewer Pipe in Laboratories to Determine Their Ordinary Supporting Strength," A. Marston, W. J. Schlick and H. F. Clemmer, Bulletin Number 47, Iowa State College. 1917.
27. "Test Program for Evaluating Design Method and Standard Designs for Precast Concrete Box Culverts with Welded Wire Fabric Reinforcing," M. R. Boring, F. J. Heger and M. Bealey, Transportation Research Record Number 518, Transportation Research Board, 1974.
28. "The Theory of External Loads on Closed Conduits in the Light of the Latest Experiments," A. Marston, Bulletin 96, Iowa State College, 1930.
29. "A Theory of Loads on Negative Projecting Conduits," M. G. Spangler, Proceedings, Volume 30, Highway Research Board, 1950.
30. "The Theory of Loads on Pipes in Ditches and Tests of Cement and Clay Drain Tile and Sewer Pipe," A. Marston and A. O. Anderson, Bulletin 31, Iowa State College, 1913.

31. "The Theory of Stresses and Displacements in Layered Systems and Applications to the Design of Airport Runways," Donald M. Burmister, Proceedings, Volume 23, Highway Research Board, 1943.
32. "A Treatise on the Mathematical Theory of Elasticity, ' E. H. Love, Dover Publications, 1927.
33. "Vertical Pressure on Culverts Under Wheel Loads on Concrete Pavement Slabs." Portland Cement Association, 1944.
34. "Bedding Factors —Trench Installations," Design Data No. 38, American Concrete Pipe Association, 1980.
35. "CP Information No. 12, Lateral Pressures and Bedding Factors", American Concrete Pipe Association, 1991.
36. "Design Methods for Reinforced Concrete Pipe and Box Sections", F.J. Heger and T.J. McGrath, Simpson, Gumpertz and Heger, American Concrete Pipe Association, 1982.

CHAPTER 5

SUPPLEMENTAL DESIGN CONSIDERATIONS AND PROCEDURES

Structural strength and hydraulic capacity are the principal design concerns for pipelines, and the theory and design procedures for these are provided in *Chapters 3* and *4*. Supplemental design considerations and procedures encountered can include:

- Joints
- Manholes
- Special fittings
- Curved alignment
- Buoyancy
- Fire resistance
- Energy dissipators
- Tunneling and jacking
- Metrication

JOINTS

The function of a pipeline generally determines performance requirements of the pipe joints. For example, the permissible infiltration or exfiltration in a sanitary sewer is usually less than that for a storm drain or culvert.

Concrete pipe manufacturers have developed joint designs to provide the following performance characteristics:

- Resistance to infiltration of groundwater and backfill material
- Resistance to exfiltration of sewage or storm water
- Control of leakage due to internal or external pressure
- Flexibility to accommodate lateral deflection or longitudinal movement
- Pipeline continuity and smooth flow line
- Infiltration of groundwater for subsurface drainage
- Ease of installation

The actual field performance of pipe joints depends primarily upon the inherent characteristics of the joint, conditions of service, and the care with which the joint is installed. The designer of a pipeline need specify only the joint performance requirements, and the pipe manufacturer will supply pipe with a joint to meet the specifications.

JOINT CONFIGURATIONS

Concrete pipe joints, *Figures 5.1, 5.2* and *5.3*, are manufactured in three basic shapes:

- Bell and spigot
- Tongue and groove
- Modified tongue and groove

Circular concrete pipe are manufactured in all three configurations, while noncircular concrete pipe shapes normally utilize the tongue and groove joint.

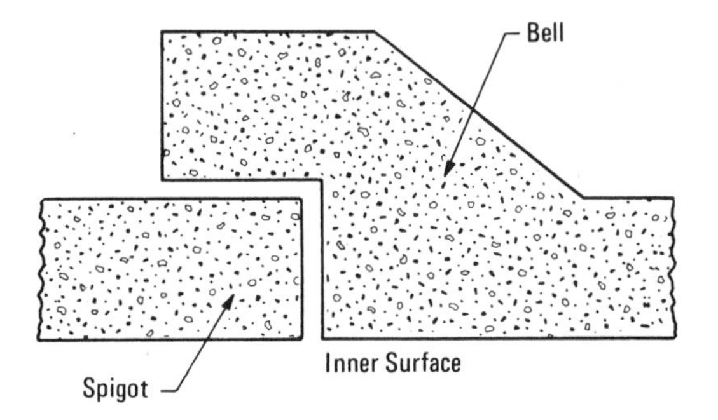

Figure 5.1. Bell and Spigot Joint.

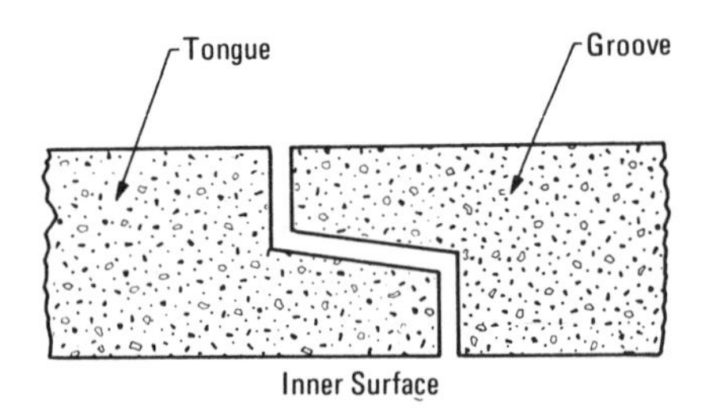

Figure 5.2. Tongue and Groove Joint.

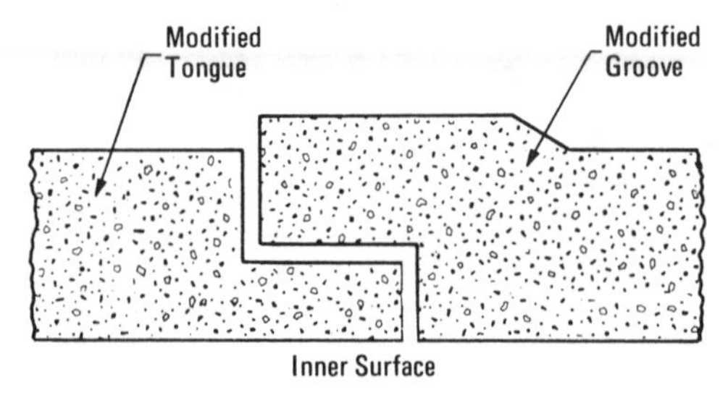

Figure 5.3. Modified Tongue and Groove Joint.

JOINT GASKETS AND SEALANTS

Gaskets and **sealants** vary in cost and inherent performance characteristics, but field performance is always dependent upon installation procedures. The most common are:

- Rubber, attached or separate
- Mastic, bulk or preformed
- Cement, paste or mortar
- External bands, cement mortar or rubber

Rubber

Rubber gaskets are of three basic types; **flat gaskets** which may be cemented to the pipe tongue or spigot, **O-ring gaskets** which are recessed in a groove on the pipe tongue or spigot and then confined by the bell or groove after the joint is completed, and **roll-on gaskets** which are placed around the tongue or spigot and rolled into position as the joint is assembled. Except for the roll-on gasket, the gasket and joint surfaces should be lubricated with a lubricant recommended by the manufacturer.

Mastic

Mastic sealants consist of bitumen and inert mineral fillers. The sealant is applied to the tongue or spigot and inserted into the bell or groove. A sufficient amount of sealant should be used to fill the annular joint space with some squeeze out.

Cement

Cement sealants consist of **cement paste** made with 1 to 1 1/2 gallons of water per cubic foot of portland cement or **cement mortar** made with a mixture of 1 part portland cement to 2 parts sand and 6 to 7 gallons of water per cubic foot of cement. The joint surfaces should be clean and soaked with water immediately before the joint is made. A layer of cement paste or mortar is placed in the lower portion of the bell or groove of the installed pipe and on the upper portion of the tongue or spigot of the pipe section to be installed. The tongue or spigot is then inserted into the bell or groove of the installed pipe until the sealant material is squeezed out on the interior or exterior surfaces. The annular joint space should be completely filled and the abutting joint sections flush and even.

External Bands

Cement mortar bands are placed around the exterior of the pipe joint. A slight depression is excavated in the bedding material to enable the mortar to be placed underneath the pipe and the external joint surface cleaned and soaked with water. Canvas or cloth **diapers** are used to hold the mortar as it is placed. Backfill material should be placed around the pipe immediately after the mortar band is in place.

Combination **rubber-mastic bands** are available to seal joints of non-circular concrete pipe. The bands are installed on the exterior surface of the pipe joint.

JOINT DETAILS

The concrete pipe industry utilizes a number of joint details to satisfy a broad range of performance requirements. These joints can vary in cost, as well as in performance characteristics, and field performance is dependent upon proper installation procedures. Consultation with local concrete pipe manufacturers will provide information on the availability, performance and cost of the various joints.

Rubber Gasket Joints

Concrete surfaces with or without shoulders on the tongue or the groove utilize compression type rubber gaskets, *Figure 5.4.* Although there is wide variation in joint dimensions and gasket cross section for this joint, most are manufactured in conformity with ASTM C 443. This joint is primarily intended for use with pipe manufactured to meet the requirements of ASTM C 14, C 76 or C 655 and may be used with either bell and spigot or tongue and groove pipe.

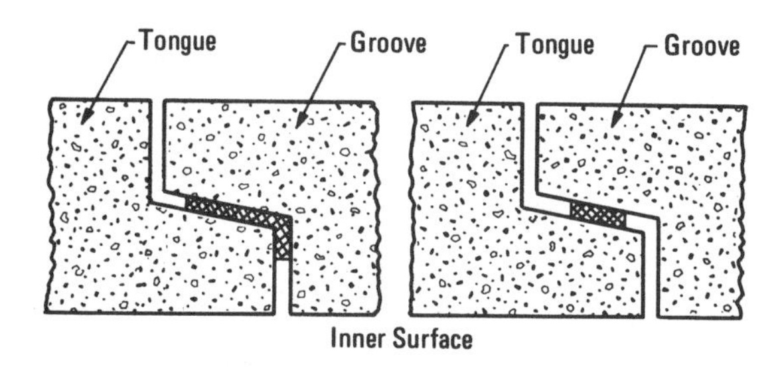

Figure 5.4. Joints with Compression Type Rubber Gaskets.

Concrete surfaces with opposing shoulders on both the bell and spigot use O-ring, circular cross section, rubber gaskets as shown in *Figure 5.5.* Basically designed for low pressure capability, these joints are frequently used for irrigation lines, waterlines, sewer force mains, and gravity or low head sewer lines where infiltration or exfiltration is a factor in the design. Meeting all the requirements of ASTM C 443, these type joints are also employed with pipe meeting the requirements of ASTM C 361. They provide good inherent watertightness in both the straight and deflected positions.

Concrete surfaces with a groove on the spigot for an O-ring rubber gasket, *Figure 5.6,* are referred to as a confined O-ring joint. These are designed for low pressure capabilities and used for irrigation lines, water lines, sewer force mains, and sewers where infiltration or exfiltration is a factor. This joint provides excellent watertightness in both the straight and deflected positions and meets the joint requirements of ASTM C 443 or C 361.

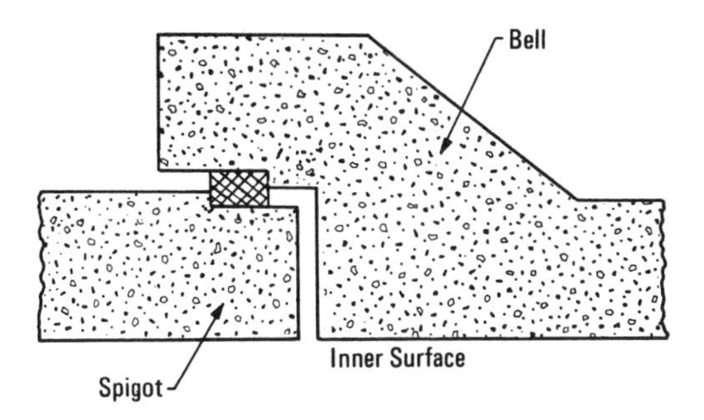

Figure 5.5. Opposing Shoulder with O-ring.

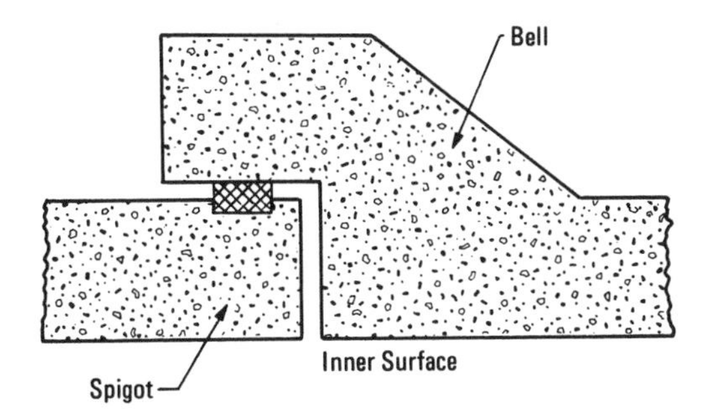

Figure 5.6. Spigot Groove with Confined O-ring.

Mastic or Mortar Joints

The performance of these joints, *Figure 5.7,* depends exclusively upon the workmanship of the contractor. Joints employing mortar joint sealants are rigid, and any deflection or movement after installation may cause cracks and leakage. Mastic sealants provide a degree of flexibility without impairing watertightness. Mastic and mortar joints are not generally recommended for any internal or external head conditions if leakage is an important consideration.

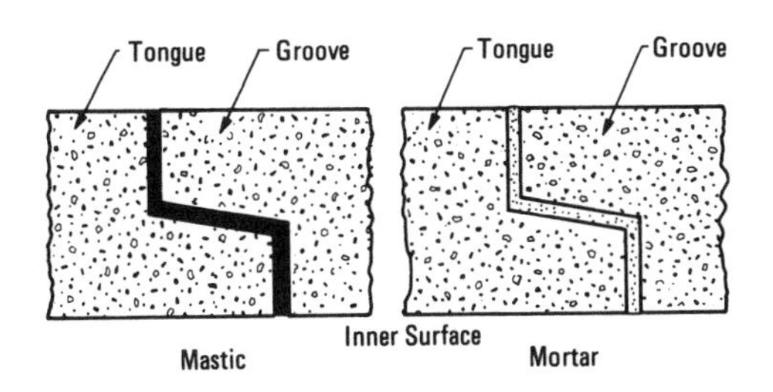

Figure 5.7. Joints Sealed with Mastic or Mortar.

External Band Joints

Another jointing system utilizes the external rubber and mastic sealing band conforming to ASTM C 877, *Figure 5.8,* or cement mortar joints. Generally limited to noncircular pipe with tongue and groove configurations, external sealing bands have provided good results in resisting external heads of the magnitude normally encountered in sewer construction.

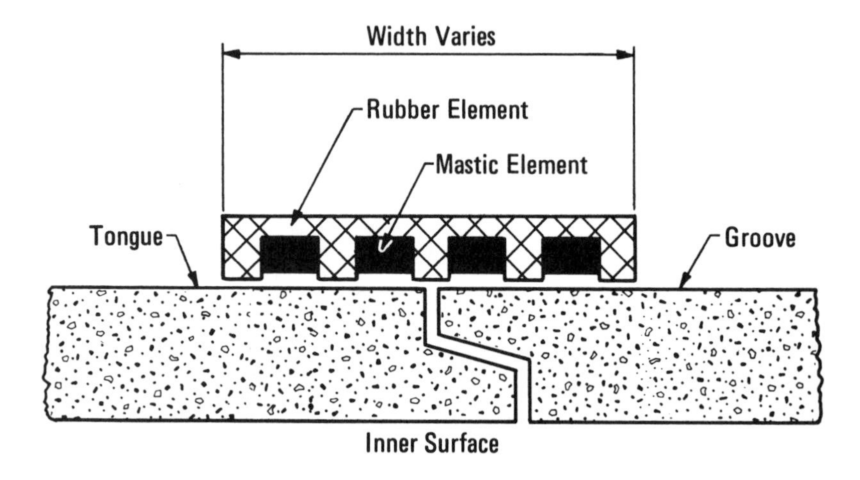

Figure 5.8. External Sealing Band.

Steel End Ring Joints

Steel end rings incorporating a groove on the spigot for an O-ring rubber gasket, *Figure 5.9,* are basically a high pressure joint for use in water transmission and distribution lines. This joint is also used for irrigation lines, sewer force mains, and sewers where infiltration or exfiltration is a factor. This joint meets the requirements of ASTM C 443 or C 361.

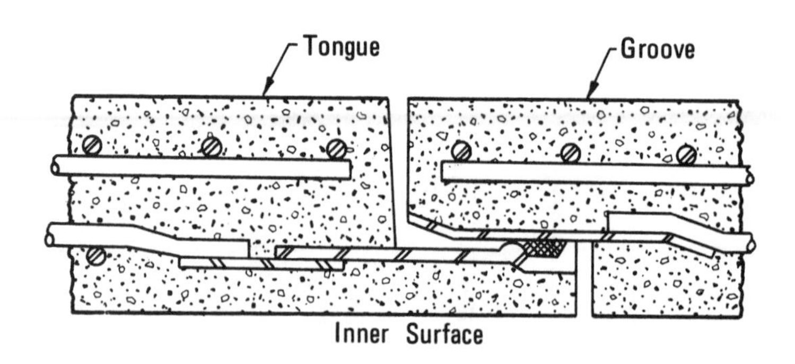

Figure 5.9. Steel End Ring with Confined O-ring.

Illustration 5.1
Lubricating O-ring joint.

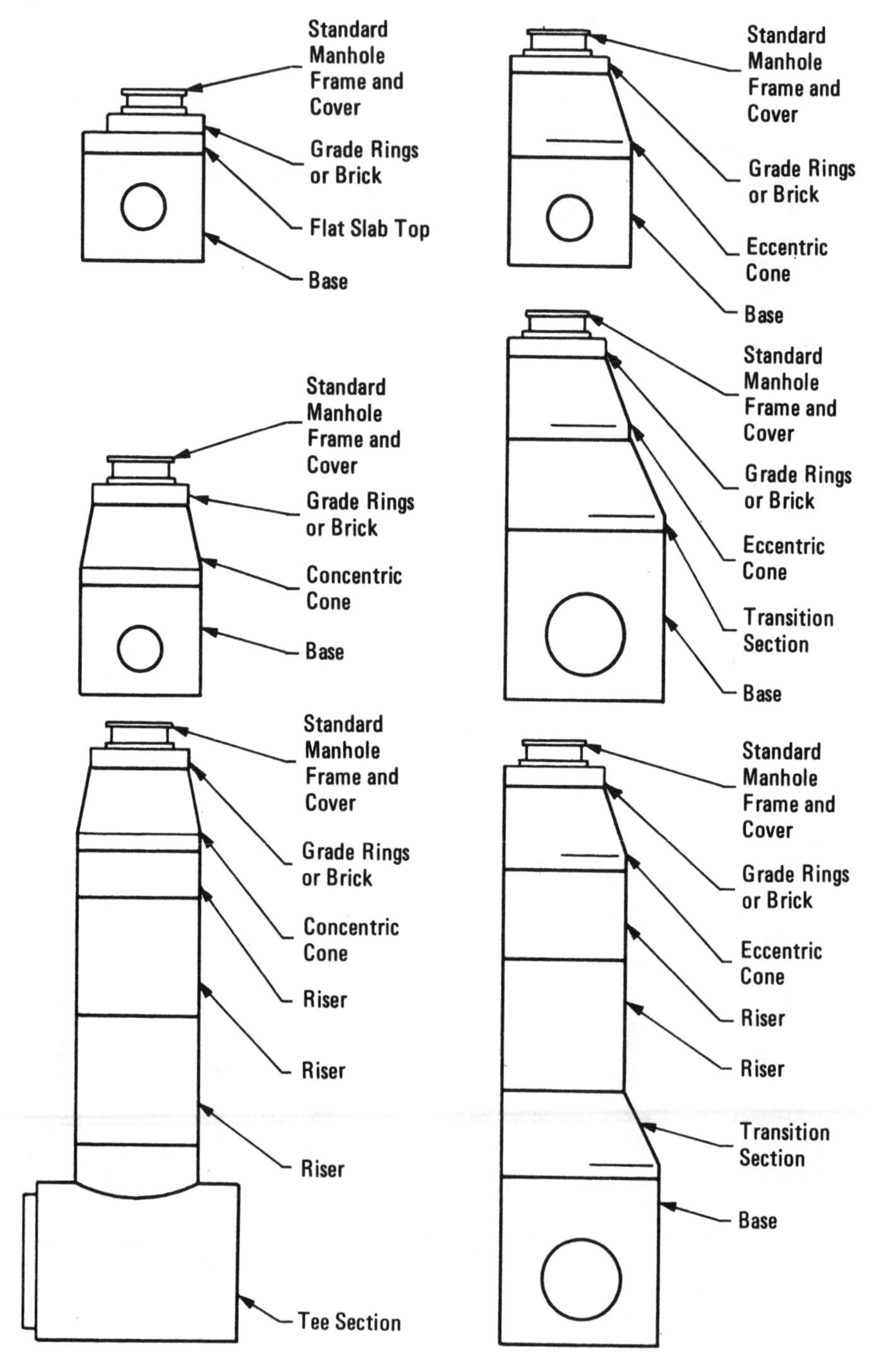

Figure 5.10. Precast Concrete Manhole Assemblies.

PRECAST CONCRETE MANHOLES

The proper functioning of a sewer system also depends on the performance of its appurtenances, with manholes being one of the most important. Precast concrete manholes offer significant savings in labor cost over cast-in-place concrete, masonry and brick manholes and are universally accepted. Precast reinforced concrete manhole sections are available throughout the United States and Canada and are generally manufactured in accordance with ASTM C 478.

The typical precast concrete manhole, *Figure 5.10,* consists of **riser sections, top section, grade rings** and, in many cases, a **precast base section** or **tee section.** Riser sections are of uniform circular cross section, usually 48 inches in diameter, but are also manufactured in larger diameters. Precast manholes are constructed with an **eccentric cone, concentric cone,** or **flat slab top.** The cone sections effect the transition from the inside diameter of the riser sections to the specified diameter of the top opening, *Figure 5.11.* Flat slab tops are normally used for very shallow manholes and consist of a reinforced slab at least six inches thick for risers up to 48 inches in diameter and eight inches thick for larger sizes. The slab has an access opening and rests on top of the riser sections.

Precast grade rings, which are placed on top of either the cone section or flat slab top, are used for close adjustment of top elevation. Cast iron manhole cover assemblies are normally placed on top of the grade rings. The manhole assembly is available with or without steps in the walls of the sections.

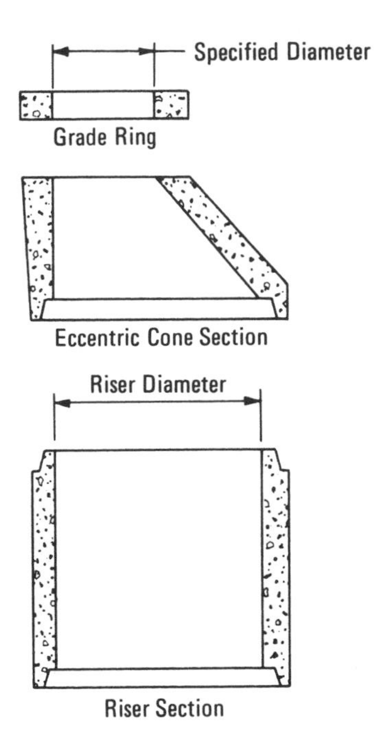

Figure 5.11. Cone Transition from Riser Diameter to Specified Diameter

MAXIMUM DEPTH

Reinforcement is primarily to resist handling stresses incurred before and during installation. Such stresses are more severe than those encountered in the vertically installed manhole. In normal installations, the intensity of the earth loads transmitted to the manhole risers is a fraction of the intensity of the vertical pressure.

To determine the allowable depth to which precast concrete manholes can be placed, it is necessary to consider the forces acting on the manhole. The most severe loading condition occurs when the water table is at the same elevation as the surface. The resultant forces acting on the manhole periphery are illustrated in *Figure 5.12*. The total force is composed of the active lateral earth force and the hydrostatic force. Both forces are uniformly distributed around the periphery of the manhole and impart no

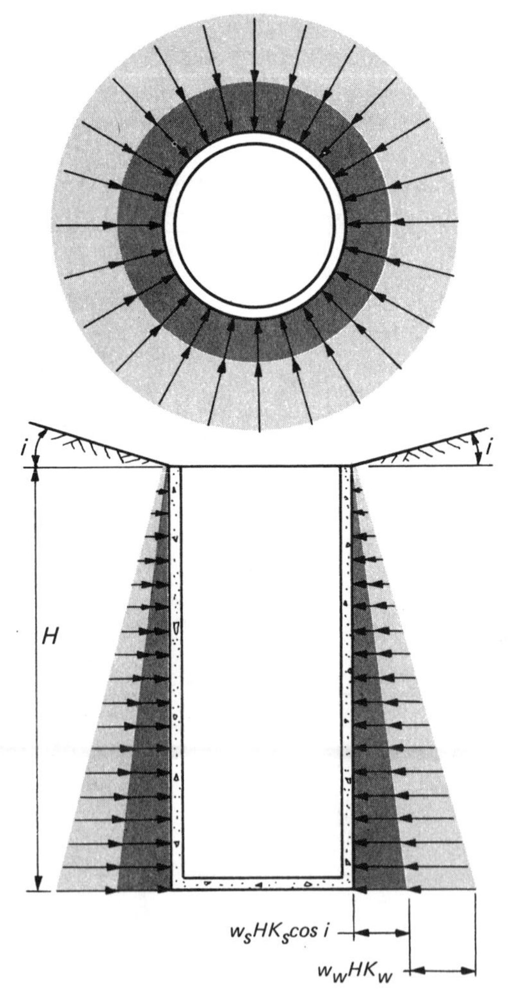

Figure 5.12. Forces Acting on Manhole.

bending moment to the manhole section. The lateral earth pressure and hydrostatic pressure at any depth within the soil mass is:

$$p = w_s H K_s \cos i + w_w H K_w \tag{5.1}$$

Where: p = total lateral earth and hydrostatic pressure, pounds per square foot
w_s = effective unit weight of the backfill material, pounds per cubic foot
H = depth of manhole, feet
K_s = conjugate ratio for soil, Rankine's lateral pressure ratio
i = angle between backfill surface and the horizontal, degrees
w_w = unit weight of water, 62.4 pounds per cubic foot
K_w = conjugate ratio for water (1.0)

In most cases i equals 0, therefore, cos i equals 1 and *Equation 5.1* reduces to:

$$p = w_s H K_s + 62.4H \tag{5.2}$$

K_s is further defined as:

$$K_s = \frac{\sqrt{\mu^2 + 1} - \mu}{\sqrt{\mu^2 + 1} + \mu} \tag{5.3}$$

Where: $\mu = \tan \phi$ = coefficient of friction for the soil
ϕ = angle of internal friction of the soil, degrees

Table 5.1 lists the normal range of the angle of internal friction for various types of soils.

For design purposes, the average value of ϕ is usually assumed to be 30 degrees. Since the tangent of 30 degrees is equal to $\sqrt{3}/3$, substitution of this value in *Equation 5.3* results in K_s equal to 0.33.

If the saturated unit weight of clay backfill is 120 pounds per cubic foot, the effective or submerged unit weight, w_s, is equal to 120 minus 62.4 or

Table 5.1. Angle of Internal Friction for Commonly Used Backfill Materials.

Backfill Material	Angle of Internal Friction, ϕ, Degrees
Plastic Clay	0 – 10
Wet, Fine Sand	15 – 30
Dry Sand	25 – 40
Gravel	30 – 40
Compact Clay	25 – 45

57.6 pounds per cubic foot due to the buoyant effect of water. Substituting the effective unit weight of 57.6 pounds per cubic foot for w_s and 0.33 for K_S, *Equation 5.2* reduces to:

$$p = (57.6H \times 0.33) + 62.4H$$

$$p = 81.6H \tag{5.4}$$

Except for the section of the manhole where the sewer line is connected, the pressure, p, will act on the manhole equally around the periphery and therefore place the section in pure compression without introducing bending moments in the concrete section in the horizontal plane. Considering one-half of the section, the compressive stress in the manhole is:

$$s = \frac{pD}{2t} \tag{5.5}$$

Where: s = unit compressive stress in ring, pounds per square foot
D = diameter of the manhole, feet
t = thickness of the manhole wall, feet

If the minimum specified wall thickness is used, the wall thickness would be one-twelfth the manhole diameter. Substituting this wall thickness and the value for p from *Equation 5.4*, and converting to pounds per square inch, *Equation 5.5* reduces to:

$$s = \frac{81.6\ HD}{2\ \frac{D}{12} \times 144}$$

$$s = 3.4H \tag{5.6}$$

The American Concrete Institute Building Code specifies allowable compressive stress as 45 percent of the ultimate compressive concrete strength. This design requirement is primarily intended for cast-in-place concrete and its application to precast and pretested concrete is considered conservative. Using 45 percent of the minimum specified compressive strength of 4000 pounds per square inch, the allowable compressive stress is 1800 pounds per square inch. Substituting this value in *Equation 5.6* and solving for H:

$$1800 = 3.4H$$

$$H = 530 \text{ feet}$$

The maximum allowable depth of a typical precast concrete manhole is in excess of 500 feet or, for all practical purposes, unlimited. Therefore, the critical or limiting factor for manhole depth is the supporting strength of the base structure or the resistance to crushing of the ends of the riser sections. The vertical force acting on the base or ends of the riser sections is dependent on the relative settlement of the adjacent soil mass and does not lend itself to precise analysis. However, if only the weight of the manhole riser and top were considered, with an allowable crushing stress of 1800 pounds per square inch, a theoretical height of over 1700 feet could be allowed. Even the most conservative approach would conclude that up to several hundred feet could be safely supported by the riser sections without end crushing, assuming provision is made for uniform bearing.

RISER JOINTS

Manhole risers and tops employ a number of joint types, such as mortar, mastic, and rubber gaskets for sealing purposes. Consideration should be given to manhole depth, the presence of groundwater, and the minimum allowable leakage rates in the selection of specific joint requirements.

PIPE TO MANHOLE CONNECTIONS

Differential settlement between the manhole and pipe may sometimes occur because of differences in bedding, vertical load and backfill settlement. If the pipe is rigidly connected to the manhole, differential settlement can induce excessive shear forces resulting in circumferential cracks in the pipe or shear failure.

Resilient connectors accommodate differential settlements and minimize the effect of shear forces. Resilient connectors also minimize leakage by providing a positive seal between manhole wall and connector and between the connector and pipe. The seal between the manhole wall and connector is made by mechanical means or by casting the connector integrally with the manhole wall. The seal between the connector and pipe is made by mechanical means or by compression of resilient material against the outside wall of the pipe. Resilient connectors are available throughout North America and are generally manufactured in accordance with ASTM C 923.

SPECIAL FITTINGS

Imaginative engineering and manufacturing capability are the only limits to possible types of special fittings. **Radius pipe** and **bends** are two examples of precast concrete pipe fittings for specific purposes. Other examples are **tees, wyes, reducers** etc., as shown in the illustrations. Special fittings often provide an economical solution to difficult engineering problems.

TEES

Tees are utilized to effect the junction of two pipelines without a manhole or junction chamber. The centerline of the intersecting pipe of a **standard tee** enters the base pipe perpendicular to, and intersects the centerline of, the base pipe, *Figure 5.13*. The centerline of the intersecting pipe of an **offset tee** is also perpendicular to the base pipe centerline but does not intersect it, *Figure 5.14*. Offset tees are frequently utilized as a manhole base for large diameter pipelines. A **cross** is a double tee.

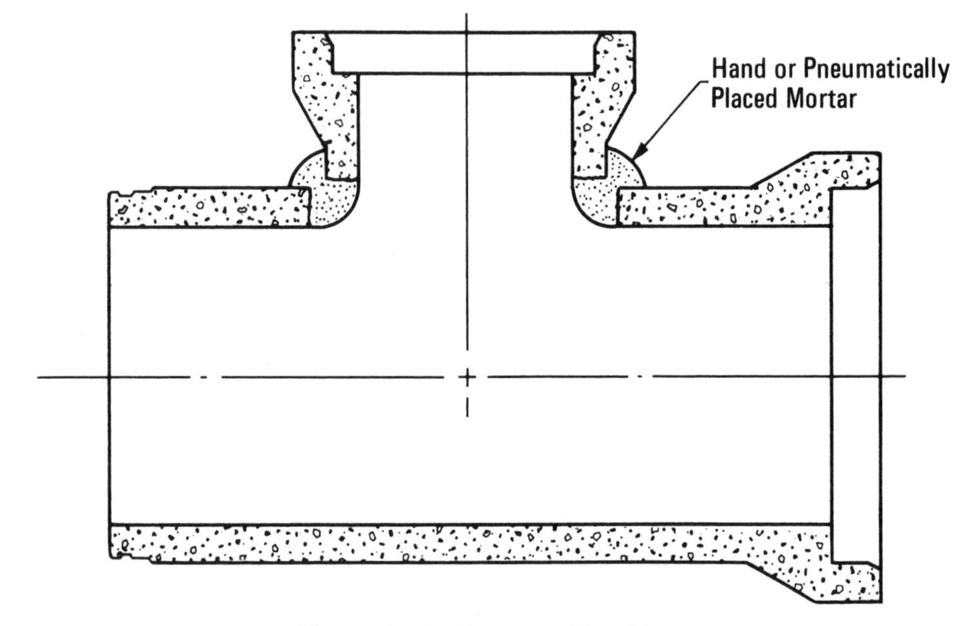

Figure 5.13. Concrete Pipe Tee.

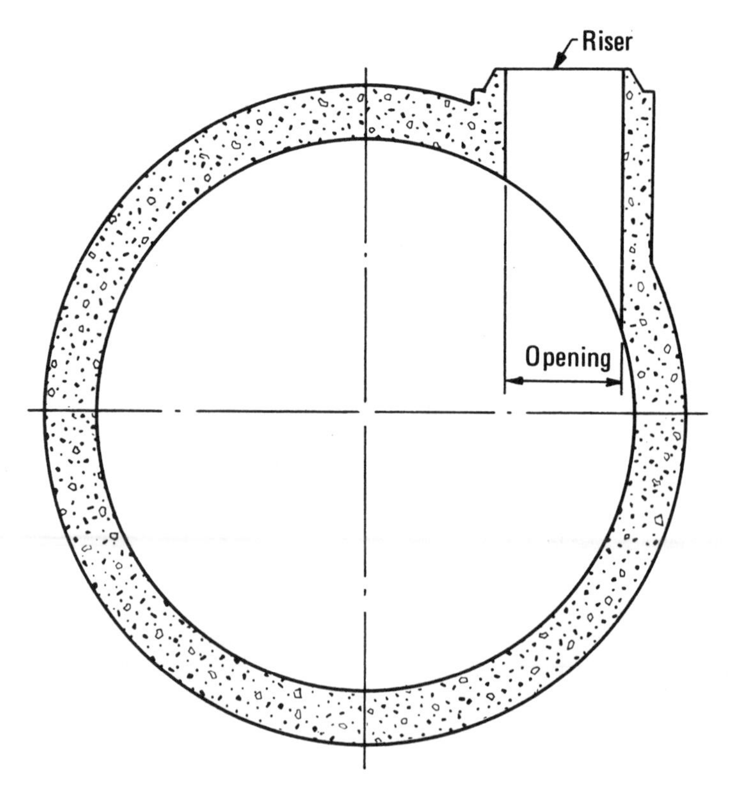

Figure 5.14. Offset Manhole Tee.

Illustration 5.2
Concrete pipe offset manhole tees.

WYES

Wyes are similar to tees except the centerline of the intersecting pipe intersects the centerline of the base pipe at an acute angle, *Figure 5.15*. Wyes are also utilized to effect the junction of two pipelines without the necessity of a manhole or junction chamber. Wyes are commonly used to connect building sewers or house laterals to a sewer main.

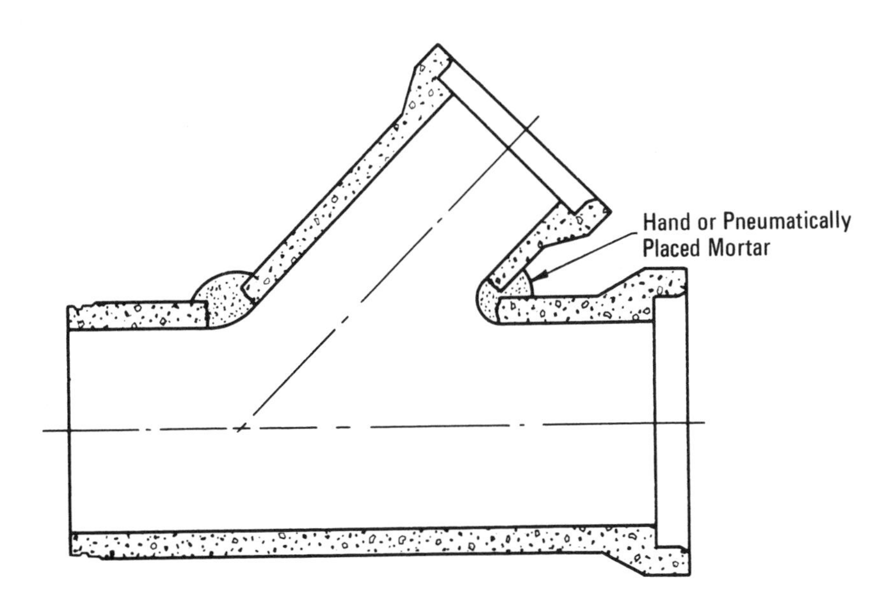

Figure 5.15. Concrete Pipe Wye.

REDUCERS

Reducers provide an in-line reduction or increase in pipe size, *Figure 5.16*. A reducer might be used in a pipeline with a constant flow where an increase in slope would permit the use of a smaller size pipe. An increase in size might be required immediately preceding the junction of two pipelines at a tee or wye where anticipated increased flow necessitates a larger size pipe.

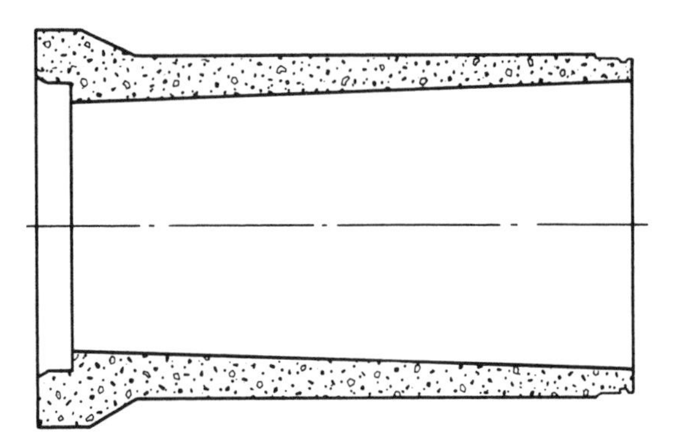

Figure 5.16. Concrete Pipe Reducer.

Illustration 5.3
Concrete pipe wye and reducer.

CURVED ALIGNMENT

Change of direction in sewers is usually accomplished at manhole structures. Grade and alignment changes in concrete pipelines can be incorporated through the use of **deflected straight pipe, radius pipe** or **bends.**

When concrete pipe is to be installed in a curved alignment, local concrete pipe manufacturers should be consulted regarding manufacturing and installation feasibility. Many manufacturers have standardized joint configurations and deflections for specific radii and economies may be realized by using standard pipe.

DEFLECTED STRAIGHT PIPE

When concrete pipe is installed in a straight alignment and the joints are in a **home,** or normal, position, the joint space or distance between the ends of adjacent pipe sections is essentially uniform around the periphery of the pipe. Starting from this home position any joint may be opened the maximum permissible amount on one side while the other side remains in the home position, *Figure 5.17*. The difference between the home and opened joint space is generally designated as the **pull.** The maximum permissible pull must be limited to that opening which will provide satisfactory joint performance. This varies for different joint configurations and is best obtained from the pipe manufacturer.

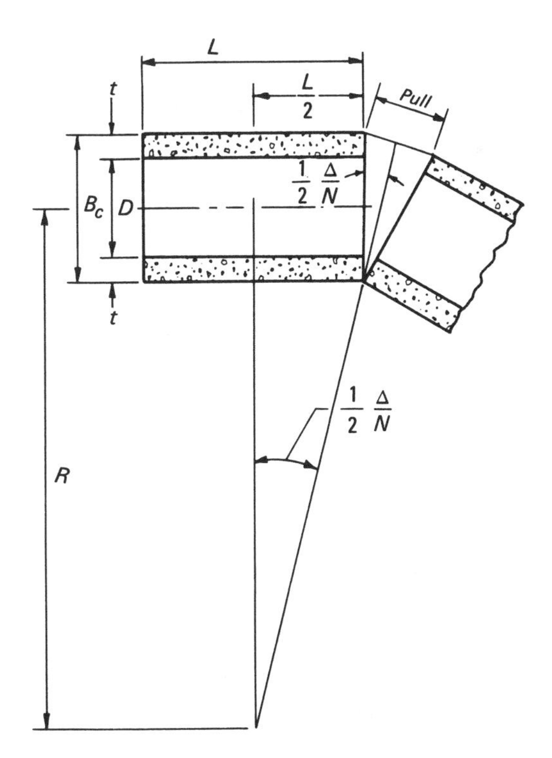

Figure 5.17. Deflection Angle Geometry for Deflected Straight Pipe.

The **radius of curvature** which may be obtained by this method is a function of the diameter of the pipe, length of the pipe sections, and the deflection angle per joint. The radius of curvature is computed by the equation:

$$R = \frac{L}{2\left(\tan \frac{1}{2}\frac{\Delta}{N}\right)} \tag{5.7}$$

Where: R = radius of curvature, feet
L = laying length of pipe sections measured along the centerline, feet
Δ = total deflection angle of curve, degrees
N = number of pipe with pulled joints
Δ/N = total deflection angle of each pipe, degrees

One-half the deflection angle, $\Delta/2N$ is defined as:

$$\frac{1}{2}\frac{\Delta}{N} = \sin^{-1}\frac{Pull}{2(D + 2t)} = \sin^{-1}\frac{Pull}{2B_c} \tag{5.8}$$

Where: $Pull$ = joint opening, inches
D = inside pipe diameter, inches
t = wall thickness, inches
B_c = outside pipe diameter, inches

When concrete pipe is installed in a curved alignment by deflecting straight pipe, *Figure 5.18,* the **point of curve,** P.C., is at the midpoint of the last undeflected pipe section, and the **point of tangent,** P.T., is at the midpoint of the last deflected or pulled pipe.

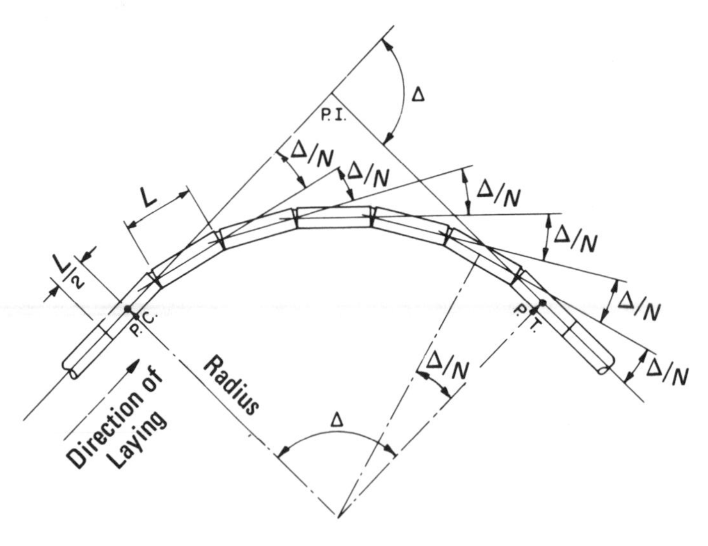

Figure 5.18. Curved Alignment Using Deflected Straight Pipe.

RADIUS PIPE

Radius pipe, also referred to as **beveled** or **mitered** pipe, incorporates the deflection angle into the pipe joint. The pipe is manufactured by shortening one side of the pipe and the amount of shortening or **drop** for any given pipe is dependent on manufacturing capability. Because of the possibility of greater deflection angles per joint, sharper curvature with correspondingly shorter radii can be obtained with radius pipe than with deflected straight pipe. The radius of curvature which may be obtained by radius pipe is a function of the deflection angle per joint, diameter of the pipe, length of pipe sections and wall thickness.

When concrete pipe is installed in a curved alignment using radius pipe, *Figure 5.19,* projections of the joints do not converge at a common point but are tangent to a common circle of diameter equal to the length of pipe sections. The point of curve is at the midpoint of the last straight pipe and the point of tangent is one half of the standard pipe length back from the

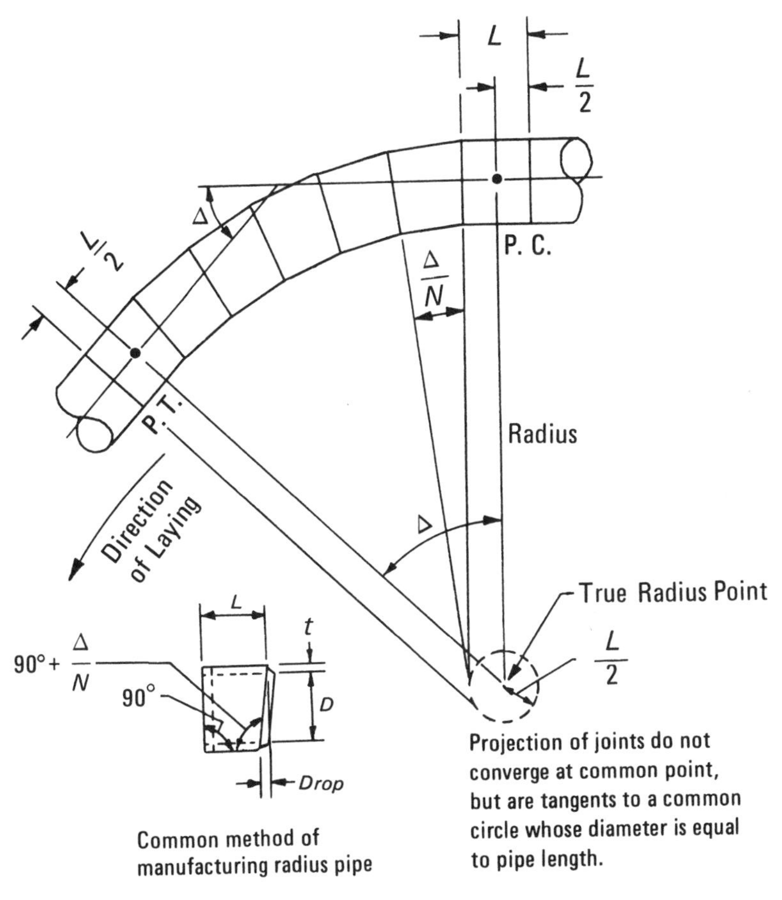

Figure 5.19. Curved Alignment Using Radius Pipe.

straight end of the last radius pipe. The required number of radius pipe is equal to the **length of the circular curve,** *L.C.*, in feet divided by the centerline length of the radius pipe, *L* minus 1/2 drop. Where possible, minor modifications in the radius are made so this quotient will be a whole number.

Referring to *Figure 5.20*:

$$\tan \frac{\Delta}{N} = \frac{L}{R + \left(\frac{D}{2} + t\right)} \tag{5.9}$$

$$\tan \frac{\Delta}{N} = \frac{Drop}{D + 2t} \tag{5.10}$$

Where:
- N = number of radius pipe
- L = standard laying length of pipe being used, feet
- R = radius of curvature, feet
- D = inside diameter of the pipe, feet
- t = wall thickness of the pipe, feet
- Δ = total deflection angle of curve, degrees
- Δ/N = total deflection angle of each pipe, degrees
- $Drop$ = length pipe is shortened on one side, feet

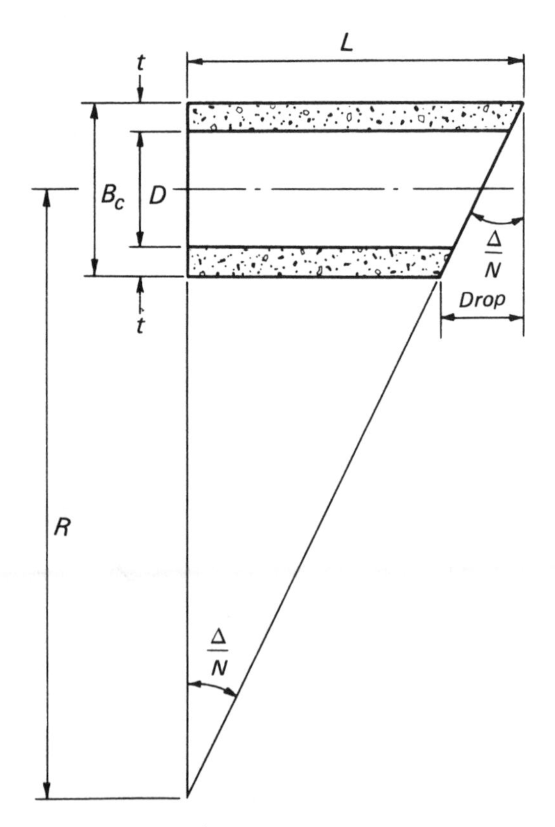

Figure 5.20. Deflection Angle Geometry for Radius Pipe.

Solving *Equation 5.9* for the radius, R:

$$R = \frac{L}{\tan \frac{\Delta}{N}} - \left(\frac{D}{2} + t\right) \qquad (5.11)$$

Substituting for $\tan \Delta/N$ from *Equation 5.10*:

$$R = \frac{L(D + 2t)}{Drop} - \left(\frac{D}{2} + t\right) \qquad (5.12)$$

Since $D + 2t = B_c$:

$$R = B_c\left(\frac{L}{Drop} - \frac{1}{2}\right) \qquad (5.13)$$

Where: B_c = outside diameter of the pipe, feet
$Drop$ = length pipe is shortened on one side, feet

Figure 5.21 is based on *Equation 5.13* and presents R/B_c ratios for drops from one inch through 15 inches, and for commonly manufactured pipe lengths. Since the maximum permissible drop for any given pipe is dependent on manufacturing capability, it is essential to coordinate the the design of radius pipe with the pipe manufacturer. Many manufacturers have standardized joint configurations and deflections for specific radii and economies may be realized by utilizing standard radius pipe.

Minimum radius of curvature obtained from the equations for deflected straight pipe or radius pipe are approximate, but are within a range of accuracy that will enable the pipe to be readily installed in correct alignment. A reasonable amount of field adjustment is possible for radius pipe by pulling the joints in the same manner as with deflected straight pipe.

Illustration 5.4
Curved alignment with concrete radius pipe.

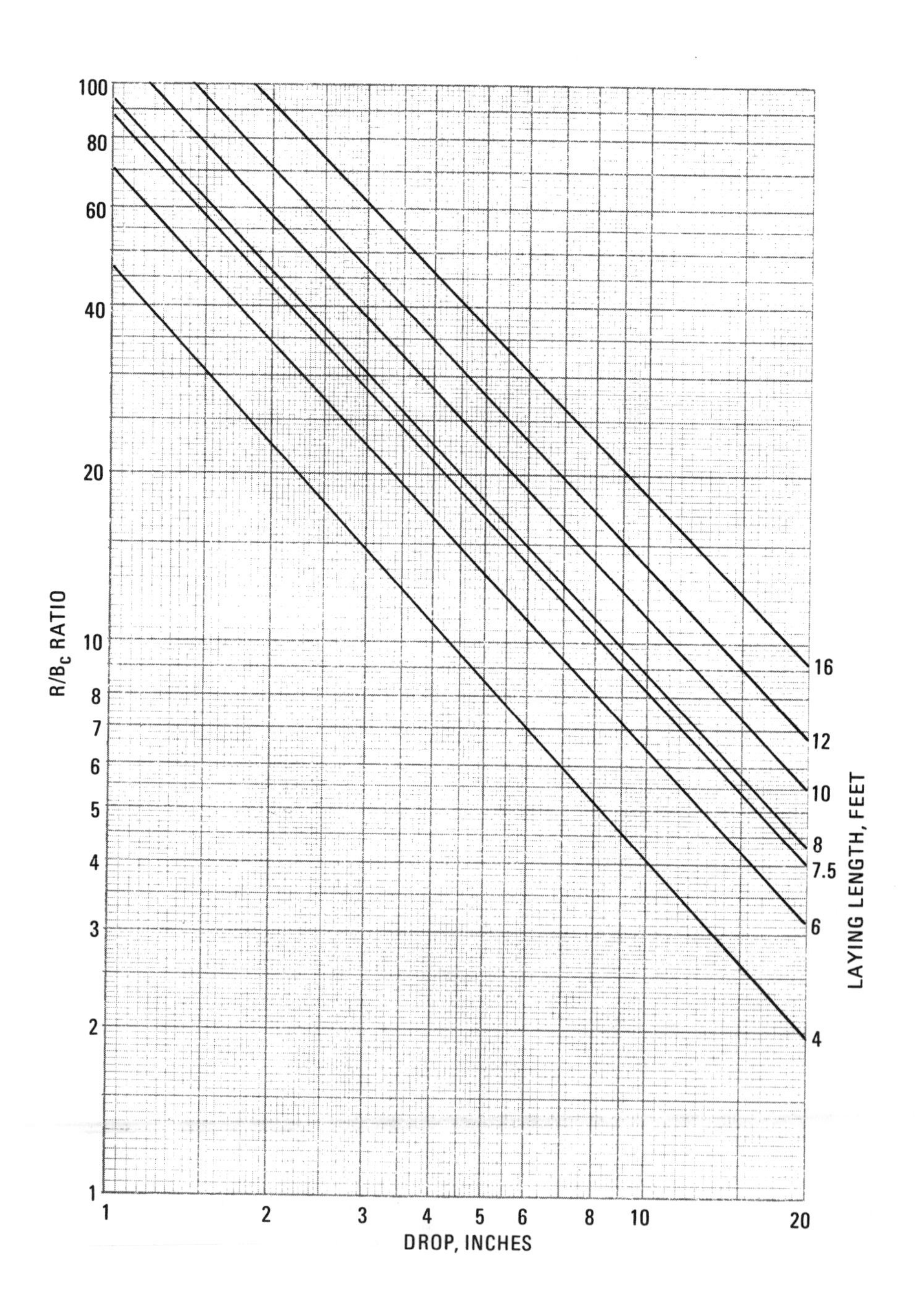

Figure 5.21. Radius of Curvature for Radius Pipe.

BENDS

Special sections can be used for extremely short radius curves which cannot be negotiated with either deflected straight pipe or with conventional radius pipe. Bends, or elbows can be manufactured to meet any required deflection angle and some manufacturers produce standard bends which provide given angular deflection per section, *Figure 5.22*.

Sharper curves can be handled by using special short lengths of radius pipe rather than standard lengths. These may be computed in accordance with the methods discussed for radius pipe. Certain types of manufacturing processes permit the use of a drop joint on both ends of the pipe, which effectively doubles the deflection.

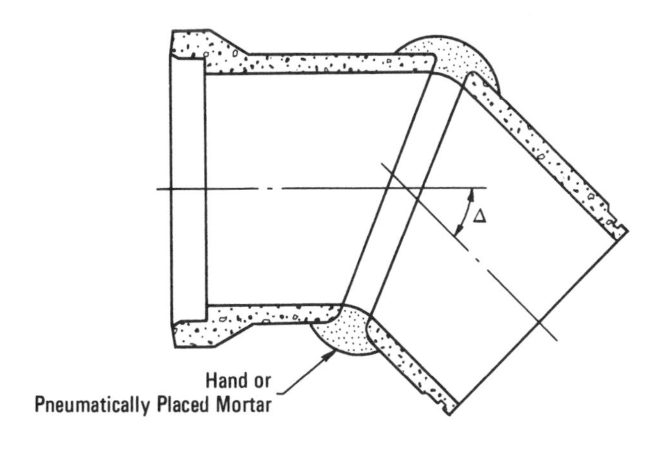

Figure 5.22. Concrete Pipe Bend.

Illustration 5.5
Concrete pipe bends.

EXAMPLE

Given: A 42-inch diameter concrete pipe storm sewer is to be installed on curved alignment corresponding to the roadway curvature. The pipe will be manufactured in 7.5-foot lengths with a 4.5-inch wall thickness. The curve data for the pipe centerline is:

P.I. = 50 + 00
P.C. = 49 + 29.6
P.T. = 50 + 63.1
Δ = 45 degrees
R = 170 feet

Find: The required pull per joint for deflected straight pipe and the required drop for radius pipe.

Solution: The required pull per joint can be determined by solving *Equation 5.7* to obtain a value for 1/2 (Δ/N):

$$R = \frac{L}{2\left(\tan \frac{1}{2}\frac{\Delta}{N}\right)}$$

$$\frac{1}{2}\frac{\Delta}{N} = \tan^{-1}\frac{L}{2R}$$

$$= \tan^{-1}\frac{7.5}{2(170)}$$

$$= 1.2636 \text{ degrees}$$

Substituting in Equation 5.8:

$$\frac{1}{2}\frac{\Delta}{N} = \sin^{-1}\frac{Pull}{2(D + 2t)}$$

$$1.2636 = \sin^{-1}\frac{Pull}{2[42 + (2 \times 4.5)]}$$

$$Pull = 2.25 \text{ inches}$$

The required drop per joint for radius pipe can be determined by solving *Equation 5.13* for *drop*:

$$Drop = \frac{2B_cL}{2R + B_c}$$

$$= \frac{2(51)(7.5 \times 12)}{2(170 \times 12) + 51}$$

$$= 2.22 \text{ inches}$$

The required drop can also be determined by use of *Figure 5.21*:

$$\frac{R}{B_c} = 40.0$$

Enter *Figure 5.21* on the vertical scale at an R/B_c value of 40.0, project horizontally to the right until the diagonal line representing a pipe length of 7.5 feet is intersected, from this point project vertically down to the horizontal scale and read a value of 2.22 inches for the required drop.

Answer: The required pull for deflected straight pipe is 2.25 inches. The required drop for radius pipe is 2.22 inches.

It is important to determine if local concrete pipe manufacturers have the capability to manufacture pipe with the required pull or drop.

BUOYANCY OF CONCRETE PIPE

The density of concrete is approximately 2.4 times that of water, but there are several installation conditions where the possibility of pipe flotation exists. Some of these conditions are: flooding to consolidate backfill; pipelines in areas which will be inundated, such as a flood plain or under a future man-made lake; subaqueous pipelines; and pipelines in areas with a high groundwater table. When such conditions exist, flotation probability should be determined.

The buoyancy of a concrete pipeline depends upon the weight of the pipe, the weight of the volume of water displaced by the pipe, the weight of the liquid load carried by the pipe, and the weight of the backfill. As a conservative analytical practice, the line can be considered empty so the weight of any future liquid load is then an additional safety factor.

PIPE WEIGHTS

The average density of concrete is 150 pounds per cubic foot, and the approximate weight per linear foot of circular concrete pipe may be calculated by the following equation:

$$W_p = \frac{\pi}{4}(B_c^2 - D^2)150 \quad (5.14)$$

Where: B_c = outside pipe diameter, feet
D = inside pipe diameter, feet
W_p = weight of pipe, pounds per linear foot

Average weights for nonreinforced and reinforced concrete sewer, storm drain and culvert pipe are listed in *Tables 5.2* and *5.3*. Most pipe manufacturers publish product data giving actual dimensions, weight per linear foot, etc. Data from these publications should be used when available.

Table 5.2. Dimensions and Approximate Weights of Circular Concrete Pipe, Bell and Spigot Joint.

ASTM C14—Nonreinforced Sewer and Culvert Pipe, Bell and Spigot Joint						
Internal Diameter, inches	Class 1		Class 2		Class 3	
	Minimum Wall Thickness, inches	Average Weight, pounds per foot	Minimum Wall Thickness, inches	Average Weight, pounds per foot	Minimum Wall Thickness, inches	Average Weight, pounds per foot
4	5/8	9.5	3/4	13	3/4	13
6	5/8	17	3/4	20	7/8	21
8	3/4	27	7/8	31	1-1/8	36
10	7/8	37	1	42	1-1/4	50
12	1	50	1-3/8	68	1-3/4	90
15	1-1/4	78	1-5/8	100	1-7/8	120
18	1-1/2	105	2	155	2-1/4	165
21	1-3/4	159	2-1/4	205	2-3/4	260
24	2-1/8	200	3	315	3-3/8	350
27	3-1/4	390	3-3/4	450	3-3/4	450
30	3-1/2	450	4-1/4	540	4-1/4	540
33	3-3/4	520	4-1/2	620	4-1/2	620
36	4	580	4-3/4	700	4-3/4	700

ASTM C76—Reinforced Concrete Culvert, Storm Drain and Sewer Pipe, Bell and Spigot Joint.				
Internal Diameter, inches	Wall A		Wall B	
	Minimum Wall Thickness, inches	Average Weight, pounds per foot	Minimum Wall Thickness, inches	Average Weight, pounds per foot
12	1-3/4	90	2	106
15	1-7/8	120	2-1/4	148
18	2	155	2-1/2	200
21	2-1/4	205	2-3/4	260
24	2-1/2	265	3	325
27	2-5/8	310	3-1/4	388
30	2-3/4	363	3-1/2	459

These tables are based on concrete weighing 150 pounds per cubic foot and will vary with heavier or lighter weight concrete.

Table 5.3. Dimensions and Approximate Weights of Circular Concrete Pipe, Tongue and Groove Joint.

ASTM C 76 – Reinforced Concrete Culvert, Storm Drain and Sewer Pipe, Tongue and Groove Joints						
Internal Diameter, inches	Wall A		Wall B		Wall C	
	Minimum Wall Thickness, inches	Average Weight, pounds per foot	Minimum Wall Thickness, inches	Average Weight, pounds per foot	Minimum Wall Thickness, inches	Average Weight, pounds per foot
12	1-3/4	79	2	93	–	–
15	1-7/8	103	2-1/4	127	–	–
18	2	131	2-1/2	168	–	–
21	2-1/4	171	2-3/4	214	–	–
24	2-1/2	217	3	264	3-3/4	366
27	2-5/8	255	3-1/4	322	4	420
30	2-3/4	295	3-1/2	384	4-1/4	476
33	2-7/8	336	3-3/4	451	4-1/2	552
36	3	383	4	524	4-3/4	654
42	3-1/2	520	4-1/2	686	5-1/4	811
48	4	683	5	867	5-3/4	1011
54	4-1/2	864	5-1/2	1068	6-1/4	1208
60	5	1064	6	1295	6-3/4	1473
66	5-1/2	1287	6-1/2	1542	7-1/4	1735
72	6	1532	7	1811	7-3/4	2015
78	6-1/2	1797	7-1/2	2100	8-1/4	2410
84	7	2085	8	2409	8-3/4	2660
90	7-1/2	2395	8-1/2	2740	9-1/4	3020
96	8	2710	9	3090	9-3/4	3355
102	8-1/2	3078	9-1/2	3480	10-1/4	3760
108	9	3446	10	3865	10-3/4	4160
114	9-1/2	3840	10-1/2	4278	11-1/4	4611
120	10	4263	11	4716	11-3/4	5066
126	10-1/2	4690	11-1/2	5175	12-1/4	5542
132	11	5148	12	5655	12-3/4	6040
138	11-1/2	5627	12-1/2	6156	13-1/4	6558
144	12	6126	13	6679	13-3/4	7098
150	12-1/2	6647	13-1/2	7223	14-1/4	7659
156	13	7190	14	7789	14-3/4	8242
162	13-1/2	7754	14-1/2	8375	15-1/4	8846
168	14	8339	15	8983	15-3/4	9471
174	14-1/2	8945	15-1/2	9612	16-1/4	10,117
180	15	9572	16	10,263	16-3/4	10,785

These tables are based on concrete weighing 150 pounds per cubic foot and will vary with heavier or lighter weight concrete.

WATER DENSITY

The density of fresh water is 62.4 pounds per cubic foot and the average density of seawater is 64.0 pounds per cubic foot. The density of brackish water will be between that of fresh water and seawater depending upon the degree of salinity. Local conditions should be investigated for specific projects.

DISPLACED WATER WEIGHT

When water is displaced, a buoyant or upward force exists, and, if the buoyant force is greater than the weight of the object displacing the water, flotation will occur. The weight of fresh water displaced per linear foot of circular pipe can be calculated by the equation:

$$W_w = \frac{\pi}{4}(B_c^2)62.4 \tag{5.15}$$

Where: W_w = weight of displaced water, pounds per linear foot

The approximate weights of the volume of fresh water displaced per linear foot of pipe are presented in *Tables 5.4* and *5.5*.

Table 5.4. Approximate Weight of Water Displaced by Circular Concrete Pipe, Bell and Spigot Joint.

ASTM C 14 – Nonreinforced Concrete Pipe, Bell and Spigot Joint			
Internal Diameter, inches	Weight of Water Displaced, pounds per linear foot		
	Class 1	Class 2	Class 3
4	9.3	10.7	10.7
6	19.3	20.6	21.0
8	33	35	37
10	49	51	55
12	70	77	86
15	109	118	127
18	154	174	179
21	216	235	258
24	281	327	342

ASTM C 76 – Reinforced Pipe, Bell and Spigot Joint		
Internal Diameter, inches	Weight of Water Displaced, pounds per linear foot	
	Wall A	Wall B
12	86	93
15	127	138
18	174	194
21	235	258
24	306	331
27	377	410
30	457	497

Table 5.5. Approximate Weight of Water Displaced by Circular Concrete Pipe, Tongue and Groove Joint.

ASTM C76—Reinforced Concrete Pipe, Tongue and Groove Joint			
Internal Diameter, inches	Weight of Water Displaced, pounds per linear foot		
	Wall A	Wall B	Wall C
12	82	87	–
15	119	130	–
18	164	181	–
21	222	239	–
24	287	306	339
27	355	381	418
30	429	465	505
33	511	560	600
36	600	660	704
42	816	885	940
48	1069	1143	1206
54	1351	1440	1504
60	1666	1764	1842
66	2020	2122	2207
72	2401	2519	2605
78	2786	2944	3043
84	3271	3401	3508
90	3752	3899	4005
96	4266	4423	4545
102	4823	4980	5109
108	5403	5580	5706
114	6017	6203	6341
120	6674	6863	7008
126	7354	7556	7709
132	8067	8282	8443
138	8826	9042	9210
144	9606	9836	10,010
150	10,418	10,662	10,844
156	11,278	11,523	11,711
162	12,157	12,416	12,612
168	13,069	13,343	13,546
174	14,031	14,303	14,513
180	15,009	15,296	15,513

BACKFILL WEIGHT

The weight of the backfill directly over the pipe assists in resisting buoyant forces. The unit weight of compacted backfill material varies with the type of material, grain size, degree of compaction, etc. For preliminary computations, however, the average values for specific gravity and unit weight of backfill materials provide sufficient accuracy.

The unit weight of inundated backfill is equal to the dry density of the backfill minus the weight of water displaced by the solid particles and can be calculated as follows:

$$w_I = w - \left(\frac{w}{SG \times 62.4} \times 62.4\right) \qquad (5.16)$$

Which reduces to:

$$w_I = w\left(1 - \frac{1}{SG}\right) \qquad (5.17)$$

Where: w_I = average unit weight of inundated backfill, pounds per cubic foot

w = average unit weight of dry backfill, pounds per cubic foot

SG = specific gravity of backfill material

The different volumes of the backfill over the pipe to be considered are illustrated in *Figure 5.23*. The volume of backfill over the haunches from the springline to the top of the pipe is equal to 0.1073 B_c^2 cubic feet per linear foot of pipe. The volume of backfill from the top of the pipe to the level of inundation equals $H_I B_c$ cubic feet per linear foot of pipe. Therefore, the weight of inundated backfill, acting downward per linear foot of pipe can be calculated by:

$$W_I = w_I(0.1073B_c^2 + H_I B_c) \qquad (5.18)$$

Where: H_I = depth of inundated backfill above top of pipe, feet

W_I = weight of inundated backfill directly over the pipe, pounds per linear foot

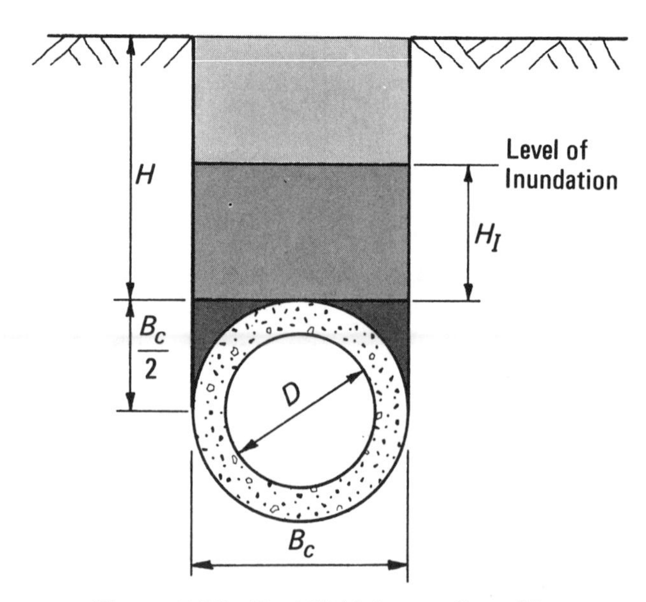

Figure 5.23. Backfill Volumes Over Pipe.

The weight of the backfill above the water level, if any, acting downward per linear foot of pipe can be calculated by the equation:

$$W_D = w(H - H_I)B_c \qquad (5.19)$$

Where: H = depth from top of pipe to surface of backfill, feet
W_D = weight of the backfill directly over the pipe, pounds per linear foot

Therefore the total weight of backfill acting downward on the pipe is the algebraic sum of *Equations 5.18* and *5.19:*

$$W_B = W_I + W_D \qquad (5.20)$$

Where: W_B = total weight of backfill directly over the pipe, pounds per linear foot

FACTOR OF SAFETY

A factor of safety ranging between 1.0 and 1.5 should be applied, based on the extent of knowledge of the proposed backfill material and site conditions. This factor of safety is applied to decrease the calculated downward force of the backfill acting on the pipe.

PREVENTIVE PROCEDURES

If the total weight of the pipe and backfill is not adequate to prevent flotation of the pipe, preventive procedures will be required. Some of the commonly used methods are:

- Increased wall thickness
- Precast or cast-in-place concrete collars
- Precast or cast-in-place concrete blocks
- Pipe strapped to piles or concrete anchor slab
- Additional backfill

When computing the volume of concrete required per linear foot for pipe anchorage, the submerged weight of concrete is used, since concrete which weighs 150 pounds per cubic foot in air weighs only 87.6 pounds per cubic foot under water.

DESIGN PROCEDURE

Following is a suggested procedure for determining the buoyancy of concrete pipe and possible measures to prevent flotation. Downward forces are considered positive and upward forces negative.

1. Determine the downward force of the pipe weight in pounds per linear foot of pipe.
2. Determine the buoyant upward force of the weight of the displaced water in pounds per linear foot of pipe.
3. Find the algebraic sum of the forces determined in Steps 1 and 2. If the resultant force is positive, the pipe will not float. If the resultant force is negative, proceed with Step 4.

4. Determine the downward force of the total weight of backfill in pounds per linear foot pipe.
5. Apply a factor of safety to determine the decreased total weight of backfill.
6. Find the algebraic sum of the downward force determined in Step 5 and the excess upward force determined in Step 3. If the resultant force is positive, the pipe will not float. If the resultant force is negative, proceed with Step 7.
7. Select and analyze the procedures required to prevent flotation.

EXAMPLE

Given: A 72-inch diameter, Wall B, ASTM C 76 reinforced concrete pipe is to be installed in a trench in a sandy coastal area with 8 feet of backfill over the top of the pipe. The groundwater table is near the surface in this area, and the natural soil is primarily sand. The sandy soil is assumed to have an in-place surface dry density of 110 pounds per cubic foot with a specific gravity of 2.65.

Find: Will the empty pipe float in the fully backfilled condition? What is the minimum depth of inundated backfill required to prevent flotation?

Solution: 1. Weight of pipe

$W_p = +1811$ pounds per linear foot (downward force), *Table 5.3*.

2. Weight of displaced water

$W_w = -2519$ pounds per linear foot of pipe (upward force), *Table 5.5*.

3. Summation of forces

$W_p + W_w = 1811 + (-2519) = -708$ pounds per linear foot of pipe (upward force).

Since the resultant force is negative, proceed to Step 4.

4. Total weight of backfill

Weight of inundated backfill

The in-place surface dry density of sand is 110 pounds per cubic foot with a specific gravity of 2.65. The unit weight of inundated backfill, *Equation 5.17*, equals:

$$w_I = 110\left(1 - \frac{1}{2.65}\right) = 68 \text{ pounds per cubic foot.}$$

The weight of inundated backfill, *Equation 5.18*, is:

$W_I = 68\,[0.1037\,(7.17)^2 + (8 \times 7.17)] = +4276$ pounds per linear foot of pipe (downward force).

Weight of dry backfill

Since the groundwater table was assumed to be at the surface, the weight of dry backfill, *Equation 5.19*, equals:

$W_D = (110)\,(8\text{-}8)\,(7.17) = 0.$

Total weight of backfill

The total weight of backfill, per linear foot of pipe, *Equation 5.20*, equals:

$W_B = 4267 + 0 = +4267$ pounds per linear foot of pipe (downward force).

5. Factor of safety:

Since precise information is not available on the density and specific gravity of the sandy backfill, a factor of safety of 1.25 will be used to reduce the assumed total weight of the backfill.

$$\frac{W_B}{F.S.} = \frac{+4276}{1.25} = +3421$$ pounds per linear foot of pipe (downward force)

6. Summation of forces:

From Step 3 the resultant upward force is −708 and from Step 5 the downward force is +3421, producing a resultant downward force of +2713 pounds per linear foot of pipe. Therefore, the empty pipe will not float in the fully backfilled condition and Step 7 is not required.

To find the minimum height of inundated backfill necessary to prevent flotation during construction, the force exerted by the inundated backfill, *Equation 5.18*, must be equal and opposite in direction to the buoyant force of the submerged pipe, −708 pounds per linear foot.

Solve for H_I

$$W_I = \frac{w_I(0.1073B_c^2 + H_IB_C)}{1.25}$$

$$H_I = \frac{1.25W_I}{w_IB_c} - 0.1073B_c$$

$$= \frac{1.25(708)}{68(7.17)} - 0.1073(7.17)$$

$$= 1.05 \text{ feet}$$

Answer: Therefore a minimum depth of slightly more than one foot of inundated backfill above the top of the pipe is required to prevent flotation.

FIRE RESISTANCE

Sanitary sewers, storm sewers, culverts and other underground pipeline systems are subject to many hazards, including the risk that combustible material such as gasoline, fuel oil, gas, industrial waste, etc., may be introduced into the pipeline either by design or accident. Fires and explosions in sewers in urban areas are not unusual occurrences. Thousands of traffic accidents occur annually involving fire and gasoline spillage.

The National Fire Protection Association has stated, *Manholes, sewers and similar underground pipes have long been recognized by fire protection engineers as constituting areas where fire and explosion hazards of some severity may exist. Modern civilization, accompanied by the increase in number of gasoline service stations, solvent disposal operations, dry cleaning establishments, fuel gas production and distribution facilities, refrigeration plants, and many other industrial activities with potentially dangerous gas or vapor by-products make the safe operation of underground structures more difficult each year.*

Flammable liquid hazards in drainage lines are greatly intensified at airports where the increased rate of handling large quantities of fuel makes spillage a frequent occurrence. Concrete pipe does not support combustion and can withstand extremely high temperatures. Numerous fires in sewers constructed with concrete pipe have occurred with little or no damage to the pipe. In fact, sewers constructed with concrete pipe have withstood explosions where other sewer materials suffered severe structural damage and had to be replaced with concrete pipe.

During a fire at O'Hare International Airport, near Chicago, Illinois, flaming fuel flowed through concrete pipe and asphalt coated corrugated steel pipe. While some slight spalling occurred in the concrete pipe, this

Illustration 5.6
Smoke billows from open manholes as burning gasoline flows through undamaged concrete pipe in Nashville, Tennessee, 1979.

spalling had a negligible effect on the service life of the pipe. The asphalt and zinc coatings on the corrugated steel pipe were destroyed. At another fire at Walker Air Force Base, Roswell, New Mexico, examination of the concrete pipe through which thousands of gallons of flaming fuel had flowed revealed no apparent fire damage.

ENERGY DISSIPATORS

The possibility of scour or erosion in the natural channel immediately downstream of the discharge outlets of culverts and storm sewers must be considered. If the **kinetic energy** of water can be transformed to **potential energy** or dissipated, resulting in a velocity reduction, the erosion will be eliminated or substantially reduced.

One method by which the kinetic energy of the flow is transformed to potential energy is illustrated in *Figure 5.24*. The concentrated flow from the pipe is distributed across the width of the downstream channel which permits the kinetic energy to be more readily absorbed in the tailwater pool and transformed into potential energy. The absorption of the flow of a tributary stream by the flow of a main stream is another example of the transformation of energy by flow distribution.

Another method of dissipating kinetic energy is illustrated in *Figure 5.25*. A general characteristic of energy dissipation is the transition from shallow to deep flow. This transition usually produces a sudden and violent churning action, commonly referred to as a **hydraulic jump**. Flow distribution and energy dissipation are often combined for maximum effect.

Much study and research has been done on energy dissipation of culvert discharges. However, the remainder of this section will be confined to a discussion and presentation of design procedures for internal energy dissipation within the concrete pipe.

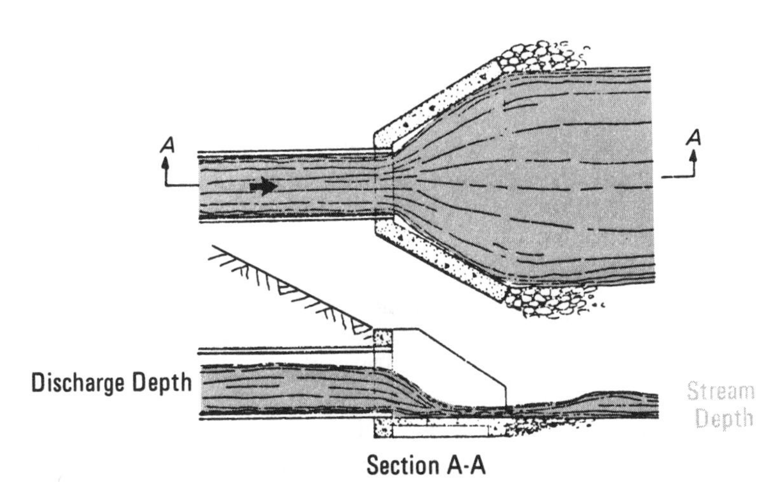

Figure 5.24. Transformation of Kinetic to Potential Energy by Flow Distribution.

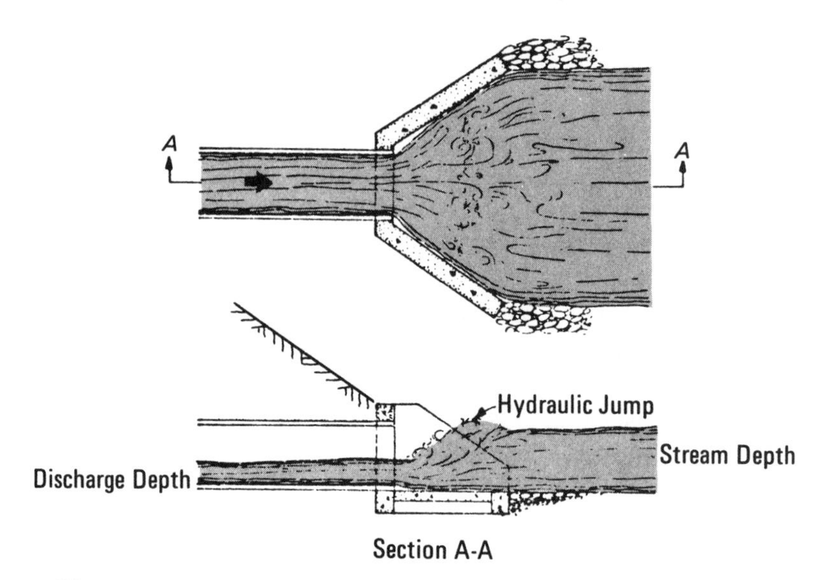

Figure 5.25. Transformation of Kinetic to Potential Energy by Hydraulic Jump and Flow Distribution.

INTERNAL ENERGY DISSIPATORS

Research conducted in the 1960's at Virginia Polytechnic Institute and State University, **VPI,** on the use of roughness elements in open channels established that excess energy in storm water flowing down steep drainage channels could be dissipated by constructing roughness elements within the channel. Since culverts operating under inlet control simulate open channel flow, application of this type of internal energy dissipation to culverts would result in more efficient utilization of the culvert barrel and reduced outlet velocities.

In 1969, the American Concrete Pipe Association contracted with VPI to investigate and determine the feasibility and applicable design procedures for using roughness elements as energy dissipators of **free surface flow** in circular concrete pipe culverts, and the results were published in 1971.

Research was based on free surface flow, therefore, full capacity of the pipe was not realized. This necessitated an increase in pipe size within the length of the culvert in which the roughness elements were placed. Based on the laboratory and field observations during this initial research, subsequent tests were conducted for **full flow** conditions occurring near the outlet end at maximum design discharge. By eliminating the criteria of free surface flow and allowing the culvert to approach full flow, it was found velocity reduction could be effected without an increase in pipe size. The results of this later research and design procedures were published in 1972.

Free Surface Flow

Since the objectives of the research were to dissipate energy and reduce high velocities associated with culverts on what are considered steep slopes, the culverts were operating under inlet control. Accordingly, the flow characteristics were observed to be one of critical flow at the entrance of the pipe with the flow accelerating down the length of the pipe until the first ring, or roughness element, was reached. At that point a hydraulic jump was formed, with extreme turbulence. The flow then encountered another roughness element while still in an agitated condition from the first and this pattern of action was repeated until a cyclic condition was reached, where the flow conditions over the roughness elements were uniform. Generally, this cyclic action was attained after the second or third element. An early conclusion was that a maximum of five rings were necessary to achieve consistent results. The agitated flow is called tumbling flow and is characterized by a greater depth over the element than before it, a fall into a valley between the elements, and a form resembling a hydraulic jump shortly before the next element. When one cycle is completed, the flow tumbles into the next cycle until the outlet is reached. Tumbling flow can only be established and maintained under less than full flow conditions, *Figure 5.26*.

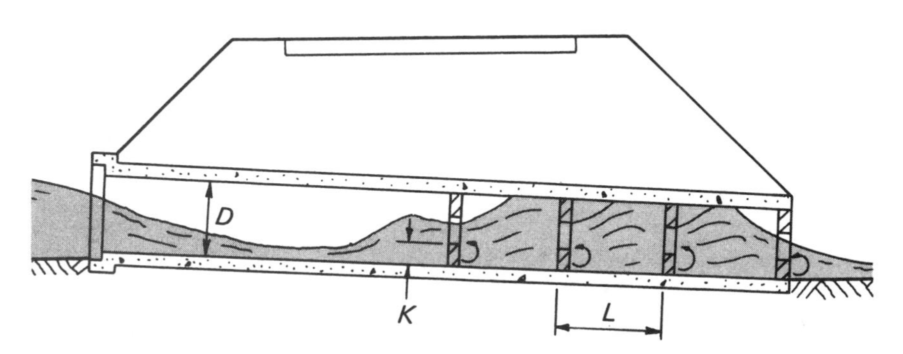

Figure 5.26. Internal Energy Dissipators with Tumbling Flow.

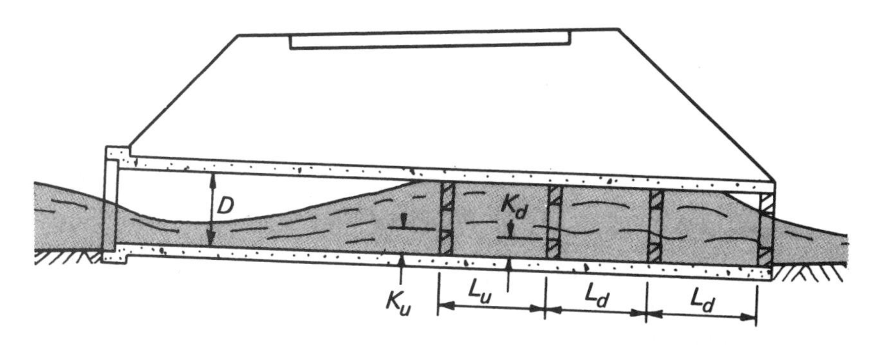

Figure 5.27. Internal Energy Dissipators with Full Flow.

Full Flow

During the VPI research on open channel flow, it was observed that if one large dissipator element was placed upstream a large hydraulic jump was created and maintained by smaller downstream elements. ACPA research validated this observation for pipe flow at maximum design discharges and concluded that three small rings preceded by one large ring at twice the small ring spacing would maintain full flow at slopes greater than 4 percent, *Figure 5.27*.

DESIGN PROCEDURES AND CRITERIA

Based on the test results, the following design procedures and criteria for full flow and free surface flow are presented.

Full Flow

1. Select required pipe size in accordance with the appropriate design procedures presented in *Chapter 3*.
2. Determine outlet velocity per *Chapter 3*.
3. Select a ring height for the three downstream elements within a range determined by:

$$0.06 \leq \frac{K_d}{D} \leq 0.09 \qquad (5.21)$$

Where: K_d = ring height of the downstream elements, inches
D = pipe diameter, inches

4. Select a ring height for the single upstream element within the range determined by:

$$0.12 \leq \frac{K_u}{D} \leq 0.18 \qquad (5.22)$$

Where: K_u = ring height of the single upstream element, inches

5. Select a spacing for the three downstream elements as determined by:

$$L_d \approx \frac{1.5D}{12} \qquad (5.23)$$

Where: L_d = Spacing of the downstream elements, feet

6. Select a spacing for the single upstream element as determined by:

$$L_u \approx \frac{3.0D}{12} \qquad (5.24)$$

Where: L_u = spacing of the single upstream element, feet

7. Determine the hydraulic cross-sectional area in square feet at the last downstream element.
8. Determine the outlet velocity by dividing the design discharge by the cross-sectional area of flow determined previously.

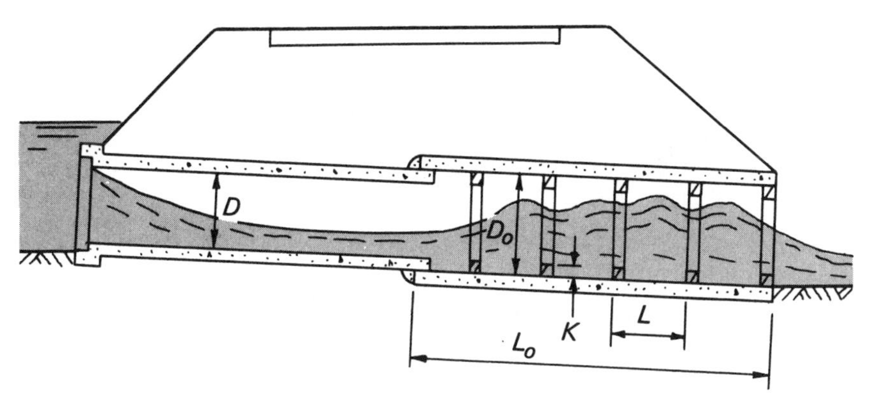

Figure 5.28. Internal Energy Dissipators with Free Surface Flow.

Free Surface Flow

If full flow design reduces outlet velocity to an acceptable level, free surface flow design, *Figure 5.28,* is not required. However, if the outlet velocity is not acceptable, continue with free surface flow design as follows:

1. Select an outlet pipe diameter within the range determined by:

$$\left[\frac{Q^2}{3.22}\right]^{1/5} \le D_0 \le \left[\frac{Q^2}{1.42}\right]^{1/5} \tag{5.25}$$

   Where: D_0 = outlet pipe diameter, feet
   Q = design flow, cubic feet per second

2. Select a ring height for the elements within the range determined by:

$$1.2 \le \frac{K}{D_0} \le 1.8 \tag{5.26}$$

   Where: K = ring height of the elements, inches

3. Select a ring spacing for the five elements within the range determined by:

$$1.5 \le \frac{L}{D_0} \le 2.5 \tag{5.27}$$

   Where: L = spacing of the elements, feet

4. Determine the approximate length of the outlet pipe by:

$$L_0 \approx 5L \tag{5.28}$$

   Where: L_0 = length of the outlet pipe, feet

5. Determine hydraulic cross-sectional area at last dissipator ring based upon critical depth as presented in *Chapter 3*.
6. Determine the outlet velocity by dividing the design discharge by the cross-sectional area of flow determined in the previous step.

EXAMPLE

Given: A 36-inch diameter concrete pipe culvert, 125 feet long with a Manning's n of 0.012 on a 4 percent slope. The design discharge, Q, has been determined to be 60 cubic feet per second and the allowable headwater, AHW, depth at the inlet is 4.5 feet.

Find: Size, spacing of roughness elements and outlet velocity for full flow conditions.

Solution:

1. By the procedures presented in *Chapter 3*, inlet control governs with an AHW of 4.5 feet.
2. Outlet velocity, as determined by procedures presented in *Chapter 3*, is 19.3 feet per second.
3. Reduction of the outlet velocity is desired, therefore select a ring height, K_d, for the three downstream elements within the range determined by *Equation 5.21*.
$$0.06(36) \leq K_d \leq 0.09(36)$$
$$2.2 \leq K_d \leq 3.2$$
$$\text{Try } K_d = 3 \text{ inches}$$
4. Select a ring height, K_u, for the single upstream element within the range determined by *Equation 5.22*.
$$0.12(36) \leq K \leq 0.18(36)$$
$$4.3 \leq K \leq 6.5$$
$$\text{Try } K_u = 6 \text{ inches}$$
5. Select a spacing, L_d, for the three downstream elements as determined by *Equation 5.23*.
$$L_d \approx \frac{1.5(36)}{12}$$
$$\text{Use } L_d = 4.5 \text{ feet}$$
6. Select the spacing, L_u, for the single upstream element as determined by *Equation 5.24*.
$$L_u \approx \frac{3.0(36)}{12}$$
$$\text{Use } L_u = 9 \text{ feet}$$
7. Determine hydraulic cross-sectional area at last ring.
$$\text{Diameter} = \frac{D - 2K_d}{12}$$
$$= \frac{36 - 2(3)}{12}$$
$$= 2.5 \text{ feet}$$
$$A = \frac{\pi D^2}{4}$$
$$= \frac{\pi(2.5)}{4}$$
$$= 4.91 \text{ square feet}$$

8. Determine outlet velocity.

$$V = \frac{Q}{A}$$
$$= \frac{60}{4.91}$$
$$= 12.2 \text{ feet per second}$$

Answer: Three downstream elements with a ring height of 3 inches and spaced 4.5 feet apart in the 36-inch diameter pipe and a single upstream element with a ring height of 6 inches and spaced 9.0 feet above the third downstream element results in an outlet velocity of 12.2 feet per second, 63 percent of the outlet velocity without internal energy dissipators.

Assuming that reduction of the outlet velocity to 12.2 feet per second is not sufficient, continue with the free surface flow design procedure.

1. Reduction of the outlet velocity is desired, therefore the outlet pipe diameter, D_0, range is determined by *Equation 5.25*.

$$\left[\frac{60^2}{3.22}\right]^{1/5} \le D_0 \le \left[\frac{60^2}{1.4168}\right]^{1/5}$$

$$4.0 \le D_0 \le 4.8$$

   Try a pipe with a diameter of 4.0 feet

2. Select height, K, of the five dissipator rings within the range determined by *Equation 5.26*.

$$1.2(4.0) \le K \le 1.8(4)$$
$$4.8 \le K \le 7.2$$
$$\text{Try } K = 5.0 \text{ inches}$$

3. Determine the range of spacing, L, of the rings by *Equation 5.27*.

$$1.5(4) \le L \le 2.5(4)$$
$$6 \le L \le 10$$

   The allowable spacing range of 6 to 10 feet permits the placement of one element in each of five pipe sections whose normal laying lengths range from 7.5 to 10 feet.

4. The approximate length of the outlet pipe, L_0, is determined by *Equation 5.28*. Assuming a spacing and pipe laying length of 8.0 feet:

$$L_0 \approx 5(8.0)$$
$$\approx 40 \text{ feet}$$

5. The cross-sectional area of flow at the last ring is found to be 6.62 square feet by the procedures presented in *Chapter 3*.

6. The outlet veloctiy is determined by dividing the design discharge, 60 cfs, by the cross-sectional area of flow determined previously, 6.62 square feet.

$$V = \frac{60}{6.62}$$

$$= 9.1 \text{ feet per second}$$

Answer: A 48-inch diameter concrete pipe, 40 feet long with five dissipator rings each five inches high and spaced eight feet apart, installed as per *Figure 5.28,* results in an outlet velocity of 9.1 feet per second, 47 percent of the outlet velocity without internal energy dissipators.

JACKING CONCRETE PIPE

Concrete pipe is frequently installed by tunneling and jacking where deep installations are necessary or where conventional open excavation and backfill methods may not be feasible. Concrete pipelines were first jacked in place by the Northern Pacific Railroad between 1896 and 1900. In more recent years, this technique has been applied to sewer construction with intermediate shafts along the line of the sewer as jacking stations. The feasibility and planning of tunneling and jacking projects should be coordinated with local concrete pipe manufacturers and jacking contractors.

Reinforced concrete pipe as small as 18-inch diameter and as large as 132-inch diameter have been installed by jacking. Since conventional jacking procedures require access by workmen through the pipe to the heading, 36-inch diameter pipe is generally the smallest practical size for most jacking operations. When jacking smaller size pipe, earth removal is accomplished by mechanical means such as augers and boring equipment.

Concrete pipe is ideally suited for tunneling and jacking. The pipe can be pushed forward immediately after the soil is excavated, providing a completed tunnel liner for protection of workers and equipment. Because of technological advances and increased experience, many pipelines are now being jacked.

JACKING PROCEDURE

A typical installation and general procedures for jacking concrete pipe are illustrated in *Figure 5.29.*

The usual construction sequence for tunneling and jacking concrete pipe is:

- Excavate jacking **pits** or **shafts**, construct jacking **abutments** or **thrust blocks**, and install **jacks**, jacking **frame** and **guide rails**.
- Begin tunnel excavation by machine, or hand, depending on conditions.
- Lower first section of pipe, position jacks and jacking frame, and jack pipe forward.
- Continue excavation, remove soil through pipe, insert succeeding sections of pipe between the lead pipe and jacks and jack forward.
- Repeat sequence, excavation, soil removal, pipe insertion and jacking, until the operation is complete.

Pits are excavated on each side. The jacks will bear against the back of the left pit so a steel or wood abutment is added for reinforcement. A simple track is added to guide the concrete pipe sections. The jacks are positioned in place on supports.

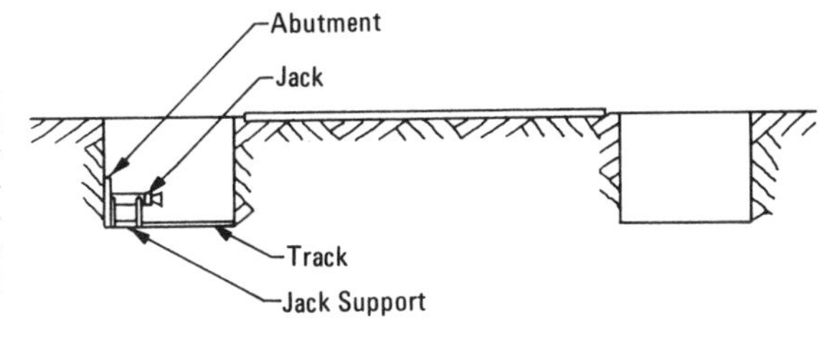

A section of concrete pipe is lowered into the pit.

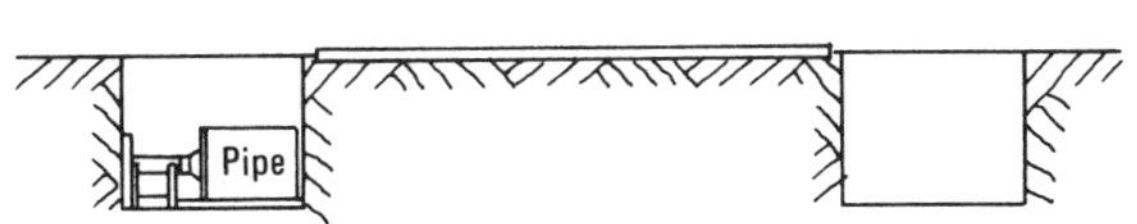

The jacks are operated pushing the pipe section forward.

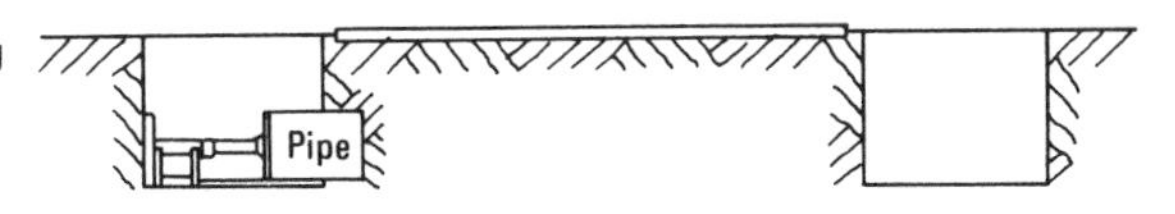

The jack rams are retracted and a "spacer" is added between the jacks and pipe.

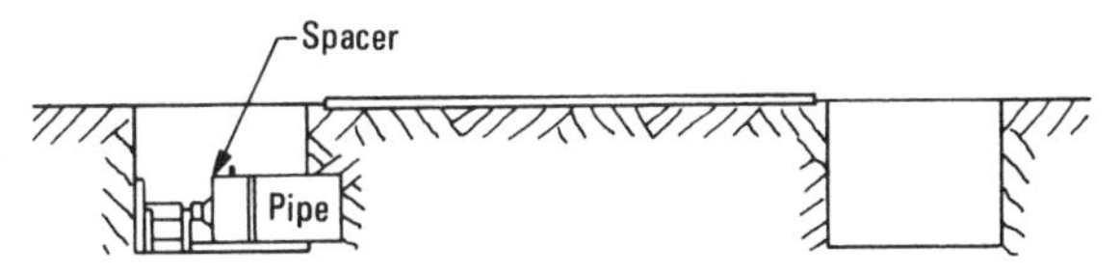

The jacks are operated and the pipe is pushed forward again.

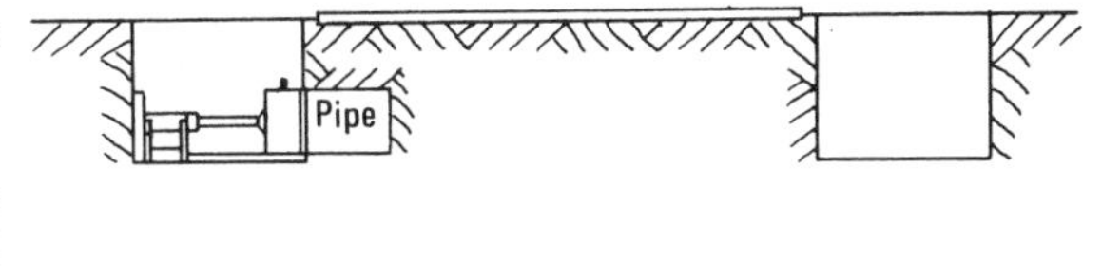

It may be necessary to repeat the above steps four and five several times until the pipe is pushed forward enough to allow room for the next section of pipe. It is extremely important, therefore, that the stroke of the jacks be as long as possible to reduce the number of spacers required and thereby reduce the amount of time and cost. The ideal situation would be to have the jack stroke longer than the pipe to completely eliminate the need for spacers.

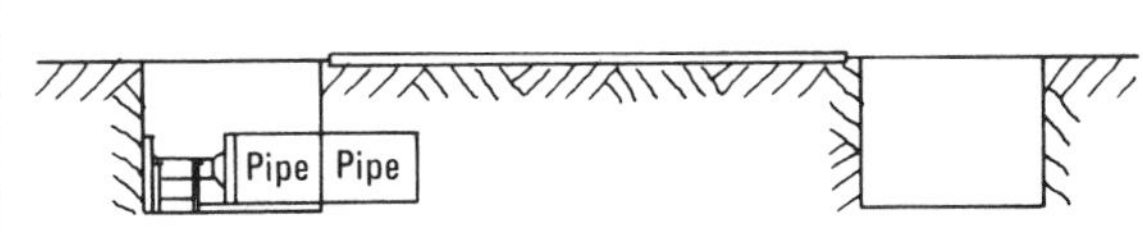

The next section of pipe is lowered into the pit and the above steps repeated. The entire process above is repeated until the operation is complete.

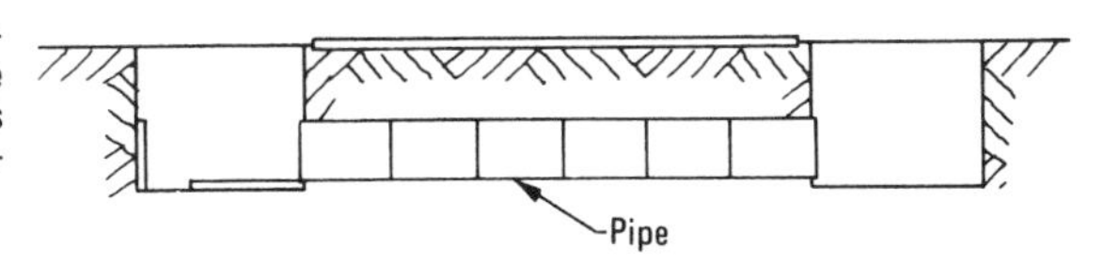

Figure 5.29. General Procedures for Jacking Concrete Pipe.

Excavation should not precede the jacking operation more than necessary. Material is trimmed so the tunnel bore slightly exceeds the outside diameter of the pipe. Such a procedure results in minimal disturbance to the adjacent soils. The lead pipe is generally contained within a **shield** projecting from the mining machine or equipped with a **cutter** or **shoe** to protect the pipe when excavating by hand. Jacked pipe tends to **set** or **freeze** when forward movement is interrupted, resulting in significantly increased frictional resistance, therefore, continous operation is desirable. Occasionally a lubricant, such as bentonite slurry, is pumped into the space between the tunnel bore and the outside of the pipe to reduce frictional resistance. After the jacked pipe have reached their final position, grout is frequently pumped into this same space to insure continous bearing with the surrounding soil.

When increased resistance develops due to soil conditions or length of run, intermediate jacking stations may be inserted at periodic intervals. The intermediate jacking station pushes only the several lengths ahead while bearing on the pipe behind. The use of intermediate jacking stations reduces axial loads on the pipe and required jacking capacity.

The number and capacity of the jacks primarily depends upon the size and length of the pipe to be jacked and the type of soil encountered. Abutments for the jacks must be strong enough and large enough to distribute the maximum capacity of the jacks to the soil behind the backstops.

LOADS ON JACKED PIPE

Two types of loads imposed upon concrete pipe installed by the jacking method are the **axial** load due to the jacking forces applied during installation and external **earth** and **live** loads.

Axial Loads

The axial or **thrust** loads are transmitted from one concrete pipe section to another through the joint surfaces. To prevent localized stress concentrations, it is necessary to provide relatively uniform distribution of the axial loads around the periphery of the pipe. This is accomplished by assuring that the pipe ends are parallel within the tolerances prescribed by ASTM standards, using a **cushion material**, plywood, between the pipe sections, and care on the part of the contractor to insure that the jacking force is properly distributed through the jacking frame and parallel with the axis of the pipe. The cross-sectional area of a standard concrete pipe wall is more than adequate to resist stresses encountered in normal jacking operations. For projects where extreme jacking pressures are anticipated due to long jacking distances or excessive unit frictional forces, intermediate jacking stations may be used, and greater care taken to avoid bearing stress concentrations.

Earth Loads

The major factors influencing the vertical earth load on pipe installed by jacking are:

- Weight of the prism of earth directly above the bore
- Upward shearing or frictional forces between the prism of earth directly above the bore and the adjacent earth
- Cohesion of the soil

A comprehensive explanation of the theory of earth loads on jacked pipe is found in *Chapter 4*.

Live Loads

Jacked installations are generally constructed at such depths of cover that effects of live loads are negligible. Highway and aircraft loads are considered insignificant at depths greater than 10 feet, however, railroad loads are considered up to 30 feet of cover. Tables for highway, aircraft and railroad loads on concrete pipe may be found in some of the references for this chapter.

METRICATION

Metrication is the conversion from a system of customary units of weights and measures to **The International System of Units, SI**. The **SI system** is based on seven units: **metre**, **m**; **kilogram**, **kg**; **second**, s; **ampere**, **A**; **kelvin**, **K**; **mole**, **mol**; **candela**, **cd**; and two supplementary units for angular measurement: the **radian**, **rad**, for plane angles; and **steradian**, **sr**, for solid angles. See *Table 5.6*. From these base units, other units are derived

Table 5.6. International System of Units, SI.

Base Units		
Metre	m	Length
Kilogram	kg	Mass (Weight)
Second	s	Time
Ampere	A	Electricity
Kelvin (Celsius)	K (C)	Temperature
Mole	mol	Elementary Entities
Candela	cd	Luminous Intensity
Supplementary Units		
Radian	rad	Plane Angle
Steradian	sr	Solid Angle
Derived Units		
Newton	N	Force
Pascal	Pa	Pressure or Stress
Square Metre	m^2	Area
Cubic Metre	m^3	Volume
Litre	L	Volume

including two of special interest to the concrete pipe industry. These are the **newton**, N, and **pascal**, **Pa**. The newton is the unit of force and is defined as *the force required to accelerate a mass of one kilogram by one metre per second per second*. The pascal is the unit of pressure or stress and is defined as *one newton per square metre*. *D*-loads, for example, are expressed in newtons per linear metre. Concrete and steel stresses are expressed in pascals. Area is expressed in square metres and volume usually in cubic metres. For fluid quantities, volume may be expressed in **litres**. Steel reinforcement areas are expressed in square millimetres per metre.

METRICATION OF CONCRETE PIPE STANDARDS

Complete SI editions for all ASTM concrete pipe standards have been developed. The values stated in either U.S. customary or SI editions are not exact equivalents, therefore, each system must be used independently. Combining values from the two systems may result in nonconformance with the specification.

CONVERSION DECISIONS

When converting from U.S. customary units to SI, the following basic decisions must be made:

- Soft or hard conversion
- Precision
- Significant figures

Soft and Hard Conversion

Soft conversion is the use of exact SI equivalents, such as 25.4 millimetres for one inch and 68.94757 megapascals for a pressure of 10 pounds per square inch. **Hard conversion** is the use of SI values, maintaining the required **precision** and **significant figures,** but not exact equivalents of customary units, such as 25 millimetres for one inch and 70 megapascals for a pressure of 10 pounds per square inch. Another example is the 0.01-inch crack *D*-load criterion which states, *The 0.01-inch crack load is the maximum load applied to the pipe before a crack, having a width of 0.01 inch measured at close intervals, occurs throughout a length of 1 foot or more*. The soft conversion is a 0.254 millimetre crack for a length of 304.8 millimetres, and the hard conversion is a 0.3 millimetre crack for a length of 300 millimetres.

Precision and Significant Figures

Degree of precision, rounding and number of significant figures are interrelated. The problems associated with this decision are illustrated by considering a permissible variation in ASTM C 76, *the underrun in the laying length of a section shall not exceed one-half inch maximum*. In U.S. customary units, one-half inch can be written decimally as either 0.5, 0.50 or 0.500 inches and each decimal place implies a different precision. Since the length of pipe is not normally measured with a micrometer, but with a

Table 5.7. SI and U.S. Customary Designated Sizes for Circular Concrete Pipe.

SI			U.S. Customary	
DESIGNATED SIZE Diameter of Pipe, mm	Permissible Variation Internal Diameter of Pipe		Diameter of Pipe	
	Minimum, mm	Maximum, mm	Inches	Millimetres
100	100	110	4	101.6
150	150	160	6	152.4
200	200	210	8	203.2
250	250	260	10	254.0
300	300	310	12	304.8
375	375	390	15	381.0
450	450	465	18	457.2
525	525	545	21	533.4
600	600	620	24	609.6
675	675	695	27	685.8
750	750	775	30	762.0
825	825	850	33	838.2
900	900	925	36	914.4
1050	1050	1080	42	1066.8
1200	1200	1230	48	1219.2
1350	1350	1385	54	1371.6
1500	1500	1540	60	1524.0
1650	1650	1695	66	1676.4
1800	1800	1850	72	1828.8
1950	1950	2000	78	1981.2
2100	2100	2155	84	2133.6
2250	2250	2310	90	2286.0
2400	2400	2465	96	2438.4
2550	2550	2620	102	2590.8
2700	2700	2770	108	2743.2
2850	2850	2925	114	2895.6
3000	3000	3080	120	3048.0
3150	3150	3235	126	3200.4
3300	3300	3390	132	3352.8
3450	3450	3540	136	3505.2
3600	3600	3695	144	3657.6

tape, one-half inch equals 0.50 inches is appropriate in this instance as the precision and has two significant figures. One-half inch is exactly 12.7 millimetres and has three significant figures. Therefore, rounding 12.7 millimetres to 13 millimetres, which has two significant figures, achieves the required precision and the number of significant figures is correct.

DESIGNATED SIZE

ASTM C 822 defines **designated size** as *The dimensional name for a particular size that may or may not be equal to or related to the dimensions used for design purposes or of the manufactured product*. When a diameter of circular pipe is specified, the designated size is used. The actual size will be between the permissible limits established by the appropriate ASTM standard. The designated SI and corresponding U.S. customary sizes for circular concrete pipe are presented in *Table 5.7*.

REFERENCES

1. "Building Code Requirements for Reinforced Concrete," ACI 318–77, American Concrete Institute, 1977.
2. "Concrete Pipe Design Manual," American Concrete Pipe Association, 1978.
3. "Concrete Pipe Installation Manual," American Concrete Pipe Association, 1978.
4. "Concrete Sewer, Storm Drain, and Culvert Pipe," ASTM C 14, American Society for Testing and Materials, 1979.
5. "Culvert Velocity Reduction by Internal Energy Dissipators," CP Info, American Concrete Pipe Association, 1972.
6. "Curved Alignment," Design Data Number 21, American Concrete Pipe Association, 1969.
7. "Definitions of Terms Relating to Concrete Pipe and Related Products," ASTM C 822, American Society For Testing and Materials, 1979.
8. "Design and Construction of Sanitary and Storm Sewers," Manual of Practice Number 37, American Society of Civil Engineers, and Manual of Practice Number 9, Water Pollution Control Federation, 1974.
9. "External Sealing Bands for Non-Circular Concrete Sewer, Storm Drain, & Culvert Pipe," ASTM C 877, American Society for Testing and Materials, 1978.
10. "Flotation of Concrete Pipe," Design Data Number 30, American Concrete Pipe Association, 1977.
11. "Jacking Concrete Pipe," Design Data Number 13, American Concrete Pipe Association, 1969.
12. "Joints for Circular Concrete Sewer and Culvert Pipe, Using Rubber Gaskets," ASTM C 443, American Society for Testing and Materials, 1979.
13. "Metric Practice," ASTM E 380, American Society for Testing and Materials, 1976.
14. "Precast Concrete Manholes," Design Data Number 12, American Concrete Pipe Association, 1969.
15. "Precast Reinforced Concrete Manhole Sections," ASTM C 478, American Society for Testing and Materials, 1979.
16. "Reinforced Concrete Culvert, Storm Drain, and Sewer Pipe," ASTM C 76, American Society for Testing and Materials, 1979.
17. "Reinforced Concrete D-Load Culvert, Storm Drain, and Sewer Pipe," ASTM C 655, American Society for Testing and Materials, 1978.
18. "Reinforced Concrete Low-Head Pressure Pipe," ASTM C 361, American Society for Testing and Materials, 1979.
19. "Resilient Connectors Between Reinforced Concrete Manhole Structures and Pipes," ASTM C 923, American Society for Testing and Materials, 1980.
20. "Roughness Elements As Energy Dissipators of Free-Surface Flow in Circular Pipes," James M. Wiggert, Paul D. Erfle and Henry M. Morris, Highway Research Record Number 373, Transportation Research Board, National Academy of Sciences, 1971.

CHAPTER 6

DURABILITY CONSIDERATIONS

Durability of a pipe material is as significant as its ability to perform intended structural and hydraulic functions. The capability of the pipe to continue to perform satisfactorily for an economically acceptable period is a fundamental engineering consideration. Unfortunately, predictions of durability cannot be made with the same degree of precision as can structural and hydraulic performance, and, in too many instances, durability is not accorded adequate consideration.

At the present time, there is no known material completely inert to chemical action and immune to physical deterioration. Concrete is no exception, but, under what might be considered *normal* exposure conditions, it has a very long life. Concrete made by the Romans from natural cement is in excellent condition after more than 2000 years of service.

Durability is concerned with life expectancy, or the endurance characteristics of a material or structure. In no type of facility is long term integrity more critical than in sewer lines and culverts. Much attention has been directed to the durability of pipe, but the vagaries of climate, soils and geology, fluid impurities, construction materials, and the construction process itself have prevented the development of a systematic and practical theory for predicting performance. The problem has been compounded by the assumed requirement that pipe must last almost indefinitely.

Concrete pipelines have a long history of excellent durability, and it is unlikely this record will change. Pipelines are beneath the ground where temperatures have very little variation, where atmospheric exposure is either not present or greatly reduced, and where the materials in close proximity to the pipe are usually nonaggressive. Laboratory test results, and damage records for cast-in-place concrete that has been exposed to atmospheric conditions, should not be related to buried precast concrete pipe until it is determined that comparable conditions will exist. Improper application of data could lead to overdesign and excessive cost.

The U.S. Bureau of Reclamation defines a durable concrete pipe as *one that will withstand, to a satisfactory degree, the effects of service conditions to which it will be subjected.* This definition contains the three variables that must be evaluated to obtain satisfactory durability; the concrete pipe, the satisfactory degree of performance, and service conditions. This chapter provides guidance to the engineer on how these variables can be evaluated, based upon current technology.

CONCRETE DURABILITY STUDIES

Many observations and analyses of field performance of pipe materials have been made. Sanitary sewer, storm sewer and culvert durability studies have been sponsored by federal agencies, state highway departments, national and local pipe associations, individual manufacturers and consultants. A tremendous quantity of data has been developed. Unfortunately, no common data base is applicable, and the three variables included in the Bureau of Reclamation definition of durability have not been precisely or uniformly defined in the studies. The net result is difficulty in comparing conclusions which often appear to be contradictory.

Reports of field studies do not provide a basis for understanding the nature of concrete pipe durability relative to specifically defined service conditions. However, engineers with a practical understanding of the subject should be able to evaluate and utilize past studies to establish and substantiate individual judgment. Of special value are studies covering the same geographical area, or areas with geological and meteorological characteristics that are similar to those of the proposed project.

Most of the portland cement concrete produced is used for cast-in-place structures, and much of the research on concrete durability relates to such applications. The Portland Cement Association, American Concrete Institute, American Society of Civil Engineers, National Association of Corrosion Engineers, various federal agencies, and individual authors have contributed an impressive quantity of technical information to the subject. A great deal of this technology, with proper interpretation, can be correlated with concrete pipe durability. Two major differences between precast and cast-in-place concrete must be understood for such correlation to be useful:

- Cast-in-place concrete is a construction material with an almost infinite scope of service in aggressive exposure conditions. Examples of severe exposure conditions range from bridge decks periodically treated with calcium chloride to plant floors subjected to spills of aggressive industrial chemicals. These types of durability problems have been the subject of much research but are outside the normal service conditions of concrete pipe.
- Concrete in modern precast concrete pipe has significantly superior durability characteristics to concrete used in cast-in-place structures.

Illustration 6.1

This section came from an aqueduct built by the Romans around 80 A.D. The original aqueduct extended 56 miles underground between Fiffel and Cologne. Trass, a slightly hydraulic natural cement occurring along the Rhine between Coblenz and Cologne, was used by Roman army engineers in constructing the aqueduct. It is a volcanic mud made up of a mixture of pumice, trachyte, quartz pebbles and some vegetable matter. Mixed with slaked lime and water, it makes a fairly satisfactory binder for the broken limestone and gravel. The walls are approximately 15 inches thick, and this section weighs 9,746 pounds.

PRECAST CONCRETE PIPE

The concrete in precast concrete pipe is of exceptionally high quality. It is produced in modern plants under close supervision, and procedures for controlling quality are used throughout every phase of manufacture. All raw materials, coarse and fine aggregates, reinforcing steel, portland cement, and the mixing water routinely undergo quality control tests. Mix designs are developed to provide optimum strength and density, and actual proportioning is controlled by precision batching equipment. A low water-cement ratio, essential for strength and durability of concrete, is an inherent characteristic of precast concrete pipe. In fact, the water content of concrete mixes for concrete pipe produced by several methods provides only slightly more water than that required to achieve proper hydration. Slumps are often referred to as less than zero, which means that the slump would remain at zero even with the addition of more mixing water.

In addition to using high quality materials, the manufacturing processes for precast concrete pipe are highly developed. Precise placement of reinforcement is obtained by positive mechanical means. Concrete is placed in steel forms and compacted under high pressures and vibration, which results in uniform and optimum consolidation and density. After a specified curing cycle, the manufacturing process is complete. The pipe is tested and must meet performance criteria in accordance with tests prescribed by ASTM standards.

Manufacturing economies dictate that the specified performance characteristics be achieved as rapidly as possible after the concrete placement

Illustration 6.2
Oval prebed concrete pipe installed about 1880 in Norwalk, Connecticut and found in excellent condition when removed in 1968.

operation. This consistently results in higher strengths than required, because the hydration of the cement must have progressed sufficiently in a few days to meet specified requirements. Hydration continues because of the moist environment in which concrete pipe is normally placed, and strength and durability can be expected to be enhanced for years under installed conditions.

Evaluation of the difference between precast concrete pipe and cast-in-place concrete structures indicates that concrete pipe has superior strength and durability characteristics. Thus, durability criteria developed for cast-in-place structures should not be applied to precast concrete pipe without modification. To do so will result in costly overdesigns.

FACTORS INFLUENCING CONCRETE DURABILITY

Specific factors that influence concrete pipe durability are **concrete compressive strength, density, absorption, cement content and type, aggregate characteristics, total alkalinity, concrete cover over the reinforcement,** and **admixtures.**

Minimum **concrete compressive strengths** of 4000, 5000 and 6000 pounds per square inch are required by ASTM standards. The strengths relate to structural, not durability, considerations and are attained within a short period of time. The 28-day compressive strengths are much higher, often exceeding 8000 pounds per square inch. Concrete compressive strengths are a function of available aggregates and cement, mix design, inherent characteristics of certain manufacturing processes, and curing procedures. Higher strength usually means overall higher quality, i.e., greater abrasion resistance, lower permeability, and greater resistance to weathering and chemical attack.

Concrete density of pipe ranges from 135 to 165 pounds per cubic foot. The higher densities are achieved by greater consolidation of the concrete, higher specific gravity aggregates, or by a combination of the two. Higher densities attained exclusively through the use of aggregates with higher specific gravity are not necessarily indicative of an improved level of concrete durability.

Absorption is an indicator of the pore structure and is considered by some to be related to the durability of the concrete. Absorption of the cured concrete is influenced significantly by the absorption characteristics of the aggregates and the inherent characteristics of the manufacturing process. Hydration of the cement, which continues under the normally favorable installed pipe environment, further reduces initial absorption values.

ASTM standards for precast concrete pipe currently require a minimum **cement content** per cubic yard of concrete. This minimum is frequently exceeded by precast concrete pipe manufacturers for a variety of reasons, but mainly because of manufacturing requirements. Other things being equal, increased cement content leads to lower absorption, higher compressive strength and increased resistance to weathering, freeze-thaw, and certain chemical environments. It also increases the probability of shrinkage cracking, which must be balanced against potential benefits.

Portland cement used in the manufacture of concrete pipe normally conforms to the requirements of ASTM C 150. Types I, II and V differ primarily in the allowable levels of tricalcium aluminate, C_3A, content. Type I has no limit to C_3A content, Type II has a maximum of 8 percent, and Type V a maximum of 5 percent. C_3A is the ingredient in cement which is principally involved in the disruptive expansion caused by sulfate reactions. Concrete made with lower C_3A contents provides greater resistance to sulfate attack. The preceding percentages are specified maximum values, but there is a great variation in the chemistry of individual portland cements. Since they are made from locally available materials, some Type I cements have less C_3A than allowed by ASTM C 150 for Type V. An economic factor to be considered in specifying cement type is the fact that Type V cement is not manufactured in all geographical areas, and, if available, may be at premium prices. Unless unusual sulfate resistance is required by the project specifications, or unless the type of cement is otherwise specified, concrete pipe is usually manufactured with Type I cement.

Aggregates used in concrete pipe must meet the requirements in ASTM C 33, except for gradation. Gradation is established by the pipe manufacturer to provide compatibility with a particular manufacturing process, to achieve optimum concrete strength, and to control permeability. ASTM C 33 provides a number of parameters covering minimum acceptable aggregate qualities. The specific hardness or abrasion resistance of the aggregate is of particular interest in durability studies. Other things being equal, harder and denser aggregates produce concrete with greater abrasion resistance. Aggregates that react with cement are rarely, if ever, a problem with pipe, because tests of aggregate sources are conducted by the individual pipe manufacturer.

Total alkalinity of concrete has a greater influence on the ability of concrete to resist acid environments than any other property. All portland cement concrete is alkaline, which means it has a pH greater than 7 and will react with acid. Total alkalinity is a measure of the total reactivity of any given mass of concrete and is expressed as a percentage of calcium carbonate equivalent. For example, concrete with a total alkalinity of 100 percent means it will react with the same quantity of acid as would an equal mass of calcium carbonate. A given mass of concrete with a total alkalinity of 40 percent will react with and neutralize twice the volume of any specific acid as would the same mass of concrete with a total alkalinity of 20 percent. Concrete pipe made with an aggregate which is nonreactive with acid, such as granite, will have a total alkalinity of 16 to 24 percent, depending upon cement content. Using a calcareous aggregate, such as dolomite or limestone, can increase the total alkalinity to as much as 100 percent. Suitable sources of calcareous aggregates are not readily available in all geographical areas. Requiring their use could increase the cost of the pipe and should be evaluated by a cost/benefit analysis.

Minimum **concrete cover** over the reinforcing steel is specified in ASTM standards. These minimum covers represent a balance between structural efficiency and durability. Assuming both structural adequacy and proper crack control, greater durability is provided against a variety of aggressive conditions by a thicker concrete cover. A modification of cover to increase durability, however, requires re-evaluation of the structural design of the pipe, and possible use of non-standard forms which could lead to significant increases in pipe costs.

Admixtures sometimes used by concrete pipe manufacturers include calcium chloride, air entraining agents and water reducing agents. Air entrainment agents, which are normally used only in wet-cast pipe, increase freeze-thaw and weathering resistance. Water reducing agents are used to provide adequate workability with drier mixes. With the same cement content, water reducing agents can reduce absorption and increase compressive strength. Calcium chloride, while accelerating setting time, tends to reduce resistance to sulfate attack. Chlorides are also related to potential reinforcement corrosion. The use of admixtures should be evaluated as to possible effects on durability performance.

Illustration 6.3
Concrete pipe sanitary sewer installed in Pine Bluff, Arkansas in 1928 was inspected in the 1950's and found in original condition.

PHYSICAL ASPECTS OF INSTALLATION CONDITIONS

There are a number of purely physical characteristics of the installation which directly and significantly influence the severity of exposure to potentially aggressive factors. These are discussed in the following paragraphs.

Pipe Wall Hydrokinetics

As shown in *Figure 6.1, Example 1,* with water at equal pressure on both sides of a pipe wall, the concrete becomes saturated, stability is reached, and no water movement takes place. In *Example 2,* there is a differential pressure, and, regardless of magnitude, a hydraulic gradient causes movement of water through the wall, along with whatever salts, alkalis, sulfates, and other chemicals are in solution in the water. Even though this movement may be imperceptibly slow, it will provide continuous replenishment of any chemicals that may be in solution. Direction of flow is highly significant. If the aggressive water were on the right of the wall, the movement of non-aggressive water through the wall would tend to mitigate any effect. In either case, with no exposure to the atmosphere, there is no concentration effect.

Examples 3 and 4 have an evaporative surface condition. The water movement is due to either a hydraulic gradient or capillary action. In either case, there would be a concentration at or near the evaporative surface of whatever chemicals are in solution. These considerations are not relevant to acid environments, since acid attack is essentially confined to the exposed surface. They are significant, however, in evaluating severity of sulfate or chloride exposures.

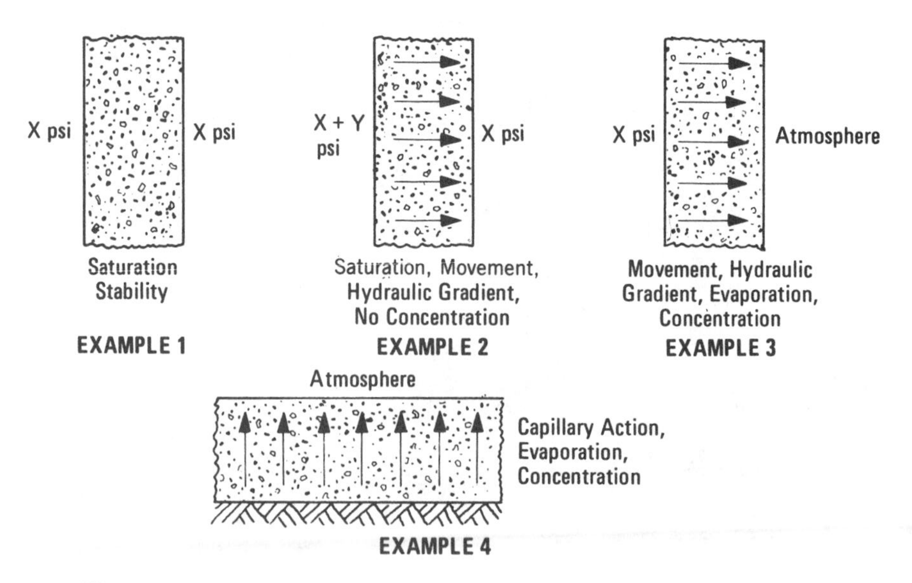

Figure 6.1. Typical Hydrostatic and Hydrokinetic Relationships.

Full atmospheric exposure, as illustrated in *Figure 6.2, Example 1,* can be a severe condition for concrete pipe. Depending upon climate and location, the exterior of the pipe could be subjected to freeze-thaw cycles, to thermal stresses, to chlorides in coastal areas, and to concentration effects of whatever salts or sulfates are in solution in the effluent.

Partial burial or immersion, as illustrated in *Figure 6.2, Example 2,* can be a similarly severe exposure condition. Only a partially evaporative surface is provided, but the concentration effects are more complex since the source of salts or sulfates may be either the effluent or moisture from the ground entering the pipe wall through capillary action and moving toward the evaporative surface.

Buried pipe usually is not exposed to freeze-thaw or thermal stresses, and concentration effects are negligible. When installed above the water

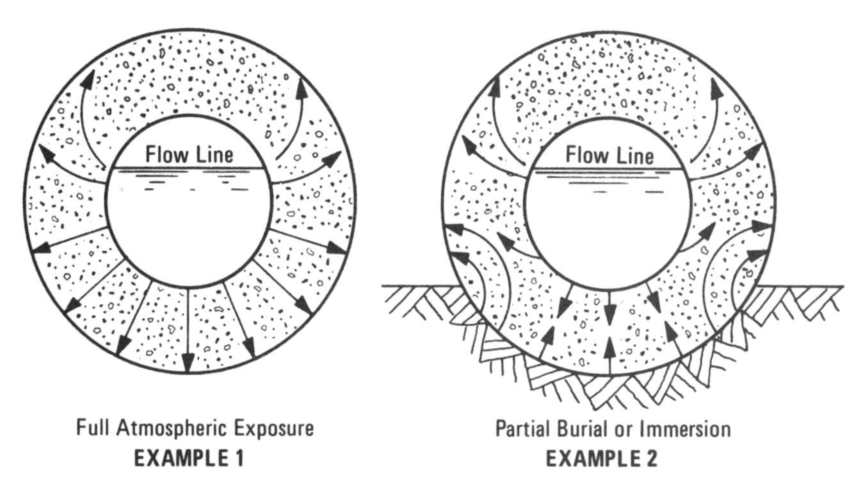

Figure 6.2. Typical Hydrokinetic Relationships Relating to Atmospheric Exposures of Concrete Pipe.

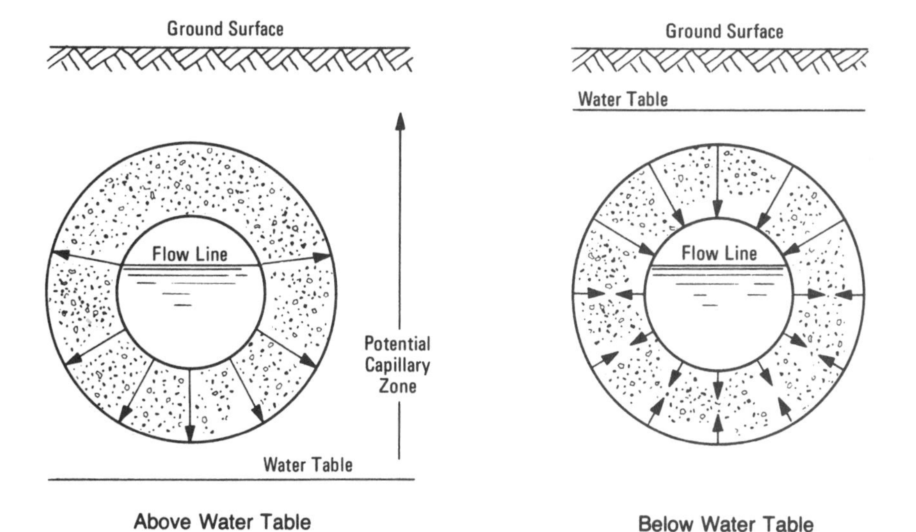

Figure 6.3. Typical Hydrokinetic Factors Relating to Buried Concrete Pipe.

table, the hydraulic gradient within the pipe wall of a partially filled pipe is toward the outside, and directly opposite when below the water table, as shown in *Figure 6.3*. The former condition is more critical for high sulfate or chloride-containing effluents, while the latter is more critical for aggressive groundwater. If the pipe is located between the minimum and maximum groundwater elevations, the hydraulic gradients would reverse on a cyclical basis.

Installation Characteristics Related to Acidic Groundwater Exposure

Certain installation characteristics have particular significance in relation to acidic groundwater exposure. The high alkalinity of concrete pipe will almost immediately neutralize acid that comes in contact with it, and the reaction will result in some loss of the concrete surface. For this reaction to continue, there must be replenishment of the acid at the concrete surface. The rate of this replenishment at the external surface of the pipe depends upon the relative permeability of the backfill and bedding material in the pipe zone, the location of the pipe with respect to the water table, and to the fluctuation of the water table. These latter characteristics have been categorized as essentially quiescent, moderately fluctuating, and grossly cyclic. A tightly compacted clay around the pipe will create a relatively impermeable zone, minimizing the potential rate of replenishment. Conversely, a permeable zone around the pipe will not impede the free movement of groundwater and tends to maximize the replenishment potential. The least potential problem with either type of zone exists when the pipe is above the water table. The situation most conducive to replenishment is a permeable zone between the high and low water table, with grossly cyclic groundwater fluctuations, where both horizontal and vertical movement of groundwater can take place. A calcareous backfill, such as limestone, can provide a highly alkaline barrier around the pipe and neutralize the acid before it can contact the pipe wall.

Thus, for any given degree of groundwater acidity, the rate of attack on any given concrete pipe is subject to extreme variation and is dependent upon installation characteristics and acid replenishment rate.

PRINCIPAL AGGRESSIVE FACTORS

This section covers specific chemical and physical factors which can be aggressive to concrete pipe and which collectively account for practically all of the durability problems that can be encountered in traditional applications of the product. These factors are:

- Acids
- Sulfates
- Chlorides
- Freeze-thaw and weathering
- Velocity-abrasion

Conditions severe enough to result in durability problems for concrete pipe are, however, quite rare. Countermeasures are also discussed, and, when required, should be included as a standard engineering design procedure.

ACIDS

When in contact with portland cement concrete, acid will attack the exposed surface and be neutralized by the alkalinity of the concrete. A given quantity of an acid will destroy a given mass of concrete, that mass being inversely proportional to the total alkalinity of the concrete. Without acid replenishment, the reaction stops.

Interior Acid Attack

Two types of **interior acid attack** are encountered. One is the **biochemical** phenomenon which can occur within a sanitary sewer. The second type relates to **acidic effluents.**

The mechanics of **biochemical acid attack** in sanitary sewers are those stated for acid attacks in general. There are, however, certain unique aspects that are experienced with this phenomenon:

- The acid involved is always sulfuric, H_2SO_4.
- Attack is confined to the interior, unsubmerged perimeter of the pipe.
- Although the total volume of acid available is small, the concentration is high, up to 5 percent, and a high percentage will react with the exposed concrete surfaces.

The development of this type of aggressive acidic environment depends upon a complex, highly unusual and specific set of sewage conditions. Present engineering technology provides the means for predicting the development and prevention or control of these specific conditions. The application of technology to prevention is an integral part of the design of sanitary sewer systems, and is discussed in *Chapter 7*. Where designs call for control rather than prevention of this phenomenon, predictable levels of acidic exposure will be present. In these instances, countermeasures for increasing the resistance of the concrete to acidic environments are available.

Highly acidic materials are usually prohibited from entering a public sewer system because **acidic effluents** are harmful to the sewage treatment process and may be harmful to the sewer. When acid is encountered, the attack is confined to the wetted interior surface of the pipe. The measure of aggressiveness of the acidic effluent is the pH, which is defined as the logarithm of the reciprocal of the hydrogen ion concentration, H^+, of a solution. A pH of 7 is neutral, neither basic nor acidic. Below 7 the material is acidic and above 7 it is basic. Since the numbers are logarithms, a pH of 5 is ten times as acidic as a pH of 6. With flowing effluent, there is constant replenishment of the acid, and the rate of attack is inversely proportional to the pH and the total alkalinity of the pipe wall. Continuous flow of effluent with a pH below 5.5 is considered aggressive and below

5.0 is highly aggressive. Intermittent flow, and cyclical increases in pH to higher values, will mitigate the rate of attack. All of these factors need to be considered in evaluating the severity of acidic conditions for any specific installation and the need for countermeasures.

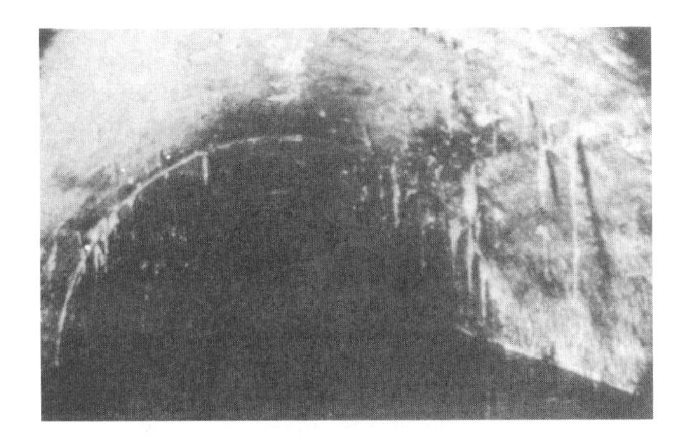

Illustration 6.4
Concrete pipe sanitary sewer inspected in Wilmington, North Carolina after 26 years of service, condition excellent.

Exterior Acid Attack

Although the chemistry is the same as for an interior attack, an exterior acid attack involves a different set of conditions. The parameters are more complicated and less predictable, and larger variations in the rate of the replenishment can be expected. However, the maximum rate of replenishment, due to the flow through soil materials, will be much slower than that encountered with an acidic effluent, with the rate frequently being almost negligible. For these conditions, pH is not the only measure needed to evaluate aggressiveness. Since pH does not measure how much acid is available to be neutralized, **total acidity,** normally expressed in terms of milligram equivalents of acid per 100 grams of soil, must be evaluated. If the total acidity is low, a very low pH can be readily increased by a small alkaline neutralization.

A meaningful description of the acidity of any given soil or groundwater must include both pH and total acidity. Of the two, total acidity is more significant, provided that the groundwater in contact with the pipe is relatively static. The greater the anticipated movement of groundwater, the greater is the replenishment rate and the significance of pH.

Measurements of pH can be accurately made in the field with a standard pH meter. Samples of soil or groundwater to be tested should be taken from the level of the proposed pipeline, as samples taken from the surface are meaningless and can be misleading. Tests should be made at regular intervals along the proposed route. If hot spots, or high acidic conditions, are encountered, their extent should be determined and a number of measurements made within the suspect area. An effective or realistic design value can be determined by a statistical evaluation of a series of soil pH readings. One, or even a few, scattered low pH values would not establish a reasonable design value. The same soil samples can be tested for total acidity using standard methods, and evaluated statistically and in conjunction with pH.

As a guideline, a pH of 5 and a total acidity of 25 milligram equivalents per 100 grams of soil indicates a potentially aggressive groundwater situation. Such conditions require a more comprehensive analysis of installation characteristics to determine if countermeasures would be necessary to insure durability. Naturally occurring groundwaters with this degree of acidity are quite rare. Man-made conditions, such as sanitary land fills and industrial waste disposal areas, are the most likely areas where this combination or greater might be encountered.

Exposure Evaluation and Countermeasures

The evaluation procedures suggested when aggressively acidic exposures are suspected or indicated are listed in *Table 6.1*.

If it is concluded that a problem exists, the following alternative countermeasures are available:

Exterior Exposure

- Use material with low permeability in pipe zone to inhibit replenishment.
- Use calcareous material in pipe zone to neutralize the acid.

Exterior and/or Interior Exposure

- Use calcareous aggregates in pipe manufacture to provide a higher total alkalinity.
- Provide increased concrete cover as sacrificial concrete.
- Use protective coatings and linings.

In sulfuric acid attack of concrete, there are secondary sulfate reactions. These are usually insignificant, and occur after the concrete has already been damaged. The use of low C_3A cement to mitigate these secondary reactions is not helpful, for it does not appreciably increase resistance to acid attack.

Table 6.1. Evaluation Procedures.

Exterior Exposure	Interior Exposure
Accurately determine pH and total acidity.	For potential bio-chemical problems in sanitary sewers, determine rate of acid development, if any.
Evaluate installation condition from the standpoint of the potential acid replenishment.	For acidic effluents, determine pH, including cyclic variations, as well as continuous or intermittent flow characteristics.

SULFATES

Sodium, magnesium and calcium sulfates in soil, groundwater, or effluent can be highly aggressive to portland cement concrete by combining chemically with certain constituents of the concrete, principally hydrates of C_3A, to form calcium sulfoaluminate. This reaction is accompanied by expansion and eventual disruption of the concrete. The situation is typical of those conditions where sulfate concentration has taken place because of an exposed, evaporative surface.

Experience with this phenomenon in the United States has primarily occurred in the alkali soils of the west and southwest and has been almost exclusively limited to cast-in-place, exposed concrete structures. The Bureau of Reclamation has wide experience in concrete construction in these areas and has developed the general criteria shown in *Table 6.2* for evaluating and dealing with this problem. These criteria apply to a wide range of exposure conditions for cast-in-place concrete where concentration effects are anticipated. Application of these criteria to buried concrete pipe is extremely conservative. They should not be applied unless evaluation of installation conditions indicates high concentration effects are likely to develop.

Table 6.2. Attack on Concrete by Soils and Waters Containing Various Sulfate Concentrations.

Relative Degree of Sulfate Attack	Percent Water-Soluble Sulfate (as SO_4) in Soil Samples	PPM Sulfate (as SO_4) in Water Samples
Negligible.	0.00 to 0.10	0 to 150
Positive[1]	0.10 to 0.20	150 to 1,500
Severe[2]	0.20 to 2.00	1,500 to 10,000
Very severe[3].	2.00 or more	10,000 or more

[1] Use Type II cement.

[2] Use Type V cement, or approved portland-pozzolan cement providing comparable sulfate resistance when used in concrete.

[3] Use Type V cement plus approved pozzolan which has been determined by tests to improve sulfate resistance when used in concrete with Type V cement.

The following summary of the experience of the Bureau of Reclamation provides the most authoritative guidelines available on sulfate attack on concrete:

Concrete Pipe

- Reducing the C_3A content of the concrete is the most direct way to increase resistance of concrete to sulfate attack.
- Steam curing increases the resistance of concrete to sulfate attack.
- Assuming equal C_3A content in the cement, higher cement content increases sulfate resistance of the concrete. For example, a 7 bag, 658 pounds, mix provides from 5 to 10 times the resistance of a 5 1/2 bag, 517 pounds, mix.

- Use of calcium chloride as an admixture reduces sulfate resistance.
- Concrete pipe has been designed using Type V cement, plus approved pozzolans, for exposure of up to 240,000 parts per million of sulfate.
- Resistance to sulfate attack decreases as absorption increases, regardless of cement type.

Exposure Conditions

- Sulfates in the soil must be water soluble.
- Concentration effects, such as those that develop at an evaporative surface, produce the most severe exposure for any given sulfate content of the water.
- Unbalanced hydraulic pressures provide the most severe exposure.

CHLORIDES

The most significant aggressive action of chlorides is corrosion of steel in reinforced concrete. Most problems occur as damage to bridge decks resulting from use of de-icing chemicals. Maintenance problems have also been encountered with reinforced concrete seawater structures, such as piling and piers, because of chloride-induced corrosion of the reinforcement.

Portland cement concrete protects embedded steel against corrosion under conditions that would be highly corrosive to bare steel. The protection is an electro-chemical phenomenon in which the high alkalinity of concrete, normally a pH around 12, passivates the steel. This passivating influence will normally remain effective as long as the pH remains above 10, even in the presence of free oxygen. The chloride ion has the ability to disrupt this protective mechanism. Research has established there is a critical chloride ion concentration at the concrete-steel interface beyond which corrosion will occur, and that oxygen must also be present to support corrosion. The greater the chloride ion concentration beyond the critical level, assuming oxygen availability, the more rapidly corrosion will progress.

Seawater has approximately 20,000 parts per million of chloride. Many concrete pipe installations are completely immersed in seawater and are performing satisfactorily after many years. This is primarily due to low oxygen solubility in high chloride waters plus the extremely low diffusion rate of oxygen through the saturated concrete cover. It is necessary to evaluate all the installation conditions to determine the probability of chloride induced corrosion. Concentration effects which generally occur along with enhanced oxygen availability can produce the critical chloride ion concentration at the steel-concrete interface that is needed to produce corrosion. These effects will more readily occur under the following conditions; low quality concrete of high permeability and porosity, cracks, and the inclusion of calcium chloride in the concrete mix.

A number of conditions can reduce the severity of chloride attack. Increased concrete cover will normally extend service life but will not prevent eventual corrosion under severe exposure conditions. High quality concrete with low permeability, and the absence of cracks and voids, will also extend the life of the pipe under severe exposure conditions but will not prevent eventual corrosion if the mechanism of chloride build-up continues. Under extreme exposure conditions, the use of barrier type protective coatings is probably the most effective alternative.

A very small precentage of concrete pipe is installed under conditions for which serious chloride build-up is probable. The American Concrete Pipe Association has not received any reports or evidence of chloride induced corrosion damage to reinforced concrete pipe.

FREEZE-THAW AND WEATHERING

Freeze-thaw damage is caused by water penetrating into concrete interstices and freezing, which generates stresses and disrupts the concrete if it does not have sufficient strength to resist these stresses. Severity of exposure is usually described by the frequency of freeze-thaw cycles. Atmospheric exposure usually accompanies freeze-thaw action, which complicates the situation. Thus, instead of a pure freeze-thaw situation, thermal stresses and evaporative surfaces with concentration effects and crystallization of various soluble salts in the pore structure could combine to provide an accelerated weathering effect.

Normally, concrete pipe is not exposed to this combined set of conditions. When it has been, however, its performance has been excellent, primarily due to the high quality of the concrete. In some circumstances, weathering exposure could be serious enough to require sealing the surface with a protective coating. Such circumstances are not common, but can occur.

VELOCITY-ABRASION

Although velocity-abrasion is a subject that has been discussed extensively, very few generally accepted conclusions have been reached. There have been very few field observations and these have provided only limited data. Invert erosion has been observed in some culverts, but it has often been a composite phenomena in which velocity-abrasion was augmented by corrosion from aggressive waters.

Velocity, by itself, does not create problems for concrete pipe within the ranges normally encountered. At velocities of 40 feet per second, or greater, cavitation effects can be serious unless the surface is smooth and internal offsets at joints are closely controlled. Within the range of velocities up to 40 feet per second, the severity of velocity-abrasion effects depends upon the characteristics of the bed load. A **bed load** is the quantity of solids being moved through the pipe by the flow velocity. Bed loads may be intermittent or continuous and vary in particle size, hardness and specific gravity. They are usually more of an engineering flow problem than a question of pipe abrasion, particularly in a sanitary or storm sewer system, and can normally be controlled by proper design.

Particle size and density are usually smallest in sanitary sewers, larger in combined and storm sewers, and largest in culverts. Specific hardness of the particles is subject to wide variation and is quite significant, because if the particles are not as hard as the concrete, the particles will be abraded rather than the pipe. Increasing the compressive strength of the concrete along with an increase in the specific hardness of the aggregate used, increases abrasion resistance.

SIGNIFICANCE OF CRACKING

The principles of reinforced concrete design are based upon the accepted concept that cracking of the concrete is necessary to permit development of the full tensile strength of the reinforcing steel. With precast reinforced concrete pipe, it became possible to utilize this cracking characteristic as a criteria for nondestructive quality control testing. This led to the development of the three-edge bearing test and the adoption by ASTM in the early 1930's of the 0.01-inch crack test as a measurable and reproducible method for determining pipe strength. This particular crack width was arbitrarily proposed by Professor W. J. Schlick of Iowa State University because a leaf gage of that dimension was readily available.

There is no structural significance to a 0.01-inch crack. It is simply the test criterion assigned by ASTM standards for reinforced concrete pipe, and the 0.01-inch crack has no meaning as a criterion of structural performance in the field.

Certainly, however, the magnitude of permissible cracks is important from the standpoint of potential exposure to aggressive factors. The 0.01-inch crack came to be widely regarded as a conservative value for the maximum width that should be accepted as nondeleterious in exposed structures. That the criterion is conservative is demonstrated by more than 50 years of experience in the United States and Canada during which there have been no reports of deleterious corrosion of reinforcement in a concrete pipe due to the existence of cracks of 0.01 inch magnitude.

EVALUATION OF CRACKS

A complete evaluation of the significance of crack widths must consider the aggressiveness of the pipe environment, the depth of crack penetration, and the thickness of concrete cover over the reinforcement.

Sources of aggressive chemical attack on concrete pipe are surface related phenomena in every case except that of chlorides. Furthermore, in order for destructive reactions to continue, there must be replenishment of the aggressive solution. The geometry of cracks which do not completely penetrate the pipe wall greatly reduce or eliminate circulation and replenishment. Reactions initiated by the penetration of aggressive waters into small cracks are soon completed and stability is reached. Cracks which completely penetrate the pipe wall are rare and present a different set of conditions. From a durability standpoint, they are of concern when aggressive liquids are involved, and installation conditions are conducive to actual movement of the liquid through the crack. Under these relatively rare conditions, replenishment will be provided and the attack would continue.

Cracks normally do not completely penetrate the wall of a reinforced concrete pipe. Ordinarily, when cracks occur, the penetration is to the depth of the reinforcement, and the maximum penetration would be to the neutral axis of the pipe wall. The geometric shape of cracks is triangular, with the maximum width at the surface and tapering to zero. Thus, the depth of penetration of any given width of surface crack is controlled by and related to the thickness of the cover over the reinforcement. The 0.01-inch crack criterion has historically been related to the standard one inch cover provided over the reinforcement in concrete pipe.

As noted earlier, chloride induced corrosion is not a surface related phenomena, and requires a very specific set of conditions. It was noted that in highly alkaline environments, pH from 10 to 12.5, not only is a critical chloride ion concentration necessary to initiate corrosion, but oxygen as well must be available to sustain the reaction. With crack widths up to 0.02 inches, and with cover depths of one inch, a high alkaline environment is maintained in the vicinity of the reinforcement. Lack of circulation within cracks of this magnitude prevents destruction of the alkaline environment and, at the same time, prevents oxygen replenishment. Any corrosion reaction initiated under these conditions is soon stifled and stability is reached.

Specifying a limitation of surface crack width of 0.01 inches in concrete pipe, even in aggressive exposure conditions, is unnecessarily conservative. From a durability standpoint, surface cracks up to 0.02 inches in width which do not completely penetrate the pipe wall, and with a minimum of one inch cover over the reinforcement, should be acceptable in an aggressive environment. Pipe with such cracks will have the same durability performance characteristics as an uncracked pipe. Consideration should be given to sealing cracks wider than 0.02 inches, particularly under conditions of severe exposure.

AUTOGENOUS HEALING

Small cracks in concrete, under damp or wet conditions, will in time be sealed by the process of autogenous healing. This natural phenomenon has been studied extensively and reported in the technical literature for over 50 years.

Two examples of the many reported in the literature will serve to illustrate autogenous healing. A piece of 30-inch unreinforced concrete pipe, when tested at Port Angeles, Washington on May 17, 1928, cracked under a three-edge test load of 2430 pounds per linear foot but did not fall apart and was laid aside. On April 8, 1931, the pipe was placed in the same position as when tested in 1928 and withstood a load of 2570 pounds per linear foot by the three-edge method. Both tests were made by the Engineer of Tests, Washington State Highway Department.

A 61-inch extra strength reinforced concrete pipe was installed under a rock fill on U.S. 410 in the State of Washington near the summit of the Cascade Mountains in 1929. Some of the pipe sections, which were provided with elliptical reinforcement, were incorrectly installed. Cracks developed in the crown and invert of the pipe which, when inspected seven years later in August of 1936, were found to have been completely sealed as the result of autogenous healing.

A generally accepted explanation of autogenous healing is that the sealing results from bonding material consisting of calcium carbonate and calcium hydroxide crystals. There is greater strength when the crack is healed under water. It is hypothesized this results from the higher concentration of carbon dioxide than found in air at 95 percent relative humidity, and in the greater ease of migration of the soluble calcium hydroxide in the paste if appreciable water is present. Strength of the bond is considered directly related to bridging of the crack and the percentage of the crack that is filled with the calcium carbonate crystals. The autogenous healing process is particularly applicable to concrete pipe, since moisture is present in considerable amount in practically all installations.

LININGS OR COATINGS

Under severe exposure to acids or chlorides, linings or coatings may provide an engineering alternative. But since these exposure conditions are rare, determination that there will be economic benefits necessitates a thorough analysis of service conditions and a realistic definition of aggressive factors encountered. Mitigating effects of short term or intermittent exposure characteristics are also relevant.

Potential alleviation of exposure conditions by modification of design details should also be explored, such as the application of the principles of sulfide control to sanitary sewer design, *Chapter 7*. Direct durability enhancement of the concrete pipe can also be considered; for example, increasing total alkalinity for greater acid resistance. Use of pipe linings or coatings as protective measures should be limited to those cases where it will provide the most cost-effective solution for the desired level of durability. Different types are commercially available and have been used in concrete pipe with varying degrees of success.

Thin linings and coatings are generally applied by brush, spray or roller. Single or multiple applications may be used, depending upon the characteristics of the material and the desired total thickness. Thin linings and coatings generally range from 10 mils to 50 mils in thickness. Dependable and uniform adherence to the concrete surface is an essential requirement for long-term performance. Careful preparation of the concrete surface is necessary prior to application.

Materials used for thin linings and coatings range from epoxies to bituminous materials such as asphalt or coal tar. Bituminous materials are particularly applicable for exterior surface sealing against chloride intrusion. Discussions of the physical and chemical properties of these materials are included in a report by American Concrete Institute Committee 515. Technical literature from material manufacturers, and concrete pipe producers, are good sources for information on specific linings and coatings.

Thick linings and coatings have a thickness in excess of 50 mils and can be expected to provide better long-term protection. They also tend to be more expensive. The two basic types of materials in this category are **epoxy resin mortars** and **polyvinyl chloride sheets.** Additional information can be obtained from the previously referenced ACI report, from manufacturers' technical literature and from pipe manufacturers and previous users.

Epoxy resin mortar linings and coatings are usually mechanically applied. The material can be applied either immediately after the pipe is manufactured, or after curing.

Polyvinyl chloride sheets, with keys projecting from one face, are placed around the inner pipe form prior to placement of the concrete. The keys project into the concrete pipe wall to form a positive mechanical bond. This application process allows any degree of the pipe periphery to be protected. Continuity of the lining is provided by heat welding or fusing each individual sheet to the next.

REFERENCES

1. "Autogenous Healing," Concrete Construction Engineering, Vol. 31, 1936.
2. "Autogenous Healing of Concrete," F. Brandeis, Beton M. Eisen, Vol. 36, No. 12, 1937.
3. "Autogenous Healing of Concrete," M. W. Loving, American Concrete Pipe Association, Bulletin 13, 1936.
4. "Autogenous Healing of Concrete," V. J. Soroker, A. J. Desov, Constructeur de Ciment Arme, Vol. 18, No. 197, 1936.
5. "The Autogenous Healing of Cement and Concrete—its Relation to Vibrated Concrete and Cracked Concrete," Leslie Turner, International Association for Testing Materials, London, 1937.
6. "The Autogenous Healing of Concrete and Mortars," H. J. Gilkey, American Society for Testing and Materials, Proceedings, Vol. 26, Part II, 1926 and Vol. 29, Part II, 1929.
7. "Autogenous Healing of Cement Paste," Kenneth R. Lauer, Floyd O. Slate, American Concrete Institute Journal, Vol. 27, No. 10, Proceedings, Vol. 52, June, 1956.
8. "Autogenous Healing in Mortars Containing Lime," F. O. Anderegg, American Society for Testing and Materials Bulletin, May, 1942.
9. "Concrete Corrosion and Concrete Protection," Imre Biczok, Chemical Publishing Co., Inc., 1967.
10. "Concrete Irrigation and Drainage Pipe in Sulfate Soils," American Concrete Pipe Association, March, 1968.
11. "Concrete Manual," U.S. Department of the Interior, Bureau of Reclamation, U.S. Government Printing Office, Eighth Edition, 1975.
12. "Concrete Pipe Handbook," H. F. Peckworth, American Concrete Pipe Association, 1967.
13. "Corrosion Protection Properties of Portland Cement Concrete," G. N. Scott, Journal AWWA, Vol. 57, No. 8, August, 1965.
14. "Durability of Concrete," American Concrete Institute, 1975.
15. "Durability of Concrete Construction," American Concrete Institute Monograph Number 4, 1968.
16. "Effects of Cracks in Reinforced Concrete Culvert Pipe," Concrete Pipe Information No. 7, American Concrete Pipe Association, February, 1976.
17. "Effects of Cracks in Reinforced Concrete Sanitary Sewer Pipe," Concrete Pipe Information No. 6, American Concrete Pipe Association, March, 1971.
18. "Electrochemical Behavior of Steel in Concrete," D. A. Hausmann, American Concrete Institute Journal, Vol. 61, No. 2, February, 1964.
19. "Fractured Concrete Test Specimens Heal and Show Increased Compressive Strength When Retested," F. T. Maddocks, California Highways, August, 1925.
20. "Guide to Durable Concrete," American Concrete Institute Journal, Vol. 74, No. 12, December, 1977.
21. "Guide for the Protection of Concrete Against Chemical Attack by Means of Coatings and Other Corrosion Resistant Materials," American Concrete Institute Journal, Vol. 63, No. 12, December, 1966.
22. "Process Design Manual for Sulfide Control in Sanitary Sewerage Systems," U.S. Environmental Protection Agency, Technology Transfer Office, 1974.
23. "Significance of Cracking in Reinforced Concrete Pipe," John G. Hendrickson, Jr., Highway Research Board Proceedings, Vol. 40, 1961.
24. "Test of a 40-ft. Reinforced Concrete Highway Bridge," D. A. Abrams, American Society for Testing and Materials, Proceedings, Vol. 13, 1913.

CHAPTER 7

DESIGN FOR SULFIDE CONTROL

Hydrogen sulfide is a highly objectional gas that can be generated from many sources. In addition to its toxicity and obnoxious odor, the gas attacks metals and can be oxidized to sulfuric acid which attacks virtually all materials. Under certain conditions, hydrogen sulfide can be generated within sanitary sewer systems. Accordingly, control of hydrogen sulfide generation and its effects within a sewer line are major design considerations.

The corrosion of concrete pipe and manholes by sulfuric acid generated from hydrogen sulfide gas has occurred in certain localities. These instances of corrosion have been given wide publicity and have created unnecessary concern in other areas. The objectives of this chapter are to:

- Establish data and procedures required to determine and evaluate the sulfide condition in existing sewer systems.
- Present procedures for correlation of existing sulfide levels with those of predictive equations.
- Present procedures for predicting sulfide levels and associated corrosion rates in a proposed new sewer.
- Present appropriate and realistic service life design methods for new sewers.

CORROSION PERSPECTIVE

Sanitary sewage is conveyed in gravity flow sewers designed to flow part full and sometimes in force mains designed to force sewage up grades under pressure. Under anaerobic conditions and where full flow does not occur, sulfide, SO_2, may be generated in sewage, combined with hydrogen and released to the atmosphere as hydrogen sulfide, H_2S. The hydrogen sulfide gas must then be oxidized to sulfuric acid, H_2SO_4, by bacteria on the unsubmerged portion of the pipe in the presence of moisture before corrosion can occur. In force mains, atmospheric release of hydrogen sulfide can take place only at the discharge end, which is the point of critical odor and corrosion problems.

In Canada and the northern part of the United States, sewer failures from sulfuric acid corrosion are almost unknown. The few cases where damage has occurred have resulted directly from the discharge of force mains. In the southern part of the United States, odor and corrosion problems are somewhat more common. Los Angeles County, California is considered a representative southern area where hydrogen sulfide has been extensively researched for many years.

Dr. Richard D. Pomeroy, an international expert on hydrogen sulfide in sanitary sewer systems and a major researcher in the Southern California area, stated in a 1970 *Public Works* article: *In the City of Los Angeles and in the trunk sewer system of the Los Angeles County Sanitation Districts, there are about 1700 miles of unprotected concrete sewers, averaging 35 years in age. About one quarter of one percent have failed for all reasons. A major part of these sewers were designed before there was any understanding of the sulfide problem; some of those failures can be blamed on that ignorance.* ***Compared to the cost of repairing the damage, millions of dollars have been saved by not putting in expensive protection in places where it was not needed.***

Hydrogen sulfide creates problems other than corrosion of concrete. For example, as a gas escaping from wastewater, manholes, pumping stations and treatment plants, it is a potent and objectional problem. The gas is toxic and lives have been lost from breathing hydrogen sulfide in sewers. Furthermore, the odor is obnoxious to persons working or living in such areas and detrimental to the economic stability of affected neighborhoods. Hydrogen sulfide also adversely affects the activated sludge process used in many treatment plants. The gas reacts directly with metals, and can corrode iron, silver, copper, cadmium and lead.

Sulfide is sometimes present in wastewaters added to sewers, particularly in certain industrial wastes. In rare instances, groundwaters with high concentrations of sulfide have leaked into sewers, but the most common source of sulfide is biological activity. To some extent this comes about by the decomposition of sulfur-containing organic matter, particularly the albuminoid proteins. In domestic wastewater, the major amount of sulfide results from the reduction of inorganic sulfur compounds. Sulfate, organic matter, and bacteria capable of bringing about the reaction that produces sulfide are present in virtually all sewers. Despite the presence of these essential elements, sulfide is not produced in all wastewater systems. In fact, severe sulfide concentrations occur infrequently. A major objective of sulfide research has been to discover the reasons why sulfide appears in some sewers and not in others.

The formation of the United States Environmental Protection Agency, **EPA,** marked a new era of environmental awareness. A vital part of EPA's national water pollution control effort is the development and dissemination of new technology for wastewater treatment systems. In October, 1974, EPA published a major report titled *Process Design Manual for Sulfide Control in Sanitary Sewerage Systems.* This manual is an excellent source of information and basis for control of corrosion and noxious conditions resulting from hydrogen sulfide in existing sewerage systems, and for design of new systems to avoid these problems. Since publication of the manual, EPA collected substantial information on odors and corrosion in municipal sewerage systems, and significant developments evolved for the control of odors and corrosion in wastewater treatment plants. Consequently, EPA included these advances in a new Design Manual for Odor and Corrosion Control in Sanitary Sewerage Systems and Treatment Plants, October 1985. The theories, methods and data presented in this chapter are principally from these manuals and the American Concrete Pipe Association Design Manual for Sulfide and Corrosion Prediction and Control, which provides step-by-step procedures and design aids for the evaluation and solution of hydrogen sulfide problems.

SULFIDE GENERATION

The mechanism of sulfide generation is described in detail in the EPA manuals and in many other published papers, but a brief review of how sulfide is formed is necessary to define those parameters critical to corrosion. Sulfate, is reduced to sulfide by sulfate-reducing bacteria which exist only in a medium completely devoid of free oxygen or other active oxidizing agents. The wastewater in a partly filled sewer is not completely anaerobic, free of oxygen, because oxygen absorbed at the surface of the stream generally reacts quite rapidly. In large sewers the oxygen concentration is very low, yet enough is present to prevent sulfate reduction in the stream.

Sulfur compounds, such as sulfate, sulfite or other inorganic or organic sulfur, must be present in the wastewater to provide the raw material for conversion to sulfide. Most domestic sewage naturally contains sufficient sulfates for this to occur but a high level of sulfates does not necessarily mean there will be a high sulfide level as other factors control the conversion process. A deficiency of sulfates will inhibit the production of sulfide even though other factors are favorable for sulfide buildup.

When there are historical or other reasons to anticipate the possibility of hydrogen sulfide problems in a proposed new sewer system, an investigation should be made at the time the system is being designed. The design can then incorporate control measures, if necessary, to prevent sulfide generation. If sulfide generation can be eliminated for the average temperature for the warmest three months of the year and the biochemical oxygen demand, *BOD,* and flow for the highest six hours of the day, it can be assumed that infrequent extremes producing a small amount of sulfide will be of little consequence.

AEROBIC SYSTEMS

Figure 7.1 depicts the processes that occur in a sewer with sufficient disolved oxygen in the sewage, aerobic, to prevent generation of sulfide in the stream. Anaerobic conditions can develop within the slime layer that forms on the submerged pipe wall. The slime layer is composed of three zones. The zone next to the pipe wall is anaerobic but inactive because of a lack of nutrients. The middle zone is also anaerobic and is the sulfide producing zone. Observations and theory indicate that sulfate and the organic nutrients

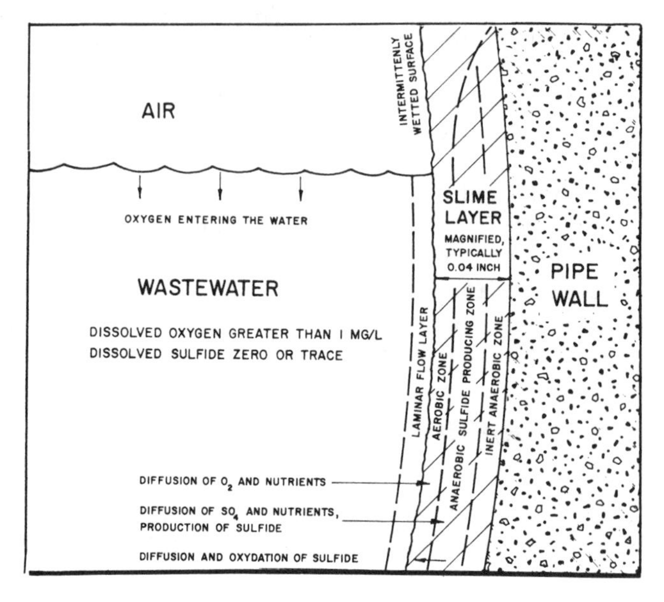

Figure 7.1. Processes Occuring in Sewers with No Sulfide Buildup.

available to the sulfate-reducing bacteria are used up in a very short distance which accounts for the inactivity of the zone next to the pipe wall. When oxygen is present in the wastewater, it diffuses into the slime layer and creates the surface zone which is aerobic. As long as the surface zone remains aerobic, sulfide diffusing out of the anaerobic zone will be oxidized and no sulfide will be present in the stream unless supplied from an extraneous source.

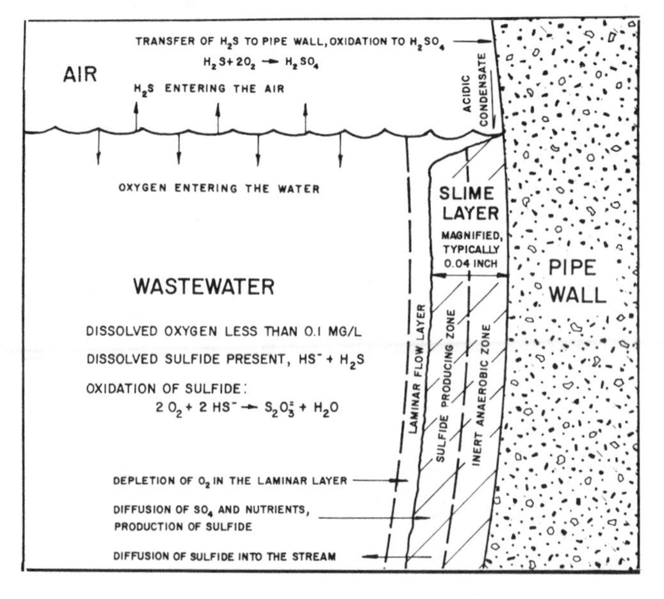

Figure 7.2. Processes Occuring in Sewers Under Sulfide Buildup.

ANAEROBIC SYSTEMS

Figure 7.2 depicts the process in a sewer with insufficient dissolved oxygen to prevent sulfide diffusion into the stream. If the oxygen concentration in the stream drops to a low level, not enough oxygen will enter the surface zone of the slime to oxidize all of the sulfide generated in the anaerobic zone. Even when the oxygen content is low enough so sulfide enters into the stream, only a small percentage may get through. Completely anaerobic conditions must be approached before all the sulfide produced can diffuse into the stream.

Sulfide in the stream is present in soluble and insoluble forms and is not harmful to concrete but may affect the sewage treatment process. Furthermore, insoluble sulfide is not involved in the concrete corrosion process. Soluble sulfide, commonly termed dissolved sulfide, consists of molecular hydrogen sulfide and sulfide ions with the percentage of each dependent on the sewage *pH*. Only molecular hydrogen sulfide is critical to the corrosion process and may be emitted to the sewer atmosphere as a gas. The gaseous hydrogen sulfide in the sewer atmosphere is not harmful to concrete, but is toxic and creates objectionable odors. Aerobic bacteria on the unsubmerged wall of the pipe, in the presence of oxygen and water, oxidize the hydrogen sulfide to sulfuric acid. A portion of this acid will run off the pipe walls back into the stream. The acid remaining on the wall will be available to react with any alkaline materials in concrete or any type of cementitious or ferrous material.

CRITICAL PARAMETERS

Hydrogen sulfide and corrosion in wastewater sewers are dependent upon the occurrence of the necessary hydraulic and water quality conditions. The critical parameters are dissolved sulfides, *pH, BOD,* temperature, dissolved oxygen, velocity, gas emission rate, rate of oxidation to sulfuric acid, concrete alkalinity, junctions, forcemains, ventilation, amount of acid runoff and flow-slope relationship.

Dissolved Sulfides and pH

The sulfide in wastewater consists of dissolved sulfides and insoluble compounds. Only the dissolved sulfide contributes to the release of H_2S to the sewer atmosphere. In wastewater with significant concentrations of heavy metal ions, such as iron and zinc, a significant fraction of the total sulfide generated may be removed as insoluble sulfide. This fraction will remain relatively constant within a system handling primarily domestic sewage and has been found to range between 0.1 and 0.3 milligrams per litre. In predicting the amount of sulfide that will be produced in a sewer, the first few tenths of a milligrams per litre produced can be considered non-reactive due to precipitation by metals.

Dissolved sulfide may total several parts per million, but the critical molecular hydrogen sulfide may be quite low because of the sewage *pH*.

Hydrogen sulfide in solution in water dissociates into the hydrosulfide ion, HS^-, and hydrogen ion, H^+, as shown by the equation:

$$H_2S \rightleftarrows HS^- + H^+ \tag{7.1}$$

The relative proportions of H_2S and HS^- in the dissolved sulfide fraction in water are primarily a function of pH, and are related by the expression:

$$\log \frac{[HS^-]}{[H_2S]} = pH - pK \tag{7.2}$$

$[HS^-]$ and $[H_2S]$ are molar concentrations of the respective constituents, and pK is the negative logarithm of the practical ionization constant as written in the arithmetic form. The value of pK varies somewhat with temperature and salinity, but has an average value of 7.0 which is sufficiently accurate for design estimates. The HS^- ion similarly dissociates into the sulfide ion, $S^=$, and the H^+ ion. However, for the pH values typically found in wastewater, the sulfide ion occurs in quite negligible amounts. Neither the sulfide ion nor the hydrosulfide ion contributes anything to the corrosion and odor problems except as precursors of hydrogen sulfide gas.

The relative amount of dissolved sulfide as H_2S depends on the pH of the wastewater. The relationship, J factor, is shown on *Figure 7.3*. At a pH of 5,

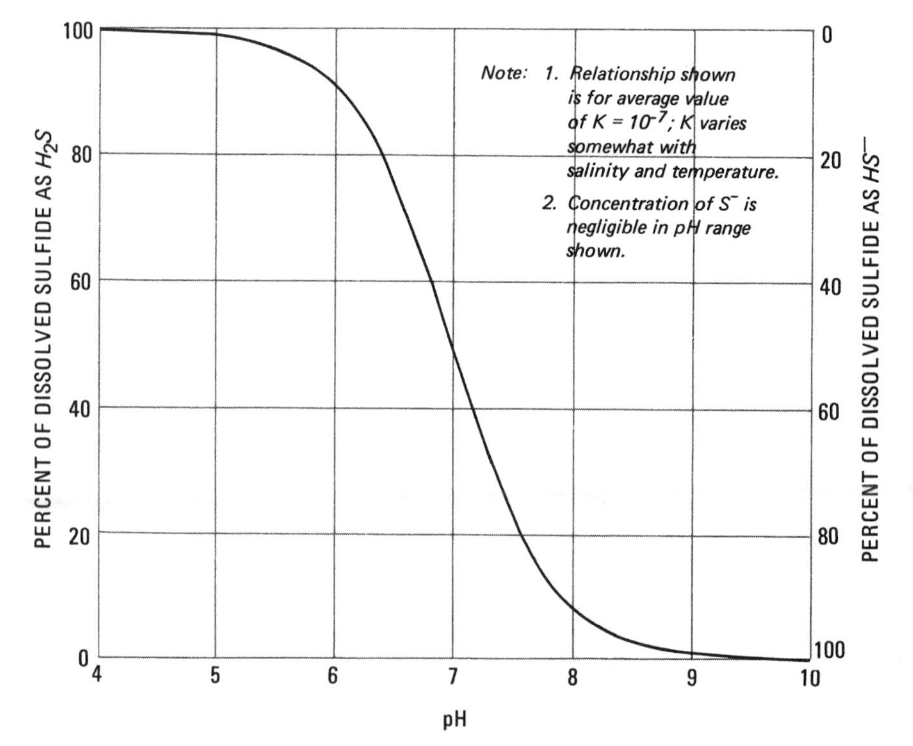

Figure 7.3. Relationship of Dissolved Sulfide Equilibrium to *pH, J* Factor.

hydrogen sulfide will be 99 percent of the dissolved sulfide. At a *pH* of 7, it will be 50 percent, and at a *pH* of 8, only 9 percent. At a *pH* of 7.5, which is the *pH* of average sewage, hydrogen sulfide will be 25 percent of the dissolved sulfide. Therefore, maintenance of the sewage flow in the high *pH* range is an important factor in reducing and eliminating sulfide and corrosion problems.

Available computer programs and the *A/B Curves* used as sulfide generation indicators are modeled for climactic conditions. Climactic conditions indicate a worst case situation, and are not representative of average annual sulfide conditions which must be used for corrosion condition analyses. The climactic conditions are defined as the average BOD_5 concentrations and temperature which occur during the highest six-hour flow period of the day for the warmest three months of the year. Predicted climactic sulfide concentrations can be adjusted to average annual concentrations as discussed in the following paragraphs.

It is necessary to determine representative average annual sulfide concentrations to avoid over-designing a system for conditions that occur only a limited percent of the time. Representative conditions for sulfide variations are sometimes difficult to determine since the conditions and resultant sulfide concentrations vary both daily and seasonally. The annual variation is usually much greater than the daily variation. Both types of variation are caused by a variety of factors including temperature, flow, *BOD*, and *pH*.

The use of average dissolved sulfide concentrations rather than peak concentrations during design becomes significant when estimating the corrosion rates. By taking the product of the annual and daily ratios of average to peak dissolved sulfide concentrations, an average annual correction factor can be approximated using the following relationship:

$$\frac{[DS]\text{ Annual Average}}{[DS]\text{ Annual Peak}} \times \frac{[DS]\text{ Daily Average}}{[DS]\text{ Daily Peak}} = C \qquad (7.3)$$

Where: $[DS]$ = dissolved sulfides, milligrams per litre
C = average annual correction factor

If sulfide concentrations are observed or predicted for summer or climactic conditions, the values should be adjusted as follows:

$$\text{Annual Average }[DS] = C \times [DS]_c \qquad (7.4)$$

Where: $[DS]_c$ = climactic dissolved sulfides measured during three warmest months or estimated from climactic conditions, milligrams per litre

Approximate values of the correction factor *C* are shown in *Table 7.1* for various $[BOD_5]_c$ concentrations and temperatures, T_c, which were obtained from data collected in several cities throughout central California. The tabular correction factors may be used for design analyses, but it is recommended that similar tables be developed for specific areas if data are available.

Table 7.1. Approximate *C* Values for Various Temperatures and $[BOD_5]_c$.[1]

$[BOD_5]_c$, milligrams per litre	T_c, degrees celsius			
	20	25	30	35
150	0.25	0.25	0.30	0.35
200	0.30	0.30	0.35	0.40
250	0.35	0.35	0.40	0.45
300	0.35	0.40	0.45	0.50

[1]C values based on central California data

BOD and Temperature

Sulfide is a higher energy form of sulfur than the sulfate from which it is derived. The source of energy that allows the conversion from sulfate to sulfide to take place is the biodegradable material dissolved in the wastewater. The quantity of this material available to fuel the process is measured by the conventional 5-day biochemical oxygen demand, $[BOD_5]$, test. $[BOD_5]$, a measure of the depletion of the dissolved oxygen in the wastewater by the decomposition and mineralization of organic matter, has proven useful in developing predictive models of sulfide generation. Therefore, the rate of sulfide generation is dependent on the flux of chemical energy to the responsible organisms. The predictive equations and sulfide indicators model the *BOD* as the driving force of sulfide generation. Of necessity, the value chosen for this parameter has to be based on the conventional 5-day *BOD* test. *BOD* values for typical wastewaters range from 100 to 300 milligrams per litre.

Temperature also affects the rate of sulfide generation. Sulfide generation may be present above 15° celsius if all other conditions for sulfide generation exist. The effect of temperature cycles on sulfide buildup is illustrated in *Figure 7.4* depicting sulfide concentrations at the end of a force main in Long Beach, California. One test was made each week for two years. An annual cycle is evident, and daily cycles would be expected also.

The combined effects of wastewater $[BOD_5]$ and temperature can be estimated by determining the effective *BOD*, $[EBOD]$, as shown in the following equation:

$$[EBOD] = [BOD_5] \times 1.07^{(T-20)} \quad (7.5)$$

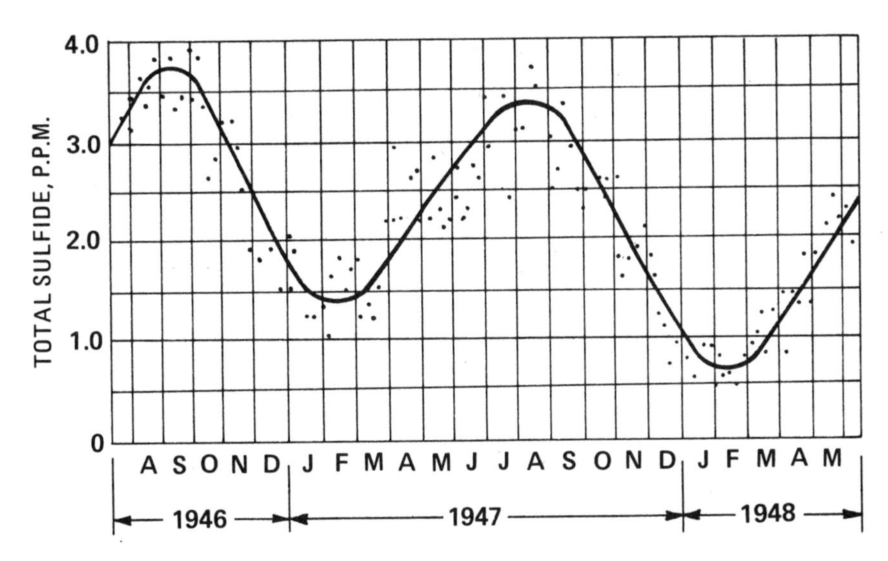

Figure 7.4. Sulfide Concentrations at End of Force Main in Long Beach.

Where: $[EBOD]$ = effective $[BOD_5]$, milligrams per litre
$[BOD_5]$ = composite average BOD_5, milligrams per litre
T = temperature, degrees celsius

When adequate wastewater quality data are available, such as year-round treatment plant influent records, $[EBOD]$ values can be estimated for any time of the year using the available $[BOD_5]$ and temperature data. The maximum sulfide generation conditions usually occur during the warmest months of the year and are not usually representative of the average annual conditions. Therefore, if adequate data are available for estimating $[EBOD]$, the average annual or seasonal sulfide generation potential can be calculated. When adequate data are not available, an acceptable method of estimating sulfide generation potential is to use maximum BOD_5 and temperature conditions and to adjust the results using available empirical correction factors.

The peak $[EBOD]$, commonly termed climactic effective BOD, is defined by the equation:

$$[EBOD]_c = [BOD_5]_c \times 1.07^{(T_c - 20)} \tag{7.6}$$

Where: $[EBOD]_c$ = climactic effective $[BOD_5]$, milligrams per litre
$[BOD_5]_c$ = climactic $[BOD_5]$, milligrams per litre
T_c = climactic temperature, degrees celsius

The climactic conditions are the average $[BOD_5]$ concentrations and temperature which occur during the highest six-hour flow period of the day for the warmest three months of the year. Climactic *BOD*, $[BOD]_c$, can be approximated as 1.25 times a flow-proportioned 24-hour composite *BOD*. If the climactic effective *BOD* is used in the sulfide generation predictive equation, the result will represent the maximum sulfide conditions that can be expected.

Dissolved Oxygen

When dissolved oxygen is present in wastewater, the major portion of sulfide passing from the slime layer into the wastewater is oxidized. The overall reaction of oxygen with sulfide produces thiosulfate:

$$2O_2 + 2HS^- \xrightarrow{\text{bacteria}} S_2O_3^= + H_2O \qquad (7.7)$$

The rate at which oxygen enters a stream with a free air surface is determined in part by the relative concentrations of oxygen in the air and

Illustration 7.1
Concrete pipe designed to meet life factor analysis being installed in the Herndon Avenue Interceptor Sewer, City of Fresno, California in 1976.

water and by the resistances which hinder movement of oxygen between two phases. In a ventilated sewer, the concentration of oxygen in the water represents the outcome of dynamic processes which influence its entry into the water and its consumption there by organisms. The rate at which oxygen is consumed is influenced by the level of oxygen available, the temperature, and the quantity and character of oxidizable substances. Increasing the oxygen concentration increases the amount of oxygen used in the slime layer but not the amount used by the wastewater stream.

All of these processes are emanable to mathematical representation and have been well studied. The rate at which oxygen is consumed in warm, rich wastewater is appreciable compared to the rate at which oxygen crosses the air-water interface in all but the most favorable circumstances. Hydraulic design considerations can bring about the circumstances that favor the entry of oxygen into the wastewater.

The hydraulic design for a new sewer can be such that the wastewater maintains dissolved oxygen throughout its length. This can be achieved by providing hydraulic structures that will produce turbulence which will overcome the resistance to oxygen entering the wastewater. Provided oxygen enters the wastewater at a rate equal to or greater than the rate at which it is used, the stream will remain aerobic and sulfide will not accumulate. In existing sewers, hydrogen sulfide problems can be controlled by injection of air or oxygen directly into the pipeline sewage flow.

Dissolved oxygen contents of approximately one milligram per litre, or greater, in the wastewater stream prevent sulfide generation (*Figure 7.1*). Less than one milligram per litre of dissolved oxygen in the wastewater indicates that sulfide generation may occur if other factors are favorable, and that further analysis is necessary.

Velocity

Consideration of velocities is important when designing a system for a long service life. Initially the average velocity may be low and then increase when the flow doubles and sometimes triples over the life of the project. It is important to perform a sulfide analysis for chronological increments of the design period since conditions usually improve with time and sulfide generation may become insignificant.

Velocity affects the rate of oxygen absorption into the wastewater, the release of hydrogen sulfide to the atmosphere, and solids buildup. Velocity also is an energy function which is used in sulfide generation indicator equations.

If the velocity of the wastewater stream is insufficient to move solids through the pipe, they will settle and provide additional sites for the generation of sulfide. The quantity of sulfide produced on or in particles suspended in the wastewater stream itself is not significant except perhaps in deep, slow-moving streams.

Observations of the effect of velocity on the slime layer are limited, but as shown in *Figure 7.5,* velocity does have a tangible effect on the transport of solids. At a velocity as low as 2 feet per second, virtually all solids are

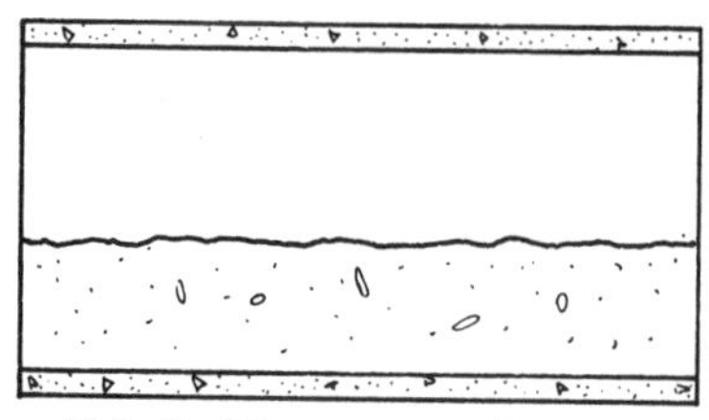

a. Velocity 2 feet per second.
Efficient solids transport. No sulfide buildup in small flows, up to 2 cubic feet per second. Sulfide buildup often observed in larger flows but only at a very slow rate.

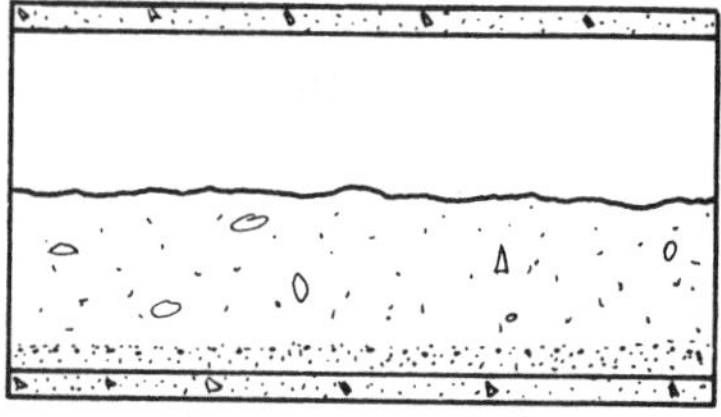

b. Velocity 1.4 to 2.0 feet per second.
Inorganic grit accumulating in the bottom. More sulfide buildup as the velocity diminishes.

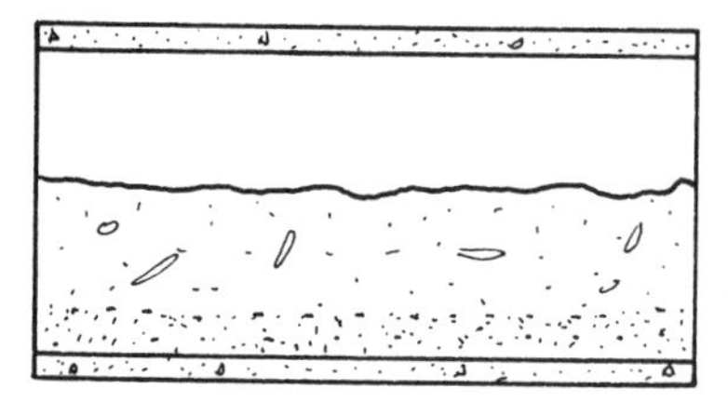

c. Velocity 1.0 to 1.4 feet per second.
Inorganic grit in the bottom, organic solids slowly moving along the bottom. Strongly enhanced sulfide buildup; severe problems expected.

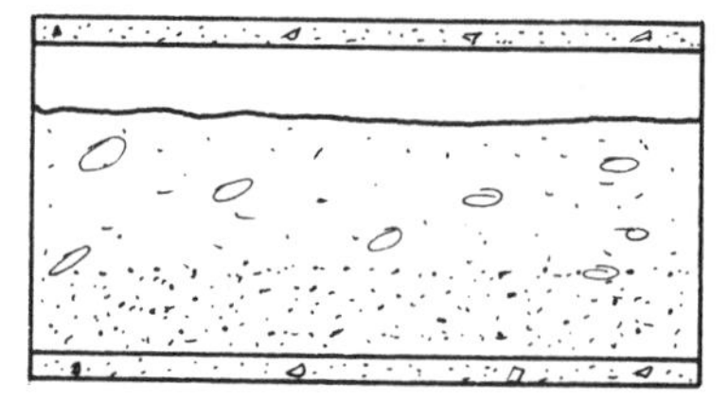

d. Velocity below 1.0 feet per second.
Much organic and inorganic solid matter accumulating, overlain with slow-moving organic solids. Sulfide problems worse than in c.

Figure 7.5. Solids Accumulations at Various Flow Velocities.

transported and no sulfide buildup has been observed in small flow quantities of up to 2 cubic feet per second. Sulfide buildup has been observed in larger flows at velocities of 2 feet per second but only at a very slow rate. At velocities between 1.4 and 2 feet per second, inorganic grit begins to accumulate in the bottom of the pipe and sulfide buildup begins and increases as the velocity diminishes. At velocities between 1 and 1.4 feet per second, more inorganic grit accumulates, organic solids move slowly along the bottom, and strong sulfide buildup and severe problems would be expected. At velocities below one foot per second, both inorganic and organic solids accumulate on the bottom of the pipe and sulfide buildup greatly increases. The importance of maintaining a minimum velocity of 2 feet per second cannot be overemphasized. A minimum velocity of 2 feet per second:

- Provides efficient solids transport
- Produces no sulfide buildup in small flows up to 2 cubic feet per second
- Produces a slow rate of sulfide buildup in larger flows

Gas Emission Rate

The rate at which hydrogen sulfide can escape from the stream to the air, under any given conditions of exposure is proportional to the molecular hydrogen sulfide level. Thus, less hydrogen sulfide will be emitted as the pH of the stream increases. The rate of hydrogen sulfide release to the atmosphere increases as the velocity and turbulence of the flow increase.

Oxidation Rate

The oxidation rate is a function of the activity of the bacteria that oxidize hydrogen sulfide to sulfuric acid. These bacteria require an adequate supply of hydrogen sulfide gas and adequate wall moisture. These two elements, necessary to the corrosion process, can be reduced by either natural or forced ventilation.

Concrete Alkalinity

The alkalinity of concrete pipe is a significant factor in resisting acid corrosion. Alkalinity is defined in terms of the amount of acid which a known mass of material can neutralize as compared to the acid neutralizing capability of pure calcium carbonate, $CaCO_3$. The alkalinity of each material used in the manufacture of concrete pipe must be known if the mix is to be designed to meet a specified value. The test method for determining the calcium carbonate equivalent of any material is a relatively simple and standard procedure. The alkalinity of the concrete cover over the reinforcement can be verified by the same method. Since the corrosion rate is inversely proportional to alkalinity, concrete with an alkalinity of 0.8 would last four times as long as concrete with an alkalinity of 0.2. Concrete pipe alkalinity can range from 0.18 to more than 1.0 depending on the cement content and type of aggregates. As an example, the alkalinity of a concrete with 594 pounds of cement per cubic yard varies with the aggregate:

- Granitic aggregate, alkalinity from 0.18 to 0.22
- 50 percent calcareous aggregate, alkalinity from 0.4 to 0.6
- 100 percent calcareous aggregate, alkalinity from 0.8 to 0.9

Junctions

Junctions can significantly affect wastewater quality parameters that cause sulfide generation. Tributary water quality parameters such as BOD_5, dissolved oxygen, temperature, and pH can affect the sulfide generation potential of a main trunk. Industrial discharges with high sulfide concentrations can cause a large increase in sulfide concentrations in the receiving gravity line. Similarly, tributary flows with little or no sulfide and possibly some dissolved oxygen can decrease the sulfide concentration in the sewer trunk and be beneficial. Each junction in the system should be analyzed individually.

The hydraulics of junctions also are important. At turbulent junctions, there can be an increased transfer of hydrogen sulfide from the wastewater to the atmosphere and an increased amount of reaeration, or oxygen transfer, into the wastewater. This process may increase the hydrogen sulfide in the gas phase in downstream reaches if hydrogen sulfide is present or the oxygen concentration of the waste stream may increase, thereby reducing the downstream potential for sulfide generation. In general, the detrimental effects of corrosion are more significant than any benefit derived from increased oxygen entrainment. Therefore, it is important that junctions be designed to minimize turbulence.

Force Mains and Siphons

Force mains and siphons which flow full are not susceptible to corrosion attack. However, sulfides generated within force main systems can cause significant problems where they outlet into gravity wastewater sewers. Force mains usually flow full creating a continuous slime layer buildup which can result in a high rate of sulfide generation. Force mains and siphons also may be operated at low velocities, or intermittently, thereby increasing the detention time and causing increased sulfide buildup.

Pomeroy's equation for predicting sulfide buildup in force mains was published over 30 years ago and has been refined to its present form:

$$S = 3.28(t)(M)[EBOD](1 + 0.48r)r^{-1} \qquad (7.8)$$

Where:
- S = total sulfides, milligrams per litre
- t = flow time, hours
- M = specific sulfide flux coefficient, metres per hour
- $[EBOD]$ = effective $[BOD_5]$, milligrams per litre
- r = hydraulic radius, feet

Based on observations of a number of force mains, it was found that the value M ranges from 0.50×10^{-3} metres per hour to 1.3×10^{-3} metres per hour. A value of 0.75×10^{-3} metres per hour was calculated using actual measured values of sulfide generation in the Sacramento area.

When designing a collection system for sulfide control, force mains and siphons should always be considered as a potential source for sulfide generation and appropriate design measures incorporated. Either aeration or chemical addition into the force main or protection of the downstream gravity sewer should be considered. Although force mains can be high sulfide contributors, the increased pressure and full flow conditions provide a good environment within which chemicals or oxygen can be added and dissolved in the wastewater. These controls can reduce the detrimental effect on a downstream gravity system.

Ventilation and Acid Runoff

If the sewer structure above the wastewater level is damp and the sewer atmosphere contains hydrogen sulfide, the hydrogen sulfide will be absorbed by the film of moisture on the wall surface. Aerobic bacteria in the film of moisture oxidizes hydrogen sulfide to sulfuric acid:

$$H_2S + 2O_2 \xrightarrow{\text{bacteria}} H_2SO_4 \qquad (7.9)$$

The acid produced by this reaction attacks the cementitious material in the wall as it trickles down into the wastewater stream.

If the sewer structure above the wastewater level is dry, there will be no film of water to absorb the hydrogen sulfide. If the wall cannot serve as a hydrogen sulfide trap, there will be no formation of sulfuric acid on the wall and hence no corrosion. However, it is very difficult to maintain a dry wall in a sewer due to temperature differentials that promote condensation on the pipe wall. Ventilation has been found to be not too highly effective in most instances where utilized in an attempt to maintain a dry wall.

Flow-Slope Relationship

Flow quantities and sewage conditions are highly erratic in small sewers. A flow, even though the velocity is so slow that solids are deposited, may remain free of sulfide because of shallow depth, low oxygen reacting rate, or service laterals. These observations led to studies which confirm the importance of the flow-slope relationship.

The results of a 1950 survey of the occurrence of sulfide in small sewers, primarily sponsored by the American Concrete Pipe Association, are shown in *Figure 7.6* and illustrate the dominant effect of slope. The results do not

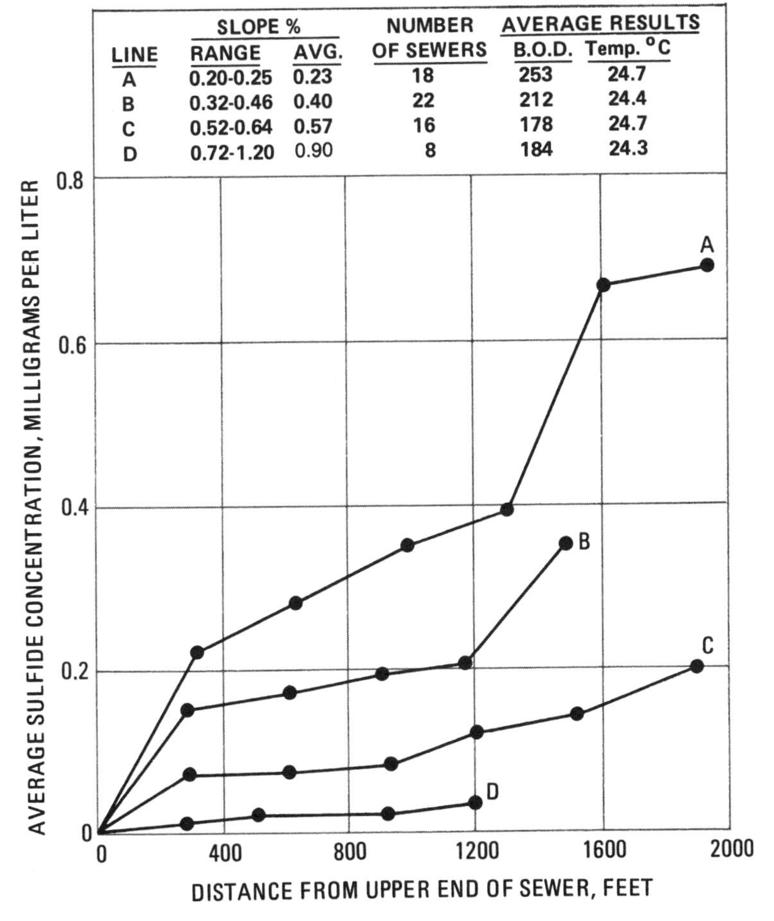

LINE	SLOPE % RANGE	SLOPE % AVG.	NUMBER OF SEWERS	AVERAGE RESULTS B.O.D.	AVERAGE RESULTS Temp. °C
A	0.20-0.25	0.23	18	253	24.7
B	0.32-0.46	0.40	22	212	24.4
C	0.52-0.64	0.57	16	178	24.7
D	0.72-1.20	0.90	8	184	24.3

Figure 7.6. Sulfide Occurrence in Small Sewers.

represent sulfide buildup as normally defined because sampling did not follow the same body of water downstream. For flow quantities up to one or two cubic feet per second, or more if the temperature is low, and at velocities not less than two feet per second, surface aeration is generally sufficient to maintain an oxygen residual in the stream and consequently suppress sulfide buildup. For larger flow quantities, aeration through turbulence is more important than surface aeration.

The rate of oxygen absorption in rivers can be expressed as proportional to the rate of loss of elevation, provided a major part of aeration occurs in falls and rapids. By applying the same principle to sewers, the overall loss of elevation occurring over a distance equal to a flow time of one hour can be considered as a crude parameter of oxygen supply. Based upon evaluation of available data, the flow-slope curves as shown in *Figure 7.7* were included in

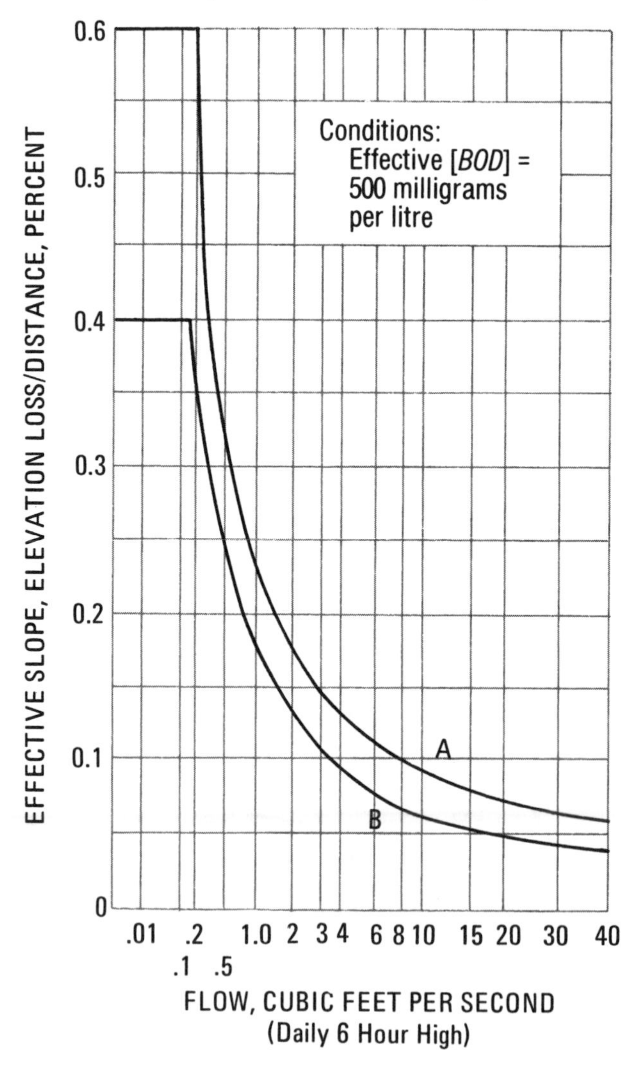

Figure 7.7. Flow-Slope Relationships—[*EBOD*] 500 Milligrams per Litre.

the EPA manuals as a guide in sulfide forecasting, but these curves cannot be used to accurately predict sulfide conditions. The purpose is to indicate an apparent trend in the effect of flow-slope combinations on sulfide buildup.

The vertical scale is the overall or effective slope defined as the elevation loss averaged over a distance equal to that required for flow times of about one hour, except for collecting sewers of minimum size where it would be the actual pipe slope. Interpretations are restricted to flow depths not exceeding two-thirds of the pipe diameter, which means there can be no pressure mains operating upstream unless some measures are taken to offset the oxygen-depleting and sulfide-producing potentials.

The curves must also be qualified as being related to effluent of specified characteristics. The temperature of sewage follows an annual cycle. *BOD* and flow quantity have diurnal, daily cycles. Flow quantities usually have long term trends. It is useful to define a climactic condition as the combination of the average *BOD* and flow quantity for the highest six-hour flow period of the day, and the average temperature for the warmest three months of the year.

SULFIDE INVESTIGATIONS

Information about sulfide conditions is important for the proper operation and maintenance of existing sewer systems and is critical for planning new construction. For planning, a thorough investigation is needed of the entire system and not limited to a part of the system where there are known problems. The purpose of the investigation is to obtain a basis for predicting probable sulfide conditions in a proposed new sewer and thereby indicate where corrective or control measures might be needed.

Two methods available to evaluate the sulfide generating characteristics of an overall sewer system are a preliminary flow-slope analysis, and, if necessary, comprehensive in-line studies. Flow-slope analyses are made first to avoid the field work required for in-line studies in non-problem areas.

FLOW-SLOPE ANALYSES

As previously stated and shown in *Figure 7.7,* flow-slope relationships were adopted by EPA as a guide to sulfide forecasting. For example, assuming the climactic [*EBOD*] for a sewer is 500 milligrams per litre, then an interpretation of *Figure 7.7* is as follows:

- **Curve A**

  While the climactic condition prevails, a system functioning with flow-slope relationships as shown by this curve will produce very little sulfide, rarely more than 0.1 or 0.2 milligrams per litre of dissolved sulfide. The annual average dissolved sulfide concentration will be only a few hundredths of a milligram per litre. For systems with effective slopes higher than those indicated by this curve, sulfide concentrations are negligible.
- **Curve B**

  While the climactic condition prevails, a system functioning with flow-slope relationships as shown by this curve may produce dissolved sulfide at concentrations of several tenths of a milligram per litre. For systems with effective slopes lower than those indicated by this curve, higher sulfide concentrations must be anticipated and some type of odor and corrosion control measures or in-line treatment required to prevent sulfide buildup.

If the climactic [*EBOD*] is higher or lower than 500 milligrams per litre, the positions of Curves A and B are altered, except that the cutoff effective slope of 0.6 percent for Curve A at small flows will remain the same, because the determining factors are hydraulic. Although the relationship between [*EBOD*] and required slope is complex, approximately similar sulfide conditions will result if the effective slopes are increased or decreased in proportion to the square root of [*EBOD*]. For example, for the Curve A condition in *Figure 7.7,* a flow of 2 cubic feet per second requires an effective

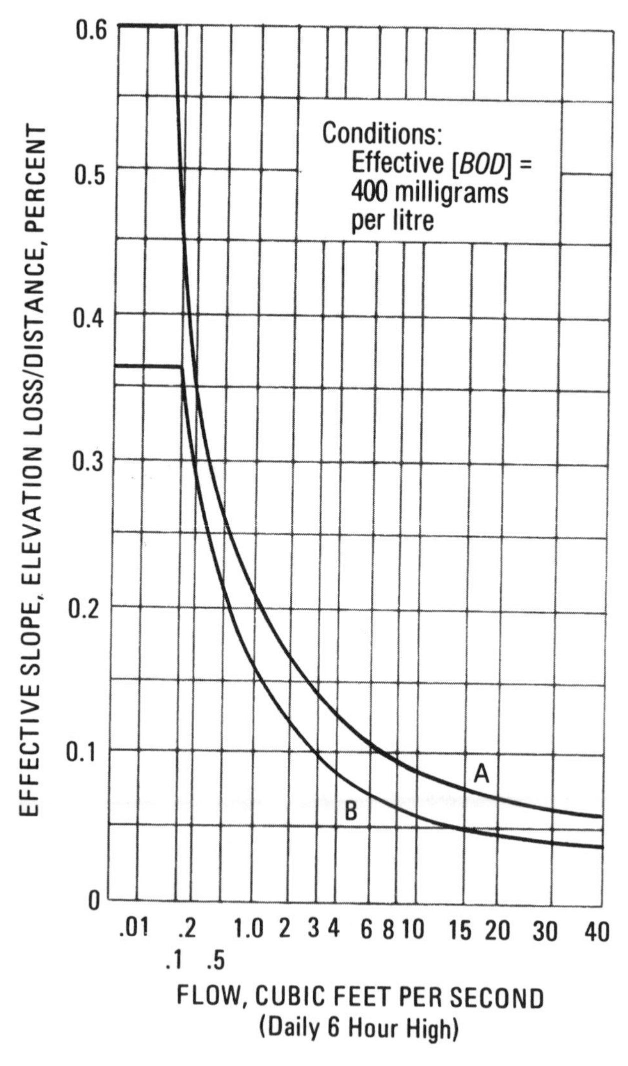

Figure 7.8. Flow-Slope Relationships—[*EBOD*] 400 Milligrams per Litre.

slope of approximately 0.175 percent. If the [*EBOD*] were 600 instead of 500 milligrams per litre, the effective slope for the Curve A condition at 2 cubic feet per second would be:

$$0.175 \text{ percent} \times \sqrt{600/500} = 0.19 \text{ percent}$$

Figures 7.8 and *7.9* indicate the positions of Curves A and B for climactic [*EBOD*]'s of 400 and 600 milligrams per litre.

The procedure for using appropriate flow-slope graphs to locate areas of possible sulfide problems, and to forecast probability of sulfide in a sewer tributary to the proposed new sewer is as follows:

1. Obtain as-built plan maps of the existing system which identify pipe

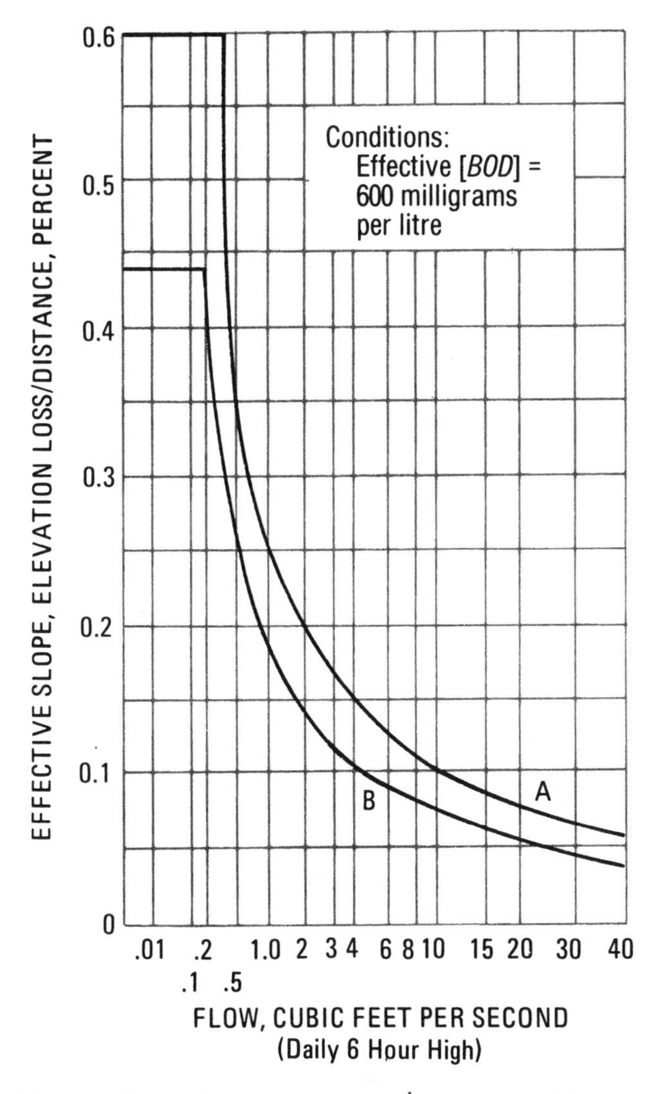

Figure 7.9. Flow-Slope Relationships—[*EBOD*] 600 Milligrams per Litre.

sizes, slopes, invert elevations, materials of construction and manhole locations. If such detailed maps do not exist, mapping should be part of the project.

2. Calculate the effective slope within a one-hour flow-through time for all collector sewers of the project. For low velocities, this distance will be approximately one to two miles. Consider street laterals in appropriate blocks and indicate the average effective slope per block.
3. On the appropriate flow-slope graph, plot the flow-slope relationship for each collector sewer. If flow quantities are not known or readily available, calculate the capacity for flow depths of 1/3 and 2/3 full and plot these as a range.
4. Locate all force mains and inverted siphons in the system as these are considered as the most probable sulfide generators. Note any sulfide control methods already in use.
5. Color code *Figures 7.7, 7.8* and *7.9.* For example, the area below Curve B could be colored red, the area between Curves A and B colored yellow, an area above Curve A equal to the area between Curves A and B colored green, and the area above the green colored blue.
6. This color code is applied to the plan map to graphically display the sulfide potential of each sewer line in the system. Street laterals would be color coded by block. For example, if a ten block area of laterals had an average effective slope of less than 0.4 percent, all those laterals would be lined red. When flows are unknown and a range of flow is plotted, the sulfide potential may fall in two or more categories. Therefore, the sewer should be lined and dash-lined with appropriate alternating colors. The actual flow during the 6-hour maximum flow period for these sewers should be ascertained by an in-line study.
7. Interpretation of the color coded plan map indicates whether a sulfide investigation and in-line studies are required and pinpoints where these should be performed. In the case of a new sewer, if all tributary areas were colored green or blue, then a safe assumption would be that the effluent entering the new sewer would be free of significant sulfide concentrations, and further, that although some sulfide might be present, the concentrations would be insufficient to create an odor or corrosion problem. If some tributary areas are colored red and yellow, indicating moderate to severe sulfide generation, then in-line sulfide studies may be required.

IN-LINE SULFIDE STUDIES

For a rational design procedure, the sulfide generating characteristics of the proposed new sewer must be estimated with reasonable accuracy. This may be accomplished in two ways. First, in-line sulfide studies of existing sewers with characteristics similar to the proposed sewer can be made. Second, the two indicators, Pomeroy's *Z* formula, *Equation 7.11,* and the *A/B Curves, Figures 7.7, 7.8* and *7.9,* on flow-slope relationships can be evaluated, and if either indicator shows the possibility of sulfide generation, the Pomeroy/Parkhurst method can be applied.

As data are accumulated by in-line studies and correlated with the sulfide predictive equation such studies may become unnecessary. Based upon in-line studies conducted by J.D. Gilbert & Associates and reported in *A Case Study, Prediction of Sulfide Generation and Corrosion in Concrete Gravity Sewers in Sacramento, California* in 1978, the less conservative coefficients in *Equation 7.13* adequately predict maximum sulfide levels within the normal range of certainty of other design parameters.

Site Selection

For the total system, refer to the color coded plan map and select those collector sewers within the one-hour flow time distance of the proposed new sewer. For the proposed new sewer, select a similar existing sewer with flow most representative of the tributary to the proposed new sewer.

Visual Inspection

The sewers selected for in-line studies should be visually inspected and information of relative importance noted. This information includes pipe material, extent of any corrosion of the sewer, manhole and manhole steps, sediment and slime depositions, hydrogen sulfide odors, evidence of manhole surcharging, etc.

Sampling

Once a test area is selected, the number and location of the sampling stations are chosen. The objective of this testing program is to determine the change in wastewater properties and composition as it flows through a pipeline. Therefore, samples must be obtained from the same specimen of sewage, termed a **slug,** as it passes the various sampling stations. Obviously then, manpower is a major factor controlling the frequency of sampling. For example, if one man conducts the tests, the distance between sampling stations must provide adequate time to draw the sample, make the tests, and move to the next station before the slug of sewage under test arrives. For a pipeline about one mile long, without junctions, a distance of 1,000 feet between sampling stations is adequate. For pipelines greater than one mile in length, the distance between stations can be doubled after the first mile. These sampling stations are for the first trial run. The data obtained are guides to the number and location of sampling stations required for subsequent test runs.

Junctions present special sampling situations which require more preparation and manpower. The procedure for a tee junction requires that the first manhole upstream from the junction be manned for each of the three branches. Samples are taken on the main pipeline at the upstream station and on the tributary line, so timed that the slug of sewage being tested in each line will arrive at the junction simultaneously. Preliminary velocity studies in the tributary line are required. The magnitude of flow is measured at time of sampling.

The optimum duration of sampling is one year or more. The next acceptable period of sampling is an interval of time encompassing the full range of sewage temperatures. If time and manpower are limited, sulfide buildup tests should be conducted during the period of the maximum 6-hour sewage flow and when sewage temperatures are at or near the maximum. The number of test runs required depends upon the consistence of the test data acquired. A minimum of three test runs is recommended. An optimum study program includes buildup tests at different levels of flow over the full range of sewage temperatures.

At the beginning of the sampling program, samples should be obtained weekly or more often and on a different weekday each time. For a 24-hour period, samples should be taken at sufficient time intervals to develop an accurate graph of the diurnal variation of sulfide concentration. Thereafter, the number of samples taken each day can be reduced. After the initial sampling program, the frequency may be further reduced, but not less than monthly. The important factor is to follow sewage temperature changes closely. During times of rapidly changing temperatures, sampling frequency should be increased.

Hydraulic Characterization

Hydraulic characterization of the sewer is necessary to correlate existing sulfide concentrations with those obtained by the sulfide prediction equation. Hydraulic characterization requires measurement of velocity, flow depth and sewer slope. Velocity and depth of flow are obtained at the time of sulfide sampling. Velocity can be measured by several methods including float-velocity, chemical slug, and flumes. The sewer slope may be field measured or taken from as-built plans. The actual hydraulic roughness coefficient, *n*, can be calculated using the Manning equation:

$$n = \frac{1.486\, R^{2/3} S^{1/2}}{V} \tag{7.10}$$

Where: V = average velocity, feet per second
R = hydraulic radius, feet
S = slope
n = roughness coefficient

Sewage Characterization

Several parameters must be monitored if the sewage is to be characterized adequately. These include the five-day biochemical oxygen demand, $[BOD]_5$; pH; temperature; dissolved oxygen, DO; sulfate, $[SO]_4$; total and dissolved sulfide concentrations; and flow quantity. The $[BOD]_5$ and $[SO]_4$ concentrations may be measured by laboratory tests on each sewage sample, or composites. The remaining five parameters must be measured immediately after obtaining the sample.

At the start of testing both total and dissolved sulfide are measured. For each sewage flow, there is a relatively constant differential between total and dissolved sulfide. Once this differential is determined, then only total sulfide must be measured. *Figure 7.10* is a sample plot of sulfide measurement indicating the various sulfide relationships. Average daily values of sulfide concentration and *pH* can be calculated by applying a correction factor, derived from the graph of diurnal sulfide variation, to the sulfide concentrations measured during a day.

The results of the first sampling and measurements may indicate the sewer is free of sulfide. Since the object is to determine the sulfide buildup characteristic, sodium sulfate in a dilute solution can be introduced into the sewer well above the first sampling station and the test procedure repeated. Using the colormetric method, one or more trials may be necessary at the first station to obtain accurate sulfide concentration when concentrations are above 1.5 milligrams per litre. The sulfide ion probe provides values accurate at all sulfide concentrations.

Since velocity is one of the determining factors of sulfide generation, it is possible for all three sulfide conditions outlined above to exist in a pipeline at some time during a 24-hour period. Therefore, for purpose of definition, the three categories which define the sulfide-generating characteristics of a

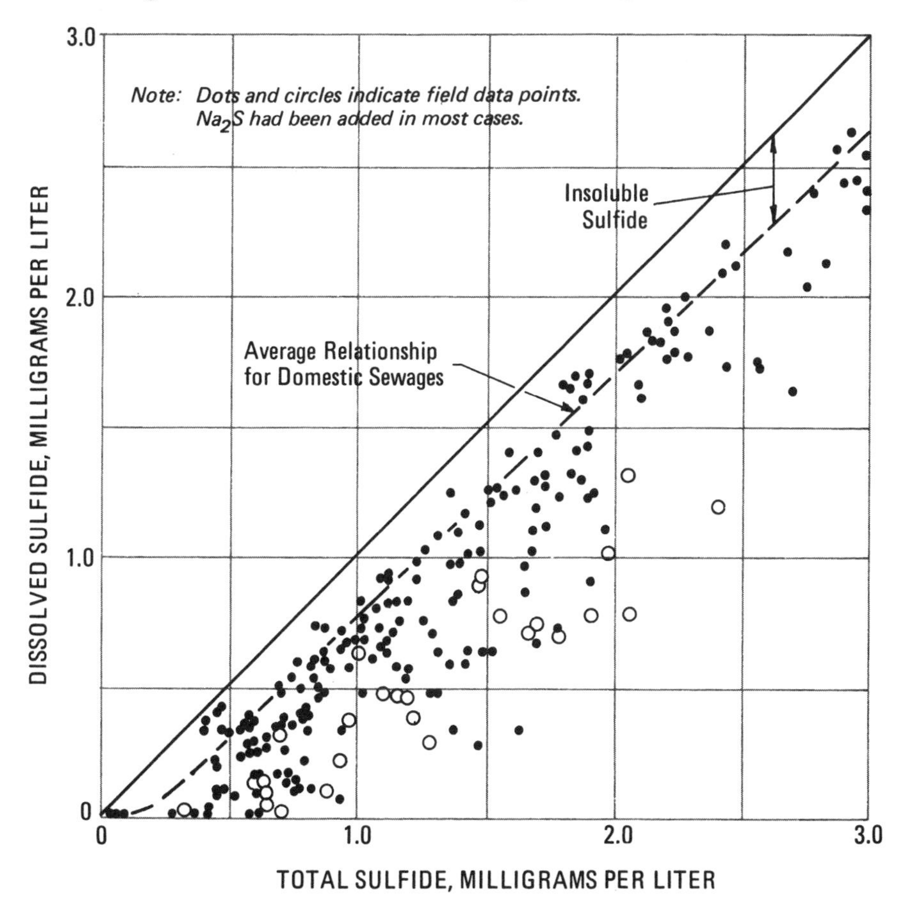

Figure 7.10. Comparison of Total and Dissolved Sulfide Concentrations in Trunk Sewers.

pipeline are based on the average velocity for the maximum 6-hour flow period.

Sufficient tests should be made to determine the average $[BOD]_5$ over the 6-hour maximum flow period. The $[BOD]_5$ of the treatment plant influent will suffice if its characteristics are similar to those of the sewer effluent under test. If 24-hour composite $[BOD]_5$ figures are used, the 6-hour maximum can be obtained with sufficient accuracy by adding 25 percent to the 24-hour value.

SULFIDE PREDICTION

The purpose of the sulfide buildup study of an existing sewer is to predict conditions in a proposed new sewer. An example of data collected from a study is shown in *Table 7.2* and plotted in *Figure 7.11.* These data are used to calculate predicted total sulfide levels which are then compared to actual values. The sulfide buildup curve may be applied directly to design a new sewer provided the slope, diameter and other factors are similar. Because of the many variables associated with a junction, it is difficult to develop a generalized mathematical expression for the effect of junctions on sulfide buildup. The measured effects of junctions can only serve as a basis for judgment in evaluating the influence that junctions may have on the sulfide buildup in a new line. It is important to note, however, that junctions decrease sulfide levels because of the effects of added turbulence and the dilution from lower sulfide level tributaries.

PREDICTIVE EQUATIONS

The 1974 EPA Manual provides equations for qualitative analysis of the sulfide generating capacity. These equations are:

- Rate of sulfide production by the slime layer
- Gains and losses of oxygen in wastewater
- Oxygen consumption in sewers
- Reaction of sulfide with oxygen
- Escape of hydrogen sulfide to the atmosphere

The objective of these equations and concepts was the development of a general model for sulfide buildup. The predictive equations for sulfide buildup were completed by Pomeroy and Parkhurst, published in *Progress In Water Technology* in 1977 and incorporated in the 1985 EPA Manual. The equations predict the hydrogen sulfide buildup in a party filled sewer at infinite time. *The predicted sulfide concentration is the peak total sulfide generated during the year.*

The Pomeroy and Parkhurst quantitative method for sulfide prediction has been proven effective by studies in California, Louisiana and Texas. The method was developed, and is applicable, only for partly filled trunk wastewater sewers when conditions are favorable for sulfide buildup. Because misleading results may be obtained under other conditions, indicators are evaluated to determine if the possibility of sulfide generation exists before using the Pomeroy/Parkhurst method.

Table 7.2. Correlation Data.[a]

RUN	d/D	R/R_f	A/A_f	b/D	P/P_f	V/V_f	R, ft	A, ft^2	b, ft
A	.54	1.05	.54	.98	.52	1.05	.394	.956	1.47
B	.55	1.06	.57	.99	.54	1.06	.398	1.01	1.49
C	.55	1.05	.56	.99	.53	1.06	.394	.990	1.49
D	.51	1.01	.52	.99	.51	1.01	.379	.920	1.49
E	.53	1.04	.53	.99	.52	1.03	.390	.938	1.49
F	.53	1.02	.53	.99	.52	1.03	.383	.938	1.49
RUN	P, ft	V, fps	BOD_5, mg/L (b)	SO_4, mg/L (b)	T, °C	pH	DO, mg/L	Total Sulfides, mg/L (c)	Dissolved Sulfides, mg/L (c)
A	2.45	1.55	130	92	26	7.7	<.5	0.3	0.25
B	2.54	1.57	130	92	27	7.7	<.5	0.25	0.15
C	2.50	1.57	130	92	27.2	7.5	<.5	0.3	0.25
D	2.40	1.49	130	92	27	7.55	<.5	0.3	0.25
E	2.45	1.52	130	92	27.1	7.5	<.5	0.25	0.15
F	2.45	1.52	130	92	27	7.5	<.5	0.45	0.25

[a] Averages made from data collected at MH 1, 5, and 8.
[b] BOD_5 and SO_4 concentrations were not monitored for each run, therefore an average was made of the data collected.
[c] Total dissolved sulfides represent net increase over test run, i.e., data zeroed at MH 1.

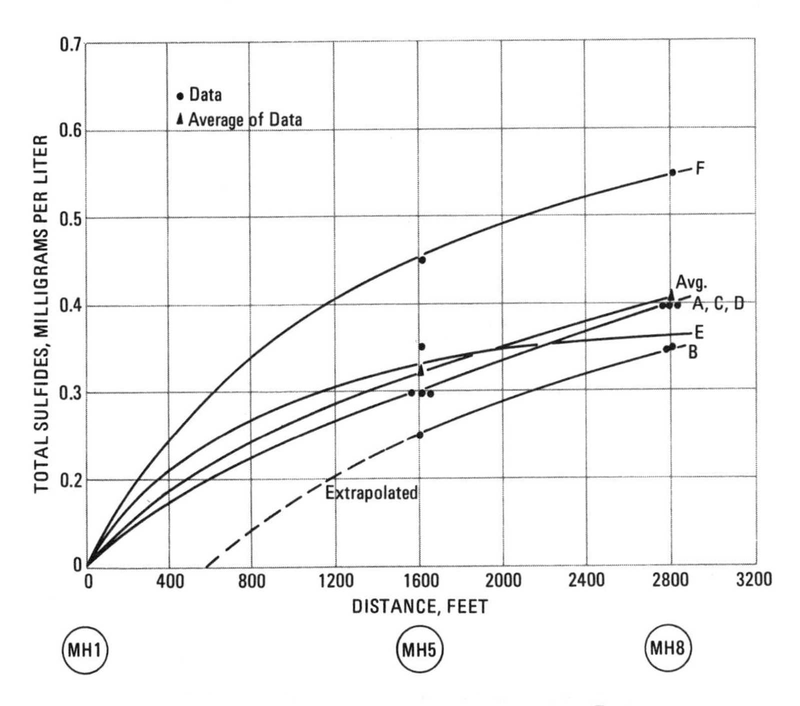

Figure 7.11. Total Sulfide Correlation Data.

SULFIDE GENERATION INDICATORS

The recommended method of analysis consists of evaluating the *Z Formula* and *A/B Curves*. If any one indicator shows that conditions are favorable for sulfide generation, then the Pomeroy/Parkhurst method is used to determine if an actual problem exists. If both indicators show no potential for sulfide generation then no further analysis is required.

Z Formula

The first equation to express the conditions necessary for sulfide generation in gravity mains was developed in 1946. This formula did not deal with the sulfide levels, but simply whether sulfide buildup might occur.

In 1950, Davy presented a more complete formula relating the Reynolds number, [*EBOD*], cross-sectional area of flow, and surface width. This work was later modified by Pomeroy to develop what is known as the *Z Formula:*

$$Z = \frac{[EBOD]}{S^{0.50}Q^{0.33}} \times \frac{P}{b} \tag{7.11}$$

Where:
- Z = defined function
- $[EBOD]$ = effective $[BOD_5]$, milligrams per litre
- S = slope
- Q = discharge, cubic feet per second
- P = wetted perimeter, feet
- b = surface width, feet

The value of Z obtained is interpreted as follows:

Z Value	Sulfide Condition
$Z < 5{,}000$	Sulfide rarely produced
$5{,}000 \leq Z \leq 10{,}000$	Marginal condition for sulfide buildup
$Z > 10{,}000$	Sulfide buildup common

The *Z Formula* has generally been successful in predicting the occurrence of sulfide problems in gravity sewers, but a degree of uncertainty still exists. For example, sulfide has been found to be present in a sewer with a Z value as low as 6,000 and absent in one system with a Z of 28,000.

A/B Curves

The second indicator used to determine sulfide generation potential is the flow-slope relationship, or *A/B Curves,* as shown on *Figures 7.7, 7.8* and *7.9.* The curves are used as indicators for sulfide forecasting but cannot be used to accurately predict sulfide concentrations.

The curves are applicable for sewers flowing less than two-thirds full. The effective slope, S_e, value used in reading the chart is the elevation drop averaged over a distance equal to flow times of about one hour. The interpretation of the curves is as follows:

- Points falling on or above Curve A indicate very little sulfide will be produced, rarely more than 0.1 or 0.2 milligrams per litre of dissolved sulfides. This results in average annual dissolved sulfide concentrations of only a few hundredths of a milligram per litre which are negligible, and no sulfide problem nor corrosion will occur.

- Points falling on or below Curve B may experience average annual dissolved sulfide concentrations of several tenths of a milligram per litre.
- Points falling between the A and B curves indicate conditions are marginal for sulfide generation

The curves must be adjusted for $[EBOD]$ values other than 500 as follows:

$$(S_e)_2 = (S_e)_1 \sqrt{\frac{[EBOD]_2}{[EBOD]_1}} \qquad (7.12)$$

POMEROY/PARKHURST METHOD

In 1977, Pomeroy and Parkhurst presented a quantitative method for sulfide prediction based upon continuing research on the sewer systems of Los Angeles County and data from other areas. The method was developed and is applicable only for partly filled sewers, and when conditions are favorable to sulfide buildup. Misleading results may be obtained under other conditions. Sulfide buildup will not occur when the wastewater contains dissolved oxygen or when nutrients are not present as indicated by a low *BOD*. The equation provides reasonably conservative forecasts for sulfide buildup rates in trunk wastewater sewers when applied to systems similar to those for which it was developed:

$$\frac{d[S]}{dt} = \frac{3.28M'[EBOD]}{r} - \frac{2.10m[S](sv)^{0.375}}{d_m} \qquad (7.13)$$

Where: $d[S]/dt$ = rate of change of total sulfide concentration, milligrams per litre-hour
M' = effective sulfide flux coefficient, metres per hour
r = hydraulic radius of the stream, feet
m = empirical coefficient for sulfide losses
$[S]$ = total sulfide concentration, milligrams per litre
s = energy gradient of the stream
v = velocity, feet per second
d_m = mean hydraulic depth, feet

The term M' is the empirically determined effective sulfide flux coefficient which controls the flux of sulfide to the wastewater stream from the slime layer. The driving force is modeled as the effective biochemical oxygen demand. The hydraulic radius, r, allows the effect on the concentration of a given flux to be greater in a small stream than in a larger stream. It is not necessary to indicate the sulfate concentration, $[SO_4]$, in the driving function since $[SO_4]$ is not generally limiting.

The term m is an empirically determined constant which represents losses of sulfide. The losses are adequately modeled as being proportional to the instantaneous sulfide level and a combination of hydraulic parameters that model oxygen entry into the wastewater stream.

The coefficients, M' and m, may be established to suit the conditions of the system under consideration. M', however, is usually about 0.4×10^{-3} metres per hour when dissolved oxygen is low, less than 0.5 milligrams per litre, and approaches zero as dissolved oxygen concentrations increase. The sulfide loss coefficient, m, varies according to the amount of sulfide losses due to various effects of oxidation. Pomeroy has suggested values for M' of 0.32×10^{-3} and for m, either a conservative value of 0.64 or a less conservative value of 0.96. Analyses by Gilbert of in-line studies conclude that the less conservative values for m adequately predict maximum sulfide levels.

Since sulfide losses are proportional to instantaneous sulfide concentration, there must be some limiting sulfide concentration at which losses equal additions. When the wastewater achieves this level, there will be no further increases in concentration. The negative term of *Equation 7.13* is proportional to the sulfide concentration. The sulfide concentration approaches a limiting concentration, $[S]_{lim}$ when the losses equal the generation and the sulfide buildup is zero. By setting *Equation 7.13* equal to zero, thus approaching the limiting hydrogen sulfide value, $[S]_{lim}$, the new equation becomes:

$$\frac{3.28M'[EBOD]}{r} = \frac{2.10m(sv)^{0.375}[S]_{\mathrm{lim}}}{d_m} \tag{7.14}$$

For the systems studied by Pomeroy and Parkhurst, suitable values for the empirical constants were found to be:

$M' = 0.32 \times 10^{-3}$, metres per hour
$m = 0.64$ *(conservative) to 0.96 (typical)*

When m is equal to 0.96 and rearranging the equation for d_m/r equal to P/b, where P is the wetted perimeter and b is the surface width of the stream, *Equation 7.14* becomes:

$$[S]_{\mathrm{lim}} = \frac{0.52 \times 10^{-3}[EBOD]}{(sv)^{0.375}} \times \frac{P}{b} \tag{7.15}$$

The difference between actual sulfide concentrations and $[S]_{lim}$ is called a sulfide deficit and declines with time. This approach to $[S]_{lim}$ follows a first order curve and is characterized by a **half life** of the deficit, $t_{1/2}$:

$$t_{1/2} = \frac{0.33d_m}{m(sv)^{0.375}} \tag{7.16}$$

Table 7.3. Proportions of $[S]_{lim}$ for Various $t/t_{\frac{1}{2}}$ Values.

$t/t_{½}$	Fraction of $[S]_{lim}$
0.1	0.07
0.2	0.13
0.3	0.19
0.4	0.24
0.5	0.29
0.6	0.34
0.8	0.42
1.0	0.50
1.5	0.65
2.0	0.75
2.5	0.82
3.0	0.88
4.0	0.94

Where: $t_{1/2}$ = half life, hours

When the flow time, or time of sulfide generation, is other than half life, the proportions of the deficit satisfied are shown in *Table 7.3.* The table is the general curve for a first order reaction. By calculating $[S]_{lim}$ and $t_{1/2}$ and applying the factors shown in *Table 7.3,* a generation curve applicable for any constant set of sewer conditions in a single reach can be established.

To calculate the sulfide generation in a series of pipe sections with changing hydraulic conditions, substituting *Equation 7.15* into *Equation 7.14* yields:

$$dt = \frac{d[S]d_m}{2.10m(sv)^{0.375}([S]_{lim} - [S])} \tag{7.17}$$

Integrating both sides of the equation and setting limits yields:

$$t_2 - t_1 = \left(\frac{1.10d_m}{m(sv)^{0.375}}\right)\left(\log \frac{[S]_{lim} - [S]_1}{[S]_{lim} - [S]_2}\right) \tag{7.18}$$

Where: $t_2 - t_1 = \Delta t$ = flow time in a given reach with constant slope, diameter, and flow, hours

$[S]_1$ = sulfide concentration at start of reach, milligrams per litre

$[S]_2$ = sulfide concentration at end of reach, milligrams per litre

By rearranging *Equation 7.18* and using a m value of 0.96, the following expression is obtained:

$$[S]_2 = [S]_{lim} - \left[\frac{[[S]_{lim} - [S]_1]}{\log^{-1}\left[\frac{(sv)^{0.375}\Delta t}{1.15\ d_m}\right]} \right] \tag{7.19}$$

Thus, wastewater which enters a reach of pipe with a uniform slope and diameter, has a sulfide concentration of $[S]_1$, and flows through the pipe for a length of time, Δt, will reach a final sulfide concentration, $[S]_2$. The value of $[S]_2$ is the maximum sulfide concentration in the pipe reach. The average sulfide concentration in the pipe reach would be less, and, therefore, use of the calculated $[S]_2$ value for design is conservative.

The value of $[S]_2$ for the first reach becomes $[S]_1$ for the second reach. By calculating $[S]_{lim}$ and t and knowing the hydraulic conditions for each reach of the system, the sulfide buildup can be calculated for a series of reaches. The Pomeroy/Parkhurst method has six logical steps:

- **Determine Hydraulic Properties:** the required properties for each reach are slope, pipe diameter and depth of flow. These properties are used to determine flow, velocity, wetted perimeter and stream width.
- **Determine Wastewater Properties:** The wastewater properties used in the indicators and Pomeroy/Parkhurst method include *BOD* and temperature. When annual data are not available, the summer or climactic conditions can be approximated. It should be remembered that if summer, or climactic, temperatures and *BOD* values are used, the sulfide concentrations should be adjusted to average annual conditions for use in corrosion analysis.
- **Determine Initial Sulfide Concentration,** $[S]_1$: When using the Pomeroy/Parkhurst method, it is necessary to determine an initial sulfide concentration, $[S]_1$. If an existing system is being analyzed or expanded, the wastewater can be sampled to determine $[S]_1$. When a new system is replacing an old one or extending an existing system, the tributary sewers can be sampled to find a representative $[S]_1$ value. The time of day and year should be noted since sulfide concentrations vary considerably daily and seasonally.

  Once an $[S]_1$ value is determined for the start of each reach, the downstream sulfide concentration, $[S]_2$, can be calculated, which becomes the $[S]_1$ value for the next reach. If there is a tributary flow at the end of the reach, the influent sulfide concentration should be measured or estimated and the $[S]_1$ value calculated using a mass balance as follows:

$$[S]_1 = \frac{[S]_m(Q_m) + [S]_t(Q_t)}{Q_m + Q_t} \tag{7.20}$$

Where: $[S]_1$ = new starting sulfide concentration, milligrams per litre
$[S]_m$ = sulfide concentration in main line above junction, milligrams per litre
Q_m = flow in main line above junction, gallons per day
$[S]_t$ = tributary sulfide concentration, milligrams per litre
Q_t = flow in tributary, gallons per day

- **Determine Limiting Sulfide Concentration, $[S]_{lim}$:** Limiting sulfide concentration, $[S]_{lim}$, values are calculated using *Equation 7.15.*
- **Determine Total Sulfide Concentration, $[S]_2$:** Values of total sulfide $[S]_2$ are calculated using *Equation 7.19.* The downstream concentration, $[S]_2$, is the maximum sulfide concentration in the reach of pipe. The average sulfide concentration throughout the reach of pipe is much less and using the $[S]_2$ value for design for an upstream reach is conservative.
- **Determine Dissolved Sulfide Design Value, $[DS]$:** As shown in *Figure 7.10,* the insoluble sulfide varies from 0.20 milligrams per litre for total sulfides of 0.5 milligrams per litre to 0.36 milligrams per litre for total sulfides of 3.0 milligrams per litre. For design, the amount of insoluble sulfide can be determined from *Figure 7.10,* or conservatively assumed to be 0.20 milligrams per litre. The dissolved sulfide design value is obtained by subtracting the amount of insoluble sulfides from the maximum sulfide concentration, $[S]_2$, and multiplying by the average annual correction factor, *C*, determined from *Table 7.1.*

If the Pomeroy/Parkhurst method indicates dissolved sulfide concentrations in each of the reaches, an evaluation of possible odor and corrosion problems would be the next step in the design process. Evaluation of odor and toxicity problems caused by hydrogen sulfide are well documented in several publications, and are beyond the scope of this handbook.

CORROSION ANALYSIS AND CONTROL

If significant sulfide levels are predicted, corrosion of the pipe may be possible. The corrosion of a cementitious sewer depends upon the supply of sulfuric acid and hence upon the rate of release of H_2S from the wastewater stream. The steps for corrosion analysis and design procedure for corrosion control are as follows:

Corrosion Analysis
- Hydraulic Properties
- Wastewater Properties
- Sulfide Flux
- Corrosion Rate

Corrosion Control

CORROSION ANALYSIS

Corrosion analysis using the results of the Pomeroy/Parkhurst method is necessary to determine the life of an existing system or in designing a new system for a desired service life.

Hydraulic Properties

The hydraulic properties necessary for a corrosion analysis are the same as those required to complete the sulfide generation analysis.

Wastewater Properties

Wastewater properties of importance in corrosion analysis include dissolved sulfide, *pH,* and the *J* factor, which is the portion of dissolved sulfide present as molecular hydrogen sulfide.

The *J* factor is dependent on *pH* and temperature. *Table 7.4* lists the correct *J* factors for 20 degrees celsius. For higher temperatures, the table should be entered with a *pH* value of 0.014 units higher for each degree celsius above 20 degrees. An equivalent correction downward can be made for temperatures below 20 degrees celsius.

Sulfide Flux

The net mass emission from the stream is the mass transfer to the pipe wall, except for generally negligible amounts of H_2S escaping entirely from the

Table 7.4. Proportions of Dissolved Sulfide Present as H_2S, *J* Factor.

pH - pK	pH if pK = 7.0	Proportion of H_2S	pH - pK	pH if pK = 7.0	Proportion of H_2S
-2.0	5.0	0.99	+0.4	7.4	0.28
-1.8	5.2	0.98	+0.5	7.5	0.24
-1.6	5.4	0.975	+0.6	7.6	0.20
-1.4	5.6	0.96	+0.7	7.7	0.17
-1.2	5.8	0.94	+0.8	7.8	0.14
-1.0	6.0	0.91	+0.9	7.9	0.11
-0.9	6.1	0.89	+1.0	8.0	0.091
-0.8	6.2	0.86	+1.1	8.1	0.074
-0.7	6.3	0.83	+1.2	8.2	0.059
-0.6	6.4	0.80	+1.3	8.3	0.048
-0.5	6.5	0.76	+1.4	8.4	0.039
-0.4	6.6	0.72	+1.5	8.5	0.031
-0.3	6.7	0.67	+1.6	8.6	0.025
-0.2	6.8	0.61	+1.7	8.7	0.020
-0.1	6.9	0.56	+1.8	8.8	0.016
-0.0	7.0	0.50	+1.9	8.9	0.013
+0.1	7.1	0.44	+2.0	9.0	0.010
+0.2	7.2	0.39	+2.5	9.5	0.003
+0.3	7.3	0.33	+3.0	10.0	0.001

sewer. Under typical sewer conditions, excluding shallow, high velocity streams or points of high turbulence, and if all the escaping H_2S is oxidized on the pipe wall, the average flux to the wall, ϕ_{sw}, is equal to the flux from the stream multiplied by the ratio of stream surface area to exposed wall area, or surface width divided by exposed perimeter:

$$\phi_{sw} = 0.45J[DS](b/P')(sv)^{3/8} \quad (7.21)$$

Where: ϕ_{sw} = hydrogen sulfide flux to pipe wall, grams per square metre-hour
J = factor relating amount of dissolved sulfide as H_2S to wastewater pH
$[DS]$ = dissolved sulfide concentration in the wastewater, milligrams per litre
b = surface width of stream, feet
P' = perimeter of pipe exposed to atmosphere, feet
s = slope of the energy line of the stream
v = stream velocity, feet per second

The dissolved sulfide, $[DS]$, concentration may be either measured or calculated from the Pomeroy/Parkhurst method. The average flux coefficient and corrosion conditions should be calculated using sulfide concentrations adjusted for daily and seasonal variations, not climactic conditions, using the appropriate C values as shown on *Table 7.1* or as determined for a specific area.

Values for ϕ_{sw} can be obtained using *Equation 7.21* or from *Figure 7.12* which was developed for specific conditions to facilitate solutions. The following example illustrates the calculations involved in determining ϕ_{sw}:

- A 30-inch diameter concrete pipe sewer 1500 feet long has been designed to carry 0.70 cubic feet per second at a relative depth of 0.15 with a 0.1 percent slope and a roughness coefficient of 0.012. The wastewater characteristics are $[BOD]_c$, 305; climactic temperature, T_c, 26 degrees Celsius; pH, 7.2; insoluble sulfide, 0.2 milligrams per litre; and total sulfide at the beginning of the reach, $[S]_1$, 1.0 milligrams per litre.
- Using the principles outlined in *Chapter 3,* the sewer hydraulic characteristics are surface width of flow, b, 1.79 feet; wetted perimeter, P, 1.99 feet; exposed perimeter, P, 5.86 feet; velocity, v, 1.52 feet per second; and mean hydraulic depth, d_m, 0.26 feet.
- Solving *Equation 7.6* for the climactic $[EBOD]$:

$$\begin{aligned}[EBOD]_c &= [BOD]_c \times 1.07^{(T_c - 20)} \\ &= 305 \times 1.07^{(26 - 20)} \\ &= 458 \text{ milligrams per litre}\end{aligned}$$

- Solving *Equation 7.15* for the limiting total sulfide value:

$$[S]_{lim} = \frac{0.52 \times 10^{-3}[EBOD]}{(sv)^{0.375}} \times \frac{P}{b}$$

$$= \frac{0.52 \times 10^{-3} \times 458}{(0.001 \times 1.52)^{0.375}} \times \frac{1.99}{1.79}$$

$$= 3.00 \text{ milligrams per litre}$$

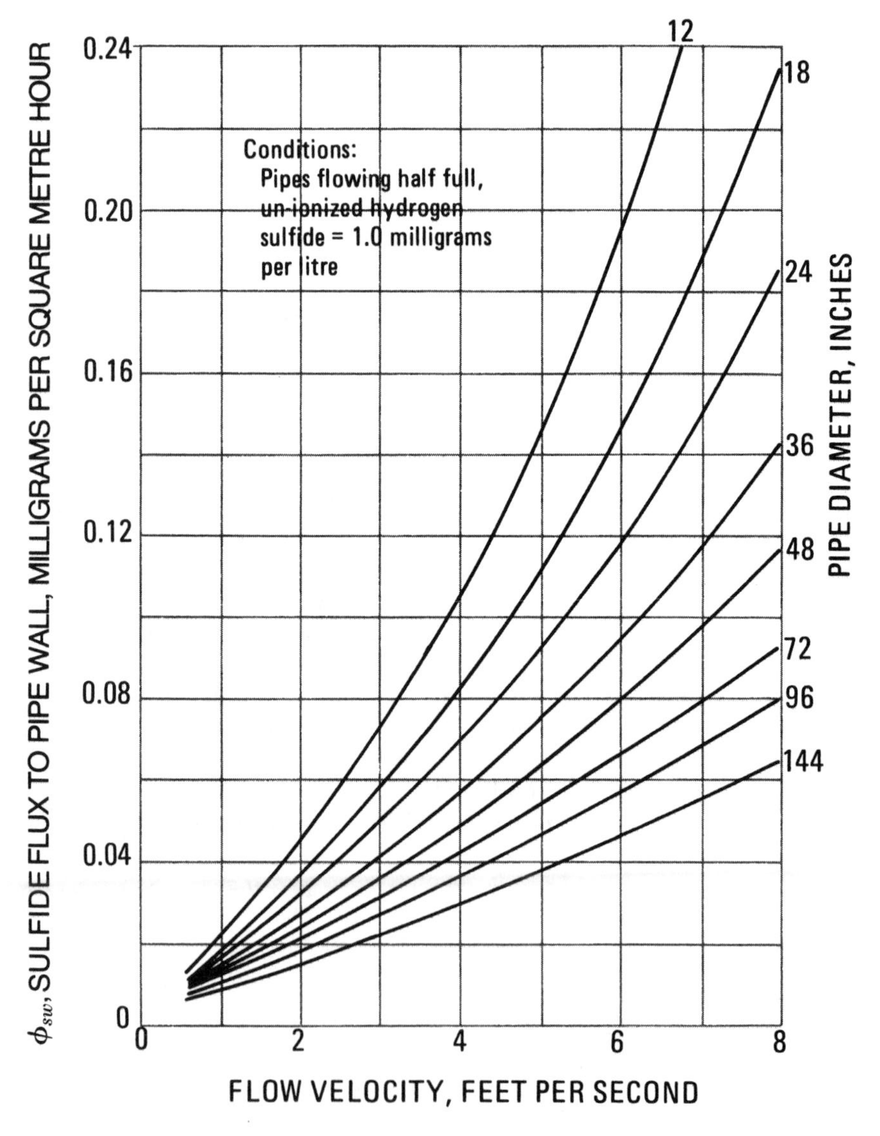

Figure 7.12. Effect of Velocity and Pipe Size on Sulfide Flux to Pipe Wall.

- The sewer flow through time is the sewer length divided by the velocity:

$$\Delta t = \frac{\text{Length}}{v} = \frac{1500}{1.52} = 987 \text{ seconds, or } 0.27 \text{ hours}$$

- Solving *Equation 7.19* for the total sulfide at the end of the reach:

$$[S]_2 = [S]_{lim} - \left[\frac{[[S]_{lim} - [S]_1]}{\log^{-1}\left| \frac{(sv)^{0.375}\Delta t}{1.15\ d_m} \right|} \right]$$

$$= 3.00 - \left[\frac{[3.00 - 1.0]}{\log^{-1}\left| \frac{(0.001 \times 1.52)^{0.375} \times 0.27}{1.15 \times 0.26} \right|} \right]$$

$$= 1.33 \text{ milligrams per litre}$$

- The climactic amount of dissolved sulfide is the total sulfide at the end of the reach minus the insoluble sulfide:

$$[DS] = [S]_2 - (\text{insoluble sulfide}) = 1.33 - 0.20 = 1.13 \text{ milligrams per litre}$$

- Adjusting the climactic to average annual dissolved sulfide, multiply by the correction factor C obtained from *Table 7.1:*

$$\text{Design value } [DS] = 1.13 \times 0.40 = 0.45 \text{ milligrams per litre}$$

- From *Table 7.4* for a pH of 7.2, the J factor is 0.39.
- Solving *Equation 7.21* for the hydrogen sulfide flux:

$$\phi_{sw} = 0.45J[DS](b/P')(sv)^{0.375}$$
$$= 0.45 \times 0.39 \times 0.45(1.79/5.86)(0.001 \times 1.52)^{0.375}$$
$$= 0.0021 \text{ grams per square metre-hour}$$

Figure 7.12 shows rates of sulfide flux to the pipe wall in pipes flowing half full. The strong upward curvature of the curves for the smaller pipe is due to increased turbulence at high Froude numbers. *Figure 7.13* provides factors to apply to rates from *Figure 7.12* to calculate the flux at other relative flow depths. The velocity input for use in conjunction with *Figures 7.12* and *7.13* must be the velocity that would prevail if the quantity of flow were such as to half fill the pipe, not the actual velocity for the actual quantity of flow.

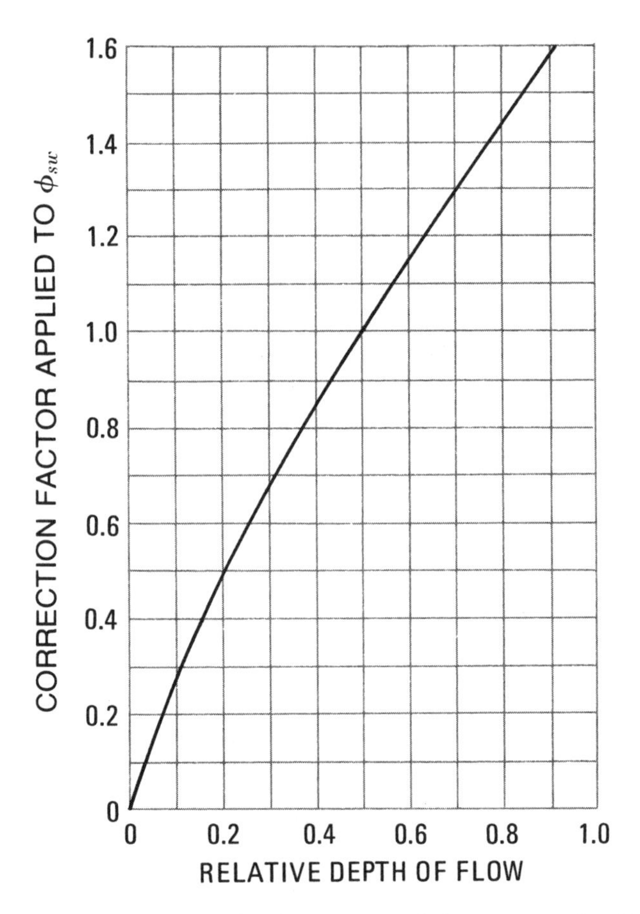

Figure 7.13. Factor to Apply to ϕ_{sw} to Calculate ϕ_{sw} for Other Than Half-Pipe Depth.

Corrosion Rate

When hydrogen sulfide is absorbed by the film of moisture on the exposed sewer wall, it supports the growth of bacteria which convert it to sulfuric acid. The rate of attack on the sewer wall by acid is thus a function of the rate at which hydrogen sulfide is delivered to the wall, ϕ_{sw}, and the capacity of the wall alkalinity to neutralize the acid. Sulfide in the amount of 32 grams is required to produce the acid to dissolve 100 grams of $CaCO_3$. A basic corrosion rate equation is developed in the EPA Manual:

$$c = \frac{0.45k\phi_{sw}}{A} \tag{7.22}$$

Where: c = corrosion rate, inches per year
k $\leq$ 1.0, a constant for the amount of sulfide oxidization and acid runoff
A = concrete alkalinity, as equivalent calcium carbonate, $CaCO_3$

The rate of corrosion, c, depends on the flux of hydrogen sulfide from the stream to the air, ϕ_{sw}, the alkalinity of the pipe material, A, the amount of hydrogen sulfide oxidized on the pipe wall and the amount of acid which runs off the wall. The last two items are accounted for in *Equation 7.22* by the factor k. No actual measurements of k have been made and the choice of a value is a matter of engineering judgment. The value of k would approach unity when the rate of acid formation is very slow and may be as low as 0.3 if acid production is rapid and much condensation is present. This phenomenon can be illustrated by two examples. If a bucket of acid were thrown onto a pipe wall, most of the acid would run off to the invert, mix with the sewage and continue downstream without reacting with the wall material. If the acid were slowly sprayed on so as to just dampen the wall, very little would run off and most would react with the wall material. Using a value of 0.7 provides a factor of safety that will assure conservative results under normal operating conditions. Therefore, it is recommended that a k factor of 0.7 be used for design to predict the corrosion rate of a sewerline.

Corrosion rates tend to increase near manholes due to increased turbulence and outgassing. In addition, it is not always possible to accurately predict future service tributary to a manhole. Therefore, it is recommended that a safety factor of 1.5 be applied to the design corrosion rate for ten pipe diameters downstream and five pipe diameters upstream from a manhole. This will assure the desired design life even if adverse conditions should develop.

CORROSION CONTROL

A strategy for design of a concrete pipe which incorporates the rate of corrosion, the thickness of concrete cover over the reinforcement, concrete alkalinity, and the desired life of the pipe is the Life Factor Design Method. In this method, the life of the pipe is defined as follows:

$$L = z/c \tag{7.23}$$

Where:

L = service life (the time required to penetrate the concrete cover over the reinforcement), years

z = concrete cover over reinforcement, inches

c = corrosion rate, inches per year

Substituting this value for c in *Equation 7.22,* the **Life Factor Equation** is:

$$Az = 0.45k\ \phi_{sw}\ L \tag{7.24}$$

The term Az is defined as the life factor and is the product of concrete alkalinity and the thickness of allowable concrete loss. In design, this thickness is the concrete cover over the inner reinforcement. A specified value of Az can be achieved by different combinations of alkalinity and concrete thickness. Thus, a project specified in terms of Life Factor allows the pipe manufacturer greater latitude in tailoring pipe design and production to current procedural and economic considerations.

The design life, L, for wastewater collection systems is generally 50 to 100 years, and is defined as the time required for corrosion to penetrate the concrete cover over the reinforcement. In some cases, sulfide generation is a problem only during the initial years if low flow and long detention times occur. Hydrogen sulfide generation may not be a problem in later years as design flow conditions are reached, and velocities increase and detention times decrease. However, when designing for a long service life with variable operating conditions, the system should be analyzed in chronological increments to avoid using the worst or the best conditions for a sulfide and corrosion analysis.

A major advantage of the concept is that the engineer can specify a **Life Factor,** Az, and the manufacturer has the maximum flexibility for producing the lowest cost product for the design life. Basic production decisions can be made on the use of partial or total calcareous aggregates, cement content, wall thickness, amount of concrete cover over the reinforcement, etc. These decisions are made on the basis of producing the required Life Factor by the most efficient combination compatible with a specific manufacturing process, equipment availability and aggregate source.

For design purposes, the Life Factor method can be simplified by appropriate charts and graphs. The information required for design are the pipe diameter and slope, the average daily flow and pH, the amount of dissolved sulfides, and an estimated value for k. The design procedure includes the following steps:

1. The velocity for the pipe flowing half full is determined.
2. The value of ϕ_{sw} is determined using *Equation 7.21* or *Figure 7.12* which relates the effect of velocity and pipe size on sulfide flux to the pipe wall under specific conditions. These conditions are for half-full flow and one milligram per litre of un-ionized hydrogen sulfide.
3. Un-ionized hydrogen sulfide is H_2S, and is determined as the J factor times the amount of dissolved sulfides. Values for the J factor are presented in *Table 7.4* and graphically in *Figure 7.3*.
4. The value for ϕ_{sw} thus obtained must be corrected directly for actual amounts of H_2S since *Figure 7.12* was developed for one milligram per litre of H_2S. For example, if the project has 1/2 milligrams per litre, one half of the curve value would be used. The value for ϕ_{sw} must be corrected directly also for other flow depths since *Figure 7.12* was developed for half-full flow. This depth correction factor is obtained from *Figure 7.13*.

The following example illustrates the Life Factor method and application:

- An interceptor sewer has been sized as a 30-inch diameter pipe to carry 3.5 cubic feet per second while flowing at 0.21 relative depth. The pipe has one-inch minimum cover over the inner cage reinforcement. A 50-year design life and a factor of safety of 1.5 have been selected. Total sulfide, [*TS*], has been determined to be 3.66 milligrams per litre and the ratio of the annual average sulfide level during the climactic period to peak has been observed to be 0.3. The insoluble sulfide, [*IS*], has been determined to be 0.2 milligrams per litre and the annual average pH has been determined to be equal to 7.2. If field data are not available, the relationship between total and dissolved sulfides can be obtained from *Figure 7.10.*

- For the conditions given, the half-full flow velocity is 5.5 feet per second.
- The annual average total sulfide is:

$$[TS] = 0.3 \times 3.66 = 1.10 \text{ milligrams per litre}$$

- The annual average dissolved sulfide, [*DS*], is:

$$[DS] = [TS] - [IS] = 1.10 - 0.20 = 0.90 \text{ milligrams per litre}$$

- From *Figure 7.12,* the uncorrected $\phi_{sw} = 0.09$
- From *Figure 7.3,* the J factor = 0.39
- From *Figure 7.13,* the depth correction factor = 0.52
- The correction for dissolved sulfides is 0.90 and therefore the corrected ϕ_{sw} is:

$$\text{Corrected } \phi_{sw} = (\text{uncorrected } \phi_{sw})\,(J)\,(\text{depth correction})\,[DS]$$

$$= 0.09 \times 0.39 \times 0.52 \times 0.9 = 0.016$$

- Assuming a moderate rate of acid production and setting k equal to 0.7, the required Life Factor is:

$$\begin{aligned} Az &= 0.45k\phi_{sw}\,L \\ &= 0.45(0.7)(0.016)(50 \times 1.5) \\ &= 0.38 \end{aligned}$$

The engineer would specify the required Life Factor of 0.38 and the pipe manufacturer would obtain the value by the method best suited to his production process. *Table 7.5* lists some combinations which could be supplied by a pipe manufacturer to furnish the required protection and life. For example, if 100 percent calcareous aggregates were used and resulted in a concrete alkalinity of 0.85, then the required cover would be:

$$\begin{aligned} z &= \frac{Az}{A} \\ &= \frac{0.38}{0.85} \\ &= 0.5 \text{ inches} \end{aligned}$$

However, the minimum cover specified is one inch. Since the actual cover is greater than the required cover, the actual Life Factor would be:

$$Az = 0.85 \times 1.0 = 0.85$$

Since the required Az was calculated based on a required safety factor of 1.5, the actual safety factor would be:

$$\begin{aligned} S.F.\ (\text{Actual}) &= \frac{Az\ (\text{Actual})}{Az\ (\text{Required})} \times S.F.\ (\text{Required}) \\ &= \frac{0.85}{0.38} \times 1.5 \\ &= 3.4 \end{aligned}$$

Table 7.5. Concrete Pipe Alternates.

Aggregates[b]	Alkalinity A[c]	Cover, z, inches		Az		Safety Factor	
		Required[d]	Actual	Required[a]	Actual[g]	Required[h]	Actual[i]
Granitic	0.20	1.9	1.9[f]	0.38	0.38	1.5	1.5
40% Calcareous	0.45	0.8	1.0[e]	0.38	0.45	1.5	1.8
100% Calcareous	0.85	0.5	1.0[e]	0.38	0.85	1.5	3.4

Note:
a. Life Factor calculated in text example.
b. Aggregate types and percentages selected for example only.
c. Alkalinity values assumed for example purposes.
d. Required cover determined by dividing require Life Factor by A.
e. Minimum cover specified.
f. Actual cover required.
g. Actual Life Factor determined by A times z.
h. Required safety factor assumed for example only.
i. Actual safety factor determined by multiplying required safety factor by actual Life Factor and dividing by required Life Factor.

ALKALINITY

ALKALINITY TESTING

The alkalinity of the concrete is determined in grams of calcium carbonate equivalent in reactivity to one gram of concrete. For typical concrete pipe with granitic aggregate, the alkalinity is approximately 0.20. With calcareous aggregate, the alkalinity may approach 0.95, which can significantly increase the life of the pipe.

Test Samples

Samples of component material for a concrete mix are obtained and should be a representative composite of the stockpiled material. Samples of concrete from a pipe are obtained by drilling two one-inch diameter cores from the interior pipe wall to the depth of the reinforcement. Each sample is placed in a separate container and dried in an oven for one to two hours at a temperature between 100 and 110 degrees Celsius. The samples are then pulverized to obtain 100 percent passing a 100-mesh sieve.

Test Procedures

Approximately one gram of a sample is placed in a beaker and 10 millilitres of water added. Then 40 millilitres of standard 1-Normal hydrochloric acid, HCl, are slowly added. When effervescence has subsided, the mixture is heated to boiling, boiled for 30 seconds and cooled. To the cooled mixture, 50-100 millilitres of water are added and titrated with a carbonate free standard 1-Normal sodium hydroxide, $NaOH$, solution. The mixture is titrated until the pH stays above 6.8 for two minutes. The final pH should be between 6.8 and 7.8.

ALKALINITY ANALYSIS

Two tests are run on each sample and the alkalinity of the material is the average of all tests. The net calcium carbonate equivalent is:

$$CaCO_3 \text{ Equivalent} = \frac{5[(ml \text{ of } HCl) - (ml \text{ of } NaOH)]}{[\text{sample mass in grams}]} \qquad (7.25)$$

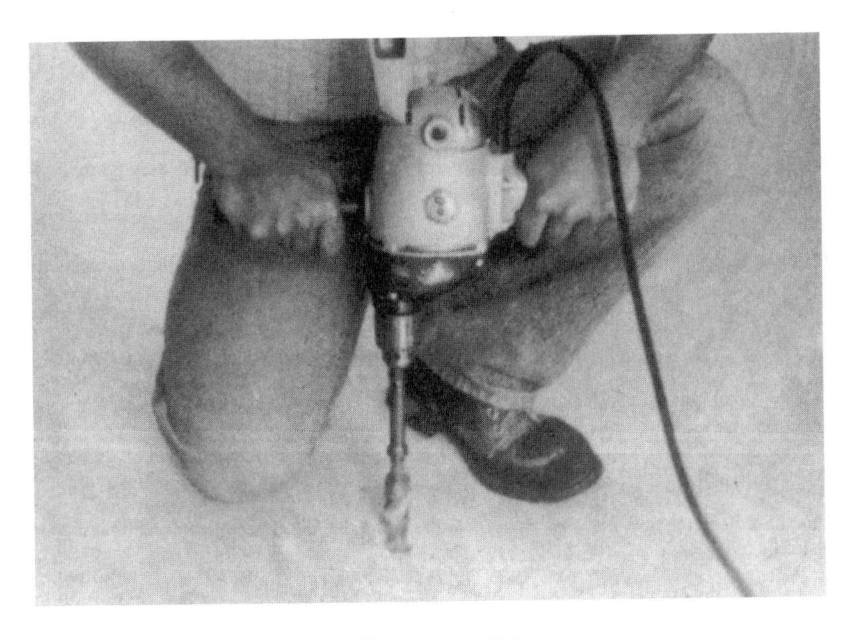

Illustration 7.2
One method of obtaining sample of cover concrete for determining alkalinity of concrete pipe.

The alkalinity of the concrete cover over the reinforcement would be used directly as the value for *A* in *Equation 7.22* and also *Equation 7.24*.

When the alkalinity of the component materials for a mix are known, the alkalinity of the resultant concrete can be determined. The analysis requires that the proportion of each material used per cubic yard of concrete be expressed as a percentage of the weight of the cured concrete. This percentage is then multiplied by the appropriate material alkalinity to obtain the alkalinity contributed to the mix by that material. For example, anhydrous cement has an alkalinity equal to about 1.18 times its weight. If 564 pounds of cement are used to produce a cubic yard of concrete weighing 4,100 pounds per cubic yard, the cement represents 14 percent of the concrete, and therefore contributes an alkalinity of 1.18 times 0.14, or 0.17, to this particular concrete mix. The contributing alkalinity of all other materials used to make the concrete would be summed to determine the total alkalinity of the concrete mix.

REFERENCES

1. "Basic Research on Sulfide Occurrence and Control," Parkhurst, Livingston, Pomeroy, and Bailey, County Sanitation Districts of Los Angeles County, Revised Draft of Final Report of Grant 10010 ENX, June 15, 1973.
2. "Biology of Microorganisms," Brock, Thomas D., Prentice-Hall, Englewood, Cliffs, New Jersey, 1970.
3. "The Control of Sulphides in Sewerage Systems," Thistlethwayte, D. K. B., Ed. Butterworths, Melbourne, Australia, 1972 and Ann Arbor Science Publishers, Ann Arbor, Michigan.
4. "A Case Study, Prediction of Sulfide Generation and Corrosion in Concrete Gravity Sewers in Sacramento, California," Gilbert, J. D. & Associates, American Concrete Pipe Association, April, 1979.
5. "Corrosion Resistant Design of Sanitary Sewer Pipe," Kienow, K. K. and Pomeroy, R. D., paper presented at Session 48, ASCE Convention, Chicago, Illinois, October, 1978.
6. "Encyclopedia of Industrial Chemical Analysis," Volume 15, Interscience Publishers Division, John Wiley & Sons.
7. "The Forecasting of Sulfide Build-Up Rates in Sewers," Pomeroy, Richard D., and Parkhurst, John D., Progress in Water Technology, Volume 9, 1977.
8. "Hydrogen Sulfide Odor Threshold," Pomeroy, Richard D., and Cruse, Henry, Journal of American Water Works Association, Volume 15, 1969.
9. "Influence of Velocity on Sulfide Generation in Sewers," Davy, W. J., Sewage and Industrial Wastes, Volume 22, 1950.
10. "Life Factor Design of RCP Sewers," Kienow, K. K., American Concrete Pipe Association, Concrete Pipe News, October, 1977.
11. "Process Design Manual for Sulfide Control in Sanitary Sewerage Systems," Environmental Protection Agency, October, 1974.
12. "Progress Report on Sulfide Control Research," Pomeroy, and Bowlus, Sewage Works Journal, Volume 18, 1946.
13. "Sanitary Sewer Design for Hydrogen Sulfide Control," Pomeroy, Richard D., Public Works, October, 1970.
14. "Sanitary Sewer Design for Hydrogen Sulfide Control Research," Pomeroy, Richard D., Sewage Works Journal, Volume 18, July, 1946.
15. "Shreveport Sewer Study," Santry, I. W., Gifford-Hill & Company, Inc., November, 1977.
16. "Standard Methods for the Examination of Water and Wastewater," American Public Health Association, New York, 12 Edition, 1965.
17. "A Study of the Use of Concrete Pipe for Trunk Sewers in the City of Delano, California," Warren, George D. II, and Tchobangolous, George, California Precast Concrete Pipe Association, September, 1976.
18. "Design Manual for Sulfide and Corrosion Prediction and Control," American Concrete Pipe Association, 1984.
19. "Odor and Corrosion Control in Sanitary Sewerage Systems and Treatment Plants," Environmental Protection Agency, October, 1985.

CHAPTER 8

PRODUCT STANDARDS AND TESTING

Standards and **testing** are critical to any product and important to the designer, specifier, owner and manufacturer. Design and manufacturing requirements for precast concrete pipe and related products are detailed in American Society for Testing and Materials, **ASTM,** standards which include acceptance procedures and test criteria. Other ASTM standards provide methods of tests for acceptance and quality control. This chapter discusses the need for standards, the types of standards and development agencies, and ASTM concrete pipe standards.

STANDARDS

For pipeline construction, the engineer develops a set of **contract documents** which become a part of the agreement with the contractor. These documents cover numerous items and requirements, from how to obtain copies of plans to final acceptance of the project. For precast concrete pipe installations, the engineer can designate the type, size and strength of pipe by referencing the appropriate ASTM or other product standard. Reference to a product standard assures the engineer that a product which has predictable performance characteristics is available. Confidence in the performance of concrete pipe that conforms to ASTM standards is the result of the rigorous, formal procedures of committees composed of experts with experience in a variety of fields and responsibilities. The benefits of such standards are economies in both product and installation performance and costs.

The pipe manufacturer also benefits from the use of standards. With standardization, the manufacturer can plan production and safely invest capital in the necessary equipment and facilities to insure volume and consistent quality. The manufacturer is also familiar with the procedures and tests the engineer will use to accept the pipe. This knowledge permits the establishment of quality control methods which result in cost savings to the user.

In addition to product standards, **project specifications** which encompass installation and pipe requirements not covered by the referenced standards are necessary. Project specifications include performance requirements, if necessary, such as, infiltration limits, testing, etc. An important function of the specifications is to clarify procedures and responsibilities to avoid disagreement.

Illustration 8.1
Excavation, bedding, pipe jointing and backfill requirements must be detailed in the project specifications.

TYPES OF STANDARDS

In North America, several hundred organizations develop **voluntary standards.** These standards are termed voluntary because participation in the system is not required by any government regulations. The organizations developing standards include professional and technical societies, industries, trade associations, public service and consumer groups, testing and inspection agencies, and national voluntary consensus organizations.

Because standards are developed in different ways, the engineer needs to be familiar with the procedures used by an organization. On a sewer or culvert project, standards produced by **ASTM,** American National Standards Institute, **ANSI,** American Association of State Highway and Transportation Officials, **AASHTO,** Canadian Standards Association, **CSA,** industries, and trade associations fit the concept of a voluntary system and could be considered national in scope. Of vital concern is whether a particular standard is a **consensus standard.** A consensus standard is defined as, *a standard produced by a body selected, organized, and conducted in accordance with the procedural standards of due process. In standards and development practice, a consensus is achieved when substantial agreement is reached by concerned interests according to the judgment of a duly appointed review authority.* Degree of consensus achieved in standards development varies and can be identified as follows:

- **Company Standard**—consensus of employees of a given organization
- **Industry Standard**—consensus of companies within a given industry and usually developed by a trade association
- **Professional Standard**—consensus of individual members of a profession and usually developed by a professional society
- **Government Standards**—consensus of employees of a government agency
- **Full Consensus Standard**—consensus of all that have an interest in the development and use of the standard

The procedures for standards of due process insure all points of view are considered in accordance with rules and regulations, and the entire process is reviewed for conformance with these procedures before any standard is approved. A full consensus standard will be technically competent and have high credibility when critically examined.

AMERICAN SOCIETY FOR TESTING AND MATERIALS

ASTM is a management system for the development of voluntary consensus standards. ASTM staff is not involved in the development of any standard. Technical research, testing and facilities are contributed voluntarily by members working within a committee structure. ASTM provides a legal, administrative and publication forum within which producers, consumers and general interest members can meet to develop standards which will best serve the needs of all concerned.

There are over 130 ASTM technical committees with jurisdiction over a wide variety of areas. Each committee must be balanced when considering a new standard or revisions to existing standards. A **balanced committee** is defined as one in which the number of producers does not exceed the combined number of users and general interest members.

Precast concrete pipe and related products are under the jurisdiction of Committee C-13 on Concrete Pipe which is a balanced committee of almost 100 members. The functions and operations of a committee can be described by following an item submitted for consideration through the required procedures. Any item submitted, whether a new standard, revision, question, request, etc., is considered. A question or request for clarification may be handled by a committee officer or a subcommittee chairman directly or submitted to the appropriate subcommittee for recommendation. Items involving new standards or revisions are submitted to a subcommittee. Any item requiring extensive development is usually assigned to a small task group appointed by the subcommittee chairman.

When a task group develops a recommendation, it is submitted to the subcommittee. After considering the recommendation, the subcommittee must formally approve submission to the full committee by letter ballot. The subcommittee can also modify the recommendation or send it back to the task group for further work. The full committee follows the same procedures and must have a letter ballot approving submission of the recommendation to ASTM headquarters. Headquarters then submits the item to letter ballot of its more than 28,000 members. Following approval, the Committee on Standards makes a final review to determine if proper procedures have been followed and, if so, the item is adopted and approved for publication.

An important point in ASTM procedures is if one negative vote is received on any letter ballot, the procedural chain is stopped and the item sent back to the subcommittee or task group for consideration of the objection. To be considered, however, a negative vote must be accompanied by a written technical or procedural objection. The time span for development of new standards can vary, but, when consensus is reached, the user is assured of a thoroughly considered, technically sound and highly credible standard.

AMERICAN NATIONAL STANDARDS INSTITUTE

ANSI was founded in 1916 by ASTM and four other societies to serve as a clearinghouse for standards activities. ANSI's role in the voluntary standard system is to reduce overlap and duplication of effort, point out where standards are needed, recognize and identify nationally accepted standards, and serve as the United States representative in international standards activities.

An ASTM standard approved by ANSI carries a dual designation, for example, ANSI/ASTM C 76. All of the ASTM precast concrete pipe standards under the jurisdiction of Committee C-13 have ANSI approval. AN-

SI also organizes, supervises, and controls the membership of committees that prepare standards for approval and publication under ANSI procedures.

AMERICAN ASSOCIATION OF STATE HIGHWAY AND TRANSPORTATION OFFICIALS

AASHTO is composed of officials from state highway and transportation agencies and ex officio members from the Federal Highway Administration, FHWA. Actions of AASHTO are not binding on individual states.

Each region has an annual meeting to discuss and vote on proposals presented by standing and special committees and to provide a forum for information exchange. Two standing committees are the Operating Subcommittee on Materials, which formally considers most ASTM standards for AASHTO approval and adoption, and the Operating Subcommittee on Bridges and Structures which is primarily responsible for structural design including concrete pipe through its Technical Committee on Culverts. This committee has jurisdiction over the Rigid Culvert Liaison Committee which has responsibilities for standards and criteria relating to the design of concrete pipe and other rigid culvert material.

ASTM standards on concrete pipe are reviewed and usually adopted by the AASHTO Materials Subcommittee with only minor modifications. Because of the time required for approval and publication, AASHTO standards are generally one revision year behind ASTM issuance of a standard.

CANADIAN STANDARDS ASSOCIATION

CSA was chartered in 1919 and is similar to ASTM. Standardization through CSA is voluntary, using the consensus principle. CSA is a national organization made up of volunteer members from business, government, labor, consumers, and associations. Standards are developed through a formal organizational structure consisting of a standards policy board, standards steering committees and technical committees established for defined areas of standardization which are responsible for the actual development of standards.

CSA also provides certification services for manufacturers who, under license, use registered CSA marks on products to indicate conformity with a standard. The certification program involves testing, examination, and follow-up procedures to determine continuing conformity with a standard.

INDUSTRY AND TRADE ASSOCIATIONS

For some materials and products, there are no ASTM or other nationally accepted standards. These are produced under company or trade association standards. These standards should be critically examined by the user due to the lack of input from user and general interest groups.

FEDERAL

The United States Federal Standardization Document System is classified into three categories; **Federal Specifications, Federal Standards,** and **Qualified Product Lists.** Federal specifications usually cover concrete pipe by reference to ASTM standards, and describe essential and technical requirements for items, materials or services bought by the federal government. The development of these specifications is coordinated with interested agencies and industry, and are mandatory for use in procurement by federal agencies. Federal standards serve a variety of purposes, and are a source of standard data for reference in federal specifications. Two major categories of standards are the **Federal Test Method Standards** which cover test methods developed by the federal government when appropriate industry standards are not available, and **Packaging, Marketing and Material Identification Standards.** Qualified product lists provide data on products which establish product quality by test prior to purchase. The purpose of these lists is to facilitate procurement of items requiring extensive testing before acceptance by federal quality control representatives.

ASTM CONCRETE PIPE STANDARDS

An ASTM standard is the result of a particular standardization effort and is a document containing a set of conditions to be fulfilled or an object for comparison. Within ASTM Committee C-13 on Concrete Pipe, four types of standards are promulgated:

- Specifications
- Methods of tests
- Definitions
- Recommended practices

SPECIFICATIONS

A **specification** is a precise statement of a set of requirements to be satisfied by a material, product, system, or service, indicating whenever appropriate, the procedure to determine whether the requirements have been satisfied. Specifications cover any of three functions:

- **Purchasing** facilitates dealings between the purchaser and supplier.
- **Standardization** provides a deliberate and possibly arbitrary choice of a limited number from the multiplicity of qualities, sizes, compositions, etc.
- **Technical data** provides technical information to the designer that is not normally required for purchase or standardization.

There are many topics specifically covered by a specification and the more important ones are:

- **Scope** amplifies the title, states the function of the specification, and notes any materials or products excluded.
- **Applicable documents** lists by designation number and complete title all documents referenced within the specification.

- **Classification** includes the types, grades, and classes of materials or products.
- **Materials and manufacture** provide general requirements regarding the materials and methods of manufacture.
- **Chemical requirements** detail requirements for the chemical composition and characteristics of the material or product.
- **Physical requirements** detail mechanical and other property requirements.
- **Permissible variations** provide appropriate tolerances.
- **Workmanship and finish** cover acceptable quality characteristics.
- **Repairs** stipulate permissible repairs and the method of acceptance.
- **Rejection** provides the basis for determining when individual items are unacceptable.
- **Marking** lists what information should be indicated on each product.

The scopes of nationally accepted ASTM specifications are as follows and similar counterpart AASHTO, CSA, and federal specifications are listed in *Table 8.1*:

- ASTM C 14 Concrete Sewer, Storm Drain and Culvert Pipe: Covers nonreinforced concrete pipe in three strength classes intended to be used for the conveyance of sewage, industrial wastes, storm water, and for the construction of culverts in sizes from 4 inches through 36 inches in diameter.
- ASTM C 76 Reinforced Concrete Culvert, Storm Drain, and Sewer Pipe: Covers reinforced concrete pipe in five strength classes intended to be used for the conveyance of sewage, industrial wastes, and storm waters, and for the construction of culverts. Class I includes pipe sizes of 60 inches through 144 inches in diameter; Class II, III, IV and V include pipe sizes of 12 inches through 144 inches in diameter. Larger sizes and higher classes are available as special designs.
- ASTM C 118 Concrete Pipe for Irrigation or Drainage: Covers concrete pipe intended to be used for the conveyance of irrigation water under low hydrostatic heads, generally not exceeding 25 feet, and for use in drainage in sizes from 4 inches through 24 inches in diameter.
- ASTM C 361 Reinforced Concrete Low-head Pressure Pipe: Covers reinforced concrete pipe intended to be used for the construction of pressure pipelines in sizes from 12 inches through 108 inches in diameter with low internal hydrostatic heads, generally not exceeding 125 feet.
- ASTM C 412 Concrete Drain Tile: Covers nonreinforced concrete drain tile with internal diameters from 4 inches to 24 inches for Standard-Quality, and 4 inches to 36 inches for Extra-Quality, Heavy-Duty Extra-Quality and Special-Quality Concrete Drain Tile.
- ASTM C 443 Joints for Circular Concrete Sewer and Culvert Pipe, with Rubber Gaskets: Covers joints where infiltration or exfiltration is a factor in the design, including the design of joints and the requirements for rubber gaskets to be used therewith for pipe conforming in all other respects to ASTM C 14, C 76 or C 655.

Table 8.1. Concrete Pipe Standards.

Type		Diameter or Size	Specification Designation			
			ASTM	AASHTO	CSA	Federal
Nonreinforced Concrete Culvert, Storm Drain and Sewer Pipe	Class 1 Class 2 Class 3	4" - 36" 4" - 36" 4" - 36"	C14	M86	A257.1	SS-P-371
Reinforced Concrete Culvert, Storm Drain and Sewer Pipe	Class I Class II Class III Class IV Class V	60" - 144" 12" - 144" 12" - 144" 12" - 144" 12" - 144"	C76	M170	A257.2	SS-P-375
Concrete Irrigation and Drainage Pipe		4" - 24"	C118			
Reinforced Concrete Low-Head Pressure Pipe		12" - 108"	C361			
Drain Tile:	Standard Quality Extra Quality Heavy-Duty Extra Quality Special Quality	4" - 24" 4" - 36" 4" - 36" 4" - 36"	C412	M178		
Joints for Circular Concrete Sewer and Culvert Pipe, with Rubber Gaskets			C443	M198	A257.3	
Perforated Concrete Pipe			C444	M175		
Precast Reinforced Concrete Manhole Risers and Tops			C478	M199		
Testing Concrete Pipe and Tile			C497	T33	A257.0	
Nonreinforced Concrete Irrigation Pipe with Rubber-Type Gasket Joints		6" - 24"	C505			
Reinforced Concrete, Arch Culvert, Storm Drain and Sewer Pipe		15" - 132"*	C506	M206		
Reinforced Concrete, Elliptical Culvert, Storm Drain and Sewer Pipe		18" - 144"*	C507	M207		
Reinforced Concrete D-Load Culvert, Storm Drain, and Sewer Pipe		12" - 144"	C655	M242		
Precast Reinforced Concrete Box Sections for Culverts, Storm Drains and Sewers		3' Span x 2' Rise to 12' Span x 12' Rise	C789	M259		
Standard Definitions and Terms Relating to Concrete Pipe and Related Products			C822	M262		
Precast Reinforced Concrete Box Sections for Culverts, Storm Drains, and Sewers with less than 2 feet of Cover Subjected to Highway Loadings		3' Span x 2' Rise to 12' Span x 12' Rise	C850	M273		
External Sealing Bands for Noncircular Concrete Sewer, Storm Drain and Culvert Pipe			C877			
Resilient Connectors Between Reinforced Concrete Manhole Structures and Pipes.			C923			
Low-Pressure Air Test of Concrete Pipe Sewer Lines			C924			
Infiltration and Exfiltration Acceptance Testing of Installed Precast Concrete Pipe Sewer Lines			C969			
Nonreinforced Concrete Specified Strength Culvert, Storm Drain, and Sewer Pipe			C985			

* Denotes Approximately Equivalent Round Size

- ASTM C 444 Perforated Concrete Pipe: Covers perforated concrete pipe intended to be used for underdrainage in sizes 4 inches and larger.
- ASTM C 478 Precast Reinforced Concrete Manhole Sections: Covers precast reinforced concrete manhole risers, grade rings and tops to be used to construct manholes for storm and sanitary sewers.
- ASTM C 505 Nonreinforced Concrete Irrigation Pipe with Rubber Gasket Joints: Covers pipe to be used for the conveyance of irrigation water with working pressures, including hydraulic transients, of up to 30 feet of head. Higher pressures may be used up to a maximum of 50 feet for 6-inch through 12-inch diameters, and 40 feet for 15-inch through 18-inch diameters by increasing the strength of the pipe.
- ASTM C 506 Reinforced Concrete Arch Culvert, Storm Drain, and Sewer Pipe: Covers arch concrete pipe to be used for the conveyance of sewage, industrial waste, and storm water and for the construction of culverts in sizes from 15-inch through 132-inch equivalent circular diameter. Larger sizes are available as special designs.
- ASTM C 507 Reinforced Concrete Elliptical Culvert, Storm Drain, and Sewer Pipe: Covers elliptically shaped concrete pipe to be used for the conveyance of sewage, industrial waste and storm water, and for the construction of culverts. Five standard classes of horizontal elliptical, 18 inches through 144 inches in equivalent circular diameter; and five standard classes of vertical elliptical, 36 inches through 144 inches in equivalent circular diameter are included. Larger sizes are available as special designs.
- ASTM C 655 Reinforced Concrete *D*-load Culvert, Storm Drain and Sewer Pipe: Covers acceptance of pipe design and production pipe based upon the *D*-load concept and statistical sampling techniques for concrete pipe to be used for the conveyance of sewage, industrial waste and storm water and construction of culverts.
- ASTM C 789 Precast Reinforced Concrete Box Sections for Culverts, Storm Drains and Sewers: Covers box sections with 2 or more feet of earth cover when subjected to highway live loads, and zero cover or greater when subjected to only dead loads, to be used for the conveyance of sewage, industrial waste, and storm water, and for the construction of culverts in sizes from 3-foot span by 2-foot rise to 12-foot span by 12-foot rise.
- ASTM C 850 Precast Reinforced Concrete Box Sections for Culverts, Storm Drains and Sewers with Less Than 2 Feet of Cover Subjected to Highway Loadings: Covers box sections with less than 2 feet of earth cover for the conveyance of sewage, industrial waste, and storm water, and for the construction of culverts in sizes from 3-foot span by 2-foot rise to 12-foot span by 12-foot rise.
- ASTM C 877 External Sealing Bands for Noncircular Concrete Sewer, Storm Drain and Culvert Pipe: Covers external sealing bands to be used for noncircular pipe conforming to ASTM C 506, C 507, C 789 and C 850.

- ASTM C 923 Resilient Connectors Between Reinforced Concrete Manhole Structures and Pipes: Covers the minimum performance and material requirements for resilient connections between pipe and reinforced concrete manholes conforming to ASTM C 478.
- ASTM C 985 Nonreinforced Concrete Specified Strength Culvert, Storm Drain, and Sewer Pipe: Covers acceptance of pipe design and production pipe based upon the specified strength concept and statistical sampling techniques for concrete pipe to be used for the conveyance of sewage, industrial waste and storm water and construction of culverts.

Illustration 8.2
The strength characteristics of precast concrete pipe as required by the appropriate manufacturing standard can be verified by the three-edge bearing test.

METHODS OF TESTS

Methods of tests describe an orderly procedure for determining a property or constituent of a material, or an assembly of materials, and represent a consensus of the best available test procedures. A method includes essential details of apparatus, test specimens, procedures, and calculations required to achieve satisfactory precision.

In addition to most of the topics included previously under the discussion of specifications, important items in methods of tests include:

- **Significance and use** contains information on the usefulness of each test procedure and provides an understanding of the meaning, suitability, and fundamental assumptions.
- **Apparatus** includes a brief description of the essential features and dimensions of apparatus and equipment.
- **Precision and accuracy** states the precision expected when the method is used by competent operators in different laboratories, and the accuracy of the method.

The scope of the nationally accepted ASTM method of tests is as follows and similar counterpart AASHTO and CSA methods are listed in *Table 8.1*:

- ASTM C 497 Determining Physical Properties of Concrete Pipe or Tile: Covers procedures for testing concrete pipe and tile.

Included in this method are the **external load crushing strength test** for concrete pipe, the **core strength test** for concrete cores, the **absorption test** for concrete pipe specimens, the **hydrostatic test** for concrete pipe sections and the **permeability test** for concrete pipe sections.

External Load Crushing Strength Test

The external load crushing strength test method describes the testing of a pipe specimen in a machine designed so that a crushing force is exerted in a true vertical plane, parallel to one diameter or the vertical centerline, and extending the full length of the wall of the specimen. The force is applied using the **three-edge bearing method** as shown in *Figures 8.1* through *8.4*, in which the test specimen is supported on two parallel longitudinal strips and the load applied through a top bearing beam.

The load is applied at a rate between a minimum of 500 and a maximum of 2500 pounds per linear foot of pipe length per minute until the formation of a 0.01-inch wide crack. The standard crack measuring gage is shown in *Figure 8.5*. A 0.01-inch crack is considered formed when the point of the gage, without forcing, will penetrate 1/16 inch at close intervals through a one foot length of crack.

If both the 0.01-inch crack and the ultimate load are required, the specified rate of loading need not be maintained after reaching the 0.01-inch crack load. The ultimate load is reached when the pipe will support no greater load. Since testing pipe to ultimate strength destroys the pipe section, destructive test procedures are costly, especially for larger size pipe and results in increased cost to the purchaser. Ultimate strength data have questionable usefulness since no correlation has been developed for the buried condition. Accordingly most agencies do not require ultimate strength testing. Some agencies do require testing to loads 10 to 15 percent greater than the specified 0.01-inch crack load and, if no such crack occurs, the pipe are accepted. Still other agencies accept pipe on the basis of inspection of reinforcement placement, production quality, and material tests.

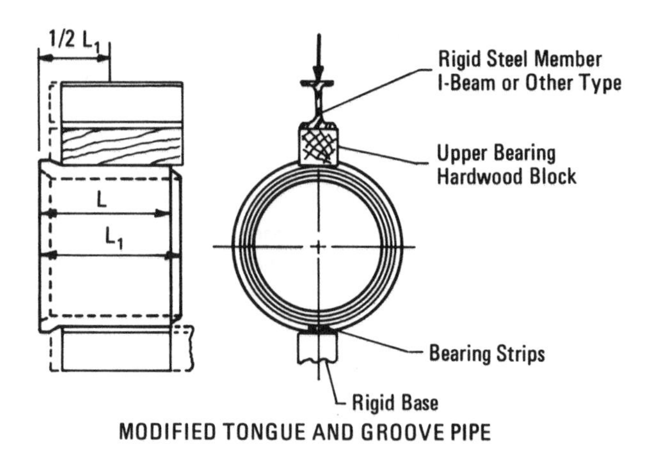

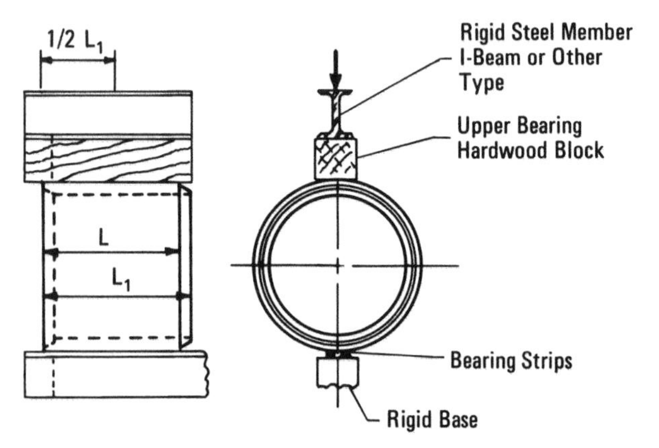

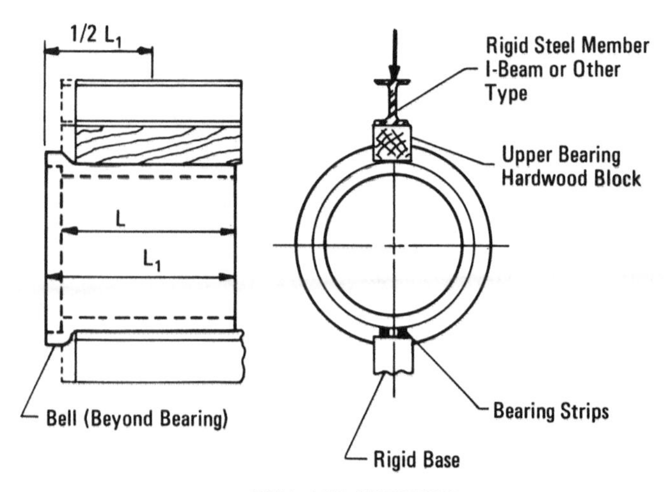

Figure 8.1. Three-Edge Bearing Test, Circular Pipe.

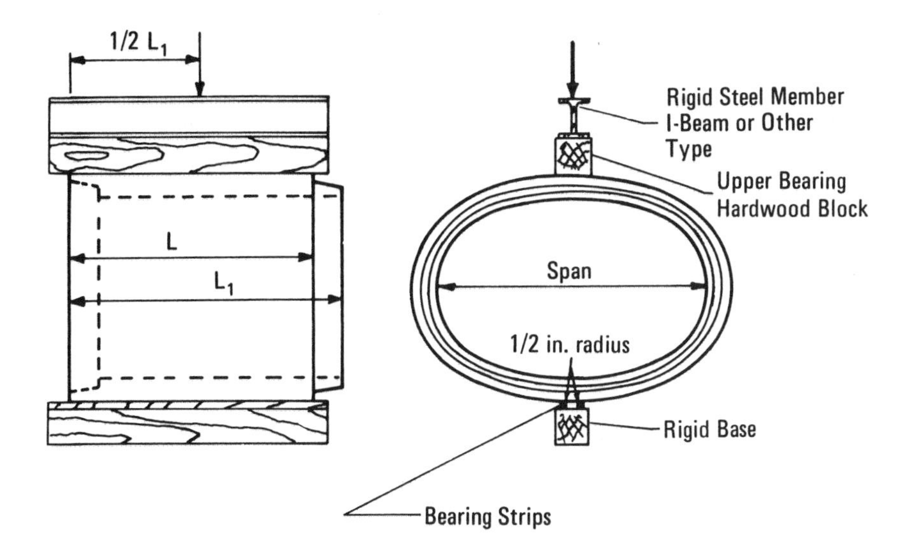

Figure 8.2. Three-Edge Bearing Test, Horizontal Elliptical Pipe.

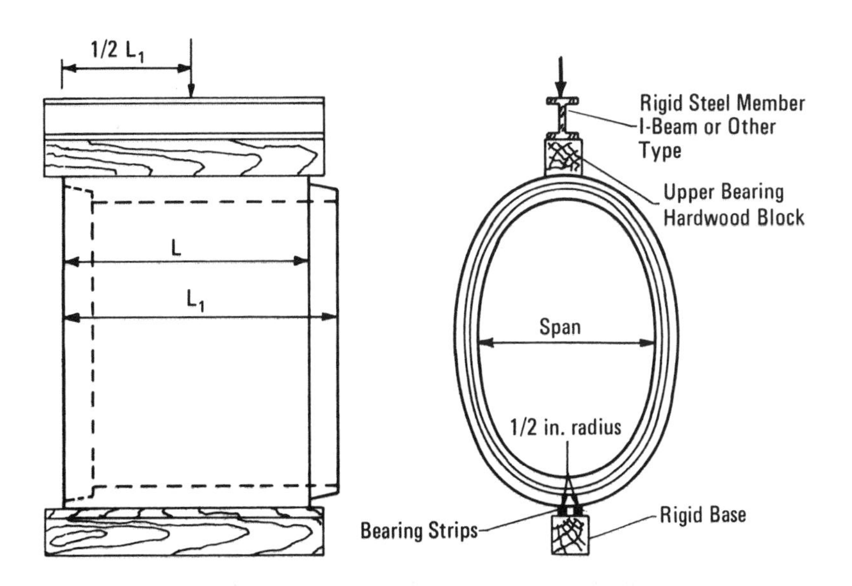

Figure 8.3. Three-Edge Bearing Test, Vertical Elliptical Pipe.

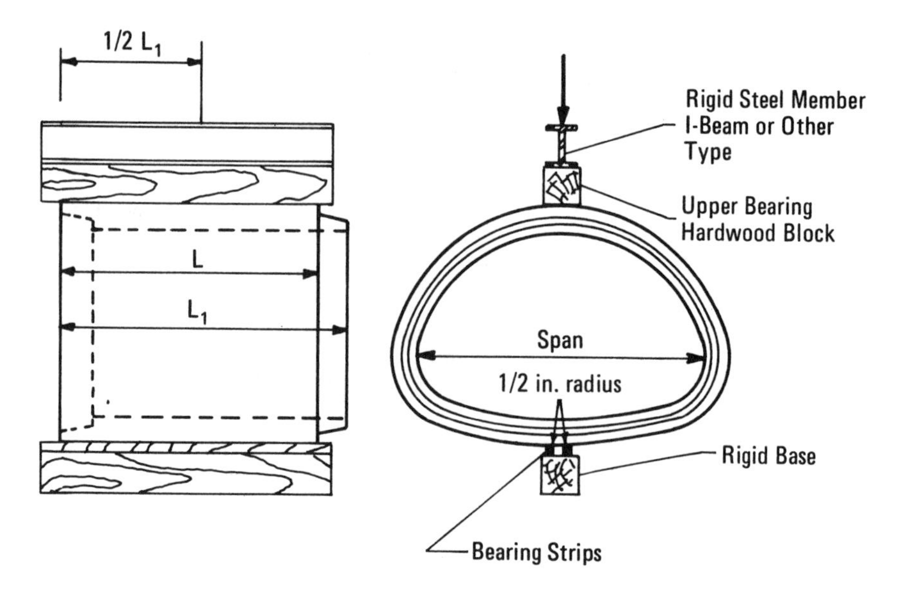

Figure 8.4. Three-Edge Bearing Test, Arch Pipe.

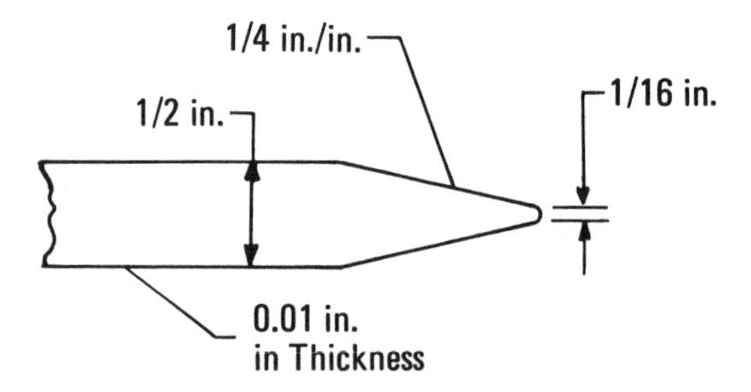

Figure 8.5. Standard Crack Measuring Gage.

Core Strength Test

The core strength test is used to determine the compressive strength of cores cut from the pipe. The core specimen should have a diameter of at least three times the maximum size of coarse aggregate used in the concrete, and a length to diameter ratio between one and two after the curved end surfaces have been removed. The core specimen is moisture conditioned by submergence in lime-saturated water before testing, unless otherwise directed by the purchaser. Strength correction factors have been developed for various ratios of core length to diameter.

Illustration 8.3
Core testing provides a more realistic determination of the concrete strength of precast concrete pipe and is the preferred method when such determination is required.

Absorption Test

The absorption test details three methods of determining absorption properties of specimens obtained from concrete pipe.

Method A

A specimen of the size specified in the appropriate concrete pipe specification is obtained from the pipe wall. The specimen is oven-dried for minimums of 24 to 72 hours, depending on the wall thickness. After weighing, the specimen is immersed in water, boiled for five hours and then left in the water to cool to room temperature for a minimum of 14 to a maximum of 24 hours. The specimen is then removed, surface dried and weighed. The dry and wet weights are used to calculate the amount of water absorbed and percent absorption.

Method B

Three specimens consisting of 1.5-inch diameter cores are taken from the two ends and center area of the pipe section being tested and oven-dried for a minimum of 24 hours. After weighing, the specimens are immersed in water, boiled for three hours, and cooled for three hours with running cold water. The specimens are then removed, surface dried and weighed. The dry and wet weights are used to calculate percent absorption as in Method A.

10-Minute Soaking Method

Specimens are the same as for Method A and may be reused for the Method A procedure, if necessary. The specimens are dried in the same manner as in Method A. After weighing, the specimens are immersed in room temperature water for 10 minutes. The specimens are then removed, surface dried and weighed. The dry and wet weights are used to calculate percent absorption.

Hydrostatic Test

The hydrostatic test is performed on a full section of pipe or two or more sections of pipe assembled with a joint gasket. The equipment for this test includes bulkheads for the pipe ends, means to secure the bulkheads, and a method to introduce and maintain internal water pressure. For a single pipe section test, the bulkhead arrangement determines whether the pipe barrel or both the barrel and joint are tested. Two or more pipe sections joined and tested provide a realistic test of the joint-gasket combination. Included are requirements for testing pipe sections in straight or deflected alignment. The exact wording on allowable leakage varies among pipe specifications but damp or wet spots and minor dripping are not considered leakage. Specifications generally allow presoaking before testing, or extended soaking before retesting.

Permeability Test

The permeability test is performed by placing a section of pipe, spigot end down, on a soft, resilient, waterproof surface, and filling the pipe with water to the level of the base of the socket. The pipe is inspected approximately 15 minutes after the test is begun, and, if the pipe shows moist or damp spots on the outer surface, the test is continued for a period not to exceed 24 hours.

DEFINITIONS

Definitions include terms relating to a single material or technology. Definitions developed by ASTM Committee C-13 are of terms found in the concrete pipe standards under the jurisdiction of Committee C-13. The scope of nationally accepted ASTM definitions is as follows and the similar counterpart AASHTO is listed in *Table 8.1*:

- ASTM C 822 Standard Definitions and Terms Relating to Concrete Pipe and Related Products: Covers words and terms used in concrete pipe standards.

RECOMMENDED PRACTICES

Recommended practices are procedures, guides, or services that may or may not be auxiliary to a test method or a specification. At the time of publication of this Handbook, ASTM Committee C-13 has approved two practices and has under consideration other practices relating to the installation of concrete pipe and procedures and criteria for testing installed pipelines. The scopes of the nationally accepted ASTM recommended practices are as follows and listed in *Table 8.1:*

- ASTM C 924 Testing Concrete Pipe Sewer Lines by Low-Pressure Air Test Method: Covers procedures for testing concrete pipe sewer lines when using the low-pressure air test method to demonstrate the integrity of the installed material and construction procedures.
- ASTM C 969 Infiltration and Exfiltration Acceptance Testing of Installed Precast Concrete Pipe Sewer Lines: Covers procedures for testing concrete pipe sewer lines for acceptance when using the water infiltration or exfiltration method to demonstrate the integrity of the installed material and construction procedures.

PLANT AIR TESTING

Precast concrete pipe manufacturers use a variety of methods and tests to assure quality products. One such test is the in-plant air test which has been in use since the early 1970's. Some manufacturers use a stamp or other symbol to mark pipe which have passed the test. Most agencies which have observed such tests accept this marking certification in lieu of requiring hydrostatic or other water-tightness tests.

Although not incorporated as an acceptance criterion in any ASTM precast concrete pipe standards, the in-plant air test is used by many manufacturers to assure that the pipe meet the requirements specified for performance. Two types of in-plant air tests have evolved, the **pressure test** and the **vacuum test.** Test procedures and equipment have been developed by individual companies although some equipment is commercially available.

PRESSURE TEST

The test is performed on single pipe sections or an assembly of pipe sections. The equipment for testing single pipe sections includes end bulkheads, a compressor, piping and valves. The configuration of the bulkheads determines whether the entire pipe or the pipe and joint are tested. When testing more than one pipe, the sections are assembled and the ends of the assembly bulkheaded and restrained. This method tests the integrity of the pipe, joint and joint material. The other equipment required is similar to that for the single pipe specimen test.

In the pressure test, air is injected into the pipe to a specified pressure. No drop in pressure, or slow drop, indicates an acceptable pipe. In most cases, however, experience indicates the test is either a go or no-go situation. Sometimes water, with or without soap, is sprayed on the outside to help locate defects. The test is of value because large samples can be economically tested.

VACUUM TEST

The test is normally performed on single pipe sections. The equipment includes a vacuum pump, bulkheads, piping and valves similar to those for the single section pressure test. The test involves removing air from the pipe to a specified pressure less than atmospheric. The ability to hold a vacuum or a slow drop indicates an acceptable pipe. Experience indicates this test is also a go or no-go situation. The test is not quantitative but provides economical testing of large samples. Other benefits include the inherent safety and economy of vacuum systems over pressurized systems.

CHAPTER 9

INSTALLATION, INSPECTION AND CONSTRUCTION TESTING

The design of a concrete pipeline assumes that certain minimum conditions of installation will be met. Acceptance criteria are established to assure that workmanship and material quality provided during construction meet the design requirements and that the pipeline will perform satisfactorily. Installation and testing are the final steps in a process that includes research, surface and subsurface investigations, design, specification preparation, pipe manufacturing and material testing.

Installation procedures are presented in this chapter together with some of the problems that might be encountered. These procedures include:

- Preconstruction planning
- Site preparation
- Ordering, receiving and handling
- Excavation
- Foundation and bedding preparation
- Jointing
- Backfilling
- Construction testing

PRECONSTRUCTION PLANNING

Adequate planning can identify and eliminate many potential problems which could produce unnecessary delays and extra costs. Preconstruction planning assists in the development of rapport among engineers, inspectors, material suppliers and construction personnel.

A plans-in-hand review at the project site is essential. This should be preceded by a review of all construction contract documents, including plans, project specifications, soil information, standard drawings and special provisions. During the field check, any questions concerning the plans and specifications can be resolved. Planning also requires all involved personnel to be familiar with the administrative requirements of the construction contract, such as wage rates, insurance requirements, change order procedures, safety regulations, etc.

Federal safety regulations for all types of construction, including sewer and culvert installations, are published by the Occupational Safety and Health Administration of the United States Department of Labor. Many states, municipalities and local agencies have also established codes of safe practice. No statement in this handbook should be construed as superceding any applicable safety code or regulation.

Good public relations with adjacent property owners and those who will be inconvenienced during the construction of the project is desirable. Preconstruction planning enables timely dissemination of project information. Information to be disseminated should include:

- Project purpose, scope and benefits
- Construction timing and sequence
- How and where to obtain information
- Emergency contacts

The type and location of installations vary, but a number of factors are common to all. Information and action on the following items will avoid delays:

- Names and addresses of agencies having jurisdiction over highways, railroads, airports, utilities, drainage, etc.
- Required easements, permits, releases or any other special stipulations
- Responsibility for notifying officials of existing utilities and, if necessary, requesting appropriate agencies to locate and mark facilities affected
- Locate bench marks, monuments and property stakes and reference all points likely to be disturbed
- Check grade and alignment, clearing requirements, and insure building connections, water mains, hydrants and other appurtenances are properly staked
- Coordinate work to be done and requirements of subcontractors
- Arrange for measurement of pay quantities and procedures for change orders, extra work orders, and force account work
- Safety regulations, equipment capabilites and requirements for traffic maintenance
- Establish forms for record keeping, progress reports, diary, etc.

SITE PREPARATION

Site preparation can significantly influence progress of the project. The amount and type of work involved in site preparation varies with the location of the project, topography, surface conditions and existing utilities. Commonly included are:

- Top soil stripping
- Clearing and grubbing
- Pavement and sidewalk removal
- Rough grading
- Relocation of existing natural drainage
- Removal of unsuitable soil material
- Access roads
- Detours
- Protection of existing structures and utilities
- Environmental considerations

ORDERING, RECEIVING AND HANDLING

Pipe manufacturers produce a wide range of pipe sizes and strengths, however, production facilities must frequently be adapted to meet specific project requirements.

ORDERING

Ordering materials is usually the contractor's responsibility, but the pipe supplier and engineer should be familiar with the proposed construction schedule to avoid mistakes and possible delays in pipe deliveries. A pipe order should include:

- Name and location of project
- Pipe size, designation and laying length
- Total footage of each designation and size
- Type of joint, gaskets or sealants
- Size and quantity of manhole base, riser and cone sections and grade rings
- Fittings and specials
- Material test requirements
- Delivery sequence and schedule
- Invoicing instructions

RECEIVING

Pipe delivered to the construction site has been plant inspected, but a field check should be made to insure that the pipe is clearly marked with the following information:

- Specification designation
- Pipe class or strength designation
- Date of manufacture
- Name or trademark of the manufacturer
- Plant identification
- Letters E or Q on pipe with elliptical or quadrant reinforcement

HANDLING

Each shipment of pipe is loaded, blocked and tied down at the plant to avoid damage during transit. However, it is the responsibility of the receiver to determine that damage has not occurred during delivery. An overall inspection of each pipe shipment should be made before unloading and total quantities of each item checked against the delivery slip and damaged or missing items recorded.

Unloading

Concrete pipe can be unloaded with conventional lifting and excavation equipment. Small diameter pipe are often unloaded by hand, with 75 to 100 pounds as the generally accepted maximum weight for one individual to handle repeatedly. Small to intermediate size pipe up to 36-inch diameter can be unloaded by manually rolling the pipe sections off the truck onto skids. Loosely piled earth should be windrowed along the unloading area near the toe of the skid to provide a cushion and to prevent the pipe from rolling beyond the designated area, *Figure 9.1*.

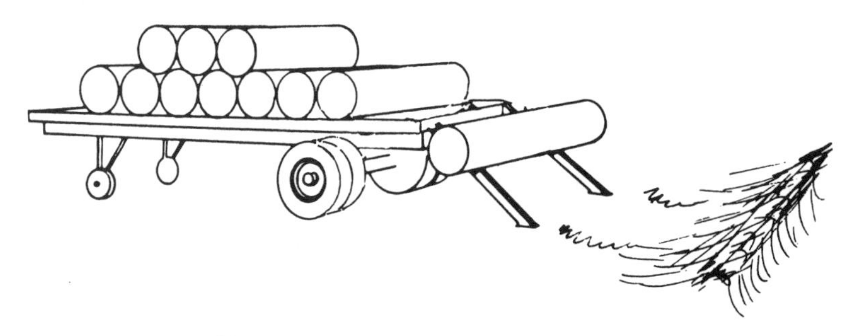

Figure 9.1. Unloading with Skids.

Larger size pipe can be unloaded with skids but should be controlled with ropes. When unloading pipe by means of ropes and skids, the pipe is lowered all the way down the skid and not allowed to roll free, *Figure 9.2*. One pipe section at a time is lowered with the rope located at the center of the pipe and securely anchored on the opposite end of the truck from which the pipe is being unloaded.

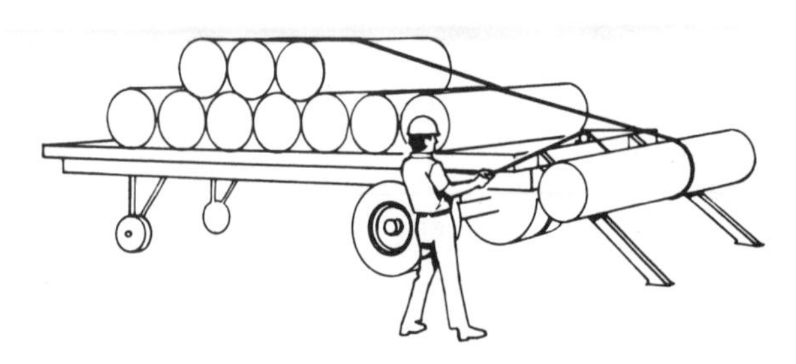

Figure 9.2. Unloading with Skids and Ropes.

Illustration 9.1
One type of automatic pipe unloader.

Lowering of the pipe must be controlled to prevent collision with other pipe sections or fittings and care taken to avoid chipping or spalling, especially to joint surfaces. Caution is necessary to insure workers are out of the path of the pipe as it is lowered down the skid. If the pipe are moved after unloading, the sections should be rolled or lifted and never dragged or rolled over rough or rocky ground.

Mechanical equipment is necessary for unloading the larger sizes of pipe and usually simplifies and speeds up the unloading of smaller pipe. When mechanical equipment is used, the lifting device which supports the pipe must provide safe handling without damaging the pipe. When pipe is provided with a lifting hole the most common lifting device consists of a steel threaded eye bar with a wing type nut and bearing plate, *Figure 9.3*.

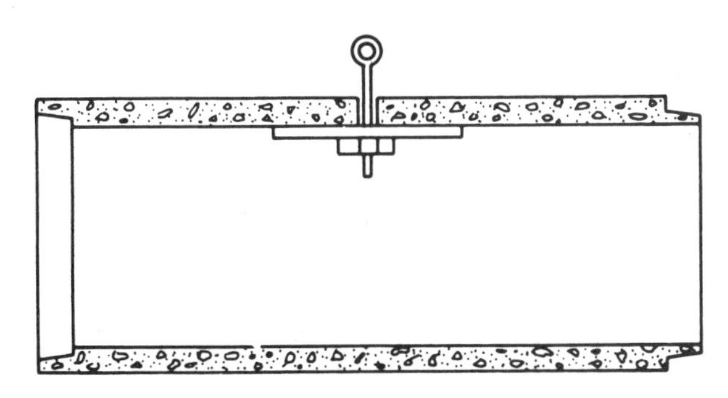

Figure 9.3. Lift Hole Device.

Many carriers are equipped with **automatic unloaders.** These unloaders consist of a forklift type apparatus mounted at the rear of a flatbed truck. The forks rotate vertically, *Figure 9.4,* rather than moving up and down, so that when the forks are in a vertical position they extend above the truck bed. This provides a backstop and cushion for the pipe sections as they are rolled to the rear of the truck for unloading. A cradle formed by the forks and unloader frame securely retains the pipe section being unloaded as the forks are rotated downward and lowered to the ground.

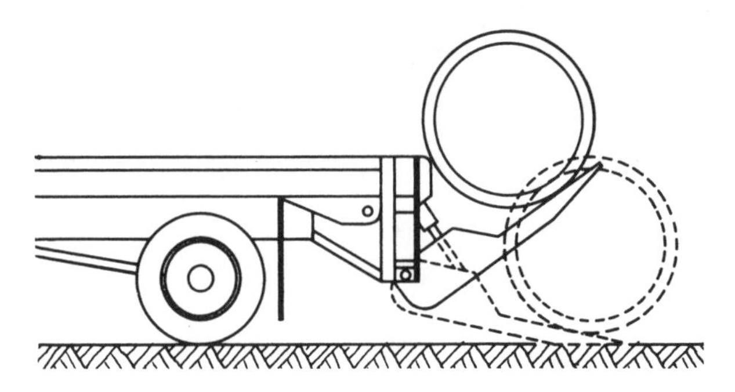

Figure 9.4. Automatic Unloader.

Distributing

Coordination of pipe delivery with installation will avoid unnecessary handling and equipment movement. For trench installations, the pipe should be placed on the trench side away from the excavated material. The sections are placed so that they will be protected from traffic and construction equipment, but close enough to the trench to permit efficient handling. For embankment installations, with pipe to be installed on a shallow bedding at approximately the same elevation as original ground, the pipe can be strung out immediately after clearing and rough grading.

Stockpiling

Stockpiling of pipe is usually made as close as possible to the point of installation. Small diameter pipe can be stockpiled in the same manner as loaded on the truck. The bottom layer is placed on a flat base and adequately blocked to prevent shifting. Each layer of bell and spigot pipe is arranged so all bells face the same direction. Bells in the next layer are reversed and project beyond the spigots of the pipe sections in the previous layer. The pipe barrel should be supported so that the bell ends are not subjected to load concentrations. Pipe should not be stockpiled in layers at the job site to a height greater than six feet.

Flexible gasket materials not on the pipe, and joint lubricating compounds, are stored in a cool dry place. Gaskets and preformed or bulk mastics need to be kept clean, away from oil, grease, excessive heat and out of the direct rays of the sun.

Illustration 9.2
Yarded concrete pipe ready for delivery.

EXCAVATION

For sewers and culverts, operations can include trenching, tunneling, backfilling, embankment construction, soil stabilization and control of groundwater and surface drainage. Adequate knowledge of subsurface conditions is essential for any type of excavation. This information is obtained from soil surveys and soil classification prior to the design phase of the project.

EQUIPMENT

Several types of excavating equipment are available. Selection of the most efficient piece of equipment for a specific excavation operation is important, since all excavating equipment has practical and economic limitations. Considerations include the type and amount of material to be excavated, depth and width of excavation, dimensional limitations established in the plans, pipe size, operating space and spoil placement. Basic equipment, shown in *Figure 9.5*, usually can be modified or adapted for use in most excavating operations.

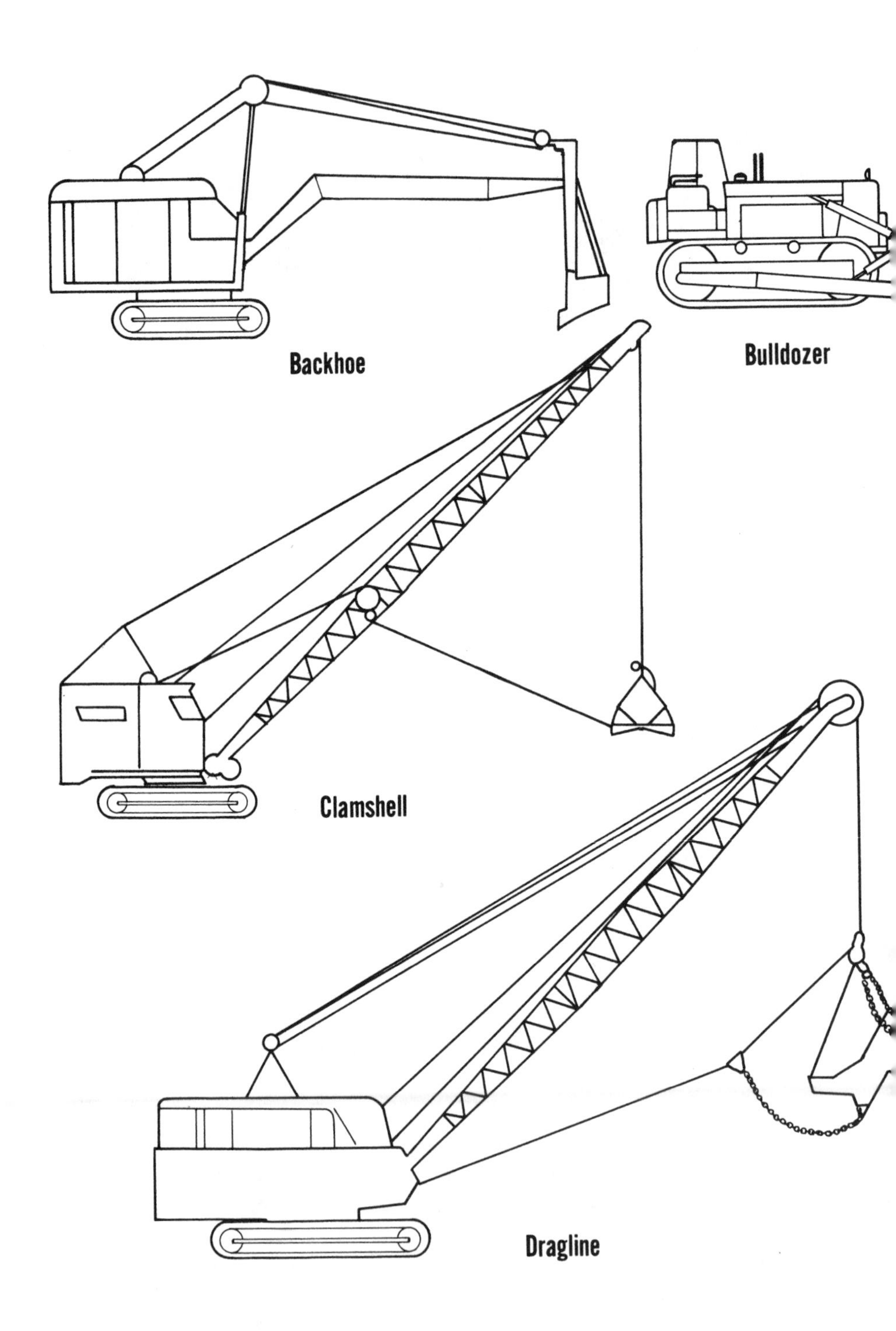

Figure 9.5. Typical Excavation Equipment.

Crawler-Mounted

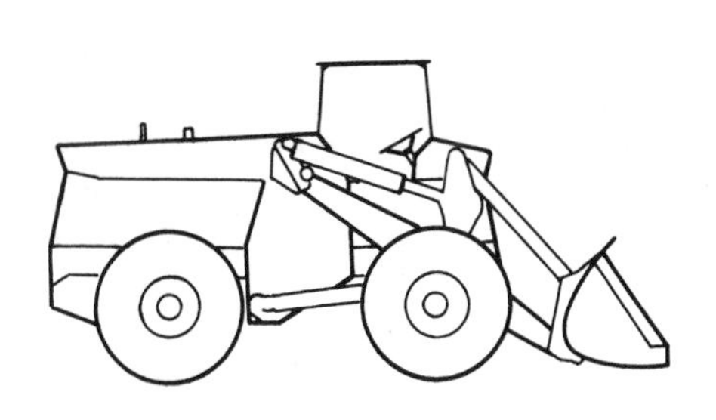

Wheel-Mounted

Front-End Loaders

Hydraulic Excavator

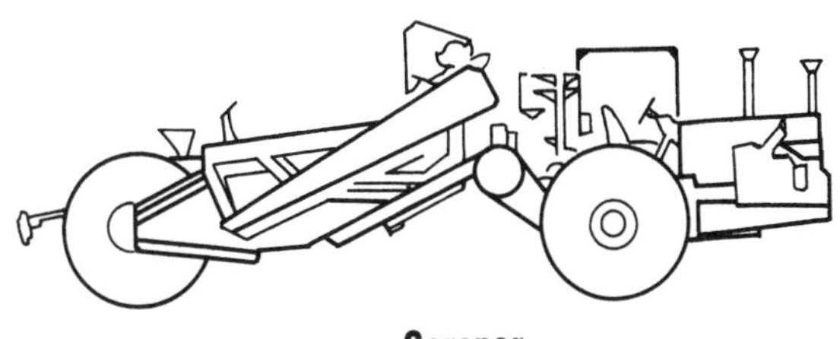

Scraper

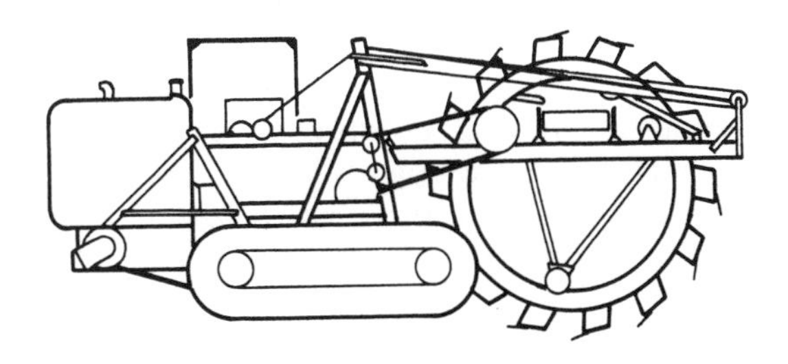

Trencher

LINE AND GRADE

For trench installation, **line** and **grade** are usually established by control points consisting of stakes, spikes, plugs or shiners set at the ground surface and offset from the proposed centerline of the pipe, and control points set in the trench. When control points are established at the surface, batter boards, tape and level, or other instruments are used to transfer line and grade to the trench bottom. Regardless, the basic procedures include:

- Stakes, spikes, plugs or shiners are driven flush with the ground surface, at 25 to 50 foot intervals for straight alignment and at shorter intervals for curved alignment.
- Control points are offset 10 feet, or some other convenient distance, on the opposite side of the trench from which excavated material will be placed.
- Control point elevations are determined, and the depth from the control point to the trench bottom or pipe invert is indicated on a guard stake next to the control point.
- A cut sheet is prepared listing reference points, stationing, offset distance and vertical distance from the control points to the trench bottom or pipe invert.

For narrow trenches a horizontal batter board is placed across the trench, *Figure 9.6,* and a nail driven in the upper edge at the centerline of the pipe. In many cases the batter board is used only as a spanning member with a short vertical board nailed to it at the pipe centerline. A stringline is then pulled tight across a minimum of three batter boards and line transferred to the trench bottom by a plumb bob. Grade is transferred to the trench bottom by means of a grade rod or other vertical measuring device.

For wide trenches the batter board may not span the width of excavation. In such cases the vertical grade rod is attached to one end of the batter board and the other end set level against an offset stringline. The length of the horizontal batter board is the same as the offset distance and the length of the vertical grade rod is the same as the distance between the trench bottom or pipe invert and the stringline. Specially designed instruments are available which incorporate a measuring tape, extendable arm and leveling device. These instruments are based on the same principle but eliminate the need to construct batter boards and supports.

The transfer of surface control points to stakes along the trench bottom is sometimes necessary because of trench depth or sloped sides. Stakes are set along the trench bottom at appropriate intervals and a stringline drawn between two or three control points. Where line and grade are established as excavation proceeds, a transit and level or laser setup is usually used.

In setting line and grade for culverts installed at about the same elevation as the original ground, control points are usually established during the construction survey. Stakes are then set along the culvert length. If

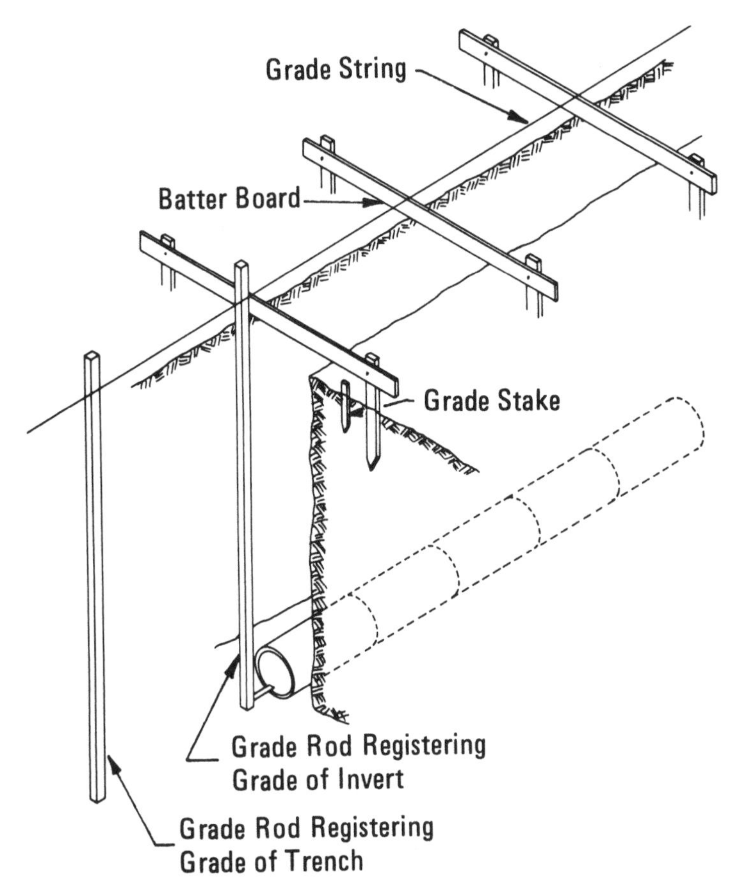

Figure 9.6. Batter Board Set-up.

the embankment is built first, and then a subtrench excavated, the same procedures as for trench excavations can be used.

When pipe is installed by the jacking or tunneling method of construction, control points must be established at the bottom of the jacking pit or work shaft. For long tunnels or curved alignment, intermediate control points are required.

Lasers can be used to set line and grade, *Figure 9.7*. Basically, the instrument projects a narrow light beam. The beam is a continuous, uninterrupted straight line which does not sag like a stringline, and can be used for distances up to 1000 feet. Since the laser is a light beam, it can be seen by either looking back at the instrument along the projection line, or intercepting the beam with a target which reflects the light.

A laser once set as to direction and grade, provides a constant reference line from which measurements can be taken at any point along the beam. A rule or stadia rod is used to measure offsets quickly and accurately The laser instrument can be mounted and operated in a manhole, set on a tripod, or placed on a solid surface inside or outside the pipe.

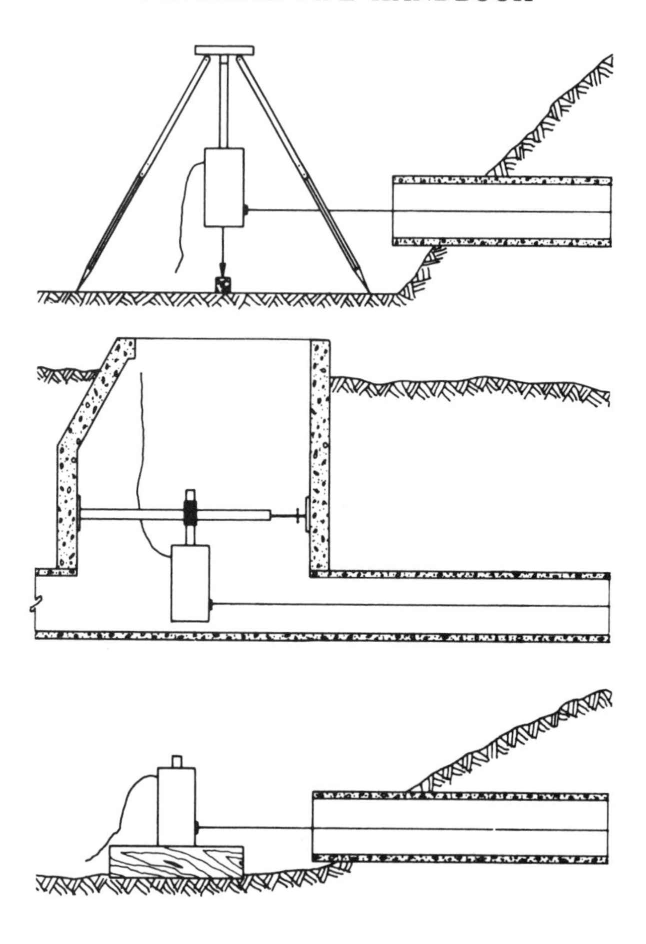

Figure 9.7. Laser System.

EXCAVATION LIMITS

Excavation, pipe installation and backfill operations should succeed each other as rapidly as possible. Avoiding long stretches of open trench will:

- Reduce equipment requirements
- Reduce sheathing and shoring required at any one time
- Prevent trench flooding
- Reduce the need to control groundwater
- Minimize disruption to existing utilities
- Simplify traffic maintenance
- Reduce safety hazards
- Permit closer supervision and inspection of the work
- Permit better quality control
- Reduce adverse environmental impacts
- Assist in maintaining better public relations

In sewer construction, the most important excavation limitations are trench width and depth. As excavation progresses, trench grades are continuously checked to obtain the elevations established on the sewer profile. Incorrect trench depths may adversely affect the hydraulic capacity of the sewer and require correction or additional maintenance after the line is completed.

The backfill load ultimately transmitted to the pipe is a function of trench width, as discussed in *Chapter 4*. The designer assumes a certain trench width in determining the backfill load, and selects a pipe strength capable of withstanding that load. If the actual trench width exceeds the width assumed in design, the load on the pipe will be greater than estimated and structural distress may result. Therefore, trench widths should

Illustration 9.3
Concrete pipe being installed in a trench.

be as narrow as established in the plans or standard drawings. Side clearance must be adequate to permit proper compaction of backfill material at the sides of the pipe, and trenches are usually designed for a width of 1.25 times the outside diameter of the pipe plus one foot. *Figure 9.8* illustrates the load carried by a pipe installed in a normal trench installation and if the width of the trench is increased, the load on the pipe is increased as shown in *Figure 9.9*.

If an excessively wide trench is excavated or the sides sloped back, the pipe can be installed in a narrow subtrench excavated at the bottom of the wider trench to avoid increase in the backfill load, *Figure 9.10*. The recommended depth of the subtrench is the vertical height of the pipe plus one foot.

For culverts installed under embankments, it may be possible to simulate a narrow subtrench by installing the pipe in the existing stream bed. When culverts are installed in a negative projection condition or by the induced trench method of construction the same excavation limits apply as for trench conditions.

For jacked or tunneled installations the excavation coincides as closely as possible to the outside dimensions and shape of the pipe. The usual procedure for jacking pipe is to equip the leading edge with a cutter, or shoe, to protect the lead pipe. As the pipe is jacked forward, soil is excavated and removed through the pipe. Materials should be trimmed approximately one or two inches larger than the outside diameter of the pipe and excavation should not precede pipe advancement more than necessary. This procedure results in minimum disturbance of the earth adjacent to the pipe.

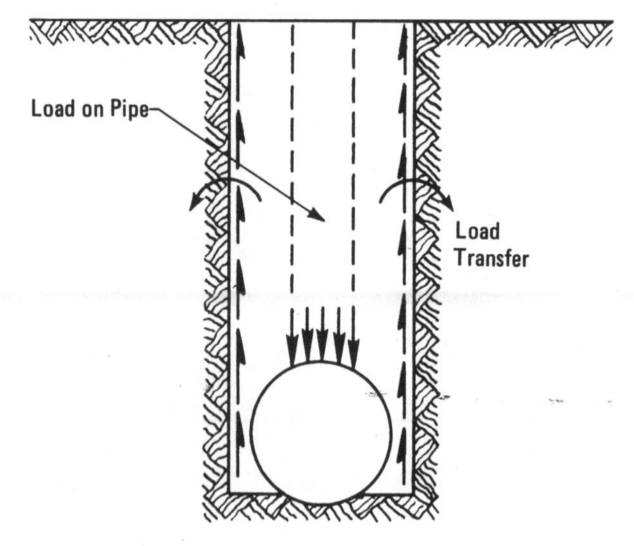

Figure 9.8. Trench Installation.

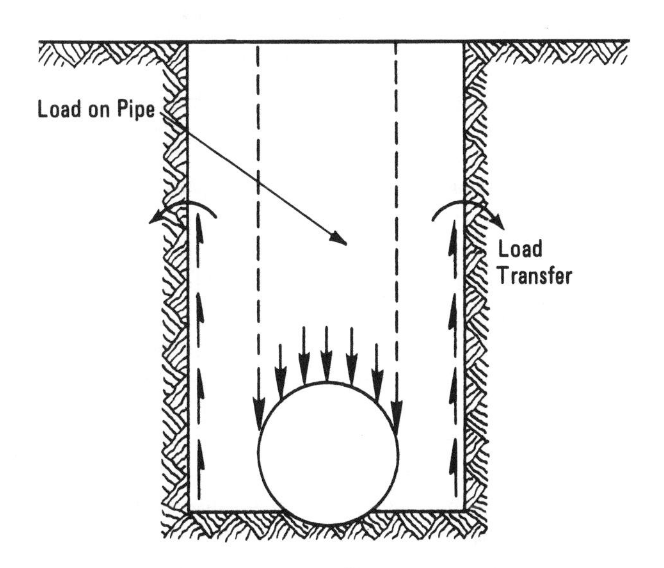

Figure 9.9. Wide Trench Installation.

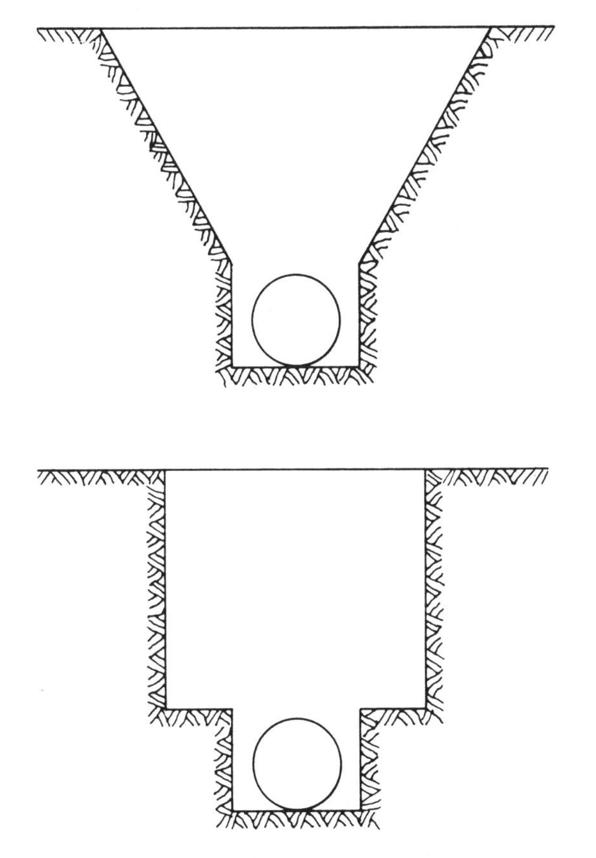

Figure 9.10. Subtrench Installation in a Wide Trench.

SPOIL PLACEMENT

The placement and storage of excavated material is an important consideration in sewer and culvert construction and influences the selection of excavating equipment, the need for providing sheathing and shoring, and backfilling operations. For trench installations the excavated material is usually used for backfill, and the material stockpiled along the trench in such a manner as to reduce unnecessary handling during backfill operations, *Figure 9.11*. The distance excavated material is placed from the trench is controlled by site conditions, dumping radius, and casting capabilities of the equipment. A general rule for spoil placement along unsupported trenches is that the minimum distance from the trench sides to the toe of the spoil bank should not be less than one half the trench depth. If the trench walls are supported, a minimum distance of three feet from the edge of the trench to the toe of the spoil bank is usually sufficient.

Stockpiling excavated material adjacent to the trench produces a **surcharge load.** The ability of the trench walls to stand under this additional load depends on the cohesive properties of the soil. Any surcharge load should be considered when evaluating the need to provide trench support. When deep or wide trenches are excavated, it may be necessary to haul away a portion of the excavated soil or spread the stockpile. If the excavated material is to be used as backfill, the stockpile should be visually inspected for rocks, frozen lumps, highly organic or plastic clays, and other objectionable material. If the excavated soil differs significantly from the type of backfill material specified, it may be necessary to remove the unsuitable soil and bring in a select backfill.

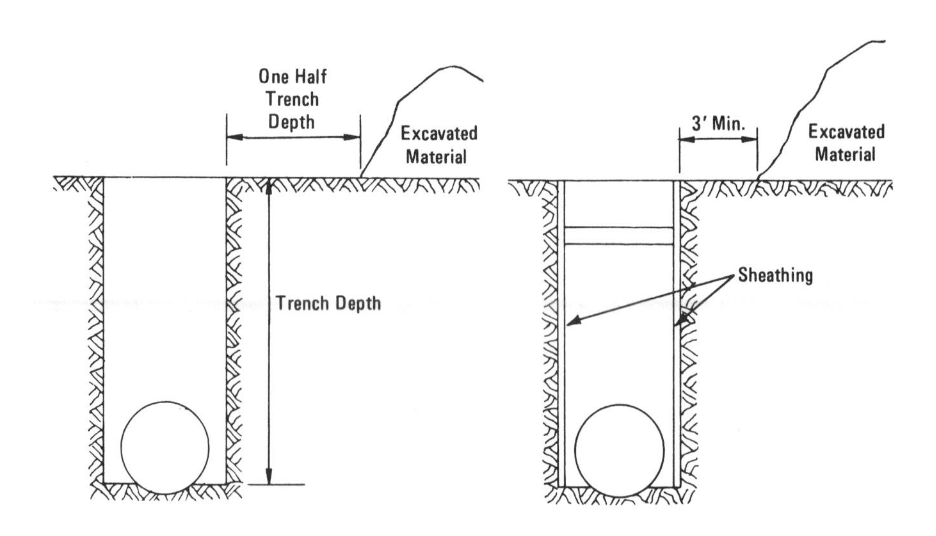

Figure 9.11. Spoil Placement.

Spoil placement for culvert installations is usually not as critical as for trench installations. If the excavated material is suitable, it can be incorporated into the embankment adjacent to the culvert.

For pipe installed by jacking the excavated material is loaded into carts or onto a conveyor system and transported through the pipe to the jacking pit. It is then lifted from the pit and hauled away or deposited in a waste bank. The rate of progress of a jacking or tunneling operation is frequently controlled by the rate of excavation and spoil removal. Preliminary investigation and advance planning for rapid and efficient removal and placement of the spoil can prevent delays and unnecessary handling.

SHEATHING AND SHORING

Trench stabilization is usually accomplished through the use of **sheathing** and **shoring,** *Figure 9.12*. The Occupational Safety and Health Administration and many states, municipalities and other local agencies have established codes of safe practice regarding support requirements for trench excavation.

The structural requirements of sheathing and shoring depend on:

- Depth and width of excavation
- Characteristics of the soil
- Water content of the soil
- Water table
- Weather conditions
- Proximity of other structures
- Vibration from construction equipment and traffic
- Spoil placement or other surcharge loads
- Code requirements

Illustration 9.4
Tight sheathing using sheet piles.

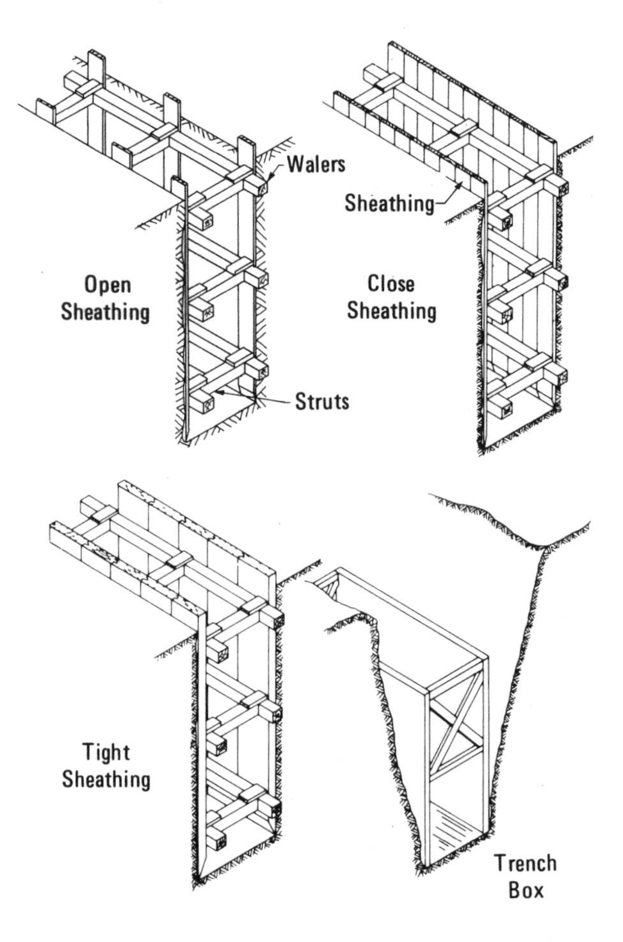

Figure 9.12. Types of Sheathing and Shoring.

Accurate evaluation of all these factors is usually not possible, so the design and application of temporary bracing systems varies considerably. However, certain methods, materials and terminology have evolved for stabilizing open trenches and serve as a general guide.

Shoring for trenches is accomplished by bracing one bank against the other, and the structural members which transfer the load between the trench sides are termed **struts.** Wood planks placed against the trench walls to retain the vertical banks are termed **sheathing.** The horizontal members of the bracing system which form the framework for the sheathing are termed **walers** or **stringers,** and the vertical members are termed **strongbacks.**

The four most common sheathing methods are:

- Open or skeleton sheathing
- Close sheathing
- Tight sheathing
- Trench shields or boxes

Open sheathing consists of a continuous frame with vertical sheathing planks placed at intervals along the open trench. This method of sheathing is used for cohesive, stable soils where groundwater is not a problem.

Close sheathing also uses a continuous frame, but the vertical sheathing planks are placed side by side so as to form a continuous retaining wall. This method of sheathing is used for noncohesive and unstable soils.

Tight sheathing is the same as close sheathing except the vertical sheathing planks are interlocked. This method of sheathing is used for saturated soils. Steel sheet piling is sometimes used instead of wood planking.

Trench shields are heavily braced steel or wood boxes which are moved along the trench bottom as excavation and pipe laying progress. Trench boxes are used to protect workmen installing pipe in stable soil where the trenches are deep and unsheathed. Trench shields are also used in lieu of other methods of sheathing and shoring for shallow excavations where the sides of the shield can extend from the trench bottom to the ground surface. When trench shields are used, care must be taken to avoid pulling the pipe apart or disrupting the bedding as the shield is moved.

Improper removal of sheathing can reduce soil friction along the trench wall and increase the backfill load on the pipe. Therefore, sheathing should be removed in increments as the backfill is placed. Additional compaction of the backfill material may be necessary to fill any voids left by the sheathing.

Illustration 9.5
Using trench box in unstable soil for concrete pipe installation.

DEWATERING

Control of surface and subsurface water is required so dry conditions will exist during excavation and pipe laying. Groundwater conditions should be investigated prior to excavation. Test borings may be required to determine the depth, quantity and direction of flow of the water table. Groundwater is usually controlled by one or a combination of the following:

- Tight sheathing
- Drains
- Pumping
- Wellpoints

If direct pumping from sumps is used, *Figure 9.13,* the pumps should be submersible or self-priming so that intermittent flows can be discharged. Diaphragm pumps are generally more suitable when a mud slurry is to be pumped, while centrifugal pumps are best for pumping large quantities of water. Regardless of the specific type of pump, a standby pump should be available in case the operating pump clogs or stops.

Lowering of the water table through the use of a **wellpoint system,** *Figure 9.14,* is an effective means of controlling groundwater in permeable soils and may eliminate the need for sheathing and shoring. A wellpoint

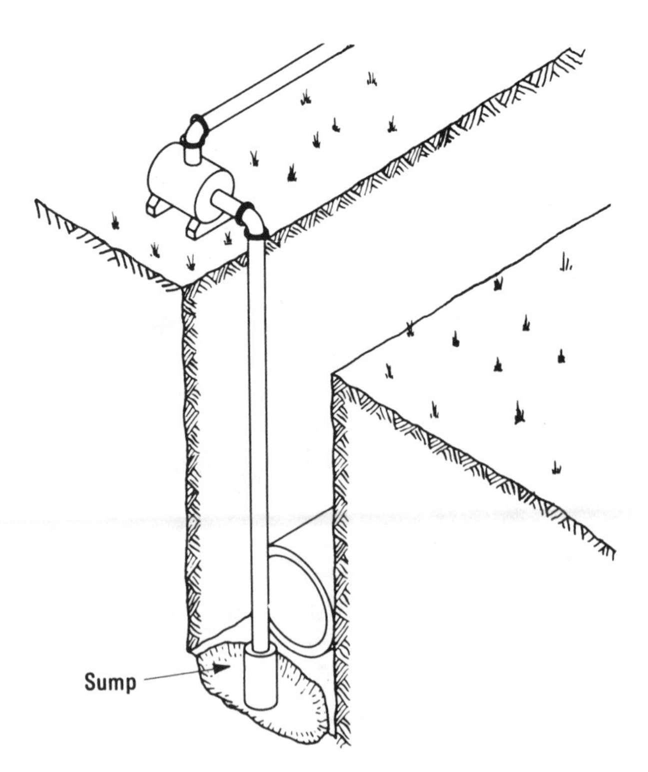

Figure 9.13. Dewatering by Pumping.

Illustration 9.6
Well point system.

system consists of one to two-inch pipe, which are jetted vertically into the water bearing soil. The wellpoints are connected to a header pipe by swing joints which permit flexibility in placement of wellpoints. The number and spacing of wellpoints are dependent on the permeability of the soil and amount of water to be removed. Spacings of three feet are common

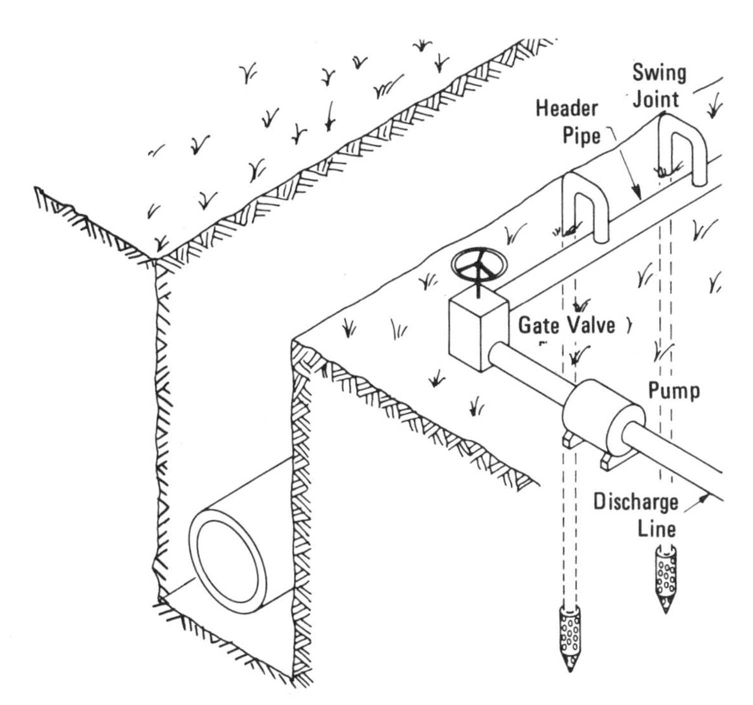

Figure 9.14. Well Point System.

for a 6-inch diameter header pipe and two feet for an 8-inch diameter header pipe. Normally 500–600 feet of header pipe are required with gate valves spaced at intervals of 100–200 feet. Lowering the water table may lead to subsidence of the ground in the surrounding area, and structures in close proximity to the dewatered area could settle or develop structural damage if precautions are not taken.

FOUNDATION PREPARATION

A stable and uniform **foundation** is necessary for satisfactory performance of any pipe. The foundation must have sufficient load bearing capacity to maintain the pipe in proper alignment and sustain the loads imposed. The foundation should be checked for hard or soft spots. Where undesirable foundations exist, they should be stabilized by **ballasting** or **soil modification**.

Ballasting requires removal of undesirable foundation material and replacement with select materials such as sand, gravel, crushed rock, slag, or suitable earth backfill. The depth, gradation and size of the ballast depends on the specific material used and the amount of stabilization required. The ballast is usually well graded from coarse to fine, having a size not more than one inch per foot of pipe diameter with three inches maximum and placed to a minimum depth of four inches.

Soil modification involves the addition of select material to the native soil. Crushed rock, gravel, sand, slag or other durable inert materials with a maximum size of three inches is worked into the subsoil to accomplish the required stabilization. Soil modification can also be accomplished by the addition of lime, cement or chemicals to the soil.

Adequate foundation stability is difficult to evaluate by visual observation. However, when concrete pipe is set on the foundation with little or no care exercised to provide a bearing surface, the weight of the pipe exerts a pressure of approximately 1000 pounds per square foot. This pressure is about the same pressure a 200 pound man would exert when standing on one foot. If the foundation can support men working in the trench without sinking into the soil, the foundation should be stable enough to support the pipe and maintain it in proper alignment.

PIPE BEDDING

Once a stable and uniform foundation is provided, it is necessary to prepare the **bedding** in accordance with the requirements of the plans, specifications or standard drawings. An important function of the bedding is to assure uniform support along the barrel of each pipe section. The bedding distributes the load reaction around the lower periphery of the pipe. The required supporting strength of the pipe is directly related to this load distribution, and several types of bedding have been established to enable specification of pipe strengths during the design phase of the project.

Pipe set on a flat foundation without bedding results in high load concentration at the bottom of the pipe, *Figure 9.15*. Bedding the pipe so that the bottom reaction is distributed over 50 percent of the outside horizon-

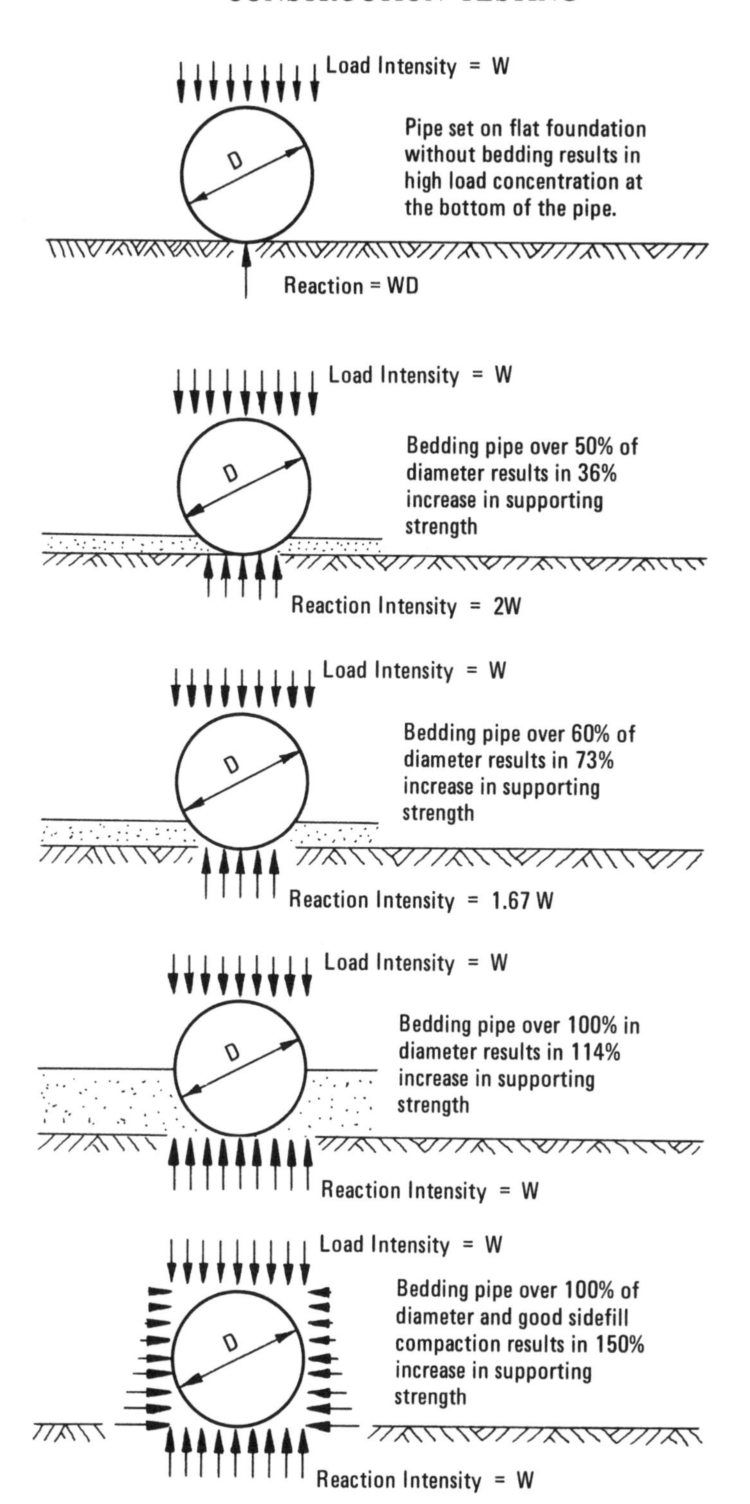

Figure 9.15. Correlation of Bedding and Supporting Strength.

tal span of the pipe results in a 36 percent increase in supporting strength; a 60 percent distribution results in a 73 percent increase for the same amount of settlement; and a 100 percent distribution results in as much as a 150 percent increase depending on sidefill compaction.

If the pipe strength specified for a particular project is based on a design assumption that at least 60 percent of the outside horizontal span of the pipe is bedded, and the pipe is actually set on a flat foundation, a pipe strength significantly greater than specified would be required. The bedding being constructed needs to be continuously compared with the requirements in the plans or specifications.

Improved construction practices enable variations in the methods used to attain the required bearing surface at the bottom of the pipe. The general classifications of beddings are presented as a guideline of what is reasonably obtainable in *Figures 9.16, 9.17, 9.18, 9.19* and *9.20*. Based on current construction practices, it is generally more practical and economical to over excavate and bed the pipe on select materials, rather than shape the subgrade to conform to the shape of the pipe.

CLASS D BEDDING

Class D bedding is used only with circular pipe. Little or no care is exercised either to shape the foundation surface to fit the lower part of the pipe exterior or to fill all spaces under and around the pipe with granular materials. However, the gradient of the bed should be smooth and true to the established grade. This class of bedding also includes the case of pipe on rock foundations in which an earth cushion is provided under the pipe but is so shallow that the pipe, as it settles under the influence of vertical load, approaches contact with the rock.

CLASS C BEDDING

With a **shaped subgrade** the pipe is bedded with ordinary care in a soil foundation, shaped to fit the lower part of the pipe exterior with reasonable closeness for a width of at least 50 percent of the outside diameter for a circular pipe, and one-tenth of the outside pipe rise for arch pipe, elliptical pipe and box sections. For trench installations the sides and area over the pipe are filled with lightly compacted backfill to a minimum depth of six inches above the top of the pipe. For embankment installations the pipe should not project more than 90 percent of the vertical height of the pipe above the bedding.

A **granular foundation** is used only with a circular pipe, and consists of a compacted granular material or densely compacted backfill placed on a flat bottom trench. The bedding material should have the minimum thickness indicated in *Figures 9.16* and *9.18*, and extend up the sides for a height of at least one-sixth the outside diameter of the pipe.

CLASS B BEDDING

For a shaped subgrade with granular foundation the bottom of the excavation is shaped to conform to the pipe surface but at least two inches greater than the outside dimensions of the pipe. The width should be sufficient to allow six-tenths of the outside pipe diameter for circular pipe and seven-tenths of the outside span for arch and elliptical pipe to be bedded in fine granular fill placed in the shaped excavation. Densely compacted backfill should be placed at the sides of the pipe to a depth of at least 12 inches above the top of the pipe.

A **granular foundation** without shaping is used only with circular pipe. The pipe is bedded in compacted granular material placed on the flat trench bottom. The granular bedding has a minimum thickness, *d,* as listed in *Figures 9.16* and *9.18,* and should extend at least halfway up the pipe at the sides. The remainder of the side fills, and a minimum depth of 12 inches over the top of the pipe, should be filled with densely compacted material.

CLASS A BEDDING

A **concrete cradle** bedding is used only with circular pipe. The pipe is bedded in nonreinforced or reinforced concrete having a thickness, *d,* as listed in *Figures 9.16* and *9.18,* and extending up the sides for a height equal to one-fourth the outside diameter. The cradle should have a minimum width at least equal to the outside diameter of the pipe plus eight inches. The backfill above the cradle is densely compacted and extends 12 inches above the crown of the pipe. In rock, especially where blasting is likely in the adjacent vicinity, the concrete cradle should be cushioned from the shock of the blasting which can be transmitted through the rock.

The **concrete arch** is an alternate to the concrete cradle for trench installations. The pipe is bedded in carefully compacted granular material having the minimum thickness shown in *Figure 9.16* and extending halfway up the sides of the pipe. The top half of the pipe is covered with nonreinforced or reinforced concrete having a minimum thickness over the

Illustration 9.7
Compacting bedding under pipe haunches.

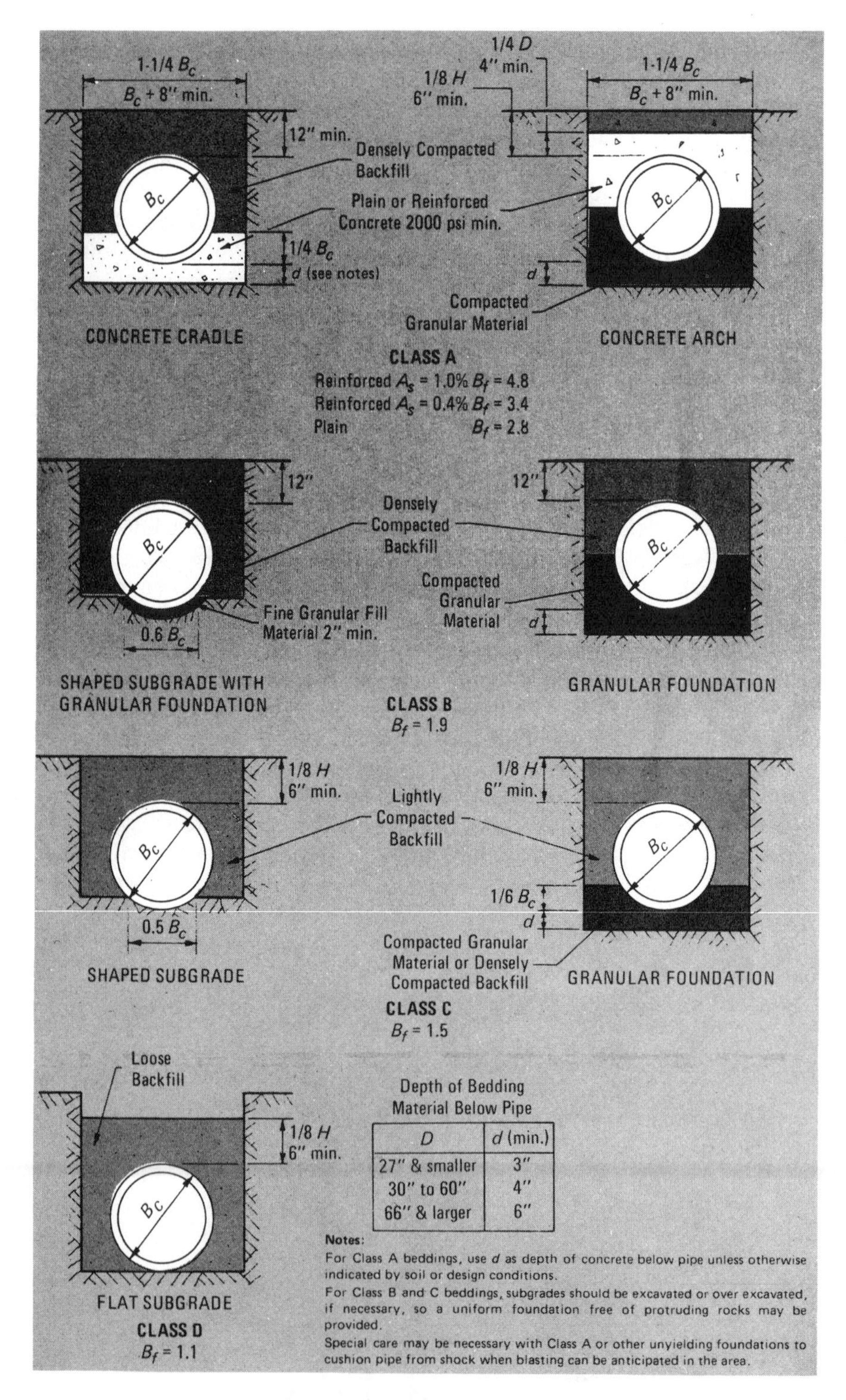

D	d (min.)
27" & smaller	3"
30" to 60"	4"
66" & larger	6"

Notes:

For Class A beddings, use d as depth of concrete below pipe unless otherwise indicated by soil or design conditions.

For Class B and C beddings, subgrades should be excavated or over excavated, if necessary, so a uniform foundation free of protruding rocks may be provided.

Special care may be necessary with Class A or other unyielding foundations to cushion pipe from shock when blasting can be anticipated in the area.

Figure 4.39. Trench Beddings—Circular Pipe.

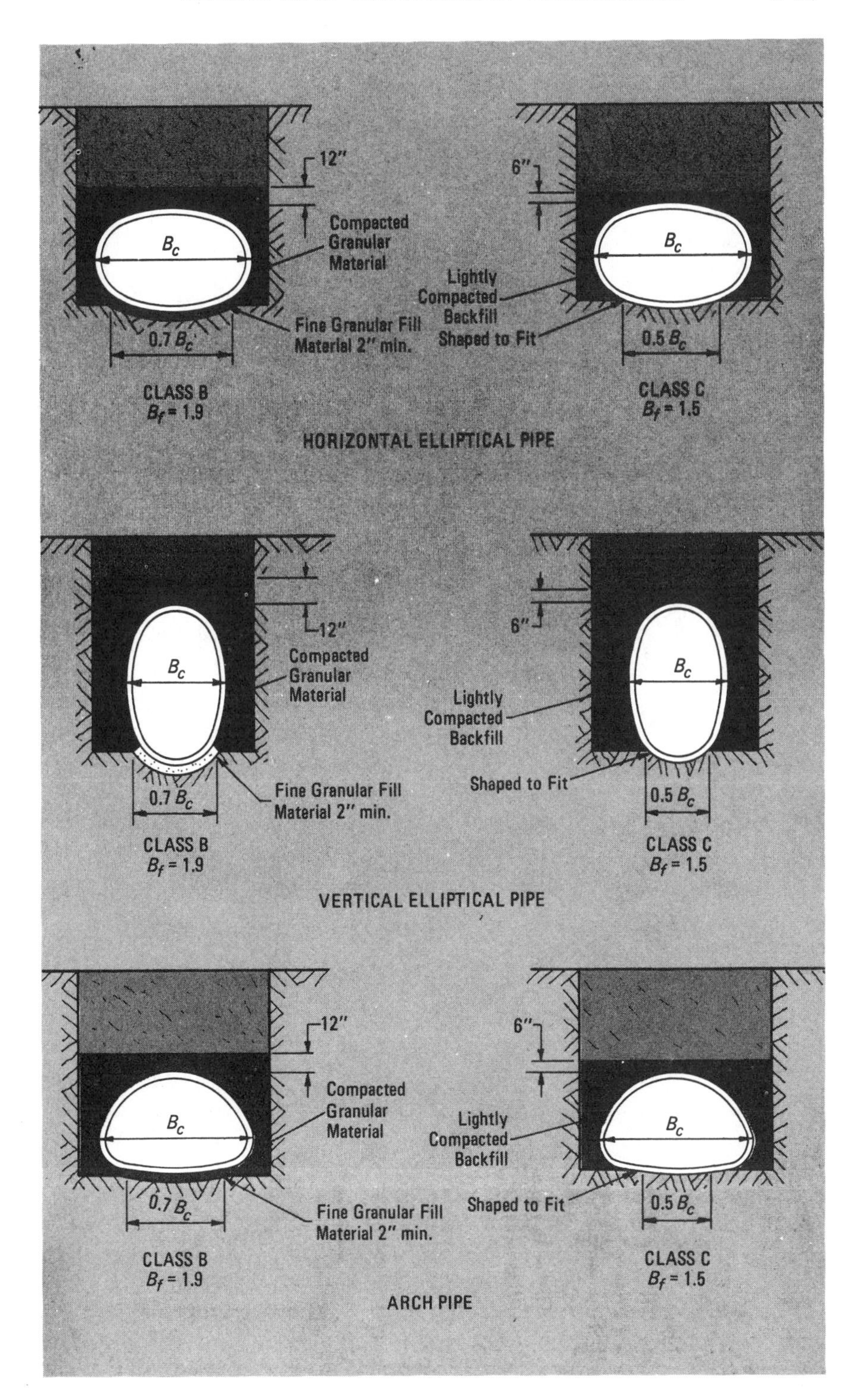

Figure 4.40. Trench Beddings—Elliptical and Arch Pipe.

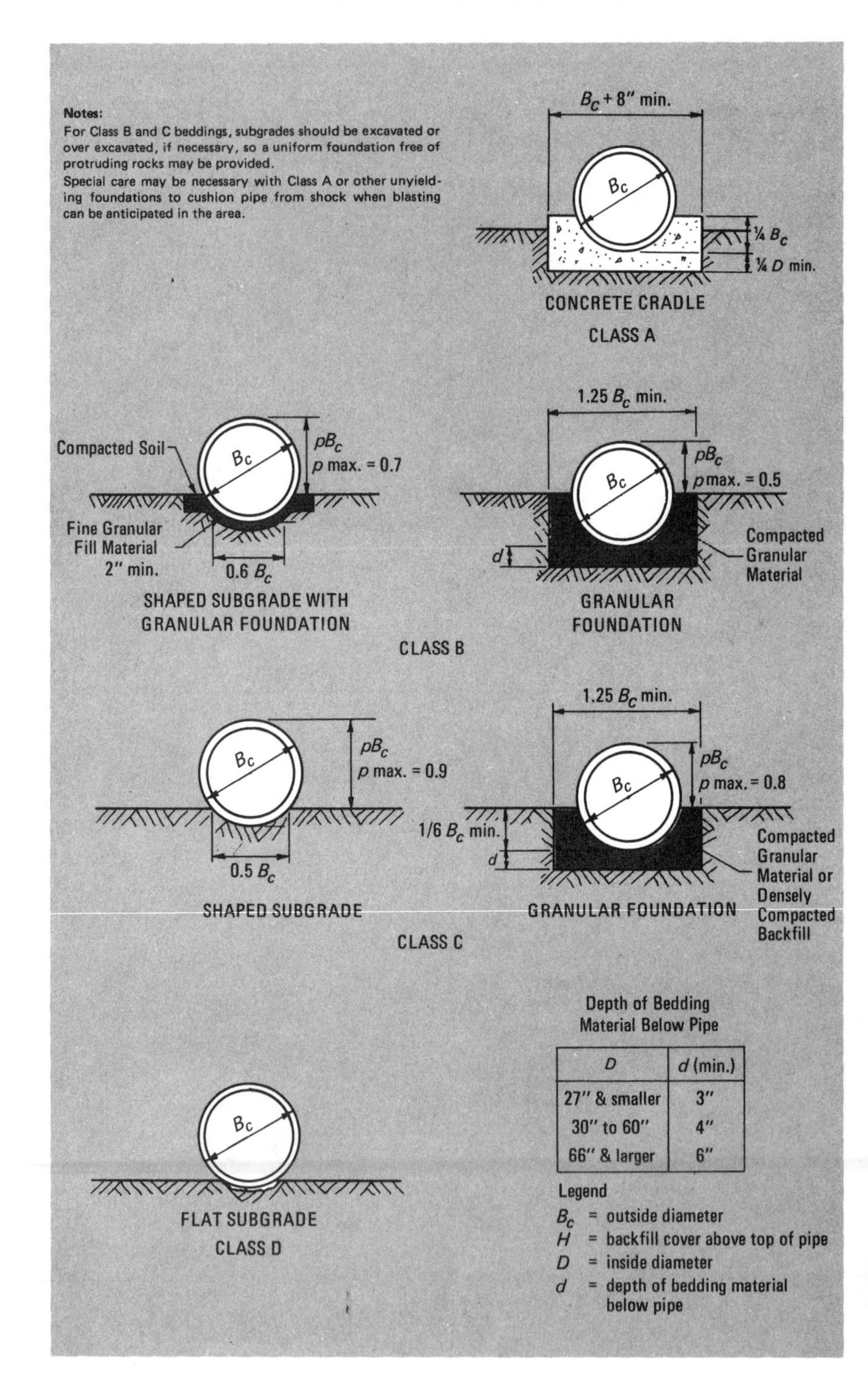

D	d (min.)
27″ & smaller	3″
30″ to 60″	4″
66″ & larger	6″

Figure 4.41. Embankment Beddings—Circular Pipe.

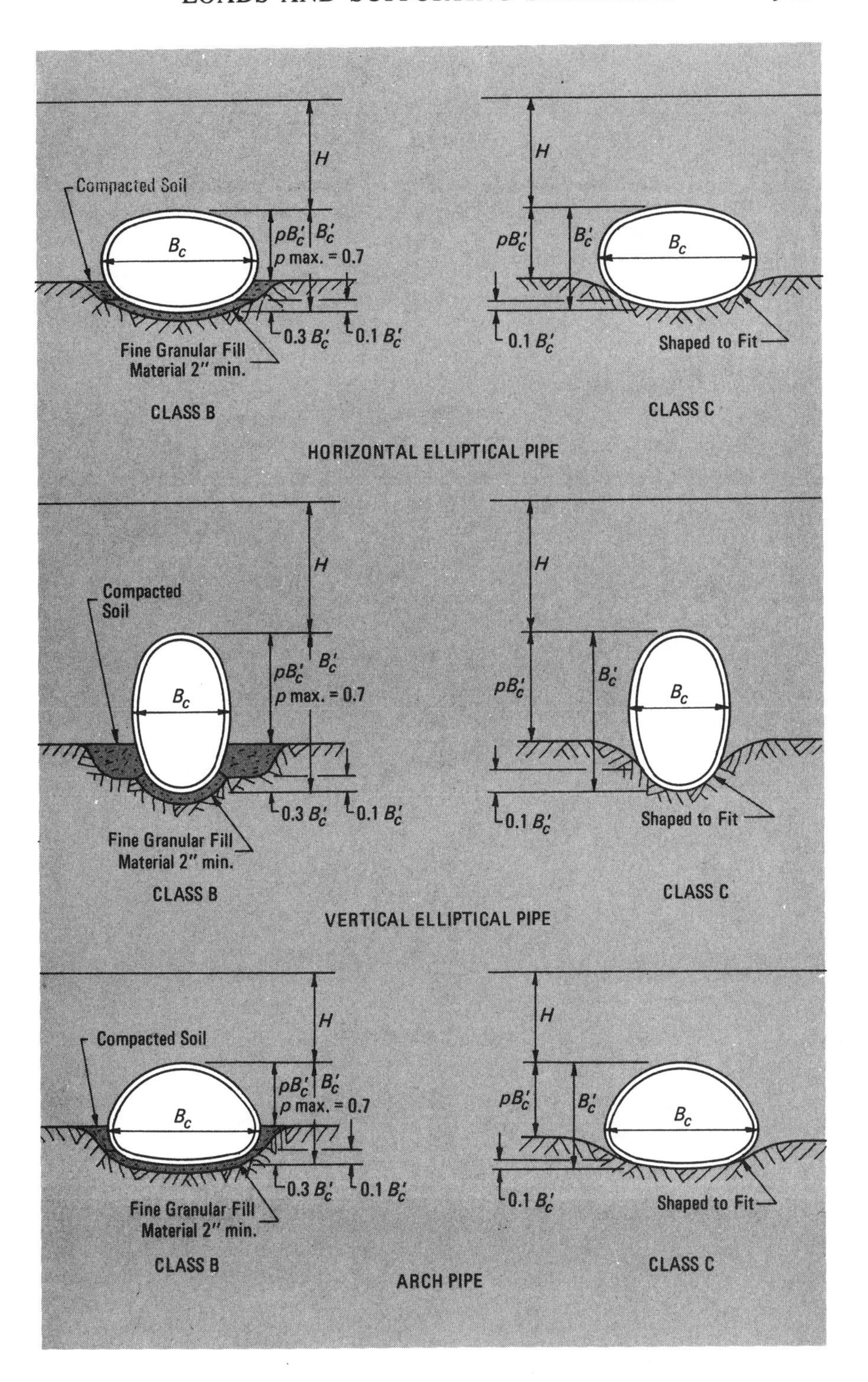

Figure 4.42. Embankment Beddings—Elliptical and Arch Pipe.

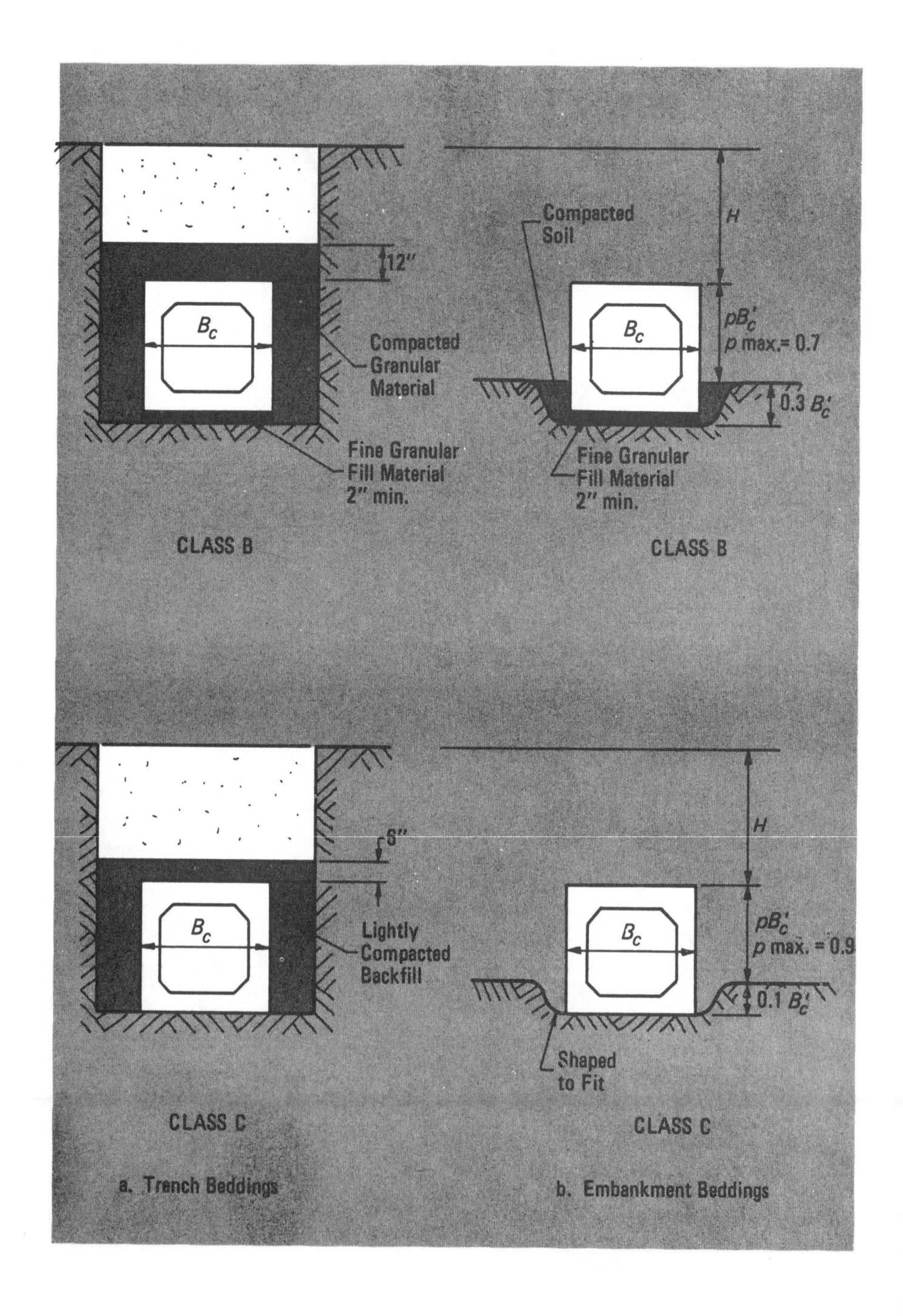

Figure 4.43. Beddings—Precast Concrete Box Sections.

top of the pipe of one-fourth the inside pipe diameter. The arch should have a minimum width at least equal to the outside diameter of the pipe plus eight inches.

BEDDING MATERIALS

Materials for bedding should be selected so intimate contact can be obtained between the bed and the pipe. Since most granular materials will shift to attain this contact as the pipe settles, an ideal load distribution can be realized. Granular materials are coarse sand, pea gravel or well graded crushed rock.

With the development of mechanical methods for subgrade preparation, pipe installation, backfilling and compaction, excellent results have been obtained with pipe installed on a flat bottom foundation and backfilled with well graded, job excavated soil. If this method of bedding is used, it is essential that the bedding material be uniformly compacted under the haunches of the pipe.

Where ledge rock, compacted rocky or gravel soil, or other unyielding foundation material is encountered, beddings should be modified as follows:

- For Class B and C beddings, subgrades should be excavated or over excavated, if necessary, so a uniform foundation free of protruding rocks is provided.
- Special care may be necessary with Class A beddings or other unyielding foundations to cushion pipe from shock when blasting can be anticipated in the area.

JOINTING

Several types of joints and sealant materials are utilized for concrete pipe to satisfy a wide range of performance requirements. All of the joints are designed for ease of installation and the manufacturer's recommendations regarding jointing procedures should be followed closely to assure resistance to infiltration of groundwater and backfill material and exfiltration of sewage or storm water. *Chapter 5* presents a detailed discussion of joints.

SEALANTS

Rubber gaskets are either **flat** gaskets which may be cemented to the pipe tongue or spigot during manufacture, **O-ring** gaskets which are recessed in a groove on the pipe tongue or spigot and then confined by the bell or groove after the joint is completed, or **roll-on** gaskets which are placed around the tongue or spigot and then rolled into position as the tongue or spigot is inserted into the bell or groove.

When gaskets are used, dust, dirt and foreign matter must be removed from the joint surfaces. For flat and O-ring gaskets, the gasket and joint surfaces are lubricated with a lubricant recommended by the manufacturer. The lubricant can be applied with a brush, cloth pad, sponge or glove. For all gaskets not cemented to the pipe, a smooth round object should be inserted under the gasket and run around the circumference two or three times to equalize stretch in the gasket.

Mastic sealants consist of bitumen and inert mineral filler and are usually cold applied. The joint surfaces are thoroughly cleaned, dried and prepared in accordance with the manufacturer's recommendations. A sufficient amount of sealant is used to fill the annular joint space with some squeeze out. Better workability of the mastic sealant can be obtained during cold weather if the mastic and joint surfaces are heated.

Cement sealants consist of portland cement paste or mortar made with a mixture of portland cement, sand and water. The joint surface is thoroughly cleaned and soaked with water immediately before the joint is made. A layer of paste or mortar is placed in the lower portion of the bell or groove end of the installed pipe and on the upper portion of the tongue or spigot end of the pipe section to be installed. The tongue or spigot is then inserted into the bell or groove of the installed pipe until the sealant material is squeezed out. Any annular joint space between the adjacent pipe ends is filled with mortar and the excess mortar on the inside of the pipes wiped and finished to a smooth surface.

Portland cement mortar bands are sometimes specified around the exterior of the pipe joint. A slight depression is excavated in the bedding material to enable mortar to be placed underneath the pipe. The entire external joint surface is then cleaned and soaked with water. Special canvas or cloth **diapers** can be used to hold the mortar as it is placed. Backfill material should be immediately placed around the pipe.

Rubber-mastic bands also can be used around the exterior of the pipe joint. The bands are stretched tightly around the barrel of the pipe and held firmly in place by the weight of the backfill material.

Regardless of the specific type of joint sealant used, each joint should be checked to be sure all pipe sections are in a **home** position. For joints sealed with rubber gaskets, it is important to follow the manufacturer's

Figure 9.21. Jointing Pipe with a Bar.

installation recommendations to assure that the gasket is properly positioned and under compression.

JOINTING PROCEDURES

Joints for pipe sizes up to 24 inches in diameter can usually be assembled by means of a bar, *Figure 9.21*. The axis of the pipe section to be installed should be aligned as closely as possible to the axis of the last installed pipe section, and the tongue or spigot end inserted slightly into the bell or groove. A bar is then driven into the bedding and wedged against the bottom bell or groove end of the pipe section being installed. A wood block is placed horizontally across the end of the pipe to act as a fulcrum point and to protect the joint end during assembly. By pushing the top of the vertical bar forward, lever action pushes the pipe into a home position.

When jointing larger diameter pipe, and when granular bedding is used, mechanical pipe pullers are required. Several types of pipe pullers or **come along** devices have been developed, *Figure 9.22*, but the basic force principles are the same.

When jointing small diameter pipe, a chain or cable is wrapped around the barrel of the pipe a few feet behind the tongue or spigot and fastened with a grab hook or other suitable connecting device. A lever assembly is anchored to the installed pipe, several sections back from the last installed section, and connected by means of a chain or cable to the grab hook on the pipe to be installed. By pulling the lever back, the tongue or spigot of the pipe being jointed is pulled into the bell or groove of the last installed pipe section. To maintain close control over the alignment of the pipe, a laying sling can be used to lift the pipe section slightly off the bedding foundation.

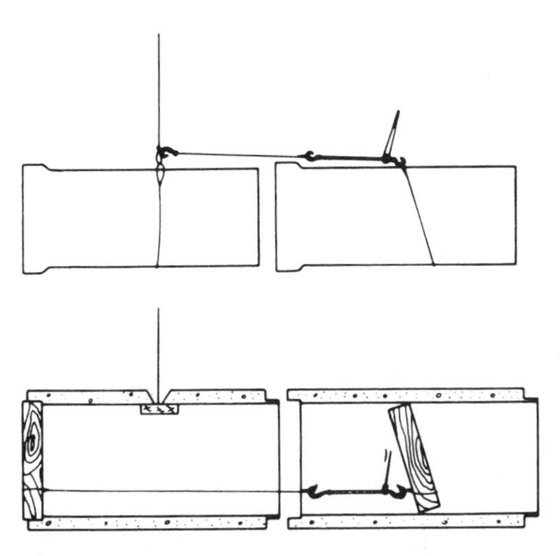

Figure 9.22. Jointing Pipe with Mechanical Puller.

Illustration 9.8
Jointing pipe with mechanical puller.

Large diameter pipe can be jointed by placing a **dead man blocking** inside the installed pipe, several sections back from the last installed section, which is connected by means of a chain or cable to a **strong back** placed across the end of the pipe section being installed, *Figure 9.22*. The pipe is pulled home by lever action similar to the external assembly. Mechanical details of the specific apparatus used for pipe pullers or come along devices may vary, but the basic lever action principle is used to develop the necessary controlled pulling force.

The use of excavating equipment to push pipe sections should be avoided unless provisions are made to prevent localized overstressing of the pipe joints. The force applied by such equipment can damage the pipe.

SERVICE CONNECTIONS

When pipe is connected to rigid structures, such as a building, manhole or junction chamber, the bedding and foundation for the pipe is highly compacted to minimize differential settlement. Differential settlement can result in the pipe being sheared or cracked at the connection. Special connectors are available which provide flexibility between the connecting pipe and the structure.

BACKFILLING

The backfill consists of two zones with separate material and compaction criteria. The first zone extends from the bedding to a plane approximately 12 inches above the top of the pipe. The second zone includes all of the remaining fill.

Illustration 9.9
This concrete pipe should have been protected by compacted granular material prior to placing rock backfill.

BACKFILLING AROUND PIPE

The load carrying capacity of an installed pipe is largely dependent on the **initial backfilling** around the pipe. Because of the importance of obtaining proper compaction of backfill material immediately around the pipe, material and density criteria are often included as part of the bedding requirements. For trench installations, where space is limited, tamping by pneumatic or mechanical impact tampers is usually the most effective means of compaction. Impact tampers which compact by static weight and kneading action are primarily useful for clay soils, while granular soils are most effectively consolidated by vibration. Where impact type tampers are used, caution should be exercised to prevent direct blows on the pipe. Backfill material should be compacted and brought up in even layers on both sides of the pipe. The backfill material should not be bulldozed into the trench or dropped directly on the pipe. Heavy vibratory equipment should not be permitted to operate directly over the pipe until a minimum of three feet of backfill has been placed.

FINAL BACKFILLING

Once the backfill material is placed around the pipe and properly compacted, the remainder of the fill is placed and compacted to prevent settlement at the surface. Several types of compaction equipment are available and certain types are best for particular soils. The steel wheeled roller is best suited for compacting coarse aggregate such as slag, coarse gravel and graded rock. The sheepsfoot roller is best suited for cohesive clays or silts, and is not suitable for use on granular soils. Rubber tired rollers, which provide static weight and kneading action, are effective for many soils. Vibratory rollers are effective for granular materials.

If the pipe is not under a roadway, sidewalk or other proposed structure, and possible settlement at the surface is not critical, flooding or jetting can be used to compact the backfill material. Water flooding and jetting are limited to compacting soils which are sufficiently permeable to dispose of the excess water and should not be used with cohesive soils. The trench is usually flooded until the backfill material is thoroughly saturated and has subsided from six to 18 inches. After initial saturation and subsidence, water is jetted into the backfill to the pipe depth at intervals varying from three to six feet. This process is repeated until the full depth of backfill material is placed.

CURVED ALIGNMENT

Changes in direction of pipelines are usually accomplished at manhole structures. Grade and alignment changes in concrete pipelines, however, can be accomplished with **deflected straight pipe, radius pipe** or **specials,** *Figure 9.23*. Since manufacturing and installation feasibility will determine the particular method used to negotiate a curve, the method must be established prior to trench excavation.

For deflected straight pipe, the joint of each section is opened on one side while the other side remains in the home position. The difference between the home and opened joint space is generally designated as the **pull.** The maximum permissible pull is limited to an opening which will provide satisfactory joint performance.

Radius pipe, also referred to as **beveled** or **mitered pipe,** incorporates the deflection angle in the pipe joint. The pipe is manufactured by shortening one side, and the amount of shortening, **drop,** for any given pipe is

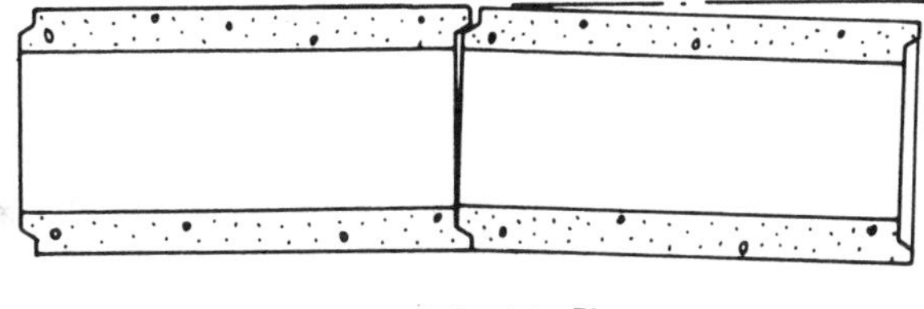

Deflected Straight Pipe

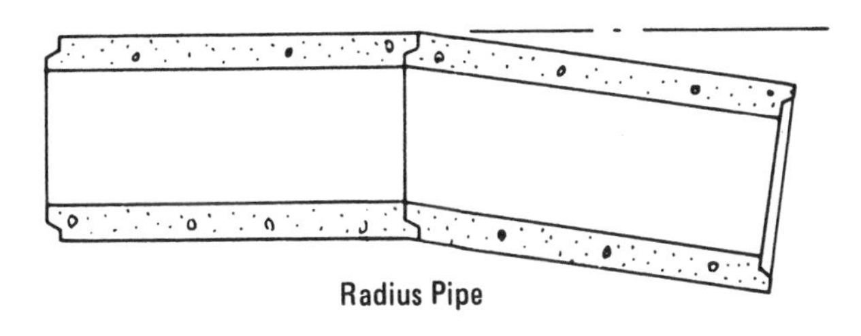

Radius Pipe

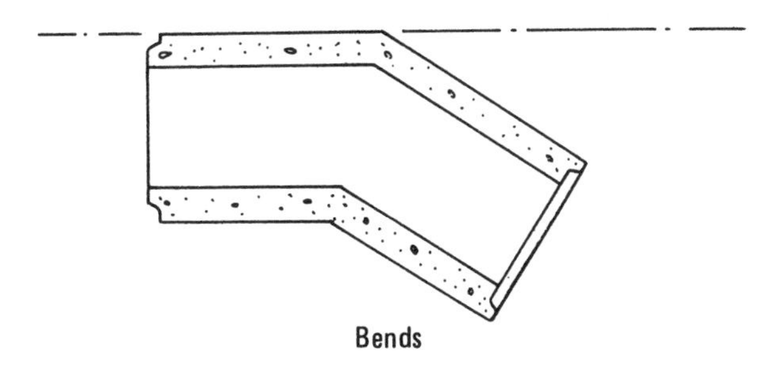

Bends

Figure 9.23. Curved Alignment.

dependent on manufacturing feasibility. Because of the possibility of greater deflection angles per joint, sharper curvature with a correspondingly shorter radius can be obtained with radius pipe than with deflected straight pipe. When establishing alignment for radius pipe, the first section of radius pipe begins one-half of a pipe length beyond the point of curvature and the last section of radius pipe extends one-half of a pipe length beyond the point of tangent, *Figure 9.24*.

Bends or other special precast sections can be used for extremely short radius curves which cannot be negotiated with either deflected straight pipe or with conventional radius pipe. Sharper curves can be constructed by using special short lengths of radius pipe rather than standard lengths.

One or more of these methods may be employed to meet the most extreme alignment requirements. Since manufacturing processes and standards vary, local concrete pipe manufacturers should be consulted to de-

Illustration 9.10
Curved alignment with deflected straight pipe.

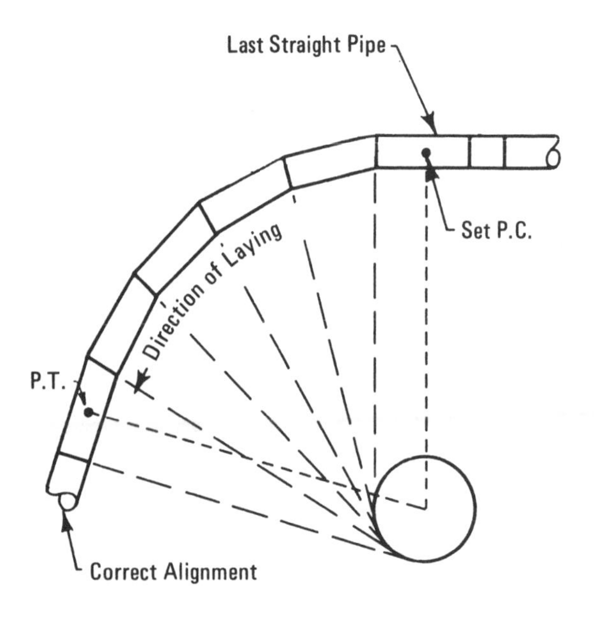

Figure 9.24. Alignment for Radius Pipe.

termine the geometric configuration of pipe sections available. Many manufacturers have standardized joint configurations and deflections for specific radii and economies may be realized by using standard pipe.

JACKING AND TUNNELING

In all jacking and tunneling operations, direction and distance are carefully established prior to beginning the operation. The first step is the excavation of **jacking pits** or shafts at each end of the proposed line. The pit must be of sufficient size to provide ample working space for the jacking head, jacks, jacking frame, reaction blocks, spoil removal and one or two sections of pipe, *Figure 9.25*. Provisions are made for the erection of guide rails in the bottom of the pit. For large pipe it is desirable to set the rails in a concrete slab. If drainage is to be discharged from the jacking pit, a collection sump and drainage pump are required.

The number and capacity of jacks depend on the type of soil, size of the pipe and jacking distance. The jacks are placed on both sides of the pipe so the resultant jacking force is slightly below the springline. Use of a lubricant, such as bentonite, to coat the outside of the pipe is helpful in reducing frictional resistance and preventing the pipe from setting when forward movement is interrupted. Because of the tendency of soil friction to increase with time, it is usually desirable to continue jacking operations without interruption until completion.

Correct alignment of the guide frame, jacks and backstop is necessary for uniform distribution of the axial jacking force around the periphery of the pipe. By assuring that the pipe ends are parallel, and the jacking force properly distributed through the jacking frame to the pipe and parallel with the axis of the pipe, localized stress concentrations are avoided. A jacking head is often used to transfer the force from the jacks or jacking frame to the pipe. In addition to protecting the end of the pipe, a jacking

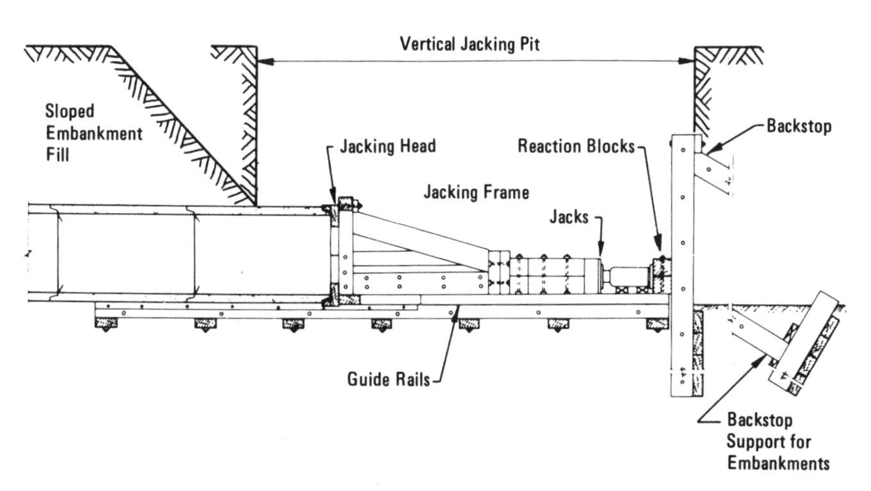

Figure 9.25. Typical Jacking Operation.

head helps keep the pipe on proper line by maintaining equal force around the circumference of the pipe. Use of a cushion material, such as plywood, between adjacent pipe sections provides uniform load distribution.

Illustration 9.11
Tunneling and jacking precast concrete pipe.

CONSTRUCTION TESTING

Tests included in the standards under which the pipe is purchased assure that pipe delivered to the job site meets or exceeds the requirements established for a particular project. The project specifications usually include acceptance test criteria to assure that reasonable quality of workmanship and materials has been realized during the construction phase of the project. Tests applicable to all storm sewer, sanitary sewer and culvert projects are soil density, line and grade and visual inspection. For sanitary sewers, leakage limits are established for infiltration or exfiltration.

SOIL DENSITY

Several test methods are available for measuring in-place soil densities. To correlate in-place densities, unit weight per cubic foot, with the maximum density of a particular soil, it is necessary to determine the optimum moisture content for maximum density and then use this as a guide to determine the actual compaction of the backfill. The most common methods used to determine optimum moisture content and maximum density are the standard tests for moisture-density relations, frequently termed Standard Proctor Test and Modified Proctor Test.

ASTM D 698 and AASHTO T 99 require placing soil in three equal layers in a mold. Each layer is compacted by 25 blows of a 5.5 pound tamper falling a distance of 12 inches. After compaction, the soil is struck off, the compacted sample weighed and the moisture content determined by drying a portion of the soil sample. Successive tests are made with increased moisture contents and the results plotted on a moisture content-density graph, *Figure 9.26*. The peak of the resulting curve is the optimum moisture content required to produce maximum density.

ASTM D 1557 and AASHTO T 180 are similar except that the soil is compacted in five layers with a tamper weighing 10 pounds falling from a height of 18 inches. It is important to note that the two tests results are not numerically interchangeable.

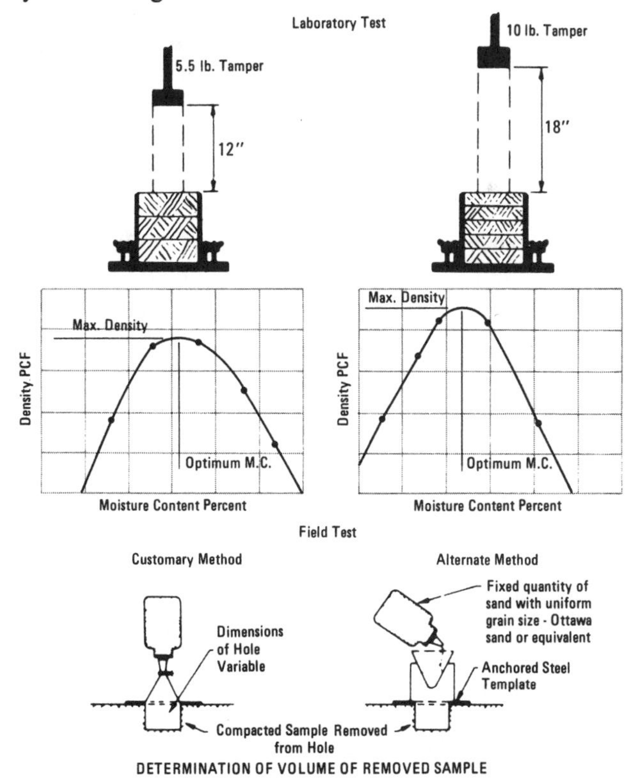

Figure 9.26. Moisture-Density Tests.

To determine the density of in-place soils, a sample is carefully cut from the compacted soil and weighed. The volume occupied by the removed sample is determined by filling the hole with dry sand of known uniform density or other suitable material. The in-place density is computed from the measured weight and volume of the sample and compared with the density of the soil at maximum compaction.

ASTM D 2922 and AASHTO T 238 are nuclear methods which provide a rapid, nondestructive technique for in-place determination of density suitable for control and acceptance testing of soils to a depth of approximately two to 12 inches depending on the testing geometry. In general, the density of the material is determined by placing a gamma source and a gamma detector either on, into, or adjacent to the material. The radiation intensity reading is converted to measured wet density by a suitable calibration curve. It should be noted that density determined by these methods is not necessarily the average density within the volume involved in the measurement and that the equipment utilizes radioactive materials which may be hazardous to the health of users unless proper precautions are taken.

ALIGNMENT

Line and grade are checked as the pipe is installed and any discrepancies between the design and actual alignment and pipe invert elevations are corrected prior to placing the backfill. Obtaining manhole invert elevations for as-built drawings, combined with visual inspection of the sewer or culvert, provide an additional check that settlement has not occurred during backfill operations.

VISUAL INSPECTION

Larger pipe sizes can be entered and examined while smaller diameter pipe must be inspected visually from each manhole or by means of TV cameras. Following is a checklist for an overall visual inspection of a sewer or culvert project:

- Debris and obstructions
- Cracks exceeding 0.01-inch wide for sanitary sewers or the larger specified allowable crack width for storm sewers and culverts
- Joints properly sealed
- Pipe invert smooth and free of sags or high points
- Pipe stubs properly grouted and plugged
- Hookups, diversions and connections properly made
- Catch basins and inlets properly connected
- Manhole frames and covers properly installed
- Surface restoration and all other items pertinent to the construction properly completed

INFILTRATION AND EXFILTRATION

The United States Environmental Protection Agency, EPA, defines **infiltration** as the *volume of groundwater entering sewers and building sewer* *connections from the soil, through defective joints, broken or cracked pipe, improper connections, manhole walls, etc.* **Inflow** is defined as the *volume of any kind of water discharged into sewer lines from such sources as roof leaders, cellar and yard area drains, foundation drains, commercial and industrial so-called "clean water" discharges, drains from springs and swampy areas, etc. It does not include and is distinguished from, infiltration.* The most effective way to control infiltration and at the same time to assure the structural integrity and proper installation of the new sewer is to establish and enforce a maximum leakage limit as a condition of job acceptance. Limits may be stated in terms of water leakage for infiltration and exfiltration tests and should include a maximum allowable **test section rate** and a maximum allowable **system average rate.**

Infiltration Testing

The **infiltration test,** *Figure 9.27,* is intended to measure the watertightness of a sewer to the infiltration of groundwater and therefore, **is only applicable if the water table level is above the top of the pipe.** Although the test is a realistic method there are inherent difficulties in applying the test criteria because of seasonal fluctuations in the water table.

EPA states that *current information indicates that a maximum allowable test section rate of 200 gallons per inch of diameter per mile of pipe per day can normally be achieved with little or no effect on construction costs. This limit is appropriate when the average depth of the groundwater is between 2 feet and 6 feet over the crown of the pipe.*

The effect of soil permeability and increased depth of groundwater on infiltration allowances must be considered. EPA recommends *infiltration allowance should reflect a consideration of the permeability of the soil, particularly the envelope around the pipe, in addition to the depth of the groundwater over the pipe.* To adjust the infiltration allowance to reflect the effect of permeable soil, an average head of six feet of groundwater over the pipe is established as the base head. With heads of more than six feet, the infiltration limit is increased by the ratio of the square root of the

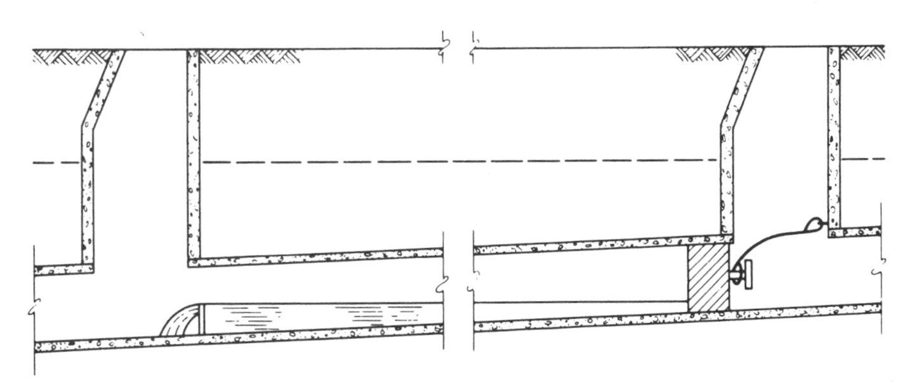

Figure 9.27. Typical Infiltration Test Arrangement.

actual average head to the square root of the base head. For example, with permeable soil and an average groundwater head of 12 feet, the 200 gallons per inch of diameter per mile of pipe per day infiltration limit should be increased by the ratio of the square root of the actual average head, 12 feet, to the square root of the base head, six feet, which results in an allowable infiltration limit of 282 gallons per inch of diameter per mile of pipe per day.

The American Society for Testing and Materials has developed Standard C 969, Standard Practice for Infiltration and Exfiltration Acceptance Testing of Installed Precast Concrete Pipe Sewer Lines. The criteria established in this recommended practice for infiltration testing follows the preceding recommendations of EPA. The practice includes procedures for preparing the sewer, conducting the infiltration test and evaluating the test results.

The infiltration test is usually conducted between adjacent manholes with the upstream end of the sewer bulkheaded to isolate the test section. All service laterals, stubs and fittings are plugged or capped at the connection to the test section to prevent the entrance of groundwater. A V-notch weir or other suitable measuring device is installed in the pipe at the downstream manhole. When steady flow occurs over the weir, leakage is determined by direct reading from graduations on the weir or by converting the flow quantity to gallons per unit length of pipe per unit of time.

Exfiltration Testing

An **exfiltration test,** *Figure 9.28,* may be specified if the groundwater level is below the top of the pipe. However, as cautioned by EPA, *Exfiltration limits, to achieve similar control of infiltration, should be set somewhat higher than the infiltration limits. Accordingly, the combined leakage from the pipe and manholes could be fixed at about 200 gallons per inch of diameter per mile of pipe per day when the average head on the test section is 3 feet.*

The effect of increased test head is accounted for in a manner similar to that for the infiltration test. The increased exfiltration limit is determined by multiplying 200 by the ratio of the square root of the actual average test

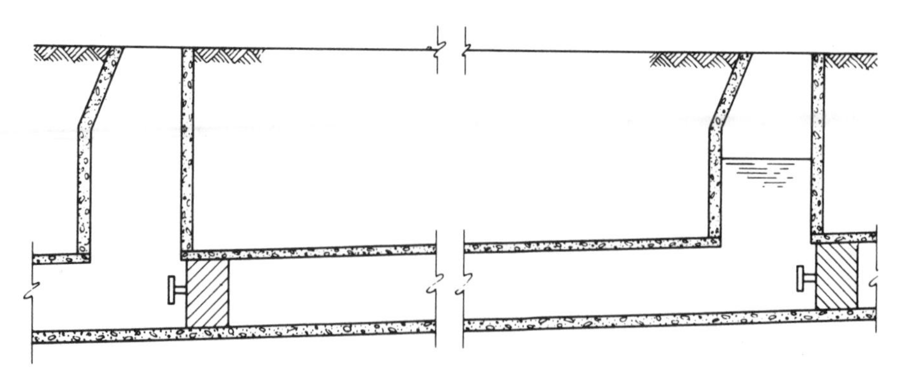

Figure 9.28. Typical Exfiltration Test Arrangement.

head to the square root of the assumed base head, three feet. For example, if the actual average test head is eight feet, the exfiltration test allowance is 327 gallons per inch of diameter per mile of pipe per day, including manholes.

EPA states, *manholes may be tested separately and independently. An allowance for manholes of 0.1 gallon per hour per foot of diameter per foot of head would be appropriate.* To exclude both manholes from the test, it is necessary to bulkhead the outlet pipe of the upstream manhole. Provision must be made in the upstream bulkhead for a standpipe.

The criteria established in ASTM Standard C 969 for exfiltration testing follows the preceding recommendations of EPA. The practice includes procedures for preparing the sewer, conducting the exfiltration test and evaluating the test results.

The test is usually conducted between adjacent manholes. All service laterals, stubs and fittings within the test section are plugged or capped to withstand the test pressure. If manholes are included in the test, the inlet pipe to each manhole is bulkheaded and the test section filled with water through the upstream manhole. Water is added at a steady rate, to allow air to escape from the sewer, until the water is at the specified level above the crown of the pipe. After absorption into the pipe and manhole has stabilized, the water in the upstream manhole is brought to the test level. At the end of the test period, drop in water elevation is measured and the loss of water calculated, or the water restored to the initial test level and the amount added used to determine leakage rate.

LOW PRESSURE AIR TESTING

The **low pressure air test,** *Figure 9.29,* was developed to detect pipe that has been damaged or improperly jointed by measuring the rate at which air under pressure escapes from a section of the sewer. In applying low pressure air testing to sanitary sewers designed to carry fluid under gravity conditions, it is necessary to distinguish between air losses inherent in the type of pipe material used and those caused by damaged pipe or defec-

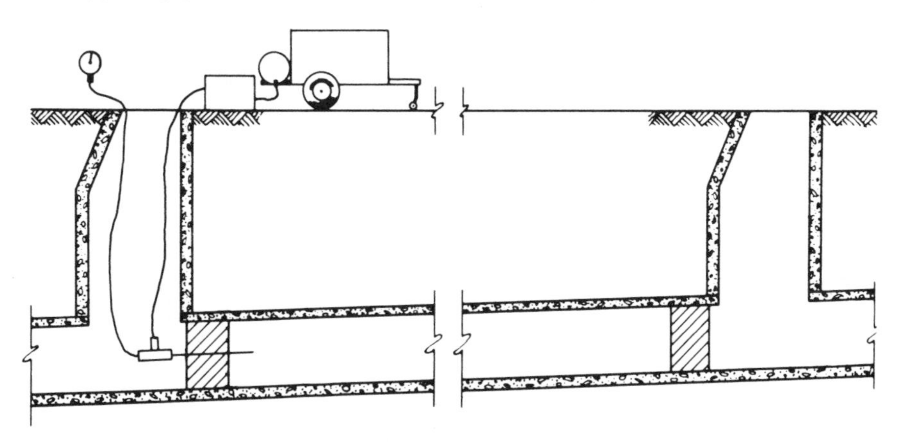

Figure 9.29. Typical Low Pressure Air Test Arrangement.

tive joints. Because of the physical difference between air and water, and the difference in behavior under pressure conditions, air loss does not necessarily mean there will be water infiltration. Depending on the porosity, moisture content and wall thickness of the pipe, a well constructed concrete sewer line which is impervious to water may still have some air loss through the pipe wall. EPA cautions, *it should be understood that no direct mathematical correlation has been found applicable between air test limits and water exfiltration limits.*

The American Society for Testing and Materials has developed Standard C 924, Standard Practice for Testing Concrete Pipe Sewer Lines by Low Pressure Air Test Method. The practice includes procedures for preparing the sewer, conducting the test and evaluating the test results. Based on field experience, the recommended practice establishes for each pipe size an appropriate allowable air loss which enables detection of any significant leak. The practice limits the maximum diameter of pipe to be tested to 24 inches for safety reasons. Larger pipe may be more conveniently accepted by visual inspection and individual joint testing.

Two air test methods are the **constant pressure method** and the **time pressure drop method.** With either method the section of pipe tested is plugged at each end. The ends of laterals, stubs and fittings to be included in the test section are plugged to prevent air leakage, and securely braced to prevent possible blowouts. Test equipment consists of valves and pressure gages to control air flow and to monitor pressure within the test section. The internal pressure is raised to a specified level and allowed to stabilize. For the constant pressure method, the air loss at a specified pressure is determined by use of an air flow measuring device. In the more commonly used pressure drop method, the air supply is disconnected and the time required for the pressure to drop to a certain level is determined. This time interval is then used to compute the rate of air loss.

In applying low pressure air testing to sanitary sewers intended to carry fluid under gravity conditions, several important factors should be understood and precautions followed:

- The air test is intended to detect defects in construction and pipe or joint damage and not to measure infiltration or exfiltration leakage under service conditions.
- Air test criteria are presently limited to pipe 24 inches in diameter and smaller.
- Plugs should be securely braced and not removed until all pressure has been released.
- For safety, no one should be allowed in the trench or manhole during the test.
- Testing apparatus should be equipped with a pressure relief device.

REFERENCES

1. "Concrete Pipe Design Manual," American Concrete Pipe Association, 1978.
2. "Concrete Pipe Installation Manual," American Concrete Pipe Association, 1978.
3. "Curved Alignment," Design Data Number 21, American Concrete Pipe Association, 1969.
4. "Design and Construction of Sanitary and Storm Sewers," Manual of Practice Number 37, American Society of Civil Engineers, and Manual of Practice Number 9, Water Pollution Control Federation, 1974.
5. "History of Sewer Line Air Testing," Concrete Pipe Information Number 9, American Concrete Pipe Association, 1979.
6. "Jacking Concrete Pipe," Design Data Number 13, American Concrete Pipe Association, 1969.
7. "Low Pressure Air Testing for Sanitary Sewers," Roy E. Ramseier and George C. Riek, Journal of the Sanitary Engineering Division, American Society of Civil Engineers, April, 1964.
8. "Low Pressure Air Testing of Sewers," William J. Chase and Harvey W. Duff, Paper Presented at a Meeting of the Pacific Northwest Pollution Control Association, November, 1965.
9. "Method of Test for Density of Soil and Soil-Aggregate in Place by Nuclear Methods (Shallow Depth)," AASHTO T 238, American Association of State Highway and Transportation Officials, 1979.
10. "Method of Test for Density of Soil and Soil-Aggregate in Place by Nuclear Methods (Shallow Depth)," ASTM D 2922. American Society for Testing and Materials. 1976.
11. "Method of Test for Density of Soil in Place by the Sand-Cone Method," ASTM D 1556, American Society for Testing and Materials, 1974.
12. "Method of Test for Moisture-Density Relations of Soils, Using 10-lb Rammer and 18-in. Drop," ASTM D 1557, American Society for Testing and Materials, 1970.
13. "Method of Test for Moisture-Density Relations of Soils, Using 5.5-lb Rammer and 12-in. Drop," ASTM D 698, American Society for Testing and Materials, 1970.
14. "Method of Test for the Moisture-Density Relations of Soils Using a 10-lb Rammer and an 18-in. Drop," AASHTO T 180, American Association of State Highway and Transportation Officials, 1974.
15. "Method of Test for the Moisture-Density Relations of Soils Using a 5.5-lb Rammer and a 12-in. Drop," AASHTO T 99, American Association of State Highway and Transportation Officials, 1974.
16. "Occupational Safety and Health Administration Regulations," Occupational Safety and Health Administration, United States Department of Labor.
17. "Sewer System Evaluation, Rehabilitation and New Construction, A Manual of Practice," EPA-600/2-77-017d, United States Environmental Protection Agency, 1977.
18. "Standard Practice for Testing Concrete Pipe Sewer Lines by Low Pressure Air Test Method," ASTM C 924, American Society of Testing and Materials, 1979.

CHAPTER 10

SOIL-STRUCTURE INTERACTION

For over fifty years, the procedures for determination of design loads on concrete pipe and the required concrete pipe supporting strength have been relatively easy to use and have resulted in a high quality, economical product. The conservative nature of these procedures is apparent because there are no known or documented structural failures due to inadequacy of the design theory. This absence of failures suggests the possibility of overdesign and that economies may be realized by judicious and technically sound modifications in design requirements and procedures.

Improvements to well established and generally accepted design procedures cannot be achieved by simplified or superficial analyses. Rather, a systematic approach is needed that includes a review of the basic assumptions of the existing method, an evaluation of new technology that has been developed, and full-scale tests to evaluate and validate theoretical studies.

A research project, to be successful in modifying or revising existing design procedures, must improve the cost effectiveness of pipeline installations. Economy is a key factor to those who design, produce, construct, operate, or maintain pipelines. If equal or better performance can be achieved at a lower cost, or if special installation conditions can be evaluated with greater confidence, then both public and private interests will be better served.

With these objectives, the American Concrete Pipe Association began a research program in 1970. The long range research program on soil-structure interaction was conducted by researchers at Northwestern University under the direction of Dr. Richard A. Parmelee. Included were full-scale tests at the Ohio Transportation Research Center, East Liberty, Ohio.

In this chapter, the various phases of the research program are reviewed and the 1979 status discussed, including:

- Research concepts
- Review of current design methods
- Research on soil-structure interaction
- Field testing program
- Design concepts
- Future design procedures

Illustration 10.1
Backfilling around research trench installation with granular material.

RESEARCH CONCEPTS

As construction techniques and materials change and improve, comparable advances in methods of analysis and design might well be anticipated. If the current technology exceeds the limits of the basic assumptions used in the derivation of a particular design methodology, the design approach must be modified or a new method developed to provide safe, economical and serviceable structures.

The analysis and design of buried pipelines is essentially a problem of soil-structure interaction. Existing design methods attempt to account for the relative stiffness between the soil and the pipe by a number of parameters which are largely empirical and have no rational basis within the context of current soil engineering theory. Empirical parameters will frequently achieve the intended goal because of the engineer's experience and good judgement. Very often, however, the use of such parameters is restricted because there is no basis for extension or generalization due to the limited ranges of applicability for which experience is available.

ACPA recognized that the design engineer lacked sufficiently clear information on the nature of the loading imposed on a buried concrete pipe, and sponsored a long range research program on soil-structure interaction. The final objective of the long range program is to formulate a procedure for the design of buried concrete pipe which will more realistically model the actual bedding and backfill conditions around the pipe.

The development of a new theory for the structural design of a concrete structure has frequently included full scale or model load tests of the structural system to validate a theoretical concept. It is not economically feasible, however, to instrument and install a sufficient number of buried pipe systems to obtain data that would encompass all conceivable combinations of conditions. Therefore, an intermediate objective of the program was the development of a soil-structure system computer model based upon finite element concepts.

REVIEW OF CURRENT DESIGN PROCEDURES

The most commonly used procedure for the design of buried concrete pipe is based to a large extent upon research conducted at Iowa State University between 1910 and 1930. This is the procedure described in *Chapter 4* and reviewed here, briefly, to identify the basic assumptions involved. Utilizing an applied mechanics approach and idealized free body diagrams, Marston developed formulas for evaluating the earth loads at the top of buried pipe in various types of installations. To simplify the process, Marston assumed that the vertical load on the pipe due to the backfill is of uniform intensity and is distributed over the total width of the pipe.

In 1933, Spangler described the importance of bedding and how to estimate the supporting strength of rigid pipe for various types of bedding. He proposed four classifications of installations to cover the range of bedding conditions normally encountered in practice, and defined these in terms of a simplified and idealized distribution of the vertical reactive force acting on the bottom of the pipe. The distinction between the three most common bedding conditions was described by Spangler in terms of the central bedding angles as shown in *Table 10.1* and *Figure 10.1*. The fourth type of bedding condition is designated as Class A in which a portion of the exterior of the pipe is bedded in concrete.

Table 10.1. Common Bedding Conditions.

Current Bedding Class Designation	Spangler's Original Description	Central Bedding Angle
D	Impermissible projection bedding	0°
C	Ordinary projection bedding	60°
B	First class projection bedding	90°

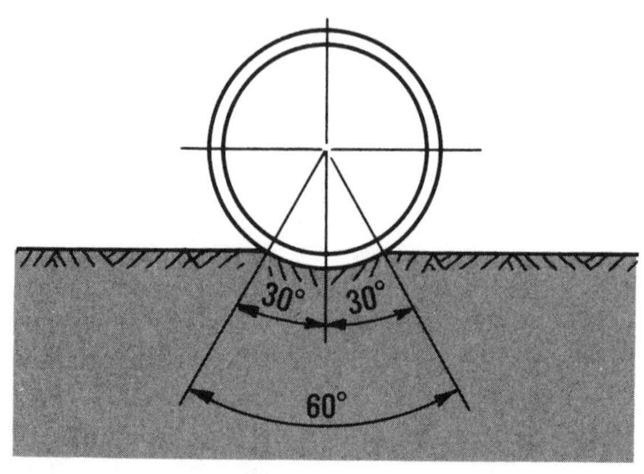

Figure 10.1. Central Bedding Angle—Class C Bedding.

The transformation of these mathematically defined loadings into actual field conditions was accomplished by Spangler with suggested installation methods as shown in *Figure 10.2*. The approach assumes that if the pipe is installed in accordance with the conditions in the drawings, the reactive load will be uniformly distributed over the central bedding angle. For field installations, the objective is to arrange the bedding to match the effect of the idealized loading assumed in the derivation of the design procedure.

The **bedding factor** is the ratio of the supporting strength of a pipe under the assumed loading for a specified bedding condition to the supporting strength of similar pipe as determined by the standard three-edge bearing test. Spangler called this ratio the load factor, however, it has been redesignated as the bedding factor, which is a more appropriate term, in order to avoid confusion with the term **load factor** used in the American Concrete Institute Building Code. The bedding factors for trench conditions are empirical constants. The bedding factors for projection conditions are calculated from an equation which was derived on the assumption that the response of the pipe can be evaluated by a linear elastic analysis.

The required strength of an installed pipe was established by Spangler as the minimum three-edge bearing test strength multiplied by the bedding factor and divided by the desired factor of safety. Under the Marston-Spangler method, a pipe is not designed to resist a system of loads produced by the bedding and backfill. Instead, the pipe is designed to withstand a specified three-edge bearing test.

Another design method was presented by Olander in 1950 in which a system of normal pressures was assumed to act on the pipe due to the earth load, water load, and dead load of the pipe. Under this approach, the associated internal stress resultants for shear, thrust and moment for various bedding angles are evaluated by linear elastic analyses, and the effect of combined loading is obtained by superposition. Utilizing conventional reinforced concrete design methods, the pipe is then proportioned to resist these stress resultants.

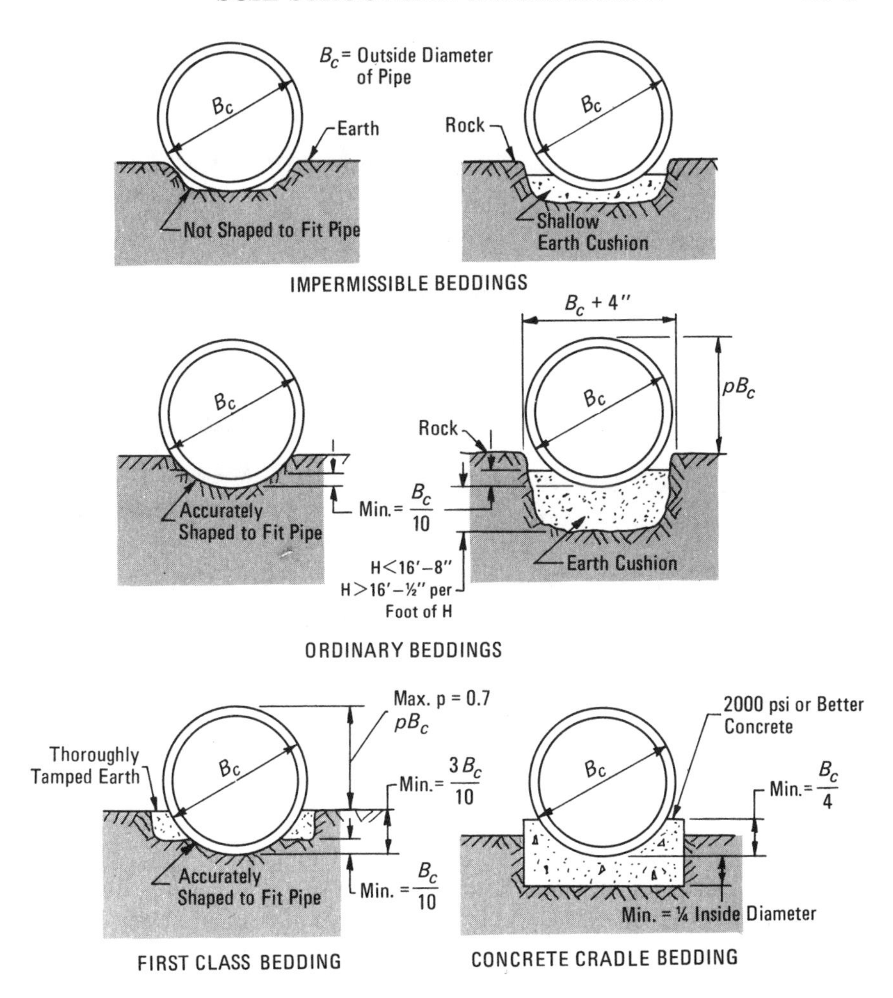

Figure 10.2. Positive Projection Installation Beddings.

RESEARCH ON SOIL-STRUCTURE INTERACTION

The response of a buried concrete pipe depends upon several characteristics of the soil-pipe system: the pipe geometry, wall thickness, and strengths of the concrete and reinforcement which were used to manufacture the pipe; the configuration and mechanical properties of the bedding and foundation soils; the mechanical properties of the backfill material, and the manner in which it was placed around the pipe; and the effect of live loads and surcharge loads which may act upon the system. The deflection and stresses in the concrete pipe are influenced by the soil, and in turn, soil deformations are influenced by the rigidity of the pipe. This interdependent behavior of the soil and pipe has been termed **soil-structure interaction** and must be taken intc account to obtain a realistic and practical evaluation of the loads acting on a buried pipeline.

Illustration 10.2
Instrumentation and circuitry inside of test pipe buried at Ohio Transportation Research Center.

Because of the complexity of the interaction, the relatively simplified theory used by Marston, Spangler and Olander cannot account for all conditions that influence the soil-structure system. By utilizing the theory of continuum mechanics, the soil-structure interaction effects can be more completely analyzed. For this more complex approach, it is necessary to utilize a numerical technique in conjunction with a digital, electronic computer. The finite element method is ideally suited for the solution of the soil-structure interaction problem.

A major objective of the ACPA research program was to develop a comprehensive finite element computer program to simulate the nonlinear behavior of a buried pipe. This development has progressed in four major steps.

STEP 1. A theoretical mathematical model was defined for a circular, reinforced concrete pipe. The model is based upon a plane strain, finite element idealization in which the elements can have nonlinear mechanical properties, and the phenomenon of cracking can be simulated.

A realistic mathematical model of concrete pipe must incorporate the effect of cracking. Progressive cracking has a significant effect upon internal stresses and displacements, as well as upon the deflection of the pipe structure. To simulate progressive cracking, a technique was developed that utilizes the activation of hinging mechanisms. The hinges are activated at finite element nodes when the stress in designated elements reaches a threshhold value. The phenomena of bond slip, slabbing and steel yield are empirically accounted for by an artificial disconnection of the steel and concrete elements.

Illustration 10.3
Three-edge bearing test of 66-inch diameter pipe.

STEP 2. The validity of the pipe model, including progressive cracking behavior, was established on the basis of a comparison with the results of an extensive program of laboratory tests of full size concrete pipe under controlled loading conditions.

STEP 3. Simplified laboratory tests were defined that could be performed on a soil to evaluate appropriate properties to be used for finite element idealization of a particular construction site. Also, a selection was made of average mechanical properties for various classes of typical soils used for the installation of concrete pipe.

When programmed on a computer, a mathematical model can handle quite sophisticated relationships for material properties. Material characterization was required to be consistent with the basic behavior assumptions inherent in the model and the degree of accuracy required in the solution. However, the performance of complicated and expensive laboratory or field tests to precisely determine the nonlinear stress-strain behavior of a soil could not be economically justified if the finite element solution was not sensitive to minor variations, if other material properties were handled in a relatively crude manner, or if the pipe design was ultimately controlled by factors other than soil response. Accordingly, the advantages and disadvantages of various ways of characterizing material behavior for soil-structure interaction problems were assessed.

After a comprehensive study, several conclusions were reached. For example, effects due to pipe diameter changes were not extremely sensitive to the specific nature of the soil properties input formulation. In contrast, response characteristics at discrete points, such as strain at a specific point in the pipe wall, were considerably more sensitive to the choice of soil properties. However, none of a variety of complex stress-strain formulations, including linear elastic, modified hypoelastic, and parabolic, yielded predictions that consistently agreed with full-scale experimental measurements better than predictions utilizing any other formulation. Results and observations have indicated that while an order-of-magnitude change in value of the soil modulus does exert some effect on the response of a soil-pipe system, the specific formulation does not produce an appreciable influence. This effect was attributed to the relative stiffness of the reinforced concrete pipe compared to the surrounding soil.

STEP 4. The ability of the finite element program to simulate the response of buried pipelines was confirmed by a comparison of the calculated and observed behaviors of a series of full-scale test installations.

Figures 10.3-10.6 show some of the results of computer simulations and observed field data from two 60-inch diameter concrete pipe installations. In *Figures 10.3* and *10.4*, a comparison is made between the measured and observed diameter changes. The mean and standard deviation of the measured data are plotted, and the change predicted by the computer solution is shown as a solid line. The deflections were calculated at heights of fill comparable to those in the field installations. The agreement between calculated and observed data for all fill heights is quite good.

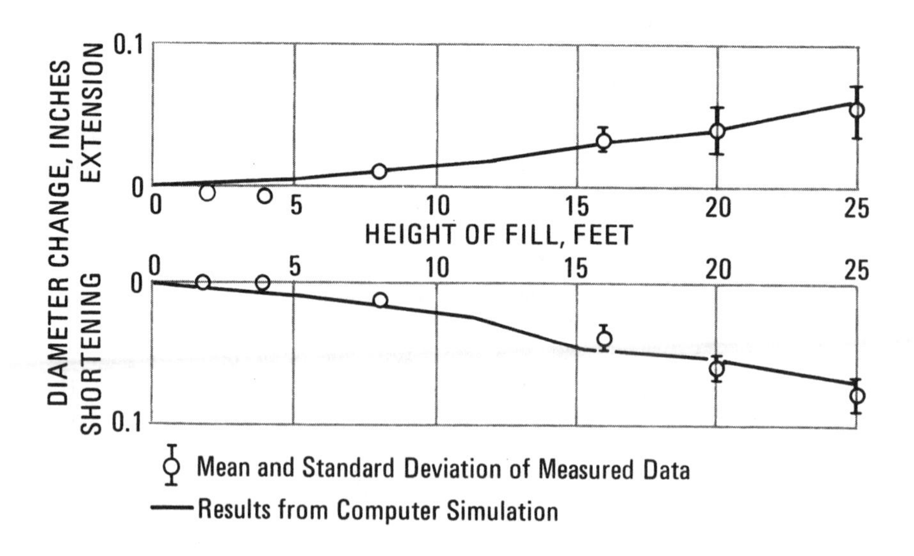

Figure 10.3. Predicted and Measured Diameter Changes–Embankment.

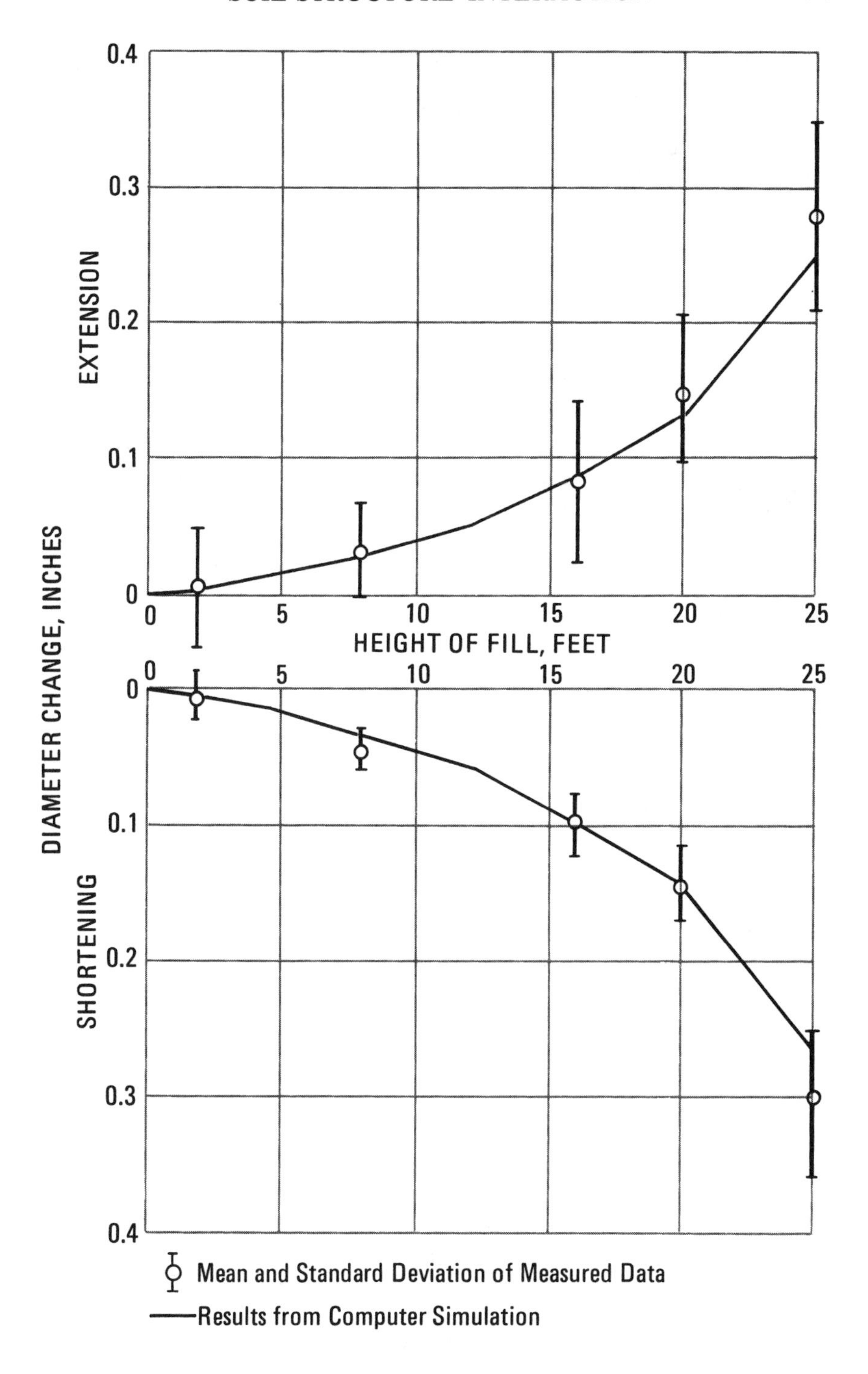

Figure 10.4. Predicted and Measured Diameter Changes—Trench.

The measured inside surface strains were converted to stress by multiplying the strain by the modulus of elasticity of the concrete. The results are compared, *Figures 10.5* and *10.6,* with the surface stress calculated from the mathematical pipe model for a fill height of 25 feet. The mean and standard deviation of the measured data are shown. For both installations, the agreement between predicted and measured data is very good.

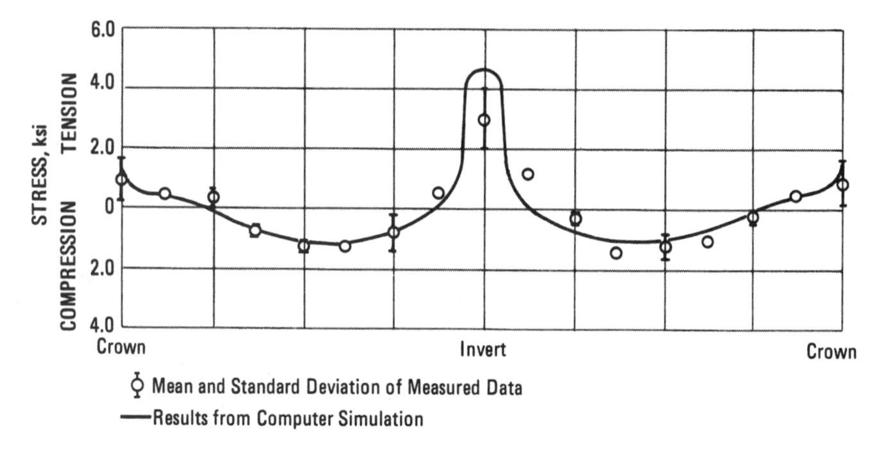

Figure 10.5. Predicted and Measured Stress Levels—Embankment.

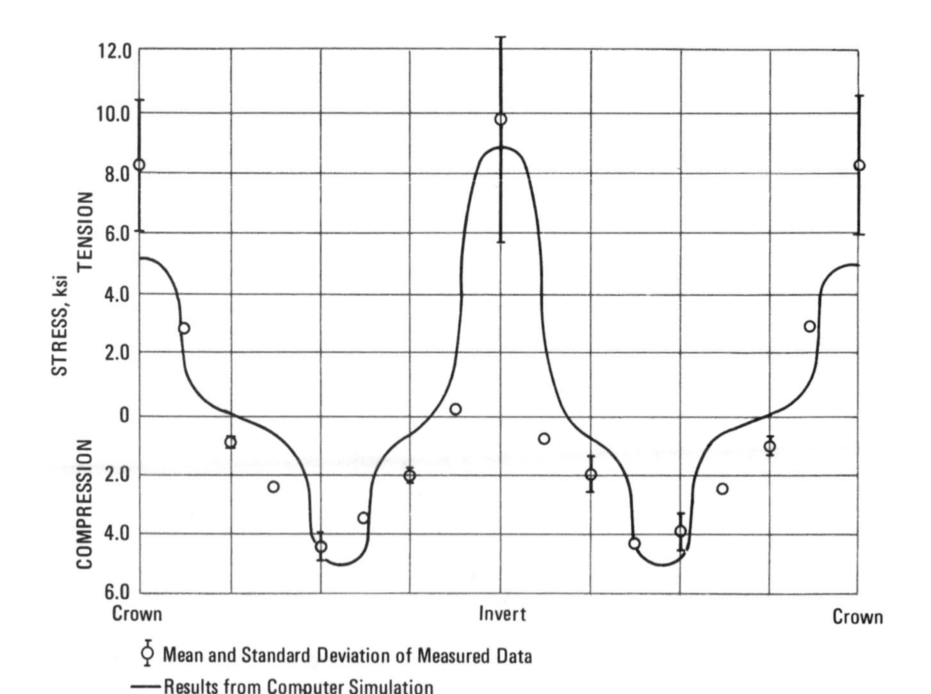

Figure 10.6. Predicted and Measured Stress Levels—Trench.

Additional validation of the finite element model was obtained from a study of the data from the Mountainhouse Creek research project installed by the State of California Department of Transportation. In each case there was satisfactory agreement between the predicted and observed response of the pipe sections up to the fill heights at which 0.01-inch cracks were recorded.

Illustration 10.4
Embankment research installation constructed under a proposed vehicle test track at the Ohio Transportation Research Center.

FIELD TESTING PROGRAM

To determine the validity with which the finite element program predicted the behavior of buried pipe, two test installations were constructed at the Ohio Transportation Research Center, East Liberty, Ohio in 1971. At each site, five sections of 60-inch diameter pipe were instrumented and backfilled with 25 feet of earth cover.

The tests were designed and conducted by the research staff of Northwestern University under the direction of Dr. Richard A. Parmelee on the basis of existing procedures. One was a trench installation and the other an embankment condition. Installation was in accordance with the Standard Specifications of the Ohio Department of Highways, and inspected by representatives of the department.

Prior to backfilling, each of the installations was instrumented to measure stresses and displacement in the soil, at the soil-pipe interface, on the inside surface of the pipe and within the pipe wall. The three types of instrumentation were:

- Strain gages
- Diameter and chord measuring devices
- Pressure cells

Strain gages were placed at intervals of 22½ degrees around the circumference, on or within the pipe walls, and at additional locations to measure longitudinal variations as follows:

- Inside surface of the pipe
- Inner cage circumferential reinforcement
- Outer cage circumferential reinforcement
- Exterior surfaces of the pipe

Two types of pressure cells were used. A 6-inch diameter cell was used for measuring the total normal stress on the pipe at the interface with the soil. For measuring pressures in the soil, 10-inch diameter cells were used. Soil settlement plates were installed throughout the backfill and over and under the pipe. Reference points for diameter and chord measurements were installed at 45-degree intervals around the pipe circumference.

Two significant conclusions from analyses of these data were that longitudinal strains along the pipe were insignificant, and that in each installation quite similar responses were observed in each half of the pipe. These findings permitted the finite element program to be based upon plane-strain concepts and a pipe model with a vertical axis of symmetry.

DESIGN CONCEPTS

An early decision made in the ACPA research program was that the design procedure for concrete pipe should be similar to the basic philosophy and techniques currently utilized to design other reinforced concrete structures such as bridges, buildings, slabs, and pavements. The basic steps of these techniques are:

- Determine appropriate loading for conditions of anticipated service.
- Evaluate various sections of the structure for maximum shear, thrust and flexural stresses.
- Proportion reinforcement at each critical cross-section using the ultimate strength method of design.
- Evaluate serviceability criteria such as creep, cracking and collapse.

Such an approach was proposed for the design of concrete pipe systems based upon the theories developed and validated in the research program. The technique has been modeled in a comprehensive design computer program termed SPIDA, an acronym for Soil-Pipe Interaction Design and Analysis. The following discussion highlights the design approach.

DEAD LOADS

The dead load effect on buried concrete pipe consists of two components:

- Weight of the pipe section.
- Pressures at the soil-pipe interface produced by the bedding and backfill materials.

Illustration 10.5
Trench research installation constructed at the Ohio Transportation Research Center.

The maximum stress resultants that are produced in the wall of the pipe by the dead load are more accurately evaluated by a rational analysis which considers the nonlinear properties of the concrete and soil materials. In addition, the analysis considers a realistic arrangement of the bedding and backfill materials, taking into account the degree of compaction that is likely to be achieved during construction. Finally, the analysis accounts for the effects of the sequential placement of the backfill materials.

MAXIMUM STRESS RESULTANTS

The analysis determines nine maximum stress resultants as follows:

- Maximum moment in the invert region
- Associated thrust at the point of maximum moment in the invert region
- Maximum moment in the springline region
- Associated thrust at the point of maximum moment in the springline region
- Maximum shear in the invert region
- Associated thrust at the point of maximum shear in the invert region
- Associated moment at the point of maximum shear in the invert region
- Maximum shear in the springline region
- Associated thrust at the point of maximum shear in the springline region

The five stress resultants at the invert region of the pipe are used for proportioning the inner cage of reinforcement. The four stress resultants at the springline region of the pipe are used for proportioning the outer cage of reinforcement.

Illustration 10.6
Soil pressure meters prior to installation in the backfill. Rods were connected to soil settlement measuring plates through the pipe access hole.

PROPORTIONING REINFORCEMENT

In the buried configuration, axial stress resulting from thrust forces is compressive at every point around the pipe. The interactive effects of this compression with both moment and shear must be considered in evaluating the cross-section and in serviceability evaluations.

There are different shear considerations in the invert and springline regions. The difference is due to radial tension action which can occur at the crown and invert when the inner reinforcement cage tends to straighten under tensile forces. Radial tension action is not a problem in the springline region because the outer reinforcement cage is subjected to tensile forces and shear action is similar to that found in conventional reinforced concrete beams. The shear criterion can also be similar but the percentage of reinforcement used in concrete pipe is much less than for conventional reinforced concrete beams.

Illustration 10.7
Three-edge bearing test of 156-inch diameter pipe.

SERVICEABILITY

Serviceability criteria for buried concrete pipe are derived from observations which are the basis for the engineering judgement reflected in project specifications. The 0.01-inch crack criterion was originally proposed by researchers Marston, Spangler and Schlick at Iowa State University in the late 1920's as a quality control standard for acceptance of pipe at a producer's plant prior to shipment and installation. Over the years, however, this criterion was improperly extended and used as a serviceability criterion for buried concrete pipe. In other reinforced concrete structures, once the reinforcement and section are proportioned, the design is checked for crack control. Similar procedures are proposed for buried concrete pipe design.

SUMMARY

The research program has produced a comprehensive computer model for design and analyses of buried pipe. With this model, any installation parameter can be effectively evaluated, including:

- Pipe size
- Bedding
- Reinforcement
- Foundation and backfill
- Earth cover over pipe

The behavior of buried concrete pipe can be predicted in a minimum of time and at a nominal cost so that alternative designs, particularly for larger size pipe, can be compared. It is likely, however, that current design procedures will be used until the concepts of SPIDA are finalized and accepted.

REFERENCES

1. "Analysis and Measurement of Soil Behavior Around Buried Concrete Pipe," R. B. Corotis and R. J. Krizek, ASTM STP 630, June, 1976, pp. 91-104.
2. "Analysis of Loads and Supporting Strengths and Principles of Design for Highway Culverts," M. G. Spangler, Proceedings, Volume 26, Highway Research Board, 1946.
3. "The Analysis of Soil-Structure Interaction of Buried Concrete Pipe," R. A. Parmelee, Proceedings, AQTE-FACE Conference on Water and the Environment, Montreal, Canada, May, 1972, pp. 89-102.
4. "An Analysis of the Design and Response of Concrete Pipe," R. A. Parmelee and T. H. Wenzel (presented at the TRB meeting, January, 1975).
5. "Analytical and Experimental Evaluation of Modulus of Soil Reaction," R. A. Parmelee and R. B. Corotis, Transportation Research Record 518, 1974, pp. 29-38.
6. "Assessment of Soil Constitutive Models for Numerical Analysis of Buried Concrete Pipe Systems," R. J. Krizek and D. K. Atmatzidis, ASTM STP 630, June, 1976, pp. 76-90.
7. "Behavior of Buried Concrete Pipe," R. J. Krizek and P. V. McQuade, Journal of the Geotechnical Engineering Division, ASCE, Volume 104, Number GT7, July 1978, pp. 815-836.
8. "Computer Aided Structural Analysis and Design of Concrete Pipe," T. H. Wenzel and R. A. Parmelee, ASTM STP 630, June, 1976, pp. 105-118.

9. "Concrete Cradles for Large Pipe Conduits," W. J. Schlick and J. W. Johnson, Bulletin Number 80, Iowa State College, 1926.
10. "Concrete Pipe Design Manual," American Concrete Pipe Association, 1978.
11. "Design and Construction of Sanitary and Storm Sewers," Manual of Practice Number 37, American Society of Civil Engineers, and Manual of Practice Number 9, Water Pollution Control, Federation 1974.
12. "The Design and Response of Circular Concrete Pipe," T. H. Wenzel, a Ph.D. Dissertation, Northwestern University, August, 1975.
13. "Design Criteria for Reinforced Concrete Pipe," R. A. Parmelee (presented at the TRB meeting, January, 1976).
14. Discussion of "Response of Corrugated Steel Pipe to External Soil Pressure," (by R. K. Watkins and A. P. Moser), R. A. Parmelee, Highway Research Record 373, 1972, pp. 109–110.
15. "Effects of Cracks in Reinforced Concrete Culvert Pipe," Concrete Pipe Information No. 7, American Concrete Pipe Association, 1977.
16. "Effects of Cracks in Reinforced Concrete Sanitary Sewer Pipe," Concrete Pipe Information No. 6, American Concrete Pipe Association, 1977.
17. "Evaluation of Modulus and Poisson's Ratio from Triaxial Tests," M. H. Farzin, R. J. Krizek, and R. B. Corotis, Transportation Research Record 537, 1975, pp. 69–80.
18. "An Evaluation of Surface Tractions on Buried Concrete Pipe," T. H. Wenzel, a Masters Thesis, Northwestern University, August, 1972.
19. "Evaluation of Stress Cell Performance," R. J. Krizek, M. H. Farzin, A. E. Z. Wissa, and R. T. Martin, Journal of the Geotechnical Engineering Division, ASCE, Volume 100, Number GT 12, December, 1974, pp. 1275–1295.
20. "Factors of Safety in the Design of Buried Pipelines," M. G. Spangler, Research Record Number 269, Highway Research Board, 1969.
21. "Field Performance of Reinforced Concrete Pipe," R. J. Krizek, R. B. Corotis, and M. H. Farzin, Transportation Research Record 517, 1974, pp. 30–47.
22. "Instrumentation and Testing of Concrete Pipe," R. A. Parmelee, R. B. Corotis, and J. H. Hemann (presented at the ASCE Structural Engineering Conference, April, 1975).
23. "Inverse Method for Determining Approximate Stress-Strain Behavior of Soils," M. H. Farzin, R. B. Corotis, and R. J. Krizek, Journal of Testing and Evaluation, ASTM, Volume 3, Number 1, January 1975. pp. 51-61.
24. "Investigation of Soil-Structure Interaction of Buried Concrete Pipe," R. A. Parmelee, Highway Research Record 443, 1973, pp. 32–39.
25. "The Iowa Deflection Formula: An Appraisal," R. A. Parmelee and R. B. Corotis, Highway Research Record 413, 1972, pp. 89–100.
26. "Loads on Negative-Projecting Conduits," W. J. Schlick, Proceedings, Volume 31, Highway Research Board, 1952.
27. "Loads on Pipe in Wide Ditches," W. J. Schlick, Bulletin 108, Iowa State College, 1932.
28. "Material Properties Affecting Soil-Structure Interaction of Underground Conduits," R. J. Krizek and J. N. Kay, Highway Research Record 413, 1972, pp. 13–29.
29. "A Model for Evaluating the Response of Buried Circular Concrete Pipe," J. E. Anderson, a Ph.D. Dissertation, Northwestern University, June, 1974.
30. "Negative Projecting Conduits," M. B. Spangler and W. J. Schlick, Report Number 14, Iowa State College, 1953.
31. "A New Design Method for Buried Concrete Pipe," R. A. Parmelee, ASTM STP 630, June, 1976, pp. 119–130.
32. "Nonlinear Soil Behavior and Its Effects on Soil-Structure Interaction," M. H. Farzin, a Ph.D. Dissertation, Northwestern University, August, 1973.
33. "Nonlinear Stress-Strain Formulation for Soils," R. B. Corotis, M. H. Farzin, and R. J. Krizek, Journal of the Geotechnical Engineering Division, ASCE, Volume 100, Number GT 9, September, 1974, pp. 993–1008.
34. "NUPIPE—A Comprehensive Program for the Design of Concrete Pipe," R. A. Parmelee and T. H. Wenzel (presented at the Second National Symposium on Computerized Structural Analysis and Design, Washington, D.C., March, 1976).
35. "A Practical Application of the Imperfect Ditch Method for Construction," M. G. Spangler, Proceedings, Volume 37, Highway Research Board, 1958.
36. "Regression Analysis of Soil Compressibility," A. S. Azzouz, R. J. Krizek, and R. B. Corotis, Soils and Foundations, (Japanese Society of Soil Mechanics and Foundation Engineering) Volume 16, No. 2, June 1976.

37. "The Response of Shallow Buried Concrete Pipe," P. V. McQuade, a Masters Thesis, Northwestern University, August, 1976.
38. "The Response of Shallow Buried Concrete Pipe," R. A. Parmelee, (presented at the TRB meeting, January, 1977).
39. "Shear Strength of Circular Concrete Pipe," D. S. Gromala, a Masters Thesis, Northwestern University, June, 1976.
40. "A Simplified Design Method for Buried Concrete Pipe," R. J. Kudder, a Ph.D. Dissertation, Northwestern University, June, 1978.
41. "Soil Engineering," M. G. Spangler and R. L. Hardy, Intext Educational Publishers, 1973.
42. "Soils Engineering," M. G. Spangler, International Textbook Company, 1966.
43. "Soil Stresses and Displacements in a Concrete Pipe Trench Installation," R. B. Corotis, T. H. Wenzel, and R. J. Krizek, Transportation Research Record 640, 1977, pp. 52-58.
44. "Soil-Structure Interaction of Concrete Pipe Systems," R. J. Krizek, R. B. Corotis, and T. H. Wenzel, ASCE Structural Division Speciality Conference, Madison, Wisconsin, August, 1976.
45. "Standard Tests for Drain Tile and Sewer Pipe," A. Marston, Proceedings, American Society for Testing and Materials, 1911.
46. "Statistical Analysis of Constrained Soil Modulus," J. Salazar Espinosa, R. J. Krizek, and R. B. Corotis, Transportation Research Record 537, 1975, pp. 59–68.
47. "Statistical Evaluation of Soil Index Properties and Constrained Modulus," R. B. Corotis, A. S. Azzouz, and R. J. Krizek, Proceedings of the Second International Conference on Application of Probability and Statistics in Soil and Structural Engineering, Aachen, Germany, September, 1975, pp. 273–293.
48. "Stress Analysis of Concrete Pipe," H. C. Olander, Engineering Monographs Number 6, United States Department of the Interior, Bureau of Reclamation, October, 1950.
49. "Stress Coefficients for Large Horizontal Pipes," J. M. Paris, General Fireproofing Co., November, 1921.
50. "Structural Behavior of Circular Reinforced Concrete Pipe-Development of Theory," F. J. Heger, Title Number 60–67, Journal of the American Concrete Institute, November, 1963.
51. "Structural Behavior of Circular Concrete Pipe Reinforced with Welded Wire Fabric," F. J. Heger, E. G. Nawy and R. B. Saba, Title Number 60-60, Journal of The American Concrete Institute, October, 1963.
52. "Structural Behavior of a Concrete Pipe Culvert—Mountainhouse Creek (Part 1)," R. E. Davis, A. E. Bacher and J. C. Obermuller, R&D Number 4-71, State of California Business and Transportation Agency Department of Public Works, April, 1971.
53. "Structural Behavior of a Concrete Pipe Culvert—Mountainhouse Creek (Part 2)," R. E. Davis, A. E. Bacher and E. E. Evans, Report Number 14034, State of California Business and Transportation Agency Department of Public Works, September, 1975.
54. "A Study of Soil-Structure Interaction of Buried Concrete Pipe," R. A. Parmelee, ASTM STP 630, June, 1976, pp. 66–75.
55. "Supporting Strength of Drain Tile and Sewer Pipe Under Different Pipe-Laying Conditions," W. J. Schlick, Bulletin Number 57, Iowa State College, 1920.
56. "The Supporting Strength of Rigid Pipe Culverts," M. G. Spangler, Bulletin 112, Iowa State College, 1933.
57. "The Supporting Strength of Sewer Pipe in Ditches and Methods of Testing Sewer Pipe in Laboratories to Determine Their Ordinary Supporting Strength," A. Marston, W. J. Schlick and H. F. Clemmer, Bulletin Number 47, Iowa State College, 1917.
58. "Synthesis of Soil Moduli Determined from Different Types of Laboratory and Field Tests," R. J. Krizek and R. B. Corotis, Proceedings of the ASCE Specialty Conference on In-Situ Measurement of Soil Properties, Raleigh, North Carolina, June, 1975, pp. 225–240.
59. "The Theory of External Loads on Closed Conduits in the Light of the Latest Experiments," A. Marston, Bulletin 96, Iowa State College, 1930.
60. "A Theory of Loads on Negative Projecting Conduits," M. G. Spangler, Proceedings, Volume 30, Highway Research Board, 1950.
61. "The Theory of Loads on Pipes in Ditches and Tests of Cement and Clay Drain Tile and Sewer Pipe," A. Marston and A. O. Anderson, Bulletin 31, Iowa State College, 1913.

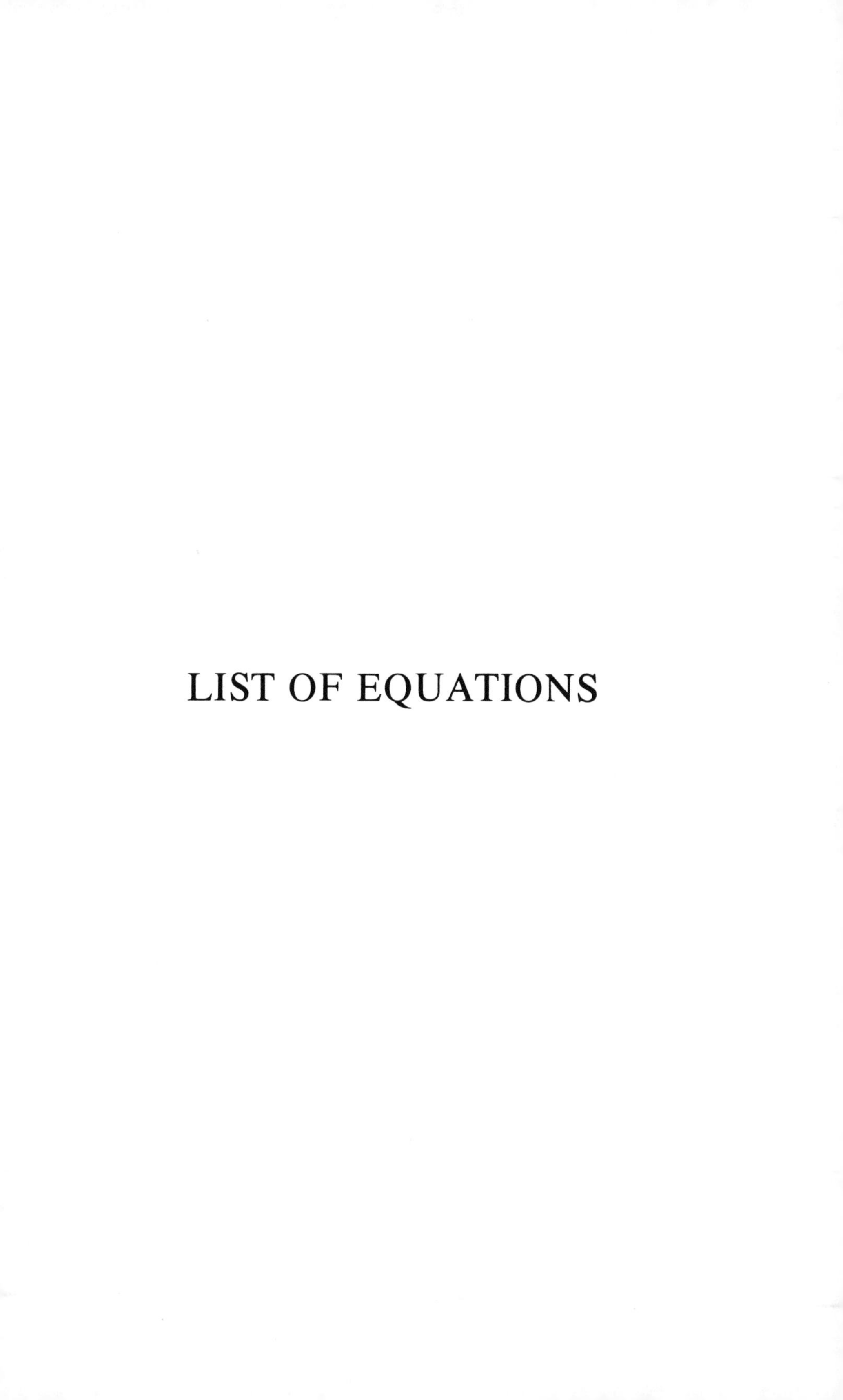

LIST OF EQUATIONS

LIST OF EQUATIONS

$$\Delta L = \frac{\Delta(d + h_v)}{S_e - S_o}$$

$$\frac{d_2}{d_1} = \frac{1}{2}\left(\sqrt{1 + 8F_1^2} - 1\right)$$

$$\Delta H = H_1 - H_2 = \frac{(d_2 - d_1)^3}{4d_1d_2}$$

$$i = \frac{C}{(d + t)^n}$$

$$A = C\ \sqrt[4]{M^3}$$

$$Q = 100p\ \sqrt{M}$$

$$T = \frac{N + 1}{M}$$

$$Q = CiA$$

$$Q = \frac{1.486}{n} AR^{\frac{2}{3}}S^{\frac{1}{2}}$$

$$H = H_V + H_e + H_f$$

$$H_f = \left[\frac{29n^2L}{R^{1.33}}\right]\frac{V^2}{2g}$$

Page

$$C_c = \frac{e^{\pm 2K\mu \frac{H}{B_c}} - 1}{\pm 2K\mu}$$

$$W_c = C_c w B_c^2$$

$$V + dV = V + (wB_c)dh \pm 2K\mu \left(\frac{V}{B_c}\right)dh$$

$$W_c = C_c w B_c^2$$

$$C_c = \frac{e^{\pm 2K\mu \frac{H_e}{B_c}} - 1}{\pm 2K\mu} + \left(\frac{H}{B_c} - \frac{H_e}{B_c}\right) e^{\pm 2K\mu \frac{H_e}{B_c}}$$

$$3HwB_c - C_c w B_c^2$$

$$2V' = 3\,(H - H_e + h)wB_c - V$$

$$d\lambda' = \left(\frac{V'}{B_c E}\right)dh$$

$$\lambda' = \int_0^{H_e} \left\{\frac{3(H - H_e + h)wB_c - V}{2B_c E}\right\}dh$$

$$\lambda = \int_0^{H_e} \left(\frac{V}{B_c E}\right)dh$$

$$\lambda + s_f + d_c = \lambda' + s_m + s_g$$

$$\lambda - \lambda' = (s_m + s_g) - (s_f + d_c)$$

$$r_{sd} = \frac{(s_m + s_g) - (s_f + d_c)}{s_m}$$

$$\lambda - \lambda' = r_{sd} s_m$$

$$\frac{3HwB_c - C_c w B_c^2}{2B_c}$$

$$s_m = \left(\frac{3HwB_c - C_c w B_c^2}{2B_c}\right)\frac{pB_c}{E}$$

$$\left[\frac{1}{2K\mu} \pm \left(\frac{H}{B_c} - \frac{H_e}{B_c}\right) \pm \frac{r_{sd}p}{3}\right] \frac{e^{\pm 2K\mu \frac{H_e}{B_c}} - 1}{\pm 2K\mu} \pm \frac{1}{2}\left(\frac{H_e}{B_c}\right)^2$$

$$\pm \frac{r_{sd}p}{3}\left(\frac{H}{B_c} - \frac{H_e}{B_c}\right) e^{\pm 2K\mu \frac{H_e}{B_c}} - \frac{1}{2K\mu} \cdot \frac{H_e}{B_c} \mp \frac{H}{B_c} \cdot \frac{H_e}{B_c}$$

$$= \pm\, r_{sd}p \frac{H}{B_c}$$

$$W_n = wB_d^2\left(\frac{e^{-2K\mu \frac{H}{B_d}} - 1}{-2K\mu}\right) \text{ when } H \le H_e$$

$$C_n = \left(\frac{e^{-2K\mu \frac{H}{B_d}} - 1}{-2K\mu}\right) \text{ when } H \le H_e$$

Page

$$W_n = C_n w B_d^2$$

$$V + dV = V + (wB_d)\, dh - 2K\mu\left(\frac{V}{B_d}\right)dh$$

$$C_n = \frac{e^{-2K\mu\frac{H_e}{B_d}} - 1}{-2K\mu} + \left(\frac{H}{B_d} - \frac{H_e}{B_d}\right) e^{-2K\mu\frac{H_e}{B_d}} \text{ when } H > H_e$$

$$r_{sd} = \frac{s_g - (s_d + s_f + d_c)}{s_d}$$

$$\frac{e^{-2K\mu\frac{H'_e}{B_d}} - 1}{-2K\mu}\left[\frac{H'}{B_d} - \frac{H'_e}{B_d} - \frac{1}{2K\mu}\right]$$

$$- \frac{H'_e}{B_d}\left[\left(\frac{H'}{B_d} - \frac{H'_e}{B_d}\right) + \frac{1}{2}\frac{H'_e}{B_d} - \frac{1}{2K\mu}\right]$$

$$= \frac{2}{3} r_{sd}p'\left[\frac{e^{-2K\mu\frac{H'_e}{B_d}} - 1}{-2K\mu} + \left(\frac{H'}{B_d} - \frac{H'_e}{B_d}\right) e^{-2K\mu\frac{H'_e}{B_d}}\right]$$

$$W_i = C_i w B_c^2$$

$$C_i = \frac{e^{-2K\mu\frac{H}{B_c}} - 1}{-2K\mu} \text{ when } H \leq H_e$$

$$C_i = \frac{e^{-2K\mu\frac{H_e}{B_c}} - 1}{-2K\mu} + \left(\frac{H}{B_c} - \frac{H_e}{B_c}\right) e^{-2K\mu\frac{H_e}{B_c}} \text{ when } H > H_e$$

Page

(4.45) Live Load on Pipe 4-43

$$W_L = \frac{W_T}{L_e}$$

(4.46) Effective Supporting Length 4-43

$$L_e = L + 1.75\left(\frac{3B_c}{4}\right)$$

(4.47) Railroad Live Load 4-44

$$W_L = Cp_0B_c(1 + I_f)$$

(4.48) Surcharge and Fill Load
(Trench Installation) 4-48

$$W_d = C_d w B_d^2 + C_s w H B_d$$

(4.49) Surcharge and Fill Load
(Embankment Installation) 4-51

$$W_c = C_c w B_c^2 + C_s w H B_c$$

(4.50) Trench Variable Bedding Factor 4-62

$$B_{fv} = (B_{fe} - B_{ft})\left[\frac{B_d - (B_c + 1.0)}{B_{dt} - (B_c + 1.0)}\right] + B_{ft}$$

(4.51) Bedding Factor for Positive Projection Embankment and
Induced Trench 4-63

$$B_f = \frac{A}{N - xq}$$

(4.52) Lateral Pressure Term (Circular Pipe) 4-63

$$q = \frac{mK}{C_c}\left(\frac{H}{B_c} + \frac{m}{2}\right)$$

(4.53) Lateral Pressure Term
(Elliptical or Arch Pipe) 4-65

$$q = \frac{pB'_cK}{C_cB_c^2}\left(H + \frac{pB'_c}{2}\right)$$

(4.54) Total Active Lateral Pressure Bounding Pipe
(Elliptical or Arch Pipe) 4-65

$$A' = \frac{KwpB'_c(2H + pB'_c)}{2}$$

$$q = \frac{A}{W_c}$$

$$q = \frac{pB'_cK}{C_cB_c^2}\left(H + \frac{pB'_c}{2}\right)$$

$$q = \frac{0.23p}{C_c}\left(\frac{H}{B_c} + 0.35p\right)$$

$$q = \frac{0.48p}{C_c}\left(\frac{H}{B_c} + 0.73p\right)$$

Pipe Supporting Strength Required $= (W_L + W_E)(F.S.)$

Pipe Supporting Strength $= T.E.B.(B_f)$

$$\text{Required T.E.B.} = \frac{(W_L + W_E)(F.S.)}{B_f}$$

$$D\text{-load} = \frac{T.E.B.}{S}$$

$$D_{ult} = \frac{(W_L + W_E)(F.S.)}{B_fS}$$

$$F.S. = \frac{D_{ult}}{D_{0.01}}$$

$$D_{0.01} = \frac{W_L + W_E}{B_fS}$$

Page

(5.1) Lateral Pressure, Saturated Condition 5-11

$$p = w_s H K_s \cos i + w_w H K_w$$

(5.2) Lateral Pressure, Angle i Equals Zero 5-11

$$p = w_s H K_s + 62.4H$$

(5.3) Conjugate Ratio for Soil, Rankine's Lateral Pressure Ratio 5-11

$$K_s = \frac{\sqrt{\mu^2 + 1} - \mu}{\sqrt{\mu^2 + 1} + \mu}$$

(5.4) Reduction of *Equation 5.2* 5-12

$$p = (57.6H \times 0.33) + 62.4H$$
$$p = 81.6H$$

(5.5) Unit Compressive Stress in a Ring 5-12

$$s = \frac{pD}{2t}$$

(5.6) Reduction of *Equation 5.5* 5-12

$$s = \frac{81.6\ HD}{2\ \frac{D}{12} \times 144}$$

$$s = 3.4H$$

(5.7) Radius of Curvature, Deflected Straight Pipe 5-18

$$R = \frac{L}{2\left(\tan \frac{1}{2}\frac{\Delta}{N}\right)}$$

(5.8) One Half the Deflection Angle, Each Deflected Straight Pipe 5-18

$$\frac{1}{2}\frac{\Delta}{N} = \sin^{-1}\frac{Pull}{2(D + 2t)} = \sin^{-1}\frac{Pull}{2B_c}$$

Page

(5.9) Tangent, Deflection Angle, Each Radius Pipe, ... 5-20

$$\tan \frac{\Delta}{N} = \frac{L}{R + \left(\frac{D}{2} + t\right)}$$

(5.10) Tangent, Deflection Angle, Each Radius Pipe 5-20

$$\tan \frac{\Delta}{N} = \frac{Drop}{D + 2t}$$

(5.11) Radius of Curvature, Radius Pipe 5-21

$$R = \frac{L}{\tan \frac{\Delta}{N}} - \left(\frac{D}{2} + t\right)$$

(5.12) Radius of Curvature, Radius Pipe 5-21

$$R = \frac{L(D + 2t)}{Drop} - \left(\frac{D}{2} + t\right)$$

(5.13) Radius of Curvature, Radius Pipe 5-21

$$R = B_c\left(\frac{L}{Drop} - \frac{1}{2}\right)$$

(5.14) Approximate Weights, Circular Concrete Pipe 5-25

$$W_p = \frac{\pi}{4}(B_c^2 - D^2)150$$

(5.15) Approximate Weight, Displaced Fresh Water 5-28

$$W_w = \frac{\pi}{4}(B_c^2)62.4$$

(5.16) Unit Weight, Inundated Backfill 5-30

$$w_I = w - \left(\frac{w}{SG \times 62.4} \times 62.4\right)$$

$$w_I = w\left(1 - \frac{1}{SG}\right)$$

$$W_I = w_I(0.1073B_c^2 + H_IB_c)$$

$$W_D = w(H - H_I)B_c$$

$$W_B = W_I + W_D$$

$$0.06 \leq \frac{K_d}{D} \leq 0.09$$

$$0.12 \leq \frac{K_u}{D} \leq 0.18$$

$$L_d \approx \frac{1.5D}{12}$$

$$L_u \approx \frac{3.0D}{12}$$

Page

(5.25) Diameter, Outlet Pipe 5-39

$$\left[\frac{Q^2}{3.22}\right]^{1/5} \leq D_0 \leq \left[\frac{Q^2}{1.42}\right]^{1/5}$$

(5.26) Ring Height, Elements..5-39

$$1.2 \leq \frac{K}{D_0} \leq 1.8$$

(5.27) Spacing, Elements 5-39

$$1.5 \leq \frac{L}{D_0} \leq 2.5$$

(5.28) Length, Outlet Pipe..5-39

$$L_0 \approx 5L$$

(7.1) Disassociation of Hydrogen Sulfide 7-7

$$H_2S \rightleftarrows HS^- + H^+$$

(7.2) Relative Proportions of H_2S and HS^- 7-7

$$\log \frac{[HS^-]}{[H_2S]} = pH - pK$$

(7.3) Average Annual Correction Factor 7-7

$$\frac{[DS]\text{ Annual Average}}{[DS]\text{ Annual Peak}} \times \frac{[DS]\text{ Daily Average}}{[DS]\text{ Daily Peak}} = C$$

(7.4) Annual Average Dissolved Sulfide 7-7

$$\text{Annual Average }[DS] = C \times [DS]_c$$

(7.5) Effective $[BOD]$ 7-8

$$[EBOD] = [BOD_5] \times 1.07^{(T-20)}$$

(7.6) Climactic Effective BOD 7-9

$$[EBOD]_c = [BOD]_c \times 1.07^{(T_c - 20)}$$

Page

(7.7) Thiosulfate Production 7-10

$$2O_2 + 2HS^- \xrightarrow{\text{bacteria}} S_2O_3^= + H_2O$$

(7.8) Sulfide Buildup in Force Mains 7-14

$$S = 3.28(t)(M)[EBOD](1 + 0.48r)r^{-1}$$

(7.9) Sulfuric Acid Production 7-14

$$H_2S + 2O_2 \xrightarrow{\text{bacteria}} H_2SO_4$$

(7.10) Manning Roughness Coefficient 7-22

$$n = \frac{1.486\, R^{2/3}S^{1/2}}{V}$$

(7.11) Z Formula 7-26

$$Z = \frac{[EBOD]}{S^{0.50}Q^{0.33}} \times \frac{P}{b}$$

(7.12) A/B Curve Adjustment 7-27

$$(S_e)_2 = (S_e)_1 \sqrt{\frac{[EBOD]_2}{[EBOD]_1}}$$

(7.13) 1977 Pomeroy Predictive Equation 7-27

$$\frac{d[S]}{dt} = \frac{3.28M'[EBOD]}{r} - \frac{2.10m[S](sv)^{0.375}}{d_m}$$

(7.14) Limiting Sulfide Concentration 7-28

$$\frac{3.28M'[EBOD]}{r} = \frac{2.10m(sv)^{0.375}[S]_{\lim}}{d_m}$$

(7.15) Limiting Sulfide Concentration 7-28

$$[S]_{\lim} = \frac{0.52 \times 10^{-3}[EBOD]}{(sv)^{0.375}} \times \frac{P}{b}$$

(7.16) Half Life 7-28

$$t_{1/2} = \frac{0.33d_m}{m(sv)^{0.375}}$$

Page

(7.17) Sulfide Generation 7-29

$$dt = \frac{d[S]d_m}{2.10m(sv)^{0.375}([S]_{lim} - [S])}$$

(7.18) Flow Time 7-29

$$t_2 - t_1 = \left(\frac{1.10d_m}{m(sv)^{0.375}}\right)\left(\log \frac{[S]_{lim} - [S]_1}{[S]_{lim} - [S]_2}\right)$$

(7.19) Final Sulfide Concentration 7-30

$$[S]_2 = [S]_{lim} - \left[\frac{[[S]_{lim} - [S]_1]}{\log^{-1}\left|\frac{(sv)^{0.375}\Delta t}{1.15\ d_m}\right|}\right]$$

(7.20) Mass Balance 7-30

$$[S]_1 = \frac{[S]_m(Q_m) + [S]_t(Q_t)}{Q_m + Q_t}$$

(7.21) Sulfide Flux to Pipe Wall 7-33

$$\phi_{sw} = 0.45J[DS](b/P')(sv)^{3/8}$$

(7.22) Corrosion Rate 7-36

$$c = \frac{0.45k\phi_{sw}}{A}$$

(7.23) Pipe Service Life 7-37

$$L = z/c$$

(7.24) Life Factor Equation 7-37

$$Az = 0.45k\phi_{sw}L$$

(7.25) Calcium Carbonate Equivalent 7-41

$$CaCO_3 \text{ Equivalent} = \frac{5[(ml \text{ of } HCl) - (ml \text{ of } NaOH)]}{[\text{sample mass in grams}]}$$

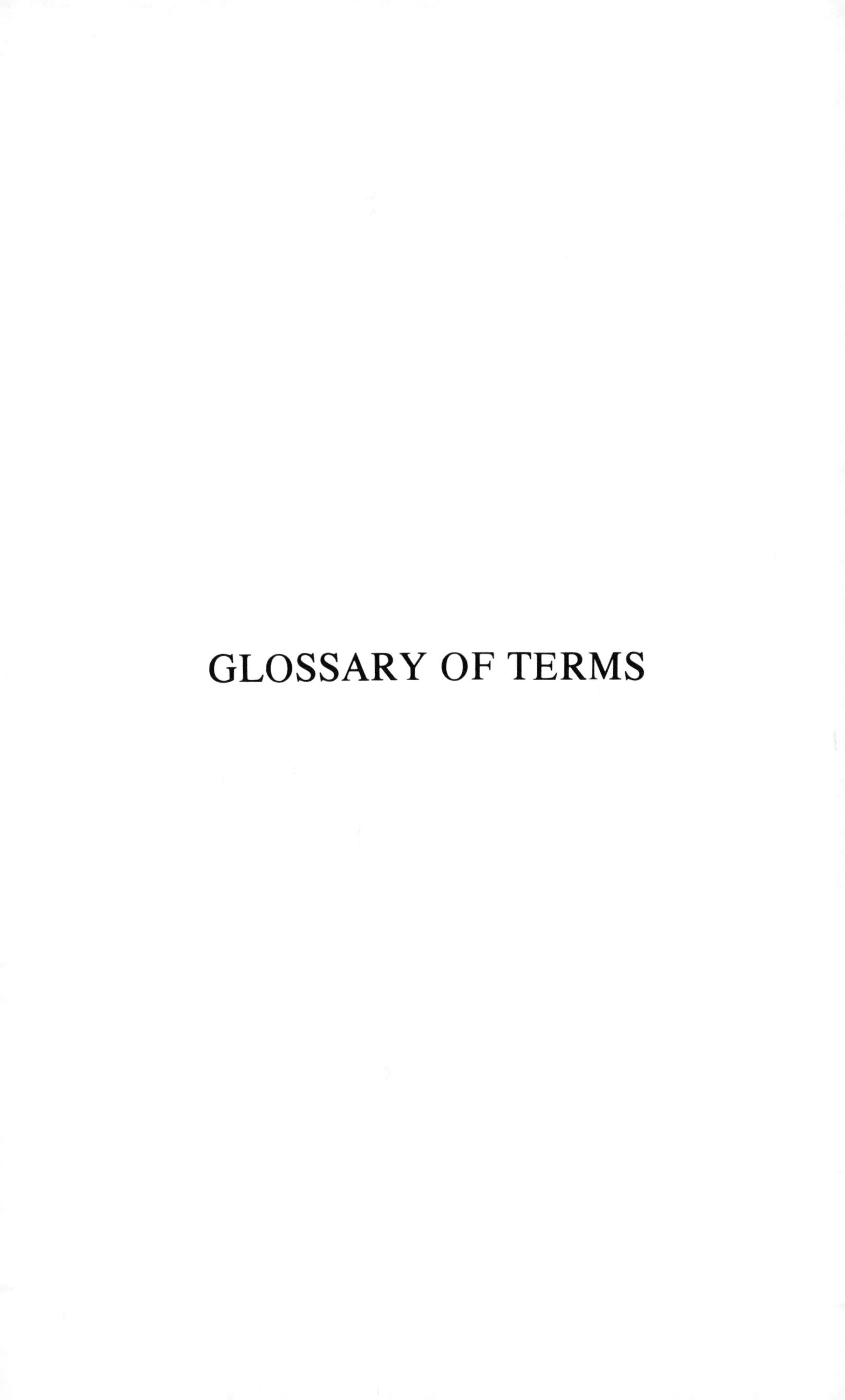

GLOSSARY OF TERMS

GLOSSARY OF TERMS

HYDRAULIC DESIGN
(Equations 3.1 through 3.32)

A	cross sectional area of flow, square feet
A	drainage area, acres
A	waterway area, square feet
A_c	cross sectional area of flow at critical flow, square feet
AHW	allowable headwater depth at culvert entrance, feet
b	surface width of fluid, feet
C	Chezy roughness coefficient
C	coefficient of runoff which is a function of the characteristics of the drainage area
C	a constant depending on frequency of occurrence of rainfall
C	Hazen-Williams coefficient related to roughness
C	Talbot discharge coefficient
D	height of culvert opening or diameter of pipe, inches or feet
d	a constant depending on rainfall duration
d	depth of flow, feet
d_1	depth of flow before hydraulic jump, feet
d_2	depth of flow after hydraulic jump, feet
$(d_{avg})_c$	average depth of flow at critical velocity, feet
d_c	critical depth, feet
d_m	hydraulic mean depth, feet
$(d_m)_c$	hydraulic mean depth at critical velocity, feet

$d(\overrightarrow{MV})$ change in momentum of the fluid free body

dt unit time

E_H heat energy

E_M mechanical energy

F Froude number

F_1 Froude number of upstream flow

$\overrightarrow{\Sigma F}$ resultant of forces applied to fluid

$(\overrightarrow{\Sigma F})dt$ impulse of the resultant force applied to fluid

f Darcy-Weisbach resistance coefficient

G weight of flow, pounds per second

g acceleration due to gravity, feet per second squared

H head loss, feet (the difference between the elevation of the entrance pool surface and the outlet tailwater surface)

ΔH head loss, feet

H_1 specific head of flow before hydraulic jump, feet

H_2 specific head of flow after hydraulic jump, feet

H_e entrance head loss, feet

H_f friction head loss, feet

H_o specific energy head, feet

H_v velocity head loss, feet

HW headwater depth at culvert inlet measured from invert of pipe, feet

h_f friction head loss, feet

h_o vertical distance between the culvert invert at the outlet and the hydraulic grade line, feet

h_V velocity head, feet

I internal energy of fluid

i rainfall intensity, inches per hour

k_e entrance head loss coefficient

L length of culvert, feet

ΔL unit length of pipe, feet

l length of pipeline, feet

M drainage area, acres or square miles

M fluid mass

M order of magnitude of annual flood peak

N length of continuous record of rainfall

n	a constant depending on storm design period
n	Kutter coefficient of roughness
n	Manning coefficient of roughness
P	fluid pressure
P/w	pressure energy of fluid
p	numerical percentage on Myer's scale
Q	flow in sewer or culvert discharge, cubic feet per second
Q	runoff, cubic feet per second
q	unit rate of flow, cubic feet per second
R	hydraulic radius, equals area of flow divided by wetted perimeter, feet
R	inside vertical rise of elliptical, arch pipe, or boxes, feet or inches
R	Reynold number
S	inside horizontal span of circular, elliptical, arch pipe, or boxes, feet or inches
S	slope of hydraulic gradient
S	slope of sewer
S_e	slope of energy gradeline
S_o	slope of culvert or pipe invert
T	rainfall recurrence interval
TW	tailwater depth at culvert outlet measured from invert of pipe, feet
t	duration of storm, minutes
t_c	time of concentration, minutes
V	velocity, feet per second
V_c	velocity at critical depth, feet per second
V_f	Darcy-Weisbach mean velocity, feet per second
$V^2/2g$	kinetic or velocity energy of fluid
v	kinematic viscosity
W	surface width of fluid, feet
W_p	wetted perimeter, feet
w	specific weight of fluid, pounds per cubic foot
Z	potential energy of fluid

LOADS AND SUPPORTING STRENGTHS
(Equations 4.1 through 4.65)

A a constant corresponding to the shape of the pipe

A_{LL} distributed live load area on subsoil plane at outside top of pipe, square feet

A_s area of transverse steel in a cradle or arch expressed as a percentage of the area of concrete in the cradle at the invert or arch at the crown

A' total active lateral pressure acting on the pipe, pounds per linear foot

B_c outside horizontal span of the pipe, feet

B'_c outside vertical height of the pipe, feet

B_d width of trench at top of pipe, feet

B_{dt} transition width at top of pipe, feet

B_f bedding factor

B_{fe} bedding factor, embankment

B_{ft} fixed bedding factor, trench

B_{fv} variable bedding factor, trench

B_t maximum width of excavation ahead of pipe or tunnel, feet

C pressure coefficient for live loads

C_c load coefficient for positive projection embankment installations

C_d load coefficient for trench installations

C_i load coefficient for induced trench installations

C_n load coefficient for negative projection embankment installations

C_s load coefficient for surcharge loads

C_t load coefficient for jacked or tunneled installations

c cohesion of undisturbed soil, pounds per square foot

D inside diameter of circular pipe, feet or inches

D-load the three-edge bearing strength in pounds per linear foot per foot of inside horizontal span

$D_{0.01}$ the maximum three-edge bearing test load supported by a concrete pipe before a crack occurs having a width of 0.01 inch measured at close intervals, throughout a length of at least 1 foot, expressed as D-load

D_{ult} the maximum three-edge bearing test load in pounds per linear foot per foot of inside horizontal span of the pipe supported by the pipe

d depth of bedding material below pipe, inches

d_c deflection of the vertical height of the pipe, inches

d_n thickness of thin horizontal soil element above pipe, feet

$d\lambda'$	settlement of thin horizontal soil element in exterior prism, feet
dV	vertical soil pressure on thin horizontal soil element above pipe, pounds per linear foot
E	modulus of elasticity, pounds per square inch
e	base of natural logarithms
$F.S.$	factor of safety
H	height of backfill or fill material above top of pipe, feet
H	height of surcharge fill, feet
H'	height of backfill or fill material above natural ground surface, feet
H_e	height of the plane of equal settlement above top of pipe, feet
H'_e	height of plane of equal settlement above natural ground surface, feet
h	distance from ground surface down to any horizontal plane in backfill, feet
h	thickness of rigid pavement, inches
I_f	impact factor for live loads
K	ratio of active lateral unit pressure to vertical unit pressure
k	Boussinesq constant for vertical stress
k	modulus of subgrade reaction, pounds per cubic inch
λ	total settlement of interior prism below the plane of equal settlement, feet
λ'	total settlement of exterior prisms below the plane of equal settlement, feet
L	length of A_{LL} parallel to longitudinal axis of pipe, feet
L_e	effective live load supporting length of pipe, feet
m	fractional part (ratio) of the outside diameter of the pipe over which lateral pressure is effective
μ	coefficient of internal friction of fill material
μ	Poisson's ratio
μ'	coefficient of friction between the backfill material and the trench walls
N	a parameter which is a function of the distribution of the vertical load and vertical reaction
N'	a parameter which is a function of the distribution of the vertical load and the vertical reaction for the concrete cradle method of bedding
P	point load, pounds
P	wheel load, pounds

p — projection ratio for positive projection embankment installations; equals vertical distance between the top of the pipe and the natural ground surface divided by the outside vertical height of the pipe

p' — projection ratio for negative projection and induced trench installations; equals vertical distance between the top of the pipe and the top of the trench divided by the trench width (negative projection) or the height of the induced trench divided by the outside horizontal span of the pipe (induced trench)

$p_{(H,X)}$ — pressure intensity at any vertical distance, H, and horizontal distance, X, pounds per square inch or pounds per square foot

p_o — intensity of distributed live load at bottom of railroad ties, pounds per square foot

p_o — live load pressure at the surface, pounds per square inch or pounds per square foot

ϕ' — angle of friction

q — the ratio of total lateral pressure to the total vertical load

R — inside vertical rise of elliptical, arch pipe, or boxes, feet or inches

R_s — radius of stiffness of the concrete pavement, inches or feet

r — radial horizontal distance from point load, feet

r — radius of the circle of pressure at the surface, inches

r_{sd} — settlement ratio

S — inside diameter of circular pipe or inside horizontal span of elliptical, arch pipe, or boxes, feet or inches

S_L — outside horizontal span of pipe (B_c) or width of A_{LL} transverse to longitudinal axis of pipe, whichever is less, feet

s_d — compression of the fill material in the trench within the height $p'B_d$ for negative projection embankment installations

s_f — settlement of the pipe into its bedding foundation, inches

s_g — settlement of the natural ground or compacted fill surface adjacent to the pipe, inches

s_m — settlement of the adjacent soil of height pB'_c for positive projection embankment installations, inches

T.E.B. — three-edge bearing strength, pounds per linear foot

U_s — uniform pressure at ground surface, pounds per square foot

V — vertical soil pressure on any horizontal plane in backfill, pounds per linear foot

V' — vertical soil pressure on any horizontal plane in exterior prism backfill, pounds per linear foot

W_c fill load for positive projection embankment installations, pounds per linear foot

W_d backfill load for trench installations, pounds per linear foot

W_E earth load, pounds per linear foot

W_i fill load for induced trench installations, pounds per linear foot

W_L live load on pipe, pounds per linear foot

W_n fill load for negative projection embankment installations, pounds per linear foot

W_p weight of pavement, pounds per linear foot

W_T total live load on pipe, pounds

W_t earth load for jacked or tunneled installations, pounds per linear foot

w unit weight of backfill or fill material, pounds per cubic foot

w vertical stress on any horizontal plane of soil under a point load applied to the surface of an infinitely wide plane, pounds per square foot

w_L average pressure intensity of live load on subsoil plane at outside top of pipe, pounds per square foot

x a parameter which is a function of the area of the vertical projection of the pipe over which active lateral pressure is effective

x' a parameter which is a function of the effective lateral support provided by the concrete cradle method of bedding

z vertical depth from point load to any horizontal plane, feet

SUPPLEMENTAL DESIGN CONSIDERATIONS AND PROCEDURES (Equations 5.1 through 5.28)

B_c outside pipe diameter, inches or feet

D diameter of the manhole, feet

D inside pipe diameter, inches or feet

D_o outlet pipe diameter, feet

Δ total deflection angle of curve, degrees

Δ/N total deflection angle of each pipe, degrees

H depth of manhole, feet

H depth from top of pipe to surface of backfill, feet

H_I depth of inundated backfill above top of pipe, feet

i	angle between backfill surface and the horizontal, degrees
K	ring height of the elements, inches
K_d	ring height of the downstream elements, inches
K_s	conjugate ratio for soil, Rankine's lateral pressure ratio
K_w	conjugate ratio for water (1.0)
K_u	ring height of the single upstream elements, inches
L	laying length of deflected pipe sections measured along the centerline, feet
L	standard laying length, long side, of radius pipe being used, feet
L	spacing of the elements, feet
L_d	spacing of the downstream elements, feet
L_o	length of the outlet pipe, feet
L_u	spacing of the single upstream element, feet
μ	tan ϕ = coefficient of internal friction for the soil
N	number of pipe with pulled joints
N	number of radius pipe
p	total lateral earth and hydrostatic pressure, pounds per square foot
ϕ	angle of internal friction of the soil, degrees
Q	design flow, cubic feet per second
R	radius of curvature, feet
s	unit compressive stress in ring, pounds per square foot
SG	specific gravity of backfill material
t	thickness of the manhole wall, feet
t	wall thickness of the pipe, inches or feet
W_B	total weight of backfill directly over the pipe, pounds per linear foot
W_D	weight of the dry backfill directly over the pipe, pounds per linear foot
W_I	weight of inundated backfill directly over the pipe, pounds per linear foot
W_p	weight of pipe, pounds per linear foot
W_w	weight of displaced water, pounds per linear foot
w	average unit weight of dry backfill, pounds per cubic foot
w_I	average unit weight of inundated backfill, pounds per cubic foot
w_s	effective unit weight of the backfill material, pounds per cubic foot
w_w	unit weight of water, 62.4 pounds per cubic foot

DESIGN FOR SULFIDE CONTROL
(Equations 7.1 through 7.25)

A	cross-sectional area of flow, square feet
A	concrete alkalinity, as equivalent calcium carbonate, $CaCO_3$
A_z	life factor
BOD	biochemical oxygen demand, milligrams per litre
$[BOD]_c$	climactic BOD, milligrams per litre
b	surface width of fluid, feet
C	average annual correction factor
c	corrosion rate, inches per year
DO	dissolved oxygen, milligrams per litre
$[DS]$	dissolved sulfide concentration in the wastewater, milligrams per litre
$[DS]_c$	climactic dissolved sulfides
d_m	mean hydraulic depth, feet
$d[S]$	incremental sulfide concentration, milligrams per litre
dt	incremental time, hours
Δt	flowtime in a given reach with constant slope, diameter and flow, hours
$[EBOD]$	effective BOD, milligrams per litre
$[EBOD]_c$	climactic $EBOD$, milligrams per litre
H^+	hydrogen ion
HS^-	hydrosulfide ion
J	factor relating amount of dissolved sulfide as H_2S to waste water pH
k	a constant for the amount of sulfide oxidation and acid runoff
L	service life, years
M	specific sulfide flux coefficient, metres per hour
M'	effective sulfide flux coefficient, metres per hour
m	empirical coefficient for sulfide losses
n	Manning roughness coefficient
P	wetted perimeter of pipe, feet
P'	perimeter of pipe exposed to atmosphere, feet
pH	negative logarithm of the effective hydrogen ion activity
pK	negative logarithm of the practical ionization constant
ϕ_{sw}	hydrogen sulfide flux to pipe wall, grams per square metre-hour
Q	flow or discharge, cubic feet per second

Q_m flow in main line above junction, gallons per day

Q_t flow in tributary, gallons per day

R hydraulic radius, feet

r hydraulic radius of the stream, feet

S slope of pipeline

$[S]$ total sulfides, milligrams per litre

S^- sulfide ion

S_e effective slope

$[S]_m$ sulfide concentration in main line above junction, milligrams per litre

$[S]_t$ tributary sulfide concentration, milligrams per litre

$[S]_1$ sulfide concentration at start of reach, milligrams per litre

$[S]_2$ sulfide concentration at end of reach, milligrams per litre

$S.F.$ safety factor

$[S]$ total sulfide concentration, milligrams per litre

$[S]_{lim}$ limiting sulfide concentration, milligrams per litre

s energy gradient of flow

T temperature, degrees celsius

T_c climactic temperature of flow, degrees Celsius

t flow time, hours

t_1 time slug of flow passes start of reach

t_2 time slug of flow passes end of reach

$t_{1/2}$ half life, the difference between actual sulfide concentration and limiting sulfide concentration, hours

V velocity of flow, feet per second

v velocity of flow, feet per second

Z Pomeroy's factor indicating possibility of sulfide buildup

z thickness of allowable concrete loss, inches

INDEX

C

D

F

G

H

Height, rings, internal energy
dissipators 5-38-42

J

K

L

M

T

U

V

W

Y

Z